The Complete Underwater Diving Manual

Compiled and Edited by
the National Oceanic and
Atmospheric Administration and
the U.S. Office of
Marine Resources

David McKay Company, Inc.
New York

10 9 8 7 6 5 4 3 2

Library of Congress Catalog Card Number: 77-78059
ISBN: 0-679-50826-0

Manufactured in the United States of America

FOREWORD

Since its inception in 1971, NOAA's Manned Undersea Science and Technology Program has been concerned both with scientific accomplishment—through the use of submersibles, undersea habitats, and diving techniques—and with the physical and biological technology required to improve the Nation's civilian underwater capability. To obtain a true understanding of our marine environment, and gain adequate knowledge of the marine resources, we must continually seek better and safer ways to explore, perform research, and undertake analysis of the underwater realm. In many situations this work must be done by men and women divers who can provide the degree of direct observation and control of experimentation, the "ground truth," that cannot be accomplished by instrumentation controlled from a remote surface location.

To help achieve these ends, this diving manual has been developed. Material presented is designed especially for the scientist-diver. The information included ranges from diving physiology to: how to perform biological surveys; how to collect geological samples; and how to dive in kelp beds and fast moving rivers. Search and recovery operations and underwater photography are also discussed, as is new information on saturation diving from shallow-water habitats.

This manual is thus designed to provide the diver with the necessary fundamentals both for safe and efficient diving, and for carrying out useful scientific investigations. The dynamic nature of underwater exploration and development dictates that the manual will need periodic revision. While the manual has been prepared primarily for NOAA scientific and working divers, we hope that it will also serve as a source of information, and will stimulate interest for the non-NOAA diver in the underwater scientific and technological community.

In this way, we at NOAA have sought to extend the capabilities of civilian diving operations, fully utilizing the most recent knowledge of diving physiology, hyperbaric medicine, underwater scientific methodology, as well as the development of new gear and operational techniques.

We wish to convey our heartfelt thanks to the many diving organizations, the leading divers and diving doctors of the Nation, and all the others who helped make this manual possible, for the invaluable contributions and review of this work they so generously made.

Publisher's note: This foreword is taken from the *NOAA Diving Manual*. Neither Howard W. Pollock nor any other NOAA employee has been connected with the David McKay Company's publication of *The Complete Underwater Diving Manual*, which is based on the *NOAA Diving Manual*.

PREFACE

This manual has been prepared for use by NOAA divers. It contains the basic information and applied diving technology needed to carry out scientific investigations as well as various tasks required of the working diver.

The manual principally addresses "shallow" water diving (surface to 300 feet), as this is the depth range in which NOAA divers primarily operate. The reader is referred to other sources for deeper mixed-gas diving procedures.

To keep the manual to a manageable size, reference material is liberally utilized throughout the text. This is especially true where detailed scientific or working procedures are encountered or where the subject matter is exhaustively treated elsewhere.

Because of the dynamic and multi-disciplinary nature of undersea exploration, it was necessary to seek the assistance of experts in many specialized fields. The task of integrating the broad and sometimes disparate material submitted by the many contributors, fell upon the Manned Undersea Science and Technology Office.

None of the specialist contributors received any remuneration for their efforts; rather their contributions were motivated by a professional desire to help produce a manual which would provide a basis for improving the capability of divers to work and learn of the sea. The reader is referred to the list of contributors and reviewers to better appreciate the number of individuals involved.

Every effort was made to include the most up-to-date information on the topics discussed. Throughout the period of preparation, new information was continually added. A point was reached, however, where deadlines dictated "no further additions." Recognizing the constantly changing technology and advances in underwater procedures, we urge our readers to advise us of new or omitted techniques, additional applications of existing techniques and other suggestions as to how the manual may be improved. Constructive criticism and recommendations for improvements on the manual should be sent directly to:

Dr. Donald C. Beaumariage, Director
Manned Undersea Science and Technology
National Oceanic and Atmospheric Administration
Rockville, Maryland 20852

In addition to expressing my appreciation to those contributing to the manual in a technical sense, special thanks must go to; Mrs. Joanne David, who served in an outstanding manner as technical editor; LCDR Laurence T. Bussey, USN and LCDR A.Y. Bryson, NOAA who, in addition to their technical contributions, played a key role in organizing, editing, and compiling the entire document.

James W. Miller, Ph.D.
Deputy Director
Manned Undersea Science and Technology

CONTRIBUTORS AND REVIEWERS

Ault, Richard L.
Smithsonian Institution
Washington, D.C.

Barr, Louis M.
NOAA, National Marine Fisheries
Service
Auke Bay Fisheries Laboratory
Auke Bay, Alaska

Breese, Denny K.
Perry Foundation, Inc.
Riviera Beach, Florida

Bryson, Abram Y. Lt. Cdr., NOAA
NOAA, Marine Resources
Manned Undersea Science and
Technology
Rockville, Maryland

Bussey, Laurence T. Lt. Cdr., USN
NOAA, Marine Resources
Manned Undersea Science and
Technology
Rockville, Maryland

Clifton, H. Edward Ph.D.
United States Department of the
Interior
Geological Survey
Menlo Park, California

Cooper, Richard A. Ph.D.
NOAA, National Marine Fisheries
Service
Northeast Fisheries Center
Woods Hole, Massachusetts

Cratin, Paul D. Ph.D.
Central Michigan University
Department of Chemistry
Mount Pleasant, Michigan

Dahl, Arthur L. Ph.D.
Smithsonian Institution
Washington, D.C.

Davis, Jefferson C. Col., USAF M.D.
San Antonio, Texas

Dill, Robert F. Ph.D.
NOAA, Marine Resources
Manned Undersea Science and
Technology
Rockville, Maryland

Earle, Sylvia A. Ph.D.
Los Angeles County Museum of
Natural History
Los Angeles, California

Egstrom, Glen H: Ph.D.
University of California, Los Angeles
Department of Kinesiology
Los Angeles, California

Ellis, Ian E.
NOAA, National Marine Fisheries
Service
Northwest Fisheries Center
Seattle, Washington

Feinstein, Stephen H. Ph.D.
University of Florida
Department of Speech
Gainesville, Florida

Given, Robert R. Ph.D.
University of Southern California
Santa Catalina Marine Biological
Laboratory
Avalon, California

Gotshall, Daniel W.
State of California
Department of Fish and Game
Monterey, California

Hamilton, R. William Jr. Ph.D.
Union Carbide Corporation
Corporate Research Department
Tarrytown, New York

Hamner, William M. Ph.D.
Australian Institute of Marine Science
Townsville, Queensland
Australia

High, William L.
NOAA, National Marine Fisheries
Service
Northwest Fisheries Center
Seattle, Washington

Hobson, Edmund S. Ph.D.
NOAA, National Marine Fisheries
Service
Marine Science Center
Avalon, California
(Author of Section 15, Marine
Animals Hazardous to Divers)

Hollien, Harry Ph.D.
University of Florida
Department of Speech
Gainesville, Florida

Jenkins, Wallace T.
Naval Coastal Systems Laboratory
Panama City, Florida

Koblick, Ian G.
Marine Resources Development
Foundation
Cabo Rojo, Puerto Rico

Lambertsen, Christian J. M.D.
University of Pennsylvania
Institute for Environmental Medicine
Philadelphia, Pennsylvania

Libby, Joseph D. Jr.
Smithsonian Institution
Washington, D.C.

Lilly, Stuart O.
Potomac Research Inc.
McLean, Virginia

Littlehales, Bates
National Geographic Society
Washington, D.C.

McAniff, John J.
University of Rhode Island
Department of Ocean Engineering
Kingston, Rhode Island

Macintyre, Ian G. Ph.D.
Smithsonian Institution
Washington, D.C.

Meckelnburg, Robert L. M.D.
Wilmington Medical Center
Wilmington, Delaware

Miller, James W. Ph.D.
NOAA, Marine Resources
Manned Undersea Science and
Technology
Rockville, Maryland

Mount, Thomas
University of Miami
Marine Laboratory
Miami, Florida

Mulherin, Paul K.
Potomac Research Inc.
McLean, Virginia

Naughton, John J.
NOAA, National Marine Fisheries
Service
Honolulu Fisheries Laboratory
Honolulu, Hawaii

Nevin, Robert F. Cdr., USN
Naval Undersea Center
San Diego, California

Peterson, Russell E. Ph.D.
University of Pennsylvania
Institute for Environmental Medicine
Philadelphia, Pennsylvania

Pratt, Harold W.
NOAA, National Marine Fisheries
Service
Narragansett Fisheries Laboratory
Narragansett, Rhode Island

Reuter, S. Harold M.D.
Houston, Texas

Roberts, William L.
Divers Den
Lancaster, Pennsylvania

Rothman, Howard B. Ph.D.
University of Florida
Department of Speech
Gainesville, Florida

Russel, Barry C.
The Australian Museum
Sydney South, Australia

Russell, Gary M.
NOAA, National Marine Fisheries
Service
Pascagoula Fisheries Laboratory
Pascagoula, Mississippi

Rutkowski, Richard L.
NOAA, Environmental Research
Laboratories
Atlantic Oceanographic and
Meteorological Laboratory
Miami, Florida

Schroeder, William W. Ph.D.
University of Alabama
Marine Science Programs
Dauphin Island, Alabama

Selfon, Paul M. M.D.
United States Department of
Commerce
Office of the Secretary
Washington, D.C.

Somers, Lee H. Ph.D.
University of Michigan
Department of Atmospheric and
Oceanic Science
Ann Arbor, Michigan

Stang, Paul R.
NOAA, Marine Resources
Coastal Zone Management
Rockville, Maryland

Stewart, James R.
University of California, San Diego
Scripps Institution of Oceanography
LaJolla, California

Stone, Richard B.
NOAA, National Marine Fisheries
Service
Atlantic Estuarine Fisheries Center
Beaufort, North Carolina

Vadus, Joseph R.
NOAA, Marine Resources
Manned Undersea Science and
Technology
Rockville, Maryland

Walter, Merritt N. Lt. Cdr., NOAA
NOAA, National Ocean Survey
Office of Fleet Operations
Rockville, Maryland

Wells, J. Morgan Ph.D.
NOAA, Marine Resources
Manned Undersea Science and
Technology
Rockville, Maryland

Wicklund, Robert I.
Perry Foundation
Riviera Beach, Florida

Wilkie, Donald W.
University of California
Scripps Institution of Oceanography
LaJolla, California

Workman, Robert D. M.D.
Taylor Diving and Salvage Co., Inc.
Belle Chasse, Louisiana

TABLE OF CONTENTS

LIST OF FIGURES

SECTION 6
GENERAL DIVING PROCEDURES

SECTION 7
WORKING DIVING PROCEDURES

SECTION 8
SCIENTIFIC DIVING PROCEDURES

SECTION 9
REGIONAL AND SPECIAL DIVING

SECTION 10
AIR DIVING

SECTION 11
MIXED GAS AND OXYGEN DIVING

SECTION 13
SURFACE SUPPORT PLATFORMS

SECTION 14
UNDERWATER SUPPORT PLATFORMS

SECTION 15
MARINE ANIMALS HAZARDOUS TO DIVERS

SECTION 16
RECOMPRESSION CHAMBERS
AND TREATMENT PROCEDURES

SECTION 17
FIRST AID

APPENDIX D
DECOMPRESSION AND TREATMENT TABLES

LIST OF TABLES

SECTION 8
SCIENTIFIC DIVING PROCEDURES

SECTION 10
AIR DIVING

SECTION 11
MIXED GAS AND OXYGEN DIVING

SECTION 12
SATURATION DIVING

SECTION 14
UNDERWATER SUPPORT PLATFORMS

SECTION 16
RECOMPRESSION CHAMBERS
AND TREATMENT PROCEDURES

APPENDIX D
DECOMPRESSION AND TREATMENT TABLES

ABBREVIATIONS

A argon
ac alternating current
acfm absolute cubic feet per minute
AM amplitude modulation
ASA American Standards Association
ata or ATA atmospheres absolute
atm or ATM atmosphere
BTU British Thermal Units
°C degrees Centigrade
cc cubic centimeter
cfm cubic feet per minute
cm centimeter
cm^2 square centimeter
cm Hg centimeter of mercury
CO carbon monoxide
CO_2 carbon dioxide
cu ft or ft^3 cubic foot
cu in or in^3 cubic inch
cu m or m^3 cubic meter
dc direct current
DDC deck decompression chamber
DOT Department of Transportation
EAD equivalent air depth
°F degrees Fahrenheit
fl oz fluid ounce
fpm feet per minute
fsw or FSW feet of sea water
ft or ' foot
g or gm gram
g/cc grams per cubic centimeter
g/l grams per liter
gm/cm^2 grams per square centimeter
H_2 hydrogen
He helium
Hg mercury
HP or hp high pressure
Hz Hertz—cycles per second
ICC Interstate Commerce Commission
I.D. or ID inside diameter
in or " inch
in Hg inches of mercury
°K degrees Kelvin
kg kilogram
kg/cm^2 kilogram per square centimeter
kHz kilo Hertz—one thousand cycles per second
kw kilowatt
lb pound
lb/cu ft or lb/ft^3 pound per cubic foot
lb/in^2 pound per square inch
lpm liters per minute
m meter
m^2 square meter
mb millibar
mg/l milligrams per liter
mg/m^3 milligrams per cubic meter
mi mile
min minute
ml milliliter
ml/l milliliters per liter
mm millimeter
mm Hg millimeters of mercury
MP or mp mid-pressure
N_2 nitrogen
$NaHCO_3$ sodium bicarbonate
NBS National Bureau of Standards
Ne neon
N/M^2 Newton per square meter
O_2 oxygen
O.D. or OD outside diameter
oz ounce
pH hydrogen-ion concentration
pO_2 or PO_2 partial pressure of oxygen
ppm parts per million
psi pounds per square inch
psia pounds per square inch absolute
psig pounds per square inch gauge
PTC personnel transfer capsule
PVC polyvinyl chloride
°R degrees Rankine
rpm or RPM revolutions per minute
SAE Standard Average European
scf standard cubic feet
scfm standard cubic feet per minute
SCUBA or scuba self contained under-water breathing apparatus
SDC submersible decom-pression chamber
SPU swimmer propulsion unit
sq cm or cm^2 square centimeter
sq ft or ft^2 square foot
sq in or in^2 square inch
sq km or km^2 square kilometer
sq mi or mi^2 square mile
TNT trinitrotoluene
v volt

THE PHYSICS OF DIVING

1.0 GENERAL

This section describes the physical laws of nature as they affect man in the water. A thorough understanding of the physical principles set forth in the following paragraphs is essential to the safe and effective performance of a diver.

1.1 DEFINITIONS

This paragraph defines the basic parameters necessary for an understanding of the physical principles of the underwater environment. The most important of these are:

1.1.1 Pressure

Pressure is a force acting on a unit area. Expressed mathematically:

$$\text{Pressure} = \frac{\text{Force}}{\text{Area}} \quad \text{or} \quad P = \frac{F}{A}$$

Pressure is usually expressed in pounds per square inch (psi) or kilograms per square centimeter (kg/cm^2).

1.1.2 Temperature

The temperature of the body is the measurement of the intensity of its heat and is produced by the average kinetic energy, or speed of its molecules. Temperature is measured by means of a thermometer, and is expressed in degrees Centigrade (°C) or Fahrenheit (°F). The quantity of heat in the body is the total kinetic energy of all its molecules and is measured in calories or British Thermal Units (BTU).

Temperature must be converted to absolute for use with the gas laws. Absolute zero is a hypothetical temperature characterized by complete absence of heat, for example, approximately $-273°$ C or $-460°$ F. This is done by adding 273 to the temperature in Centigrade units or 460 to the temperature in Fahrenheit units. Expressed mathematically:

$$°\text{Kelvin (°K)} = °\text{C plus } 273$$

$$°\text{Rankine (°R)} = °\text{F plus } 460$$

Temperatures measured in Centigrade may be converted to Fahrenheit using the following formula.

$$°\text{F} = (1.8 \times °\text{C}) + 32$$

Temperatures measured in Fahrenheit may be converted to Centigrade using the following formula.

$$°\text{C} = \frac{(°\text{F} - 32)}{1.8}$$

1.1.3 Heat

Heat is energy that causes an increase in the temperature of matter to which it is added and a decrease in the temperature of matter from which it is removed, provided that the matter does not change state during the process. Quantities of heat are measured in calories or BTU.

1.1.4 Density

Density is defined as mass per unit volume. Expressed mathematically:

$$\text{Density } (D) = \frac{\text{Mass}}{\text{Volume}}$$

Density is usually in pounds per cubic foot (lb/cu ft) in the English system, and in grams per cubic centimeter (g/cc) in the metric system.

**Table 1-1
Conversion Factors,
Metric Units
to U.S. Units**

	Metric Units		U.S. Units
Pressure			
	1 gm/cm²	=	0.394 inch of fresh water
	1 kg/cm²	=	14.22 psi
		=	32.8 feet of fresh water
		=	28.96 inches of mercury
	1 cm Hg	=	0.193 psi
		=	0.446 foot of fresh water
		=	0.394 inch of mercury
	1 cm of fresh water	=	0.394 inch of fresh water
Volume and capacity			
	1 cc or ml	=	0.061 cu in
	1 cu m	=	35.31 cu ft
	1 liter	=	61.02 cu in
		=	0.035 cu ft
		=	33.81 fl oz
		=	1.057 quarts
Weight			
	1 gram	=	0.035 oz
	1 kg	=	35.27 oz
		=	2.205 lb
Length			
	1 cm	=	0.394 in
	1 meter	=	39.37 in
		=	3.28 ft
	1 kilometer	=	0.621 mi
Area			
	1 cm²	=	0.155 sq in
	1 m²	=	10.76 sq ft
	1 sq km	=	0.386 sq mi

1.1.5 Specific Gravity

Specific gravity is the ratio of the density of a substance to the density of fresh water at 4° C. Fresh water has a specific gravity of 1.0, with substances heavier than fresh water having specific gravities greater than 1.0, substances lighter than fresh water having specific gravity less than 1.0. The human body has a specific gravity of approximately 1.0, varying slightly from one person to another.

In many parts of the world the metric system of measurement is used rather than the "English" system presently used in the United States. Table 1–1 gives conversion factors from metric to U.S. units.

1.2 PRESSURE

To a diver under the water, pressure is the result of two forces: the weight of the water over him, and the weight of the atmosphere over the water. Table 1–2 provides the factors required for converting various barometric pressure units. As a practical matter, the pressures experienced by a diver can be viewed as follows:

1.2.1 Atmospheric Pressure

Atmospheric pressure results from the weight of the atmospheric gases and acts on all bodies or structures in the atmosphere. Atmospheric pressure acts in all directions at any specific point. Since it is equal in all directions the effects are usually neutralized. At sea level atmospheric pressure is 14.7 psi or 1.03 kg/cm². At higher elevations, this value decreases. Pressures above 14.7 psi are often expressed in atmospheres. For example, one atmosphere is 14.7 psi, 10 atmospheres is 147 psi, and 100 atmospheres is 1470 psi.

Figure 1–1 shows equivalent pressures in the most commonly used units for both altitude and depth.

1.2.2 Hydrostatic Pressure

Hydrostatic pressure results from the weight of water (or any fluid) and acts upon any body or structure immersed in the water. Like atmospheric pressure it is equal in all directions at a specific depth. Hydrostatic pressure is most important to a diver. It increases at a rate of 0.445 psi per foot of descent (1 kg/cm² per 9.75 meters) in seawater and 0.432 psi per foot of descent (1 kg/cm² per 10 meters) in fresh water. This is shown graphically in Figure 1–2.

1.2.3 Absolute Pressure

Absolute pressure exerted on a submerged body is the sum of the atmospheric pressure and the hydrostatic pressure. Absolute pressure is measured in "pounds per square inch absolute" (psia) or "kilograms per square centimeter absolute" (kg/cm² absolute).

Table 1-2
Conversion Table
for Barometric
Pressure Units

	Atm	N/M²	bars	mb	kg/cm²	gm/cm² (cm H₂O)	mm Hg	in Hg (''Hg)	lb/in² (psi)
1 Atmosphere =	1	1.013×10^5	1.013	1013	1.033	1033	760	29.92	14.70
1 Newton/M² (N/M²) =	$.9869 \times 10^{-5}$	1	10^{-5}	.01	1.02×10^{-5}	.0102	.0075	$.2953 \times 10^{-3}$	$.1451 \times 10^{-3}$
1 bar =	.9869	10^5	1	1000	1.02	1020	750.1	29.53	14.51
1 millibar (mb) =	$.9869 \times 10^{-3}$	100	.001	1	.00102	1.02	.7501	.02953	.01451
1 kg/cm² =	.9681	$.9807 \times 10^5$	.9807	980.7	1	1000	735	28.94	14.22
1 gm/cm² (1 cm H₂O) =	968.1	98.07	$.9807 \times 10^{-3}$	.9807	.001	1	.735	.02894	.01422
1 mm Hg =	.001316	133.3	.001333	1.333	.00136	1.36	1	.03937	.01934
1 in Hg (''Hg) =	.0334	3386	.03386	33.86	.03453	34.53	25.4	1	.4910
1 lb/in² (psi) =	.06804	6895	.06895	68.95	.0703	70.3	51.70	2.035	1

(National Aeronautics and Space Administration 1973)

1.2.4 Gauge Pressure

Gauge pressure is the difference between absolute pressure and a specific pressure being measured. Pressures are usually measured with gauges that are balanced to read "0" at sea level when they are open to the air. Gauge pressure is therefore converted to absolute pressure by adding 14.7 if the dial reads in psi or 1.03 if the dial reads in kg/cm².

1.2.5 Partial Pressure

In a mixture of gases, the proportion of the total pressure contributed by a single gas in the mixture is called the *partial pressure*. The partial pressure contributed by a single gas is in direct proportion to its percentage of the total volume of the mixture. (See Paragraph 1.5.1).

1.3 BUOYANCY

Archimedes' Principle explains the nature of buoyancy.

"A body immersed in a liquid, either wholly or partially, is buoyed up by a force equal to the weight of the displaced liquid."

Using Archimedes' Principle to establish the buoyant force, we can establish the buoyancy of a submerged body by subtracting the weight of the submerged body from the weight of the displaced liquid.

If the total displacement, that is, the weight of the displaced liquid is greater than the weight of the submerged body, the buoyancy will be positive, and the body will float or be buoyed upward. If the weight of the body is equal to that of the displaced liquid, the buoyancy will be neutral, and the body will remain suspended in the liquid. If the weight of the submerged body is greater than the displaced liquid, the buoyancy will be negative, and the body will sink.

The buoyant force of a liquid is dependent upon its density, that is, its weight per unit volume. Fresh water has a density of 62.4 pounds per cubic foot or 1.01 grams per cubic centimeter. Seawater is heavier, having a density of 64.0 pounds per cu ft or 1.04 g/cc. Therefore, a body will be buoyed up by a greater force in seawater than in fresh water making it easier to float in the ocean than in a fresh water lake.

Lung capacity can have a significant effect on the buoyancy of an individual. With full lungs the diver displaces a greater volume of water and therefore is more buoyant than with exhaled lungs. Other individual differences include bone structure and bone weight and obesity or leanness. This explains why certain individuals float easily while others do not.

A diver wearing a wet suit is usually required to

**Figure 1-1
Equivalent Pressures,
Altitudes, and Depths**

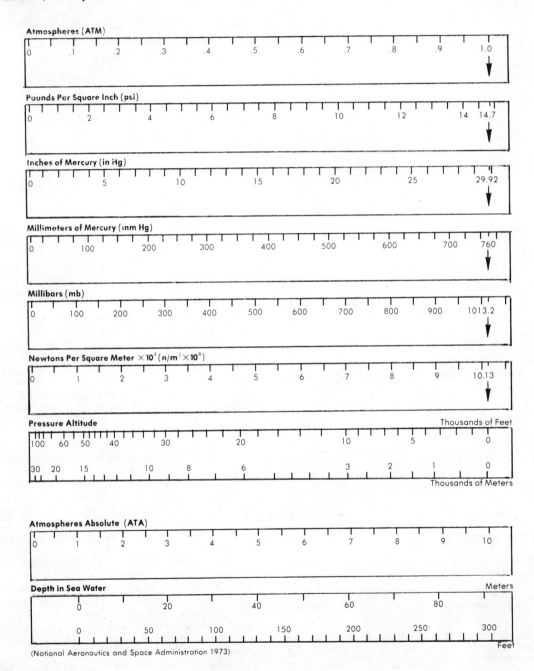

(National Aeronautics and Space Administration 1973)

NOAA Diving Manual

**Figure 1-2
The Effects of
Hydrostatic Pressure**

At the Surface
1 Atmosphere Absolute, 14.7 psi
The flotation device is fully expanded.

At 33 Feet
2 Atmospheres Absolute, 29.4 psi
(½ Surface Volume) Because of hydrostatic
pressure, the same volume of air in the
flotation device is reduced to only ½ its
surface lifting capacity.

At 132 Feet
5 Atmospheres Absolute, 73.5 psi
(⅕ Surface Volume) Because of hydrostatic
pressure, the same volume of air in the
flotation device is reduced to only ⅕ its
surface lifting capacity.

add weights to his body to provide the negative buoyancy that allows him to descend. At the working depth, buoyancy should be adjusted so that the diver is neutral and can accomplish work without the additional physical effort of counteracting positive (upward) or negative (downward) buoyancy.

1.4 DIVING GASES

A diver is totally dependent on a supply of breathing gas while under water. Two methods of providing breathing gases are generally employed. The diver may be supplied with gas from an umbilical, or may carry the breathing gas supply with him. The second method is called SCUBA (scuba) for "Self-Contained Underwater Breathing Apparatus."

Many combinations of breathing gases are used. Air is the most common, but the use of other mixtures for special diving situations is increasing. The following paragraphs describe the gases most commonly used in diving operations.

1.4.1 Air

Air is a mixture of gases (and vapors) containing nitrogen (78.084), oxygen (20.946), argon (0.934), carbon dioxide (0.033) and other rare gases (0.003). Compressed air is the most commonly used breathing gas for diving applications (See Section 10).

1.4.2 Oxygen (O₂)

Oxygen is a colorless, odorless, and tasteless gas. It is only slightly soluble in water. It can be liquefied at $-183°$ C at atmospheric pressure and will solidify when cooled to $-218.4°$ C. Oxygen is the only life supporting gas used by the human body. The other gases breathed from the atmosphere, or those breathed by a diver in a gas mixture, serve only as a vehicle and a diluent for the oxygen. Oxygen is dangerous when excessive amounts are breathed under pressure. This harmful effect is called oxygen poisoning (See Paragraph 2.3).

1.4.3 Nitrogen (N₂)

Nitrogen is a colorless, odorless, and tasteless gas. It is chemically inert and is incapable of supporting life. Its boiling point is $-196°$ C. Nitrogen is commonly used as a diluent with oxygen in a diving gas mixture, but has several disadvantages as compared

with some other gases. Nitrogen, when breathed under increasing partial pressure, has a distinct anesthetic effect, producing a disorder called "nitrogen narcosis" characterized by a loss of judgment and disorientation (See Paragraph 2.2.3.4).

1.4.4 Helium (He)

Helium is found in the atmosphere only in trace amounts. It has the lowest boiling point of any known substance, $-268.9°$ C. Helium is colorless, odorless, and tasteless and is used extensively in deep diving gas mixtures as a diluent for oxygen. It has some disadvantages, but not of the severity of nitrogen. Breathing helium-oxygen mixtures causes temporary speech distortion (Donald Duck-like voice) which hinders communication. Helium also has a high thermal conductivity, which results in rapid loss of body heat. It is used because of its lower density and lack of narcotic effect upon the diver at depth.

1.4.5 Carbon Dioxide (CO₂)

Carbon dioxide is produced by various natural processes such as animal metabolism, combustion, and fermentation. It is colorless, odorless, and tasteless. Although carbon dioxide is not generally considered poisonous, in excessive amounts it is harmful to the diver. While some CO_2 is necessary, unconsciousness will result when it is breathed under increasing partial pressure (See Paragraph 1.5.1 and Paragraph 2.1.3.2). For example, a person should not breathe air containing more than 0.02 atmospheres partial pressure CO_2 (U.S. Navy Diving-Gas Manual 1971). Divers must be concerned with the partial pressure of carbon dioxide in a breathing supply. In the case of closed- and semi-closed-circuit breathing systems, the removal of excess CO_2 generated by breathing is essential to safety.

1.4.6 Carbon Monoxide (CO)

Carbon monoxide is a poisonous gas. It is described here because of its potential lethality. It is colorless, odorless, tasteless, and is difficult for the individual to detect. Carbon monoxide is produced by incomplete combustion of hydrocarbons, as in the exhaust systems of internal combustion engines. Carbon monoxide also may be produced in overheated oil-lubricated compressors. A level of 10 parts per million should not be exceeded in a pressurized breathing system. Great care should be taken when scuba cylinders are being filled, since a possible source of contamination may be the exhaust systems of the air compressor itself. Proper precaution must be taken to ensure adequate ventilation of all spaces where cylinders are filled.

1.4.7 Argon, Neon, Hydrogen (A, Ne, H₂)

Argon, neon, and hydrogen have been used experimentally as diluents with oxygen to form breathing gas mixtures; however, these gases are not normally used in diving operations.

1.5 GAS LAWS

The behavior of all gases is affected by three factors: the temperature of the gas, the pressure of the gas, and the volume of the gas. The relationships between these three factors have been defined in what are termed the Gas Laws. Five of these, Dalton's Law, Boyle's Law, Charles' Law, Henry's Law, and the General Gas Law are of special importance to the diver.

1.5.1 Dalton's Law

Dalton's Law states:

"The total pressure exerted by a mixture of gases is the sum of the pressures that would be exerted by each of the gases if it alone were present and occupied the total volume."

In a gas mixture, the proportion of the total pressure contributed by a single gas is called the partial pressure of that gas. An easily understood example is that of a container at atmospheric pressure (14.7 psi). If the container were filled with oxygen alone, the partial pressure of the oxygen would be 1 atmosphere. Now, if the same container at 14.7 psi (1 atmosphere) were filled with dry air the partial pressures of all the constituent gases would contribute to the total pressure, as shown in the following tabulation:

Percent of Component × Total Pressure (Absolute) = Partial Pressure

Gas	Percent of component	Atmospheres partial pressure
N₂	78.08	0.7808
O₂	20.95	.2095
CO₂	.03	.0003
Other	.94	.0094
Total	100.00	1.0000

If the same container, say a scuba cylinder was filled with air to 2,000 psi (137 ata), the partial pressures of the various components would reflect the increased pressure in the same proportion as their percentage of the gas, as illustrated in the following tabulation:

Gas	Percent of component	Atmospheres partial pressure
N₂	78.08	106.97
O₂	20.95	28.70
CO₂	.03	.04
Other	.94	1.29
Total	100.00	137.00

Observe that while the partial pressures of some constituents of the gas, particularly CO_2, were fairly small at atmospheric pressure, they increased significantly at higher pressures. The implications of Dalton's Law are highly significant and should be understood by the diver (See Section 2).

1.5.2 Boyle's Law

Boyle's Law states:

"For any gas at a constant temperature, the volume will vary inversely with the *absolute* pressure while the density will vary directly with the absolute pressure."

Figure 1-3
Boyle's Law

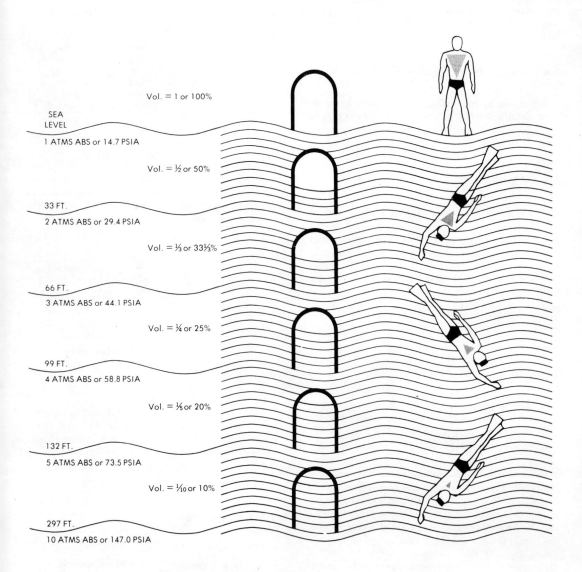

Boyle's law applied to depth versus volume and pressure.

Stated mathematically, at a constant temperature, Boyle's Law is:

$$PV = K, \text{ for each gas}$$

where

P = absolute pressure
V = volume
K = constant

Boyle's Law is important to the diver in that it relates the change in volume of a gas caused by the change in pressure due to depth and defines the relationship of pressure and volume in breathing gas supplies. The following example will illustrate the use of Boyle's Law.

Example 1 (Boyle's Law)

An open diving bell with a volume of 24 cubic feet is to be lowered into the sea from a surface support ship. No air is supplied to or lost from the bell. Calculate the volume of the air space in the bell at the 33-foot depth, the 66-foot depth and the 99-foot depth level.

Step 1 — Boyle's Law (at surface)

$$P_1V_1 = K$$

P_1 = pressure at surface in psia
V_1 = volume at surface in cu in
K = constant

Step 2 — Boyle's Law (at 33 feet water)

$$P_2V_2 = K$$

P_2 = pressure at 33 feet in psia
V_2 = volume at 33 feet in cu in
K = constant

Step 3 — Equating the constants K at the surface and at 33 feet, we have the following equation

$$P_1V_1 = P_2V_2$$

Transposing to determine the volume at 33 feet, V_2:

$$V_2 = \frac{P_1V_1}{P_2}$$

P_1 = 1 atmosphere (ata)
P_2 = 2 atmospheres
V_1 = 24 cu ft
$$V_2 = \frac{1 \text{ ata} \times 24 \text{ cu ft}}{2 \text{ ata}}$$

V_2 = 12 cu ft

Note that the volume of air in the open bell has been compressed from 24 to 12 cubic feet in the first 33 feet of seawater.

Step 4 — Using the method illustrated above to determine the air volume at 66 feet:

$$V_3 = \frac{P_1V_1}{P_3}$$

P_3 = 3 ata

$$V_3 = \frac{1 \text{ ata} \times 24 \text{ cu ft}}{3 \text{ ata}}$$

V_3 = 8 cu ft

Step 5 — For 99-foot depth, using the method illustrated previously, the air volume would be:

$$V_4 = \frac{P_1V_1}{P_4}$$

P_4 = 4 ata
V_4 = 6 cu ft

As the depth increased from the surface to 99 feet, the volume of air in the open bell was compressed from 24 cubic feet to 6 cubic feet.

In Boyle's Law the temperature of the gas was considered to be a constant value. However, temperature significantly affects the pressure and volume of a gas; therefore, it is essential to have a method of calculating this effect. To a diver, knowing the effect of temperature is essential, because the temperature deep in the oceans or in lakes is often significantly different from the air temperature at the surface. The gas law that describes the physical relationships of temperature upon the pressure and volume is known as Charles' Law.

1.5.3. Charles' Law

Charles' Law states:

"For any gas at a constant pressure, the volume of the gas will vary directly with the *absolute* temperature. For any gas at a constant volume, the pressure of the gas will vary directly with the *absolute* temperature."

Figure 1-4
Gas Laws

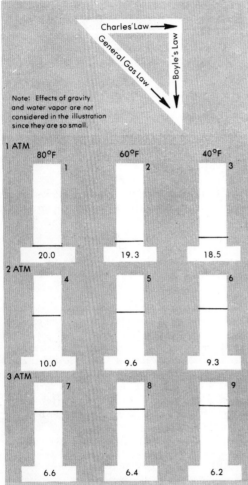

Note: Effects of gravity and water vapor are not considered in the illustration since they are so small.

Instructions:

(1) A uniform bore sealed-end tube with 20 divisions is inverted in a container of water at 80 degrees F and one atmosphere pressure. The conditions of temperature and pressure are then changed as illustrated to explain the three gas laws.

(2) Steps 1,2,3; 4,5,6; 7,8,9 (horizontally) illustrate Charles Law, i.e. the reduction of volume with reduction in temperature at a constant pressure.

(3) Steps 1,4,7; 2,5,8; 3,6,9 (vertically) illustrate Boyle's Law, i.e. at a constant temperature the volume is inversely related to the pressure.

(4) Steps 1,5,9; 3,5,7 (diagonally) illustrate the General Gas Law i.e. a combination of Charles' and Boyle's Laws.

Illustration: Morgan Wells

Stated mathematically:

$$\frac{P_1}{P_2} = \frac{T_1}{T_2} \text{ (volume constant)}$$

$$\frac{V_1}{V_2} = \frac{T_1}{T_2} \text{ (pressure constant)}$$

P_1 = initial pressure (absolute)
P_2 = final pressure (absolute)
T_1 = initial temperature (absolute)
T_2 = final temperature (absolute)
V_1 = initial volume
V_2 = final volume

To illustrate the use of Charles' Law, an example similar to the one previously used to illustrate Boyle's Law can be used.

Example 2 (Charles' Law)

A closed diving bell of 24 cubic feet capacity and atmospheric pressure is lowered from the surface to a depth of 99 feet in the ocean. At the surface, the temperature of the air is 80° F. At 99 feet the temperature is 33° F. Calculate the pressure in the bell when it is 33° F at the 99-foot level.

Because the volume of the closed bell is the same at the surface as it is at 99 feet, the decrease in the pressure is due to the change in the temperature. Therefore. using Charles' Law:

$$\frac{P_1}{P_2} = \frac{T_1}{T_2} \text{ (volume constant)}$$

P_1 = 14.7 psia (atmosphere pressure)
T_1 = 80° F + 460° F = 540° Rankine
T_2 = 33° F + 460° F = 493° Rankine

Transposing:

$$P_2 = \frac{P_1 T_2}{T_1}$$

$$P_2 = \frac{14.7 \times 493}{540}$$

$$P_2 = 13.42 \text{ psia}$$

Note that the pressure fell below atmospheric pressure due to the drop in temperature.

Example 3 (Charles' Law)

To further illustrate Charles' Law, consider the following example:

An open diving bell of 24 cubic feet capacity is lowered into the ocean to a depth of 99 feet. At the surface the temperature is 80° F, at depth the temperature is 45° F. What is the volume of the gas at 99 feet?

From Example 1 illustrating Boyle's Law, we know that the volume of the gas was compressed to 6 cubic feet when the bell was lowered to the 99-foot level from pressure effects above. The application of Charles' Law then illustrates the further reduction of volume due to temperature effects.

$$\frac{V_1}{V_2} = \frac{T_1}{T_2}$$

where

$V_1 =$ volume at depth, 6 cu ft
$T_1 = 80° \text{ F} + 460° \text{ F} = 540° \text{ Rankine}$
$T_2 = 45° \text{ F} + 460° \text{ F} = 505° \text{ Rankine}$

Transposing:

$$V_2 = \frac{V_1 T_2}{T_1}$$

$$V_2 = \frac{6 \times 505}{540}$$

$$V_2 = 5.61 \text{ cu ft}$$

1.5.4 Henry's Law

Henry's Law states that "The amount of any given gas that will dissolve in a liquid at a given temperature is a function of the partial pressure of that gas in contact with the liquid and the solubility coefficient of the gas in the particular liquid." Since a large percentage of the human body is water the law simply states that as one dives deeper and deeper, more gas will dissolve in the body tissues and that upon ascent, the dissolved gas must be released. The significance of this phenomenon coupled with the comparatively slow rates of solution in and release of gas from body tissues are developed fully in the discussion of decompression (See Paragraph 10.2).

The formula for Henry's Law is:

$$\frac{VG}{VL} = \alpha P_1$$

$VG =$ volume of gas dissolved at STPD (Standard Temperature Pressure Dry)
$P_1 =$ partial pressure in atmospheres of that gas above the liquid
$VL =$ volume of the liquid
$\alpha \ \ =$ Bunson solubility coefficient at specified temperatures

1.5.5 The General Gas Law

Boyle's and Charles' Law can be conveniently combined into what is known as the General Gas Law. This is expressed mathematically as follows:

$$\frac{P_1 V_1}{T_1} = \frac{P_2 V_2}{T_2}$$

where

$P_1 =$ initial pressure (absolute)
$V_1 =$ initial volume
$T_1 =$ initial temperature (absolute)

and

$P_2 =$ final pressure (absolute)
$V_2 =$ final volume
$T_2 =$ final temperature (absolute)

Example 4 (General Gas Law)

Let us again consider the open diving bell of 24 cubic feet capacity lowered to 99 feet in seawater from a surface temperature of 80° F to a depth temperature of 45° F. Determine the volume of the gas in the bell at depth.

The General Gas Law states:

$$\frac{P_1 V_1}{T_1} = \frac{P_2 V_2}{T_2}$$

$P_1 = 14.7$ psia
$V_1 = 24$ cu ft
$T_1 = 80° \text{ F} + 460° \text{ F} = 540° \text{ Rankine}$
$P_2 = 58.8$ psia
$T_2 = 45° + 460° \text{ F} = 505° \text{ Rankine}$

Transposing:

$$V_2 = \frac{P_1 V_1 T_2}{T_1 P_2}$$

$$V_2 = \frac{(14.7)(24)(505)}{(540)(58.8)}$$

$$V_2 = 5.61 \text{ cu ft}$$

This is the same answer as derived from a combination of Example 1 and Example 3 which were used to demonstrate Boyle's and Charles' Laws.

1.6 GAS FLOW (VISCOSITY)

There are occasions where it is desirable to determine the rate at which gas flows through orifices, hoses, and other limiting enclosures. This can be approximated for a given gas by employing Poiseuille's Law of Laminar Flow.

Poiseuille's Law of Laminar Flow:

$$V = \frac{\Delta P \pi}{8 L \eta}$$

V = gas flow, in $\text{cm}^3 \cdot \sec^{-1}$

ΔP = pressure gradient between 2 ends of tube, in $\text{dynes} \cdot \text{cm}^{-2}$

r = radius of tube, in cm

L = length of tube, in cm

η = viscosity, in poise

This equation can be used only in relatively simple systems where flow is laminar and which do not include a number of valves or restrictions. For practical applications the diver should note that as resistance is increased, the flow is reduced in direct proportion. Therefore, if the length of a line is doubled, the pressure must be doubled in order to maintain the same flow.

Nomograms for flow resistance through diving hoses can be found in the U.S. Navy Diving-Gas Manual.

1.7 MOISTURE IN BREATHING GAS

Breathing gas must have sufficient moisture for comfort. Too much moisture in a system can increase breathing resistance and produce congestion; too little can cause an uncomfortable sensation of dehydration in a diver's mouth, throat, nasal passages, and sinus cavities (U.S. Navy Diving Manual 1973). Air or other breathing gases supplied from surface compressors or tanks can be assumed to be dry. This dryness can be reduced by removing the mouthpiece and rinsing the mouth with water or introducing a small amount of water inside a full face mask. The use of gum or candy to reduce dryness while diving can be dangerous. The mouthpiece should not be removed in water which may be polluted.

1.7.1 Condensation in Breathing Tubes or Mask

Expired gas contains moisture that may condense in the breathing tubes or mask. This water is easily blown out through the exhaust valve and, in general, presents no problem. In very cold water freezing of the condensate can occur. Should the freezing of the condensate become serious enough to block the regulator mechanism, the dive should be aborted.

1.7.2 Fogging of the Mask

Condensation of expired moisture or evaporation from the skin may cause fogging of the face mask glass. Moistening of the glass with saliva, liquid soap, or commercially available anti-fog compounds will reduce or prevent this difficulty.

1.8 LIGHT AND UNDERWATER VISIBILITY

To function effectively in an underwater environment, a diver must understand the factors affecting his visual perception. The principal physical factor affecting visibility in the water is that light behaves differently in the denser water medium than it does in air. As light passes from a medium of one density to another, the light rays are bent and the effect known as "refraction" occurs. Refraction can cause an object to appear larger or smaller than its true size, and to appear in other than its true position. Refraction occurs at the surface, between the water and air interface, as well as at the interface between the water and the diver's mask.

With the eye functioning normally, refraction between air and water causes nearby objects to appear larger and closer than they actually are. This accounts for the difficulty often experienced by novice divers in attempting to grasp objects

Figure 1-5
Objects Under Water
Appear Closer

under water. The object appears to lie at a distance which is, in reality, approximately ¾ of its actual distance. This is shown in Figure 1–5. Beyond a distance of approximately 4 feet, however, this phenomenon partially tends to reverse itself. Reduced brightness and contrast, combined with the lack of normal visual distance relationships, cause faraway objects to again appear larger, but to appear farther away than they actually are. This distortion occurs even under optimum conditions of clear water and good lighting. Conditions of reduced lighting and/or increased turbidity will further impair the accurate perception of size and distance. Depending on the severity of the conditions involved, misinterpretation of size and distance due to refraction can be overcome or compensated for with experience and training (Kinney et al. 1968a).

"Diffusion" while occurring in air is further intensified under water. Light rays are diffused and scattered by the water molecules and particulate matter. At times diffusion is helpful in that it scatters light into areas that would otherwise be in shadow or have no illumination, at other times it is annoying because of the backscatter it produces which interferes with vision and underwater photography, particularly when artificial lighting is required.

1.8.1 Visibility of Colors

Distortion of underwater visibility is not limited to size and distance. A variety of factors may combine to alter the accurate perception of color. The use of colored paints on objects is an obvious means of changing their visibility either by enhancing their contrast with the surroundings or by camouflaging them to merge with their background. The problem of determining which colors will be most and least visible under water is, however, much more complicated than it is in air. Transmission of light through air does not appreciably change its spectral composition, but transmission through water can alter the appearance beyond recognition. Certain conditions of lighting and water hue may, for example, cause the color red to be perceived as black. This is readily explained when one considers that we see red objects on the surface because of the reflected red light. Because sea water absorbs red, no red light reaches the object, hence if it is a red reflector it appears as black. In the same way, a blue object in green water will also appear black, and a blue-green object in

ocean water and a yellow object in green water will resemble an object that was white or pale grey on the surface. Red and blue-green objects in green water and yellow and dark blue objects in clear ocean water will retain their color to considerable depths. Some substances with more than one peak in their spectral reflectance curve may appear quite different in color on land than under water. Blood is a good example: at the surface the reflectance maximum in the green is swamped by the red, but at depth the water absorbs the long wavelength red light and blood appears green. Both the quantity and quality of such changes depend on the particular body of water involved and the light source used. For this reason, the selective use of specific colors for underwater identification should result from actual on-site experimentation. Some experimental work has been done on the visibility of colors under water (Kinney et al. 1968b). Table 1–3 gives the results of these experiments, which were conducted by divers using spherical floats painted with different colors and illuminated by different types of light sources. The diver, the colored float, and the light source were at a depth of about 2 meters.

To summarize, as sunlight enters the water and travels to depth, red light is filtered out at relatively shallow depths in clear water. Orange is filtered out

Table 1-3
Colors That Give Best Visibility Against a Water Background

Water Condition	Natural Illumination	Incandescent Illumination	Mercury Light
Murky, turbid water of low visibility (rivers, harbors, etc.)	Fluorescent yellow, orange and red	Yellow, orange, red, white (no advantage in fluorescent paint)	Fluorescent yellow-green and yellow-orange
	Regular yellow, orange and white		Regular yellow, white
Moderately turbid water (sounds, bays, coastal water)	Any fluorescence in the yellow, orange or reds	Any fluorescence in the yellow, orange or reds	Fluorescent yellow-green or yellow-orange
	Regular paint of yellow, orange, white	Regular paint of yellow, orange, white	Regular yellow, white
Clear water (Southern water, deep water off-shore, etc.) (See Note)	Fluorescent paint	Fluorescent paint	Fluorescent paint

Note: With any type of illumination, fluorescent paints are superior.
    a. With long viewing distances, fluorescent green and yellow-green.
    b. With short viewing distances, fluorescent orange is also excellent.

next, then yellow, green, and blue. The filtering of various colors is not solely dependent on depth. Other factors, such as salinity, turbidity, or the degree of pollution have effects on the color filtering properties of the water. The above order could even be reversed in turbid water (Kinney et al. 1968b, Mertens 1970).

In general, the components of any underwater scene (weeds, rocks, encrusting animals, etc.) all tend to approach the same color as the depth or viewing range increases and are distinguished by differences in brightness and not of color. However, some colors (deep blue and yellow in clear blue water, or red and blue-green in yellow-green water) do tend to contrast strongly in color against the general scenery, and objects painted in these colors would be relatively easy to find. Fluorescent colors are always conspicuous because they emit light at wavelengths which are rarely present under water. Thus, not only do fluorescent objects retain their colors at all depths where there is light enough for color vision, but they are extremely unlikely to be displayed against a background of similarly fluorescent objects.

1.8.2 Dark Adaptation

Anytime there is a significant decrease in the

level of ambient light the eye must adapt accordingly. This can occur for the diver when he enters the water following exposure to bright sunlight especially if the water is dirty or as he descends to greater depths. As the light level decreases there is a switch from the day vision system where there is color vision, to the night vision system where there is not. While a substantial degree of dark adaptation occurs in the first ten minutes, the complete process may require over 30 minutes if the ambient brightness level just prior to entering the water was very high. This adaptation process accounts in part for the apparent loss of perceived color as the diver goes deeper. It also accounts for the feeling that the light level has increased as the diver remains on the bottom.

Although the diver's descent rate far exceeds the rate of dark adaptation, certain precautions may be taken prior to making a dive where the underwater light level is significantly below that on the surface. This is especially important during dives where bottom time is short and visual observation is important.

The night vision system of the eye is relatively insensitive to red light. If a red filter is worn over the faceplate for 30 minutes or so prior to diving, the eye reacts as though it were dark and adapts accordingly. Once the light becomes dim, the red filter is removed. Because high visual sensitivity is reached sooner when this procedure is used, visual tasks can be performed effectively at the beginning of a dive instead of 20-30 minutes later. If it is necessary to momentarily return to the surface the red filter should be worn, as exposure to bright sunlight will instantly destroy the dark adapted state of the eye.

1.9 ACOUSTICS

Sound is the result of vibrations being transmitted through some form of matter to the ear. Sound travels more rapidly through denser substances. Water is denser than air and, for this reason, is a better conductor of sound. A diver will hear sounds more clearly and at a greater distance than in air.

Underwater hearing is affected by several conditions not encountered in the atmosphere. These include:

1. Reverberations of sound resulting from reflections from the bottom.

2. Gradients and discontinuities in the water resulting from thermal and salinity conditions and microorganisms.

3. Noises caused by water movement and passing ships and marine life.

4. Type of head covering.

With the head submerged, the auditory localization ability of a diver is seriously impaired. In air sound travels at the rate of about 1,100 feet/second. The slight amount of time that elapses between the instant the sound wave hits one ear and then the other ear permits an individual to judge the direction from which the sound came. Sound travels in water at the rate of about 4,900 feet/second. The difference in time between the instant the sound wave hits one ear and then the other is so slight that the sound seems to surround the diver. However, recent studies have shown that humans possess some ability to localize sound under water. Localization is best for low frequency or broad band signals (less than 6000 HZ) (Feinstein 1973).

Sound is transmitted through water as a series of pressure waves. High intensity sound is transmitted by correspondingly high intensity pressure waves. A diver may be affected by a high intensity pressure wave that is transmitted from the water surrounding him to the open spaces within the body (ears, sinuses, lungs). The pressure wave may create increased pressure within these open spaces, which

could result in injury.

The sources of high intensity sound or pressure waves include underwater explosions and, in some cases, sonar. Low intensity sonars, such as depth finders and fish finders do not produce pressure waves of an intensity dangerous to a diver. However, some military anti-submarine sonar equipped ships do pulse high intensity pressure waves dangerous to a diver. It is prudent to suspend diving operations if a high powered sonar transponder is being operated in the area.* Underwater explosions are discussed in the following paragraph. The use of explosives is discussed in Paragraph 4.12.

1.10 UNDERWATER EXPLOSIONS

An underwater explosion produces a pressure wave that emanates outward from the source of the explosion in all directions. The pressure wave characteristics of an underwater explosion consist of an initial shock wave followed by a less pronounced pressure wave. The initial high intensity shock wave is the result of the violent liberation of high pressure gas produced by the explosion. The subsequent pressure wave is caused by the collapse of the gas pocket produced by the explosive charge.

The initial high pressure shock wave is the most dangerous and always travels away from the source of the explosion. Less severe pressure waves follow the high pressure wave very closely. Considerable turbulence and movement of water in the area of a high-order explosion is in evidence for an extended period of time after the explosion.

A number of factors affect the intensity of the shock wave and the pressure waves that follow the shock wave (Greenbaum and Hoff 1966). Each should be evaluated in terms of the particular circumstance in which the explosion occurs.

1. *The size of the explosive charge and the type of explosive utilized.* Some explosives produce a high-order, short duration explosion, resulting in a high level pressure wave of short duration. Other explosives produce lower order explosions that result in less intense but longer duration shock and pressure waves, which do more damage at a longer range. It is imperative that the characteristics of the explosive to be utilized be carefully evaluated prior to use, to estimate the type and duration of the shock and pressure waves.

2. *The character of the bottom.* Aside from the

---

*Robert D. Workman, M.D., 1973: personal communication.

fact that rock or other bottom debris may be propelled through the water by the explosion, the bottom conditions may have a dampening or amplifying effect on the shock and pressure waves. A soft bottom may tend to dampen the effect, while a hard bottom may amplify the effect. The contour of the bottom is an important consideration, as rock strata, ridges, and other topographical features may affect the direction of the shock and pressure waves, as well as produce secondary reflecting waves.

3. *The depth of the water.* At great depth, the pressure waves are attenuated through a greater water volume and thus reduced in intensity. An explosion near the surface is not attenuated to the same degree.

4. *The distance a diver is from the explosion.* In general, the farther away from the explosion, the greater the attenuation of the pressure wave and the less intensity. This factor must be considered in the context of the bottom conditions, depth of water, and reflection of shock and pressure waves from underwater structures and topographical features.

5. *The degree of submersion of the diver.* A fully submerged diver receives the total effect of the shock and pressure wave passing across his body. If a diver is only partially submerged with his head and upper parts of the body out of the water, the effect of the shock and pressure wave on his lungs, ears, and sinuses may be reduced; however, air will transmit some portion of the explosive shock and pressure wave. The head, lungs, and intestines are the parts of the body most vulnerable to the pressure effects of an explosion.

The following formula (Greenbaum and Hoff 1966) provides a means of estimating the pressure on a diver resulting from an explosion of tetryl or TNT. Note that this formula is not applicable to other explosives and should be used only to estimate the level of pressure on the diver in conjunction with factors described above.

$$P = 4,333 \frac{W^{1/3}}{r}$$

where

$P =$ pressure on the diver in pounds per square inch

$W =$ weight of the explosive (tetryl or TNT) in pounds

$r =$ range of the diver from the explosion in yards

A sample calculation shows that a 600-pound charge at a distance of 50 feet exerts a pressure of 2,180 pounds per square inch. Since a pressure wave of 500 pounds per square inch is sufficient to cause serious injury to the lungs and intestinal tract, a pressure wave over 2,000 pounds per square inch would certainly be fatal. Even a pressure wave of 500 pounds per square inch could cause fatal injury under certain conditions.*

It is prudent practice to limit the pressure a diver experiences from an explosion to a pressure less than 50 to 70 psi or best, to remove the diver from the water at the time of the explosion.

For scientific experimental work, very low order explosions are sometimes used to blast loose samples or create pressure waves through substrata. Each of these cases must be evaluated in terms of diver protection. Bottom conditions, degree of submersion of the diver, or protective measures afforded the diver can modify the effects of an explosion and are to be considered in planning a dive in which explosive experimentation is involved. Also, divers should be cautioned against diving nearby when sub-bottom profiling is being conducted using high-pressure air or high electrical discharges.

*Robert D. Workman, M.D., 1973: personal communication.

SECTION 2
DIVING
PHYSIOLOGY

DIVING PHYSIOLOGY 2

2.0 GENERAL

This section is intended to provide the diver with some basic knowledge as to how the body reacts to physiological stresses imposed under water, and how to compensate for these stresses, and to physical limitations. The diver should study the text and become familiar with the terminology necessary to understand and describe any symptoms or physical dysfunctions experienced. Table 2-1 contains the definitions of commonly used diving medical terms.

2.1 CIRCULATION AND RESPIRATION

The activity of each cell of the body consists of a variety of delicate reactions which can only take place under well-defined chemical and physicochemical conditions. The chief function of the circulatory system is to maintain conditions around the cells that are optimum for their activity. The regulation of cardiac output and the distribution of the blood are central problems of the physiology of circulation.

Respiration is the process whereby an appropriate interchange of gases, oxygen and carbon dioxide, occurs between the tissues and the atmosphere. During respiration, air enters and leaves the lungs via the nose or mouth—the pharynx—the larynx—the trachea and the bronchial tubes. The bronchial tubes enter the lungs and divide and re-divide into a branching network—ending in the terminal air sacs and alveoli. The alveoli are surrounded by a thin membrane. The interchange of gases takes place across this membrane where the blood in the tiny pulmonary capillaries takes up oxygen and gives off carbon dioxide. This process is shown schematically in Figure 2-1.

Preliminary to a study of diving physiology, it is necessary to acquire a rudimentary grasp of circulation and respiration and an acquaintance with certain problems associated with the air-containing compartments of the body as they are affected by pressure changes experienced during diving.

2.1.1 Circulatory System

The heart is divided longitudinally into the right and left hearts, each consisting of two communicating chambers, the auricles and ventricles. Blood is pumped by the right ventricle into the pulmonary artery, through the pulmonary capillaries, and back to the left heart through the pulmonary veins. The left heart pumps the blood into the aortic artery which distributes it to the various bodily organs. This distribution is accomplished by a continual branching of arteries which become smaller and smaller until they become capillaries. The capillaries have a thin wall through which the interchange of substances between blood and tissue takes place. The blood from the capillaries flows into venules, then into the veins and is returned to the heart. In this way, carbon dioxide produced in the tissues is removed, transported to the lungs and discharged. This process is shown schematically in Figure 2-2.

During exercise, there is an increase in frequency and force of the heart beat as well as a constriction of the vessels of the skin, alimentary canal and quiescent muscle. Peripheral resistance is increased and arterial pressure rises. Blood is expelled from the spleen, liver, skin, and other organs which also augments the inflow, thus the output of the heart. This augmented output is distributed mainly to the organs where vessels are least constricted or actually dilated—namely, the brain, the heart, and any active muscles. Thus, the body responds to exercise by sending additional blood (oxygen) to those areas most actively involved.

2-1

Table 2-1
Definitions of
Diving Medical Terms

1. **Aerodontalgia**   Small gas pockets in the central pulp of a tooth.

2. **Alveolus**   A small membranous sac, which is the end portion of the respiratory system in the lung, wherein the gaseous exchange takes place.

3. **Anoxia**   The total lack of oxygen.

4. **Apnea**   The cessation of breathing for short intervals of time.

5. **Bradycardia**   Slowness of the heart beat.

6. **Bronchi**   Fibro-muscular tubes connecting the trachea to the smaller portions of the respiratory tract.

7. **Carotid Sinus**   A small dilatation in the carotid artery in the neck just below its bifurcation that is surrounded by an extensive nerve network, and which is sensitive to pressure changes within the carotid artery, ensuring arterial pressure is maintained at a suitable level.

8. **Chemoreceptor**   Carotid and aortic bodies sensitive to changes in the partial pressures of oxygen and CO_2 in the blood, playing an important part in the regulation of respiration.

9. **Cyanosis**   A bluish discoloration of the skin from deficient oxidation of the blood.

10. **Dysbarism**   A general term applied to any clinical condition caused by a difference between the surrounding atmospheric pressure and the total gas pressure in the various tissues, fluids, and body cavities.

11. **Dyspnea**   Difficulty of breathing due to depth increase.

12. **Edema**   Excessive amount of fluid in tissues.

13. **Embolus**   A clot or other plug brought by the blood from another vessel and forced into a smaller one so as to obstruct the circulation.

14. **Eustachian Tube**   A canal, partly bony and partly cartilaginous, connecting the pharynx with the tympanic cavity serving as an air channel by which air pressure within the tympanic cavity is equalized with that outside.

15. **Expiration**   Expelling air from the lungs.

16. **Expiratory Reserve**   The amount of air that can be exhaled out of the lungs after normal expiration.

17. **External Ear**   That portion of the ear from the outermost portion to the tympanic membrane encompassing the external canal.

18. **Hemorrhage**   The loss of blood from the vascular system.

19. **Hypercapnia**   Undue amount of carbon dioxide in the blood, causing overactivity in the respiratory center.

20. **Hyperventilation**   Breathing excessively fast.

21. **Hypoxia**   Failure of the tissues to receive enough oxygen.

22. **Inner Ear**   That portion of the ear located within the bony confines of the temple bone, and containing the organs of equilibrium and hearing.

23. **Inspiration**   Drawing air into the lungs.

24. **Inspiratory Reserve**   The maximum amount of air that can be breathed in after normal expiration.

25. **Mediastinum**   That portion of the chest cavity, located between the right and left lungs, containing the heart, the major vessels and some of the major nerves traversing from the neck to the abdomen.

26. **Middle Ear**   That portion of the ear between the tympanic membrane and the bony enclosure of the semicircular canals. This portion contains the three bony otoliths for the transmission of the movement of the tympanic membrane and also contains the opening of the eustachian canal.

27. **pH**   A symbol representing hydrogen ion concentration in a fluid, thus indicating acidity or alkalinity.

28. **Pneumothorax**   The presence of air or gas in the pleural cavity resulting from a rupture of an alveolus allowing the pleural space to come into equilibrium with the external pressure.

29. **Residual Volume**   The amount of air left in the lungs after a maximal expiratory effort.

30. **Sinuses**   Cavities within the bones of the skull lined by epithelium and connected by small openings to the nasal passageways.

31. **Tachycardia**   Excessive rapidity of heart beat.

32. **Thrombus**   A plug or clot in a blood vessel or in one of the cavities of the heart.

33. **Tidal Volume**   The volume of the air breathed in and out of the lungs during normal respiration.

34. **Trachea**   That portion of the breathing apparatus that extends from the posterior oropharynx or the posterior portion of the mouth to the chest cavity.

35. **Tympanic Membrane**   A thin membranous partition separating the external ear from the middle ear.

36. **Vital Capacity**   Maximal volume of air which can be expired after maximal inspiration.

2.1.2 Mechanism of External Respiration

The chest wall encloses a cavity, the volume of which is altered by rhythmic contraction and relaxation of muscles. This thoracic cavity contains the lungs which are connected with outside air through the bronchi, the trachea, and the upper respiratory passages (See Figure 2–1). When a change is made in the volume of the thoracic cavity, a decrease or increase in pressure occurs within the internal chambers and passages of the lungs. Air is thereby caused to flow into or out of the lungs through the respiratory passageways until the pressure everywhere in the lungs is equalized to the external pressure. This equilibrium is upset when the chest wall is again moved and the lungs assume a new volume. Respiratory ventilation takes place by rhythmic changes of this sort. It is affected by muscular action of the diaphragm and chest wall under control of the nervous system which itself is responding to changes in blood oxygen and carbon dioxide levels. The normal respiratory rate at rest varies from about 12 to 16 times a minute. During and following heavy exertion, this rate may be increased severalfold.

In the normal resting position of the chest wall, that is, at the end of natural expiration, the lungs contain about 2.5 liters of air. Even when one voluntarily expels all the air possible, there still remains about 1.5 liters of *residual air*. The volume of air that is inspired and expired during rest is referred to as *tidal air* and averages about 0.5 liters per cycle. The additional volume (beyond the resting expiratory position of 2.5 liters) which can be taken in during a maximal inspiration, varies greatly from individual to individual but ranges from about 2 to 6 liters. The total breathable volume of air, called the *vital capacity*, depends upon the

**Figure 2-1
The Process
of Respiration**

**Figure 2-2
The Circulatory System**

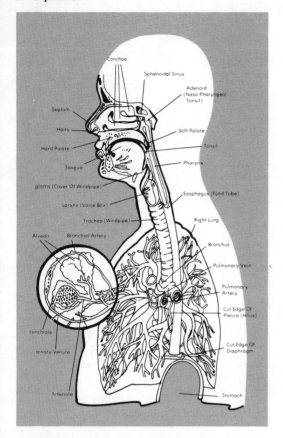

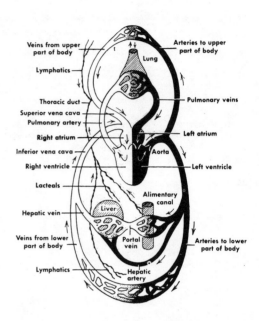

Diagram of circulation of the blood. Arterial, or oxygenated, blood is shown in black; venous blood is shown in white. Lymphatics are black knotty lines. From McClendon, J.F.: Physiological Chemistry, ed 7, St. Louis, 1946, The C. V. Mosby Co.

size, development, and physical condition of the individual. Vital capacity is defined as the maximal volume that can be expired after maximal inspiration. A reduction in vital capacity limits the ability to respond adequately to a demand for increased ventilation during exercise. Because diving can require strenuous exercise, cardiovascular or respiratory disorders may seriously limit or prevent an individual from actively participating.

2.1.2.1 Pulmonary Ventilation

Air drawn into the lungs is distributed through smaller and smaller air passages until it reaches the honeycomb-like alveoli or air sacs through which the exchange of respiratory gases takes place (See Figure 2–1).

The rates at which oxygen may be supplied and

carbon dioxide removed from the lungs depend upon several factors: (1) the composition and volume of the air supplied through the respiratory passages, (2) the partial pressures of respiratory gases in the blood, and (3) the duration of exposure of a given volume of blood to alveolar air. In a normal individual in good physical condition other factors influencing respiratory exchange are not likely to be significant.

At rest, about 0.5 liters of oxygen are utilized by the tissues per minute. During exercise a maximal exchange of about 3.5 liters or more of oxygen per minute may take place. The flexibility of the ventilatory system is accomplished by increased movement of the chest, and by increased heart action propelling blood through the pulmonary capillaries, and by increased differences in partial pressures of oxygen and carbon dioxide during exercise. Figure 2–3 depicts oxygen consumption as a function of work rate. Normally, despite wide differences in rates of gaseous exchange between resting and heavy exercise conditions, the blood leaving the lungs is almost completely saturated with oxygen.

2.1.2.2 Blood Transport of Oxygen and Carbon Dioxide

Blood can take up a much greater quantity of oxygen and carbon dioxide than can be carried in simple solution. Hemoglobin, which is the principal constituent in red blood cells and gives the red color to blood, has a chemical property of combining with oxygen and with carbon dioxide and carbon monoxide. The oxygen-carrying capacity of the blood is increased by virtue of its normal hemoglobin content by a factor of about 50. The reaction between oxygen and hemoglobin is governed primarily by the partial pressure of oxygen. At sea level where there is normally an oxygen partial pressure of 150 millimeters of mercury the alveolar hemoglobin becomes about 98 percent saturated in terms of its capacity to form oxy-hemoglobin. In the tissues where the partial pressure of oxygen is normally about 20 millimeters of mercury, more than half of this oxygen is given up by hemoglobin and made available to the tissues. It is apparent that persons lacking a sufficiency of hemoglobin, i.e., anemic persons, will be deficient in their capacity to carry oxygen. Hence, they will be less fit as divers.

Hemoglobin will also combine readily with carbon monoxide which may be present in contaminated air (See Paragraph 2.1.3.4).

The blood contains a small amount of carbon dioxide in simple solution, but a greater amount is found in chemical combinations such as carbonic acid, bicarbonate, or combinations thereof. All the forms of carbon dioxide tend toward chemical equilibrium with each other. Of some advantage with respect to the transport of respiratory gases is the fact that the taking up of oxygen by hemoglobin in the lung capillaries actually favors the unloading of carbon dioxide, at the same time, while the absorption of carbon dioxide into the blood in the tissues favors the release of oxygen.

2.1.2.3 Gas Exchange in the Tissues

The exchange of oxygen and carbon dioxide between the blood and body cells is in opposite directions. Oxygen, being continually used up in the tissues, exists there at a lower partial pressure than in the blood. Carbon dioxide is produced inside the tissue cells, thereby making its partial pressure there higher than that of the blood reaching the tissues. Therefore, blood supplied by the arteries gives up oxygen and receives carbon dioxide during its transit through the tissue capillaries. The rate of exchange of these respiratory gases and the total amount of gas movement is dependent upon the respective partial pressure differences, since the exposure time of blood in the tissue capillaries is adequate for practically complete equilibration to be established. When tissues are more active the need for oxygen is greater. The increased oxygen is supplied not from an increase in the oxygen content of the arterial blood which is already approximately at maximum, but by a larger volume of blood flow through the tissues and by a more complete release of oxygen from a given volume of the blood. There can be a ninefold increase in the rate of oxygen supplied to active tissues.

2.1.2.4 Tissue Need for Oxygen

All living tissues need oxygen but tissues that are especially active during exertion, such as skeletal muscle, need correspondingly greater amounts of oxygen. The brain, however, is made up of tissue that has an extraordinarily high and nearly steady requirement for oxygen. Although the nervous system represents only about 2 percent of the body weight, it requires about 20 percent of the total circulation and 20 percent of the total oxygen used by the body per minute at work or at rest. If the oxygen supply is precipitously and completely cut off and the lungs emptied by a full expiration, consciousness may be lost in about one-quarter of a minute, respiratory failure will occur within a minute, and irreparable damage to higher centers of the brain will occur within 3 to 5 minutes (See Paragraph 2.1.3.1).

2.1.2.5 Summary of Respiration Process

The process of respiration includes seven important phases (U.S. Navy Diving Manual 1973).

1. Breathing or ventilation of the lungs.
2. Exchange of gases between blood and air in the lungs.
3. The transportation of gases carried by the blood.
4. Exchange of gases between blood and body tissues.

5. Exchange of gases between the tissue fluids and cells.

6. Use and production of gases by the cells.

7. Return of waste products.

Each phase of this process is important to the life of the cells, and must be maintained constantly by the respiratory and circulatory systems.

2.1.3 Respiratory Problems

While most physiological problems associated with diving are related to breathing gases at the high pressures encountered under water, respiratory problems may manifest themselves at the surface as well. In general, these problems relate to inadequate transportation of oxygen to the cells and to the removal of carbon dioxide. Several of the common respiratory problems are *hypoxia; carbon dioxide excess; asphyxia, suffocation, strangulation; and carbon monoxide poisoning.* Each of these is discussed in the following paragraphs.

2.1.3.1 Hypoxia

The term hypoxia, or oxygen shortage, is used in any situation in which tissue cells fail to receive or are unable to obtain enough oxygen to maintain their normal function. Hypoxia can result from interference with any phase of the oxygen transport process.

Hypoxia will stop the normal function of cells, with the cells of brain tissue being most susceptible. Unconsciousness and death can occur before effects on other cells are apparent. Sudden unconsciousness may occur or, if onset is gradual, orientation or the ability to think clearly or to perform certain tasks will be decreased. Confusion, and difficulty in standing, walking, and maintaining coordination, will follow. The victim of hypoxia may be unaware he is in trouble, while drowsiness, weakness, and unconsciousness increase. Blueness of the lips and skin develops when the blood is unable to absorb enough oxygen to regain its red color, but this is not readily noticeable under water. Unconsciousness will develop almost at once in sudden severe hypoxia. Consciousness is usually lost when the partial pressure of oxygen reaches 0.10 atmospheres; i.e., the equivalent of breathing a 10 percent oxygen mixture at atmospheric pressure. Below this level, permanent brain damage and death will follow quickly (U.S. Navy Diving Manual 1973).

If a diver suffering from severe hypoxia is not rescued quickly, the interference with brain function will cause failure of breathing control. If given fresh air promptly before his breathing stops, he will usually regain consciousness shortly and recover completely. If breathing has stopped but heart action continues, artificial respiration may enable oxygen to reach the brain and revive the breathing control center so that spontaneous breathing will resume. It is difficult to know that the heart action has stopped completely, so efforts at resuscitation must be continued until medical attendants pronounce a victim dead. A particular danger of hypoxia is that, as it progresses, it causes a false sense of euphoria (well-being) which may prevent the diver from taking corrective action soon enough.

WARNING

There Is No Natural Warning by Which the Diver Can Be Sure of Detecting the Onset of Hypoxia.

2.1.3.2 Carbon Dioxide Excess (Hypercapnia)

An excess of carbon dioxide in the tissues can be caused by interference with the process of carbon dioxide transport and elimination. In diving, carbon dioxide excess occurs either because of an excess of the gas in the breathing medium or because of interference with eliminating the carbon dioxide produced. There is only about 0.033 percent in clean fresh air. In most diving situations the source of the excess carbon dioxide is the diver's own metabolic processes. The proper carbon dioxide level in the body is maintained by breathing a sufficient amount to dilute and exhale the carbon dioxide produced and delivered to the lungs. For breathing to be effective, the air inhaled must contain a minimum of carbon dioxide. Inadequate helmet or mask ventilation or failure of the carbon dioxide absorption system of closed or semiclosed circuit breathing systems may produce an excess of carbon dioxide in the gas breathed.

All tissues are affected with the brain being the most susceptible. Confusion and drowsiness become more severe as the excess increases to levels of 0.10 and 0.15 atmospheres partial pressure. Above 0.15 atmospheres partial pressure, muscle spasms and rigidity can occur. If a diver loses consciousness because of excess carbon dioxide alone, he usually revives quickly when the lungs are ventilated with fresh air. Aftereffects include headache,

**Figure 2-3
Oxygen Consumption
as a Function
of Work Rate**

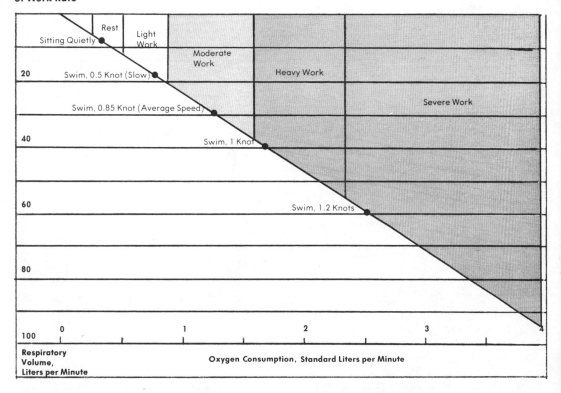

nausea, dizziness, and sore chest muscles.

Figure 2–4 shows the relation of physiological effects of carbon dioxide for different concentrations and exposure periods. In Zone I, no perceptible physiological effects have been observed. In Zone II, small threshold hearing losses have been found and there is a perceptible doubling in depth of respiration. In Zone III, the zone of distracting discomfort, the symptoms are mental depression, headache, dizziness, nausea, "air hunger," and a decrease in visual discrimination. Zone IV represents marked physical distress leading to dizziness and stupor, with inability to take steps for self-preservation. The final state is unconsciousness (U.S. Navy Diving-Gas Manual 1971).

The bar graph at the right, for prolonged exposures of 40 days, shows that concentrations of carbon dioxide in air of less than 0.5 (0.005 ata partial pressure) percent (Zone A) cause no biochemical or other effects, concentrations between 0.5 and 3.0 (0.005–0.03 ata partial pressure) per-

cent (Zone B) cause adaptive biochemical changes, which may be considered a mild physiological strain, and concentrations above 3.0 (0.03 ata partial pressure) percent (Zone C) cause pathological changes in basic physiological functions.

It is recommended that, for normal diving operations, ventilation rates be provided that result in carbon dioxide partial pressures corresponding to Zones I and II for short-term exposure, and to Zones A and B for long-term exposures.

Increased carbon dioxide in the breathing mixture stimulates the respiratory center to increase the breathing rate. Carbon dioxide at 0.02 atmospheres partial pressure will generally increase breathing noticeably, but overexertion, with the consequent increase in breathing rate, may mask the increase of breathing rate resulting from increased carbon dioxide in the breathing mixture.

With 0.05 atmospheres partial pressure an uncomfortable sensation of shortness of breath occurs. There are large differences in the response

2-7

**Figure 2-4
Relation of Physiological
Effects to Carbon Dioxide
Concentration
and Exposure Period**

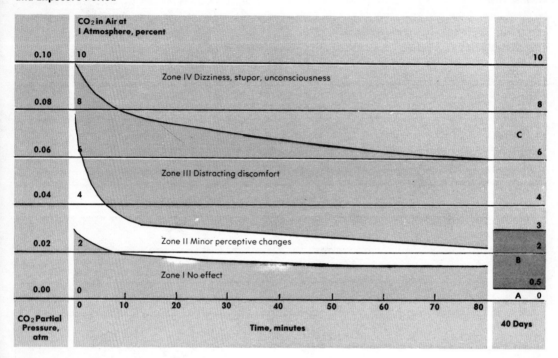

between individuals in the reaction to carbon dioxide. The amount of work, the depth, and the breathing medium are factors which will also alter the effect on breathing. Deliberate reduction of breathing will cause a carbon dioxide buildup, therefore, an adequate ventilation rate is required to effectively remove carbon dioxide from the lungs.

WARNING

Skip Breathing Is Never a Safe Procedure as Carbon Dioxide Buildup Gives Little or No Warning Symptoms.

Other conditions which increase the likelihood of carbon dioxide poisoning include severe exertion, high partial pressure of oxygen, high gas density, and breathing apparatus with excessive dead space or high breathing resistance.

2.1.3.3 Asphyxia, Suffocation, and Strangulation

Asphyxia means the existence of both hypoxia and carbon dioxide excess in the body. Asphyxia results if breathing ceases for any reason. It occurs

if a breathing gas low in oxygen and high in carbon dioxide is breathed. The term suffocation is sometimes used to indicate stoppage of breathing from any cause, and resulting asphyxia.

Strangulation means stoppage of breathing due to obstruction of the airway, such as crushing of the windpipe, lodging of a foreign body in the windpipe, spasm or swelling of the larynx, or the inhalation of water or vomitus. A victim will struggle violently and try to breathe in spite of the obstruction, before losing consciousness from asphyxia. Artificial respiration will produce little movement of air unless the obstruction is removed (See Paragraph 17.4).

2.1.3.4 Carbon Monoxide Poisoning

Carbon monoxide in inspired air combines with hemoglobin in the red blood cells, rendering them incapable of carrying oxygen to the tissues. Tissue hypoxia results even though there is sufficient oxygen in the air breathed. Hemoglobin combines with carbon monoxide about 200 times more readily than with oxygen, so very small concentrations can be dangerous to life (U.S. Navy Diving Manual 1973). The combination is red in color so that an unnatural redness of lips and skin may occur rather than the blueness usually associated with hypoxia. This redness may not occur, however, so that carbon monoxide poisoning cannot be discounted in a person with normal or pale skin. Because oxygen is not delivered to tissues in sufficient quantities, the symptoms are identical to other types of hypoxia. A sudden onset of unconsciousness may occur if the concentration of carbon monoxide is high enough to cause rapid poisoning without awareness of weakness, dizziness, or confusion. If more gradual in onset, pounding headache, nausea, and vomiting may occur.

Two likely sources of contamination of breathing gas by carbon monoxide are the exhaust from a gasoline or diesel engine and the "flashing" of oil vapors in an oil lubricated compressor. It is essential that air intakes on compressors used to provide breathing air in filled tanks be protected from this source of carbon monoxide contamination (See Paragraph 5.1.3).

When unconsciousness in a diver occurs, carbon monoxide must be considered as a possible cause. Often recompression will be carried out simply because cerebral decompression sickness and air embolism cannot be ruled out. Administration of oxygen at a safe depth in a recompression chamber using the treatment procedures described in Section 16 can be of great value in treating carbon monoxide poisoning. If a victim resumes breathing and regains consciousness after a reasonably short period of treatment, the chances of complete recovery are good.

2.1.3.5. Excessive Resistance to Breathing

Any breathing apparatus used by a diver under water will increase the work of breathing to some extent. If the breathing resistance is high, adequate breathing may be difficult even during ordinary exertion, and impossible during hard work.

Breathing is significantly affected by the equipment a diver uses. Resistance to the flow of breathing gas is caused by demand regulators, valves, hoses, and other appurtenances of a life support system. Well-designed equipment minimizes the resistance to the flow of breathing gas.

The resistance to breathing is complicated by the characteristics of gases flowing through tubes of varying sizes and configurations which are used in the breathing apparatus. Gases moving through tubes of optimal design will flow "in line" or in *laminar* flow until restrictions or the dimensions of the tube cause the air molecules to begin moving in a circular fashion or *turbulent* flow. The increased effort required to move gas in turbulent flow is significant. It is also known that the resistance to flow goes up as the square of the increased flow rate. That is, doubling the flow rate will result in four times the resistance which must be overcome (See Paragraph 1.6). This is a significant problem with small bore snorkels, small diameter exhaust valves or inadequate breathing tubes. Thus, snorkels should be large diameter (approximately 3/4 inch) with no unnecessary bends, corrugations, or obstructions and exhaust valves should be large enough to keep the exhalation resistance as low as possible.

Breathing resistance is not a problem in "free-flow" helmet-type diving apparatus except for the effects of increased density of the breathing mixture at depth.

The position of the demand valve or breathing bag (in closed-circuit scuba) is critical in relation to internal pressure in the lungs, to avoid unbalanced hydrostatic pressure causing increased breathing resistance (Figure 2–5). As work of breathing increases, a diver is uncomfortable during work, and respiratory muscles become fatigued so that the work level is limited. As the work of breathing increases, the body reaches a point where it will accept increased carbon dioxide rather than perform the respiratory work required to maintain normal carbon dioxide in the tissues (U.S. Navy Diving Manual 1973). This can lead to carbon dioxide intoxication.

2.1.3.6 Overexertion

It is possible for divers to exceed their work capacity before realizing they are in trouble from overexertion. When this occurs under water, the problem is considerably more serious than on land. The sensation of suffocation can produce panic and a serious accident. The diver may begin hyperventilating, thus demanding air at a higher rate than the regulator can provide.

WARNING

The Diver Should Stop All Activity, Relax, and Allow the Breathing Rate to Gradually Return to Normal.

If strenuous work is anticipated, a few rapid breaths should be taken prior to entering the water to test the breathing apparatus. Underwater work should be properly paced to avoid overexertion.

2.1.3.7 Excessive Dead Space

"Dead space" in a diving system is that space in which residual exhaled air remains. A diver exhaling into a full face mask may return some of this exhaled gas to the lungs. The amount is a function of the dead space volume within the mask. A well-designed mask has minimum dead space. Dead space may not be readily apparent in a casual examination; therefore, special equipment is used to measure this ineffective volume by determining how much exhaled gas is actually rebreathed.

Full face masks may add as much as 0.5 liters of ineffective space requiring ventilation with each breath (U.S. Navy Diving Manual 1973). This can seriously limit a diver's ability to do work because of the additional breathing required if a CO_2 buildup occurs. This is not a problem with a "free-flow" helmet. An increase in carbon dioxide in the tissues will occur with any amount of added dead space, because the added breathing required will produce more carbon dioxide and more is inhaled. The use of oral-nasal masks inside the full face mask is effective in reducing dead space yet permitting the use of communication systems in the mask (See Paragraph 4.5.2).

2.1.3.8 Hyperventilation and Breath-Holding

The respiratory system utilizes both carbon dioxide (CO_2) and oxygen (O_2) tensions in the body to stimulate the process of breathing. Rising CO_2 tension and falling O_2 tension are monitored by biological sensors in the body which normally trigger the breathing response when the levels are appropriate. Hyperventilation (rapid unusually deep breathing in excess of the necessary rate for the level of activity), interferes with the normal operation of the respiratory control mechanism. Hyperventilation lowers the CO_2 level in the body below normal, a condition known as *hypocapnia*. This normally results in a feeling of lightheadedness. Over a longer period of time, weakness, faintness, headache, and blurring of vision can result. It may, however, prevent the control mechanism from responding until CO_2 tension has risen above, or O_2 tension has fallen below, the level necessary

to maintain consciousness.

Extended breath-holding after hyperventilation is not a safe procedure. During the longer breath-hold, the diver's oxygen level can fall to a low value before he realizes that he must return to the surface and resume breathing. The oxygen level is lowered because exertion not only causes oxygen to be used up faster but decreases the sensitivity of the CO_2 breakpoint mechanism. This permits the O_2 level to go even lower than it would otherwise. When the diver ascends, the drop in partial pressure of oxygen in the lungs may be sufficient to stop further uptake of oxygen completely. At the same time, the partial pressure of CO_2 in the lungs also drops, and gives a false sense of relief from the need to breathe.

Hyperventilation initiated by anxiety and/ or physical stress may result in unconsciousness or muscle spasms. The diver may not be aware of the pending problem. In the water this can result in drowning. Some individuals are more susceptible to hypocapnia than others; however, loss of consciousness and muscle spasms could probably be induced in almost anyone with sufficiently prolonged hyperventilation.

Both scuba and surface-supplied divers should be aware of the problems associated with hyperventilation. If the diver notices that he is involuntarily hyperventilating, he should take immediate steps to slow his breathing rate. A scuba diver should notify his buddy and, if feasible, promptly ascend. When reaching the surface, the lifejacket should be inflated. The diver should not attempt to swim to the boat or shore unaided as unconsciousness may be imminent. A tender should continuously monitor the diver's breathing for signs of hyperventilation. If the diver starts to hyperventilate, he should be asked to stop work and rest. Once on the surface, holding the breath for short periods will aid in replenishing low CO_2 levels and possibly avert further complications. Drowning and the hyperventilation syndrome are discussed in detail by Prasser (1969).

2.2 EFFECTS OF PRESSURE

The effects of pressure on divers may be divided into two principal categories: (1) those that are direct and mechanical; and (2) those that come about because of changes in the partial pressure of inspired gases.

With each 2-foot increase in depth of seawater, the pressure increases by almost 1 psi. Each 33 feet

**Figure 2-5
Effects of Hydrostatic
Pressure on Location
of Breathing Bags Within
a Closed-Circuit Scuba**

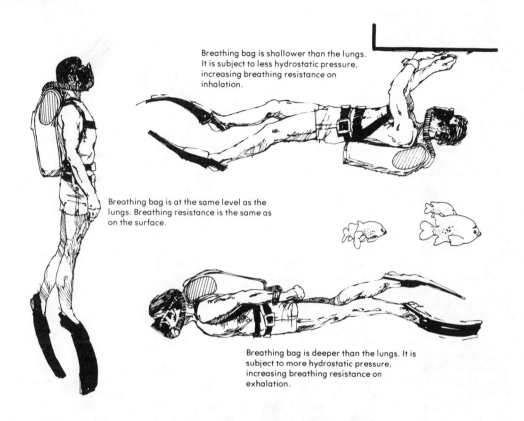

Breathing bag is shallower than the lungs. It is subject to less hydrostatic pressure, increasing breathing resistance on inhalation.

Breathing bag is at the same level as the lungs. Breathing resistance is the same as on the surface.

Breathing bag is deeper than the lungs. It is subject to more hydrostatic pressure, increasing breathing resistance on exhalation.

of descent in seawater increases the pressure by an additional atmosphere (14.7 psi).

The lungs and respiratory passages contain air at all times. In addition to the major air channels which include the nose, mouth, throat, larynx or voice box, and trachea, there are a number of side compartments issuing from the upper respiratory passages which are of importance in diving physiology. These include the eustachian tubes and the paranasal sinuses. During exposure of the body to pressure changes, as in diving, air contained in these cavities will undergo compression since the pressure of air delivered from the scuba is equilibrated to the surrounding hydrostatic pressure. The pressure of air breathed in and out of the lungs and respiratory passages will therefore also change in accordance with changes in the surrounding hydrostatic pressure.

2.2.1 Direct Effects of Pressure During Descent

Increased pressures can be tolerated providing they are uniformly distributed throughout the body. However, when outside pressure exceeds that inside the body air spaces, the difference in pressure may distort the shape of the involved tissues, causing injury to them. This is called *barotrauma*. The earliest signs are discomfort in the ears and sinuses, and swelling of tissues and blood vessels. As the pressure difference increases, small blood vessels rupture and heavy bleeding ensues.

Pressure in such spaces as the sinuses and the middle ear must be equalized on descent, or pressure differences will develop across their walls. Once equalized at a given depth, the air must also

2-11

vent freely during decrease of pressure. The effects of pressure on various parts of the body are discussed in the following paragraphs.

2.2.1.1 The Ears

Figure 2–6 illustrates the principal parts of the ear. *Aerotitis* (middle ear "squeeze") may be prevented by learning how to equalize pressure through the eustachian tubes, which lead from the middle ear cavity behind the eardrum to the upper expanded portion of the throat behind the nasal cavities above the palate.

Air contained within the eustachian tube is not in free communication with the throat in all individuals. This passageway is often relatively long and narrow, leaving the sides of the tube collapsed together, thereby making the passage of air in either direction, i.e., into or out of the middle ear compartment, somewhat difficult.

The passage of air from the middle ear outwards is ordinarily easier to accomplish than the admission of air into the middle ear from the throat. Consequently greater difficulty is generally experienced in equalizing the ears during descent. Air in the middle ear will tend to be compressed during descent and will require the addition of compressed air from the throat at successively greater depths in order to prevent inward rupture of the eardrum or hemorrhage from the mucous membranes lining the middle ear.

Successful methods of equalizing pressure are swallowing, yawning, or blowing against closed mouth and nostrils. When eustachian tube blockage prevents the equalization of pressure in the middle ear, causing painful inflammation with possible rupture of the eardrum, pain will be experienced in the first few feet of descent. Further descent will increase the pain, stretch the eardrum, and dilate and eventually rupture the blood vessels in the eardrum. The lining of the middle ear space is rich with blood vessels. These blood vessels may, upon serious pressure differentials between the pressure in the blood and the lower pressure in the middle ear space, expand, hemorrhage, and, in an extreme case, burst. Rupture of the eardrum may be caused by as little as three pounds of pressure differential which can take place anywhere in the water column.

Infections including a head cold, sinusitis, or sore throat can seriously interfere with the equalization of pressure in the middle ear and sinuses. However,

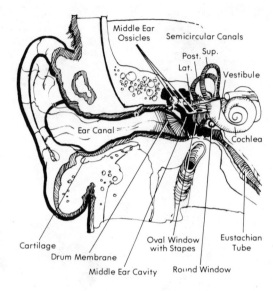

Figure 2-6
Principal Parts
of the Ear

a mild or slight head cold should not interfere with diving if a diver feels reasonably well and can equalize pressure without difficulty.

There are some prophylactic measures that can be employed for mild nasal congestion. A topical nasal decongestant (nose spray) — long acting type — 15 to 20 minutes prior to entering the water. Oxymetazoline is particularly effective. Use of a systemic decongestant, i.e., Pseudoephedrine, 15 to 20 minutes prior to entering the water may also be effective. A word of caution is necessary since it is possible that the diver may have a rare idiosyncratic reaction to the medication such as extreme drowsiness from an antihistamine, or excessive swelling of the nasal membranes shortly after using a spray. Disaster could result if this occurred in the water. For this reason all newly prescribed decongestant medications should be used on a trial basis at some period prior to diving.

Problems of equalization may also be avoided if extra care is used on descent. Some simple steps are:

■ Descend feet first, preferably down the anchor

line or a drop line. Advance of the lower body portions before the eustachian tube areas permits a more gradual equalization of pressure to the middle ears.

- Self-inflation of the middle ear should be carried out actively and conscientiously every two to three feet of descent. It may even be necessary to introduce the finger and thumb under the mask to squeeze the nostrils closed; this will flood the mask to adequately pressurize. It is well to inflate the middle ears prior to entering the water in anticipation of pressure changes.

- If pain develops, ascend a few feet and work on inflation, as outlined above. It is sometimes helpful to move the jaws or head from side to side or to move the head backward and forward. If inflation is impossible, abort the dive.

WARNING

Never Dive With an Upper Respiratory Congestion or Infection.

Cold water entering the external ear canal can upset the balance of a diver until the water in the external canal has been warmed by body heat. Pressure imbalance between the two sides of the eardrum can also be a contributing factor. Vertigo is often experienced as a result of such conditions.

Treatment of mild ear damage is symptomatic. Analgesics are indicated when pain is intense. Pain usually subsides gradually. If pain persists, thereby suggesting infection, systemic antibiotics and nasal and systemic vasoconstrictors are indicated to promote drainage and combat infection.

When the eardrum is ruptured, blood may drain through the external auditory canal but may not be visible. Retained blood is usually absorbed within a few days with no impairment of hearing. If the rupturing of the eardrum occurs in the water, vertigo may also be experienced; again, this will pass upon warming of the water in the middle ear. Local application of medication to the ear canal is ordinarily not advised, and care should be exercised to prevent water from entering the external auditory canal until healing is complete. This may take days or weeks, depending on the severity of the injury.

Another concern for the diver is ear infection. The prevention and treatment of this problem is found in Paragraph 17.2.5.

2.2.1.2 The Sinuses

Figure 2–7 shows the location of the sinus cavities.

Ordinarily, air in the sinuses behind the cheek and the brow and within the smaller sinuses situated in the roof of the nasal passages has free access to the respiratory passages through openings into the nose. However, in some instances the sinus openings may be abnormally small, chronically inflamed or acutely inflamed during a head cold. If any of these conditions exist, changes in depth will be marked by feeling tension, pressure, or pain in the region of the sinus involved. Vasoconstrictors may be helpful, as in barotitis, but if infection develops, as indicated by persistent pain, systemic antibiotics may be required. See Paragraph 2.2.1.1 for use of decongestants.

2.2.1.3 The Lungs

As long as normal breathing takes place with an ample breathing supply, the lungs and airways will equalize pressure without difficulty. If the breath is held during pressure increase, no difficulty arises until the total volume of air in the lungs is compressed to less than the residual volume. Pulmonary congestion, swelling, and hemorrhage of lung tissue then occurs in what is generally called "*thoracic squeeze.*" Figure 2–8 shows pressure effects on lung volume.

In breath hold diving, no high pressure air is available to the lungs. Pressure compresses the diver's chest and raises his diaphragm: pressure equalization results from the fall in lung volume, i.e., Boyle's Law ($P_1V_1 = P_2V_2$). Lung volume limits the extent of tolerable compression. Descending to 33 feet will cut lung volume in half. Compression down to residual volume (the amount of air in the lungs after forceful expiration) can be tolerated. When chest compression exceeds this limit, tissue trauma results. Fluid from capillaries and the tissues then enters the alveoli and the air passageways; gross hemorrhaging may occur. Mild lung barotrauma will cause only pain and slight exudation, which is quickly reabsorbed upon ascent. In dire cases, the lungs may be seriously damaged. Blood from the lungs may be coughed up after the dive. This form of trauma generally responds well to conservative treatment consisting of general supportive care, prevention of infection, and intermittent positive-pressure inhalation therapy (Schaefer et al. 1968).

Spraying of bronchodilators and aerosols, with gravitational drainage if hemorrhage or bruising has been severe, may prove beneficial.

Pulmonary edema (swelling) due to fluid in the lungs may follow the use of breathing apparatus with high inspiratory resistance. In an effort to maintain adequate lung ventilation during moderate activity, high negative pressure within the lungs may result in damage to small veins, seepage of fluid through membranes, and rupture. Coughing and shortness of breath are symptoms. X-rays of the chest may show patchy pulmonary infiltration, which clears within 24 hours without specific therapy.

Trauma to the lungs caused by compression is possible in pressure chambers if an individual stops breathing during compression, either voluntarily by breath holding, or involuntarily by unconsciousness, windpipe or tracheal obstruction, or convulsions.

2.2.1.4 The Teeth

Pain in the mouth associated with an increase or decrease of pressure is seen infrequently. Whatever pain does occur is usually in the teeth of the upper jaw and associated with adjacent sinus changes evident on X-ray. Freedom from dental abnormality has been frequent enough in these cases to suggest that maxillary-sinus squeeze is the causative factor. It is possible that the presence of small gas bubbles in the tooth pulp may permit the soft tissue to be squeezed during pressure decrease. However, this theory has not been confirmed by dental examination.

2.2.2 Direct Effects of Pressure During Ascent

WARNING

A Diver Experiencing Blowup, or Overpressure Accident, Must Immediately Be Examined by a Physician to Rule Out Gas Embolism.

During pressure decrease, the air contained in body cavities expands. Normally, the air vents freely, and there are no difficulties. If breathing is normal during ascent, the expanding lung air is exhaled freely. However, if the breath is held, or there is a localized airway obstruction, the expand-ing air is retained causing overinflation and over-pressurization of the lungs. For example, the air in the lungs at a depth of 66 feet gradually expands to *three times* its volume during ascent to the surface. The air volume can expand to the point of maximum inspiration safely, assuming the absence of airway obstruction. With further pressure decrease, over-expansion and, later, overpressurization of the lungs results in progressive distension of the alveoli. Such overdistension may be generalized with breath holding or insufficient exhalation, or localized because of partial or complete bronchial obstruction due to bronchial lesions, mucus, or bronchiospasm. Problems of lung overinflation can occur during ascent from depths as shallow as 7–10 feet if the breath is held. Several of the most commonly encountered physiological difficulties associated with pressure during ascent are included in the following paragraphs. Each may be prevented by breathing normally during ascent providing there is no localized airway obstruction.

WARNING

Do Not Hold Breath While Ascending.

Figure 2–9 shows the possible consequences of overinflation of the lungs.

2.2.2.1 Pneumothorax

Distended alveoli or temporarily enlarged fluid-filled blisters (emphysematous blebs) may rupture the membrane lining the chest (parietal pleura), causing *pneumothorax.*

Under pressure, this is extremely dangerous, because trapped intrapleural gas expands with continuing pressure decrease as the diver surfaces causing increased pressure in the chest cavity. The lungs may be collapsed by this pressure, and the heart and other vital organs may be pushed out of their normal position. Symptoms include sudden severe pain, reduction of breathing capability, and coughing of frothy blood.

The rapidity of development can cause sudden respiratory and circulatory difficulty, impaired cardiac function, or death from shock. Early diagnosis and prompt treatment with thoracentesis are essential. If recompression is required for concomitant conditions, the pneumothorax must be vented or released by a chest tube or other device before ascent is accomplished.

**Figure 2-7
Location of
Sinus Cavities**

**Figure 2-8
Pressure Effects
on Lung Volume**

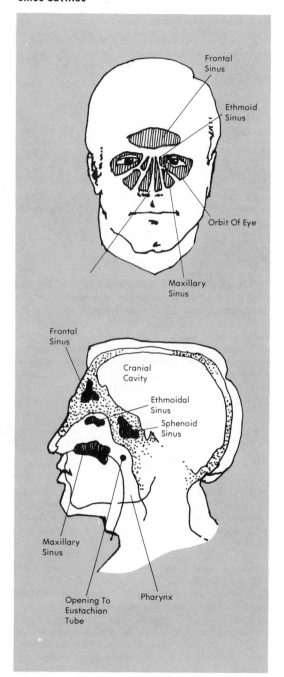

Frontal Sinus

Ethmoid Sinus

Orbit Of Eye

Maxillary Sinus

Frontal Sinus

Cranial Cavity

Ethmoidal Sinus

Sphenoid Sinus

Maxillary Sinus

Opening To Eustachian Tube

Pharynx

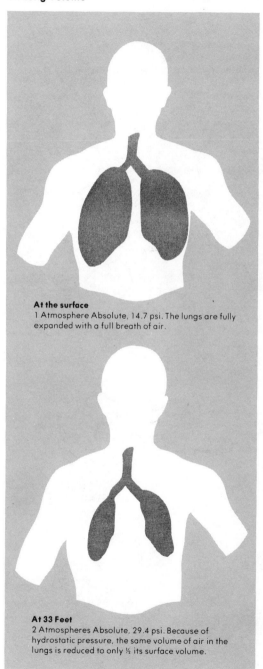

At the surface
1 Atmosphere Absolute, 14.7 psi. The lungs are fully expanded with a full breath of air.

At 33 Feet
2 Atmospheres Absolute, 29.4 psi. Because of hydrostatic pressure, the same volume of air in the lungs is reduced to only ½ its surface volume.

**Figure 2-9
Complications From Expansion
of Air in the Lungs
During Ascent**

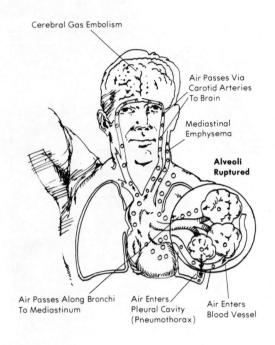

Cerebral Gas Embolism

Air Passes Via
Carotid Arteries
To Brain

Mediastinal
Emphysema

**Alveoli
Ruptured**

Air Passes Along Bronchi
To Mediastinum

Air Enters
Pleural Cavity
(Pneumothorax)

Air Enters
Blood Vessel

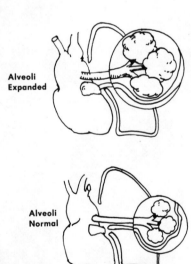

**Alveoli
Expanded**

**Alveoli
Normal**

2.2.2.2 Mediastinal Emphysema

Mediastinal emphysema is the result of air being forced into the tissues about the heart, the major blood vessels, and the trachea (windpipe) in the middle of the chest.

Gas trapped in the spaces between tissues may expand rapidly with continuing decompression, causing impaired venous return. The symptoms of mediastinal emphysema are pain under the sternum and, in extreme cases, shortness of breath or fainting due to interference with circulation as the result of direct pressure on the heart and large vessels. Treatment in mild cases of mediastinal emphysema is symptomatic. In more severe cases, oxygen inhalation may aid resolution of the trapped gas. For severe, massive mediastinal emphysema, recompression is required.

2.2.2.3 Subcutaneous Emphysema

Subcutaneous emphysema, which may be associated with mediastinal emphysema, is a result of air being forced into the tissues beneath the skin of the neck extending along the facial planes from the mediastinum. Unless it is extreme (characterized by a crackling of the skin), the only symptoms of subcutaneous emphysema are a feeling of fullness in the neck and a change in the sound of the voice. Oxygen breathing will accelerate the absorption of this subcutaneous air.

2.2.2.4 Gas Embolism

The most serious result of pulmonary overpressurization is the dispersion of alveolar gas into the pulmonary venous system. The gas is carried to the heart, and then into the systemic circulation, resulting in gas emboli in the coronary, cerebral, and other systemic arterioles. Gas bubbles continue to expand with further decrease of pressure, increasing the severity of clinical signs.

The clinical features of traumatic arterial gas embolism may occur suddenly or be preceded by dizziness, headache, or great anxiety. Unconsciousness, cyanosis, shock, and convulsions follow quickly. The convulsions may be severe and recurrent, and may require heavy sedation. Motor and sensory deficits occur in various degrees and distribution. Death results from coronary or cerebral occlusion with cardiac arrhythmia, respiratory failure, circulatory collapse, and shock. Physical examination may reveal (1) air bubbles in the retinal vessels of the eye; (2) Liebermeister's sign (a sharply defined area of pallor in the tongue); (3) marbling of the skin; (4) hemoptysis; (5) focal or generalized convulsions; or (6) other neurological abnormalities. A chest cold or bronchitis can cause problems resulting from coughing, increased breathing resistance in airways, and the risk of gas embolism resulting from temporary obstruction of an air passage. Diving with a chest cold or bronchitis should be avoided.

The only effective treatment of gas embolism is recompression to reduce the size of the bubbles, force them into solution, and thus restore effective circulation. A recompression chamber is required. Treatment prior to recompression is merely symptomatic. A patient should be kept in the head-down position, which may help to keep bubbles from reaching the brain. Placing the patient on the left side helps to maintain cardiac output, which may be impaired because the large amount of air has decreased the efficiency of the pumping action of the heart. In nonfatal cases, residual paralysis, myocardial necrosis, and other ischemic injuries may occur if recompression is not immediately carried out, and may occur in adequately treated patients if there is a delay in initiating therapy. Although most surgical and medical therapeutic pressure facilities will operate at 2 to 3 atmospheres absolute, they must have the capacity to reach 6 atmospheres absolute safely. *Central nervous system decompression sickness is clinically similar to gas embolism and the treatment for both requires a recompression chamber.* Treatment such as oxygen inhalation, body positioning (head-down 15 degree angle), and hypothermia are only partially effective without recompression. However, these steps must be taken until a recompression chamber can be reached (See Paragraph 16.3.4).

2.2.2.5 Overexpansion of the Stomach and Intestine

In the stomach and large intestine there is ordinarily a liter or more of gas entrapped. Since the intestines are surrounded by soft tissues, the compression and reexpansion of these air bubbles is ordinarily not noticeable and carries no special hazard. If, while diving, one tends to swallow air, it may be necessary to expel gas by belching or by passing gas per rectum, in the course of ascent. For the same reason, eating large amounts of gas producing foods prior to diving is not recommended.

An excess of gas in the stomach or intestine during ascent may cause marked discomfort and vasovagal effects. In an extreme case, breathing difficulty may be experienced. The causes of air swallowing, such as chewing gum during pressure exposure, should be avoided.

2.2.3 Indirect Effects of Pressure

The indirect effects of pressure result from changes in the partial pressures of the gases in the breathing medium. The mechanism of these effects include saturation and desaturation of body tissues with dissolved gas, and changes of body functions by abnormal gas tensions.

2.2.3.1 Nitrogen Absorption and Elimination

At sea level the body tissues are equilibrated with dissolved nitrogen equal to the partial pressure of nitrogen in the lungs. Upon exposure to altitude or pressure, the partial pressure of nitrogen in the lungs will change and the tissues will either lose or gain nitrogen to reach a new equilibrium with the nitrogen pressure in the lungs. Taking up nitrogen in tissues is called *absorption* or uptake. Giving up nitrogen from tissues is termed *elimination*. In air diving, nitrogen absorption occurs when a diver is exposed to an increased nitrogen partial pressure. Elimination occurs when pressure decreases. This is true for any inert gas breathed.

The process of absorption consists of several phases, which include transfer of inert gas from the lungs to the blood, then from the blood to the various tissues through which it flows. The gradient for gas transfer is the partial pressure difference of the gas between the lungs and blood and the blood and the tissues. The volume of blood flowing through tissues is usually small compared to the mass of the tissue, but over a period of time the gas delivered to the tissue will cause it to become equilibrated with that carried in solution in the blood. The rate of equilibration with the blood gas depends upon the volume of blood flow and the respective capacities of blood and tissues to absorb dissolved gas. For example, fatty tissues hold significantly more gas than watery tissues and will thus take longer to absorb or eliminate excess inert gas.

The process of elimination is the reverse of absorption. During ascent, and after surfacing, the tissues lose excess inert gas to the circulating blood by diffusion, the gradient being the difference between the inert gas partial pressure in each tissue and that in the blood vessels after the blood has equilibrated to the gas in the lungs. The amount of inert gas that can be taken up in the blood is limited, so the tissue inert gas tension falls gradually. As in absorption, the rate of blood flow and the amount of inert gas dissolved in the tissues and blood determine the rate of elimination. After decompressing to the surface or ascending to a shallower level, elimination at the new level may require 24 hours or more.

During decompression, the blood and tissues can hold gas in supersaturated solution to some degree, without bubbles being formed. A supersaturated solution is one in which the blood and tissues hold more gas than is possible at equilibrium at the particular temperature and pressure. Because of the ability of the blood and tissue to become supersaturated for short periods of time, a diver can ascend at least part of the way regardless of the depth and duration of his dive. An outward gradient is established and inert gas is eliminated from body tissues. This permits the diver to ascend further after some period of time. The process is continued until a diver can reach the surface. The diver's body will still contain inert gas in supersaturated solution in some tissues, but this is normally safe if kept within proper decompression limits, and if further pressure reduction such as ascending to altitude does not take place (See Paragraph 6.4).

The basic principles of absorption and elimination of gas are the same for any inert gas breathed. Differences exist in the solubility and rates of diffusion of gases in water and fat. Helium is much less soluble in tissues than is nitrogen and diffuses faster. Thus, helium saturation may occur somewhat more rapidly than for nitrogen. It would appear that the more rapid saturation and desaturation that occurs with helium could require less decompression after long deep dives than when air is breathed. However, somewhat deeper decompression stops are required with helium to prevent it from coming out of solution as bubbles. As a result, some of this advantage is lost. The greatest advantage in the use of helium-oxygen mixtures is the freedom from narcosis and the decrease in breathing resistance, rather than a decompression advantage.

2.2.3.2 Decompression Sickness

If the elimination of gas by blood flowing through the lungs is inadequate to parallel the rate of reduc-

tion of external pressure, the amount of supersaturation of gas in the tissues may permit the gas to come out of solution in the form of bubbles. Bubbles forming in the blood stream will block circulation, while bubbles in tissues will distort the tissues as the bubbles expand. Symptoms occurring depend on the location of the bubbles, whether in joints, muscles, bones or nerves. When the brain is affected, dizziness, deafness, paralysis and unconsciousness can occur. Bubbles in the spinal cord can cause paralysis and loss of feeling in parts of the body affected. Bubbles in respiratory systems cause choking and asphyxia. Skin bubbles produce itching and rash. Involvement of the brain and spinal cord can cause severe disabilities that can threaten the life of a diver if treatment is not initiated promptly. Treatment of decompression sickness consists of recompressing the diver to a depth sufficient to cause the bubbles to return to solution. When symptoms and signs are cleared, careful decompression to the surface again should follow, so that bubbles do not again form (See Paragraph 16.3.1).

Prevention of decompression sickness can usually be accomplished by adhering to the proper decompression table. Even though the correct decompression procedure is followed, cases of decompression sickness sometimes occur. Factors which may increase the likelihood of decompression sickness even when proper tables are used include excessive obesity, loss of sleep, fatigue, use of alcohol and its aftereffect, dehydration, various illnesses, particularly those which affect the circulatory system, and anything that causes poor physical condition and poor circulation. Heavy exertion and cold during a dive also contribute to excess inert gas being absorbed and interferes with its elimination during decompression. Anything that impedes blood flow, such as a cramped position, interferes with inert gas being eliminated (U.S. Navy Diving Manual 1973). It is important to note that the significant individual differences which exist with respect to physical condition and the effects of environmental parameters, also play an important role in susceptibility to decompression sickness.

WARNING

Symptoms of Decompression Sickness Can Occur as Long as 24 Hours Following a Dive.

A device known as a doppler bubble detector has demonstrated the ability to detect gas bubbles in the blood stream and tissues. The device utilizes high frequency sound waves which, when passed through blood vessels or tissues, indicate when bubbles of gas are present by a noticeable change in the frequency of the sound emitted from the device. These devices are being used experimentally and show great promise for the future.

2.2.3.3 Aseptic Bone Necrosis (Dysbaric Osteo-necrosis)

Aseptic bone necrosis refers to destructive changes in bone, in which the relative density of the affected bone is increased by sclerosis, as well as cystic changes. Neither of these are of infectious origin. These changes have been noted in many conditions such as chronic alcoholism, pancreatitis, sickle-cell anemia, during the use of systemic steroids, and in caisson workers and divers. The development of changes in the hips and shoulder joints of caisson workers with crippling effects from joint breakdown was first noted in 1888, but the disease has not had much attention in divers who generally observe more conservative decompression.

Many caisson workers experience a high incidence of bends as a result of inadequate decompression time. It is felt that some of the bubbles causing pain in joints may have lodged in the arteries that supply blood circulation to bone, blocking the flow of blood for a period of time. If the blockage and stagnation of blood flow lasts for 12 hours or more, the bone cells thus affected may die (Kindwall 1972). If the lesions occur in the head of bones as the femur or humerus, the weakened underlying bone that supports the cartilage covering the bone will collapse with weight-bearing and activity, causing the joint surface to break down and become irregular. Pain occurs with movement of these joints accompanied by muscle spasms around the joint and inability to use the joint in a normal manner.

Lesions also occur in the shafts of long bones, but these never cause symptoms or disability though the bony scars of increased density may appear on X-ray after deposition of the new bone occurs, with healing of the area. Few changes are seen in the knees and rarely in the elbows, wrists, or ankles (Kindwall 1972).

It appears that aseptic bone necrosis can occur after only one severe instance of decompression sickness, though a time period of months must elapse before evidence of bony change can be seen

by X-ray of the affected bones. Frequency of exposure to pressure, number of cases of bends, adequacy and promptness of recompression treatment, and the amount of pressure exposure have been listed as possible factors related to likelihood of developing bone lesions.

The cause of aseptic bone necrosis has still not been demonstrated beyond doubt. The highest incidence occurs in workers who have used inadequate decompression procedures or who have experienced bends on one or more occasions. There is some evidence that fat emboli may occlude circulation of blood vessels in bone and other tissues, and thus may be a factor in development of hip lesions in the chronic alcoholic with a fatty liver, or following pressure exposure in which bends occur.

In patients with gout, lesions of the hip joints have contained sodium urate crystals, which may have been a factor in the destruction of the joint surface. Lesions of bone in workers exposed to pressure may not become apparent on X-rays of the joints for 4 months to 5 years after the pressure exposure.*

A 3-year survey of 350 full-time divers in the British Navy tabulated a 5 percent incidence of aseptic bone necrosis, in which half of the affected divers had no evidence of decompression sickness while using Royal Navy decompression tables only.* The British Navy's decision has been not to permit divers with joint lesions to continue to dive.

2.2.3.4 Inert Gas Narcosis

Among the major factors likely to cause performance impairment in divers at increased ambient pressures is inert-gas narcosis. Although the common inert gases (nitrogen and helium) associated with diving are physiologically inert under normal conditions, they have distinct anesthetic properties when the partial pressure is sufficiently high. The problem of compressed air "intoxication" has long been recognized by divers and researchers.

There are several theories as to the basic cause of inert gas narcosis including: increased carbon dioxide tension; impairment of carbon dioxide diffusion in the alveoli; increased oxygen pressure and anxiety or claustrophobia. The divergent opinions as to the cause may to some extent be explained by the fact that, at raised barometric pressures there are simultaneous increases in alveolar oxygen pressure, alveolar nitrogen pressure, and gas density. Experiments where the subjects are exposed to "normal"

* *Robert D. Workman, M.D., 1973; personal communication.*

air at different barometric pressures will therefore not permit any differentiation between these factors as to their possible narcotic effects (Hesser 1963). In spite of such divergent opinions as to the basic cause, there seems to be no doubt that the anesthetic properties of high nitrogen pressure constitutes an important causative factor.

Narcosis is characterized by symptoms similar to alcohol intoxication. It becomes evident at a depth of about 100 feet. Beyond this depth, most compressed air divers show some impairment of thought, judgment, and the ability to perform tasks that require mental or motor skill. Such impairment, even if mild, obviously constitutes a potential hazard to the diver's safety. Most divers lose their effectiveness at about 200 feet, and at about 250 feet, the average diver will be unable to function well enough to ensure his own safety.

Like alcohol, the effects of nitrogen vary with the individual. By conscious effort, the hazards can be minimized within certain limits. The sequence of events for the average man under the influence of high-pressure nitrogen in a breathing medium of air is as follows:

- 100–150 feet: Light head, increasing self-confidence, loss of fine discrimination, and some euphoria.
- 150–200 feet: Joviality and garrulousness, perhaps some dizziness.
- 200–250 feet: Laughter may be uncontrolled and approach hysteria. Power of communication lessened, and mistakes made in simple motor and mental taks. May be peripheral numbness and tingling. Less attention paid to personal safety. Delayed response to signals and stimuli.
- 300 feet: Depression, and loss of clear thinking. Impaired neuromuscular coordination.
- 350 feet: May approach unconsciousness, with the additional danger of oxygen poisoning (Miles 1966).

Several predisposing factors may advance the onset of symptoms and ameliorating factors may help to increase the tolerance to nitrogen narcosis. Alcohol taken prior to pressurization greatly enhances the nitrogen effect and should be avoided. Fatigue will increase susceptibility, as will any circumstance causing retention of carbon dioxide. In the inexperienced diver, anxiety is likely to advance the onset of symptoms. However, experience, strong will, and frequent deep diving all help to increase the tolerance to high-nitrogen tensions. The principles of prevention lie in common sense and proper diving procedures.

To treat inert gas narcosis the diver simply ascends to shallower depths. Except for general tiredness, recovery is usually immediate and complete.

2.3 OXYGEN POISONING

Low-pressure oxygen poisoning can occur if more than 60 percent oxygen is breathed at 1 atmosphere of pressure for 12 hours or more. Lung irritation with coughing and painful breathing can develop (U.S. Navy Diving Manual 1973). A form of pneumonia, with lung damage, can develop if the exposure is continued. When oxygen is administered for long periods of time, sufficient dilution with air usually is done to prevent such occurrences. During long pressure chamber exposures, a diver may be exposed to a partial pressure greater than 0.6 atmospheres of oxygen for a sufficient time to produce lung irritation (U.S. Navy Diving-Gas Manual 1971).

High-pressure oxygen poisoning can occur when divers are exposed to more than 1 atmosphere of oxygen for a period of minutes to hours. The lower the oxygen partial pressure, the longer the time before symptoms develop. Because it is the partial pressure of oxygen itself which causes toxicity, the problem can occur while breathing mixtures of oxygen with nitrogen or helium at depth. No time limitations apply if the partial pressure of the oxygen is maintained between 0.2 and 0.5 atmospheres (U.S. Navy Diving-Gas Manual 1971).

Other factors which may contribute to the onset of oxygen toxicity are: degree of exertion, amount of carbon dioxide inspired and retained; and basic individual differences in susceptibility.

Early **symptoms of oxygen poisoning** may appear before generalized convulsions, and thus serve as a warning to lower the oxygen partial pressure or terminate the exposure. Muscular twitching particularly of the face and lips may occur. Nausea and dizziness occur intermittently. Tunnel vision, abnormalities of hearing, ringing in the ears, difficulty in breathing, or the inability to take a deep breath may occur. A diver may become anxious, confused, fatigued, and uncoordinated in his movements. These symptoms may not be noticed early enough to terminate the exposure before convulsions occur.

Breathing air at atmospheric pressure after the onset of symptoms may restore tolerance and permit the resumption of oxygen breathing. Deep breathing or hyperventilation may help to avoid the onset of convulsions if initiated at the onset of the warning symptoms.

Convulsions are the most serious direct consequence of oxygen poisoning. The victim becomes unconscious during the convulsion, followed by semiconsciousness, restless agitation, and random movements. When this occurs with a diver under water, the danger of drowning is great. Gas embolism may be induced by bringing the diver up or decreasing chamber pressure when he is not breathing regularly during the generalized muscular spasms of the convulsive seizure. Removal of the oxygen mask or ventilating with air will be effective in decreasing oxygen until breathing is resumed and pressure can be safely decreased. Figure 11–1 describes the, relationship of the percentage of oxygen in the breathing mixture to partial pressure and depth.

If convulsions occur in a decompression chamber, the tender should keep the victim from thrashing against hard objects and injuring himself. Inserting a mouth bit will prevent damage to the victim's tongue from self-inflicted bites. He should then be turned onto his abdomen with the head to one side to aid breathing.

The mechanism of oxygen toxicity appears to result from interference with the functioning of the enzyme systems involved with cell metabolism. Since no safe drugs are available for use in preventing oxygen poisoning, the observance of depth-time limits and the avoidance of excessive exertion and carbon dioxide retention are important to prevent its occurrence.

2.4 EFFECTS OF COLD (HYPOTHERMIA)

Hypothermia is a condition in which the deep tissue or "core" temperature of the body falls below the normal physiological range, about 97° F (36° C) and is the temperature at which malfunctions in normal physiology begin to occur (Beckman 1963). If the core temperature continues to drop below 36° C, serious consequences usually develop. At about 34° C temporary amnesia may occur, between 30°–32° C cardiac irregularities commence and unconsciousness may result. If the core temperature of a diver should decrease to 32° C therefore, his operational usefulness would cease and the mission should be terminated.

Because water has a specific heat, approximately 1000 times greater than air, and a thermal conductivity 25 times greater than air, the body loses heat much faster in water than in air of the same temperature. Fortunately, the thermo-regulatory system of the body is highly sensitive to stimulation in specific areas, i.e., the hands, feet, and head, so that the body's heat generating systems are activated before the core temperature is seriously affected. Thus, the fact that the hands and feet get cold first is an advantage, in that dives are terminated before the core temperature has a chance to drop appreciably.

At temperatures below 35.7° C the defense mechanisms of the body are activated. These mechanisms take the form of shivering, which can increase basal body heat production by about 5 to 7 times; or by vaso-constriction which reduces blood flow to periphery thus reducing heat loss. The heat regulating system is so sensitive that moderate changes in surrounding water temperature can produce an alternating vaso-dilation and vaso-constriction.

In addition to losing body heat by conductive losses from the skin, there is a significant loss (15 to 24 percent of the total body heat loss) by evaporation from the lungs and by heating the inspired air. This percentage range is dependent on the humidity of the inspired air, i.e., the drier the air the greater the evaporative heat loss.

It is obvious from the above that the diver must wear protective clothing when exposed to cold water or when exposed to moderately warm water for long periods. Because of the large individual differences in cold tolerance, each diver must determine the most suitable protection for himself. There are a variety of diving suits available ranging from standard foamed neoprene wet suits, dry suits, to specially heated suits. These are described in Paragraphs 4.8 and 9.3.2.

Chilling, even if not severe enough to threaten life, will produce loss of dexterity and sense of touch in the hands, making it difficult for a diver to do useful work or even control his diving equipment. Shivering causes a lack of coordination and may make it difficult for a diver to hold his mouthpiece in place. Ability to think clearly and short term memory may also be seriously affected by cold.

Figure 2-10
Ice Diving

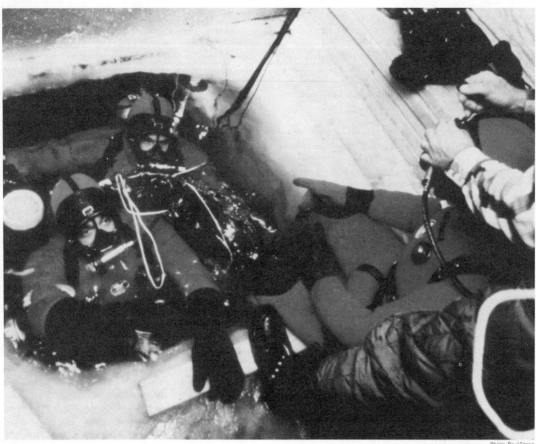

Photo: Paul Stang

It has been well established that dives in cold water must be planned so that the diver's tasks are both simple and few. Because of the effect of cold on short term memory complicated sequences of tasks are extremely difficult to carry out.

A diver surfacing from a dive in cold water needs to be rewarmed as rapidly as possible, and should be completely warmed, as demonstrated by sweating, before he dives again. A hot bath or water-heated suit is preferable to a shower for rewarming.

WARNING

If the Dive Approached No Decompression Limits or Required Decompression, Caution Should Be Exercised in the Application of Extreme Amounts of External Heat as It May Stimulate Bubble Formation.

Exercise to generate internal heat is also helpful to speed up the process. The diver should then change into warm, dry clothing and continue some mild exercise to improve heat production and circulation. Hours of time may be required to restore all the body heat lost. Drinking alcohol is not beneficial. It increases circulation of blood to the skin, and speeds the loss of body heat if the surroundings are cold. Hot, nourishing liquids such as soup are useful.

SECTION 3
TRAINING
OF DIVERS

TRAINING OF DIVERS 3

3.0 GENERAL

There are many types of organizations throughout the country offering diver training.

Some representative organizations are:
- National Oceanic and Atmospheric Administration (NOAA)
- U.S. Navy
- Recreational diving associations
- Commercial diving schools
- Universities
- Local diving shops

Most organizations accept students on the basis of interest, the ability to pass a complete physical examination and basic swimming tests.

Types of training vary from the basic scuba course to advanced and specialized training.

NOAA requirements for the training of divers are found in the NOAA Diving Regulations contained in Appendix C.

3.1 SELECTION

Applicants for diver training should be volunteers. Some of the tasks divers may perform require strenuous physical exertion. Applicants should be in good physical condition. A physical examination and a general swimming test to indicate a reasonable degree of watermanship, should be required prior to the applicant being accepted for training.

3.1.1 Physical Examination

The physical examination should include the following:

Ears, nose and throat — to assure against chronic or acute conditions that would preclude adjusting to pressure changes or use of personal diving equipment.

Cardiovascular — to determine if disease is present that would inhibit active exercise.

Respiratory — include a chest X-ray to establish that free passage of air and free gas exchange is possible.

Visual acuity — to establish that the applicant's visual status is compatible with diving.

Other areas — the examination should include the following to establish that the applicant's condition is within normal limits:

    Gastrointestinal
    Serological
    Neuromuscular
    Endocrinological
    Neuropsychiatric
    Central nervous system
    Dermatological

Details of these examinations and evaluation criteria for NOAA divers are contained in Appendix C.

3.1.2 Swimming Test

All applicants for diver training should successfully perform the following swimming exercises without equipment showing a noticeable degree of confidence and good watermanship to the satisfaction of a designated examiner.

1. Swim 300 yards using the crawl, sidestroke, and backstroke
2. Swim under water for a distance of 50 feet without surfacing
3. Stay afloat for 30 minutes.

3.2 BASIC SCUBA TRAINING

Even though the specific requirements of divers may differ, the following general guidelines should be considered a minimum for a diver's basic training. Training should be composed of a combination of classroom teaching and "in-the-water" instruction.

1. Each prospective diver should receive at least

10 hours of classroom instruction on general diving principles, diving equipment, safety, general diving operations, etc. This instruction should include, but need not be limited to the following:

a. Diving physics
   (1) Pressure
   (2) Buoyancy
   (3) Diving gases
   (4) Gas laws
   (5) Thermal conductivity
   (6) Light and sound.
b. Diving physiology and medical aspects (including first aid)
   (1) Hypoxia — breath holding
   (2) CO_2 toxicity
   (3) CO toxicity
   (4) O_2 toxicity
   (5) Effects of pressure during ascent and descent
   (6) Lung overpressurization accidents
   (7) Decompression sickness
   (8) Flying after diving
   (9) Nitrogen narcosis
   (10) Heat loss
   (11) Exhaustion
   (12) Hyperpnea
   (13) Panic syndrome
   (14) Drowning
   (15) Cardiopulmonary resuscitation.
c. Deep, decompression, repetitive, and altitude diving
d. Diver equipment use and maintenance
e. Diving environments and marine life
f. Underwater communications
g. Light salvage
h. Search and recovery
i. Dive planning.

2. At least 15 hours of in-water training, using scuba, by a certified instructor should be given the prospective diver. This training should include, but need not be limited to the following:

a. Drown proofing
b. Diver equipment
c. Buoyancy control
d. Controlled emergency free ascent
e. Open water entries and exits
f. Buddy breathing
g. Limited visibility diving
h. Underwater navigation
i. Search and recovery
j. Scuba rescue

k. Gear removal and replacement in water
l. Full-gear surface snorkel swimming
m. Weight belt ditching.

3. A minimum of two open water dives should be performed by the prospective diver in conditions and at depths as similar as possible to those he will encounter during his anticipated operational dives. A diver who completes a basic course which consists of only the minimum requirements outlined above should not attempt any type of working dive or any dives under adverse conditions. The diver should only make observational dives under ideal conditions. He should dive with more experienced divers not with divers who have just completed a basic scuba course. Each diver in a buddy pair should be capable of aiding the other during an emergency.

3.3 ADVANCED SCUBA TRAINING

Advanced training is designed to increase the skills of the diver in underwater activities and to broaden his knowledge in specialized areas. Emphasis is placed on practical application of subjects discussed in the classroom. Training should be composed of classroom teaching and "in-the-water" instruction consisting of the following general guidelines.

1. Each student should receive at least 20 hours of classroom instruction which should include but need not be limited to the following subject areas: diving physics and physiology, equipment, general diving procedures, search and recovery, light salvage, low visibility, navigation, environment and decompression diving.

2. At least 20 hours of instruction should be in open water with as many varied situations and conditions presented as possible. This training should include an evaluation of basic skin and scuba skills, scuba rescue training and open water dives which relate to the classroom subject areas.

3. A minimum of ten open water dives should be performed using varied surface diving platforms and underwater environmental conditions.

3.4 SCUBA INSTRUCTOR TRAINING

Most organizations that conduct scuba training have designated instructors. Individuals may be designated as instructors based on their level of experience and knowledge.

Recreational diving associations sponsor courses designed to evaluate a diver's knowledge, waterman-

Figure 3-1
Demonstrating
Emplacement of
Transect Marker

Photo: Laurence Bussey

ship and teaching ability. Successful completion of one of these courses is required for instructor certification.

3.5 SPECIALIZED TRAINING

Specialized training may be required to perform a specific task, to use specialized or advanced equipment, to dive in unfamiliar diving environments, and to instruct others in diving. Some examples of specialized training are:

1. Cave diving
2. Cold water diving
3. Ice diving·
4. Diving at high elevations
5. Diving in high currents
6. Wreck diving
7. Kelp diving
8. Underwater photography
9. Use of underwater tools
10. Surface supplied umbilical diving
11. Operation of decompression chambers
12. Mixed gas diving
13. Closed circuit scuba
14. Diving from underwater habitats
15. Diver lock-out submersibles
16. Saturation diving
17. Underwater scientific procedures.

Each of these specialized areas is discussed in other sections of this manual.

The end result of a training program for divers should produce:

- A diver who has reached a level of comfort with his equipment and the environment that permits him to operate confidently.
- A diver who can discriminate and make appropriate decisions when confronted with an underwater problem.
- A diver who can operate safely and efficiently when executing the tasks to which he is assigned.

By continuing to maintain a high level of proficiency through regular physical exercise and frequent diving, an individual will possess the knowledge, strength, endurance, and flexibility to safely perform work required in the underwater environment.

DIVING EQUIPMENT

4.0 GENERAL

The variety of missions and functions requiring the services of a diver call for the availability of many items and types of equipment. All diving equipment has its special function, and all must be of high reliability and maintained in good working order. The use of untried equipment must be limited to those special situations where precautions and proven backup systems are available. This section discusses the equipment that is in general use and has the proven reliability to support a diver and assist him in accomplishing his assigned task.

Basic equipment includes life support units, which supply the diver with the breathing gas at the pressure and temperature that satisfy his respiratory requirements and provide for thermal protection. Also included are those items which, *under normal conditions* are not essential to life support, but rather assist a diver in overcoming or adapting to the unique problems encountered in the underwater environment. Fins and wet suits are examples of these items of equipment. They are not normally required to support a diver's life under water, but do enable him to perform more efficiently. Also discussed are those specialized diver's tools or instruments designed for the performance of underwater tasks.

Various types of life support equipment are available to meet the many demands of the underwater environment and the specialized tasks to be performed. Each has its advantages and limitations. A diver equipped with scuba carries his breathing gas with him, independent of the surface. Umbilical-supplied equipment provides the diver with breathing gas from a source either on the surface or submerged, through an umbilical. The primary advantages of self-contained diving include equipment portability, diver mobility, and reduced surface support requirements. Primary disadvantages are limited gas duration and related

depth limitations, limited ability to perform heavy work, and lack of effective voice communications. In addition, the freedom of the scuba equipped diver, which provides the major advantage, gives rise to certain negative physical, physiological, and psychological considerations, such as a feeling of insecurity in cold, dark waters, freedom to move too far from a habitat or surface support, and a diver's almost complete dependence upon himself to recognize and correct difficulties.

Scuba equipment is available in three basic configurations: Open-circuit scuba, closed-circuit scuba, and semi-closed-circuit scuba.

Open-circuit scuba is by far the most widely used configuration. This unit provides for "one time" use of each volume of the breathing gas supplied by the high pressure (HP) cylinders. The breathing gas flows from the cylinders through a regulator to the diver's mouthpiece during inhalation. Exhaled gas is discharged into the water. Air is the most common breathing medium used with open circuit scuba. The cylinders can be charged with a mixture of gases other than air, but, due to the complexity and expense associated with mixed gas diving, it is not generally undertaken with open-circuit scuba.

Closed-circuit scuba, as the name implies, involves a recirculation of the breathing gas after exhalation and continuous rebreathing, with no intentional loss of gas to the surrounding water. A diver inhales gas from a container such as a breathing bag and exhales through a purifying canister back into the breathing bag. A high-pressure gas cylinder or flask replenishes the gas in the breathing bag as it is expended through respiration. Carbon dioxide generated by the body and released during respiration is removed by an absorbent in the purifying canister. The breathing medium used in closed-circuit scuba diving may be pure oxygen or mixed gas, depending on the system used.

**Figure 4-1
Open Circuit
Scuba Equipment**

**Figure 4-2
Upstream Valve**

**Figure 4-2a
Downstream Valve**

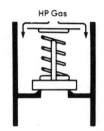

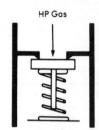

Failure of this valve cuts off the diver's air supply.

Failure of this valve allows the air supply to free-flow to the diver.

Photo: U.S. Divers

Semi-closed-circuit scuba is a modification of the closed-circuit system, which allows a partial rebreathing but provides for a continuous purge to prevent buildup of inert gas (nitrogen, helium, etc.) in the breathing bag.

Closed and semi-closed-circuit scuba provide for more efficient utilization of the compressed breathing medium through rebreathing than does the open-circuit system. Closed- and semi-closed systems, therefore, permit efficient utilization of the costly gas mixes necessary for diving to depths not safely attainable on air. The closed-circuit scuba further enables a diver to mingle less obtrusively with marine life because of the absence of exhaust bubbles. The primary disadvantage of both closed- and semi-closed-circuit scuba is system complexity, necessitating correspondingly rigid maintenance and diver training requirements.

4.1 OPEN-CIRCUIT SCUBA

The open-circuit scuba system is shown in Figure 4–1. It is a one-piece funtional unit consisting of several individual components. The first is a cylinder assembly, which stores the breathing gas under pressure and provides a diver with a supply of breathing gas. The second is a regulator assembly, which reduces the pressure of the high-pressure breathing gas to ambient pressure and provides the gas to the diver upon demand. The diver then exhausts the gas directly into the water.

4.1.1 Demand Regulators

The demand regulator is used to reduce the pressure of breathing gas in high pressure cylinders to ambient pressure and provide the gas to a diver on demand, using the pressure differential created by the respiratory action of the diver's lungs as the metering signal. Most regulators automatically adjust to changes in depth and the diver's respiration rate, and conserve the gas supply by delivering only the quantity of breathing gas required. To understand the operation of a regulator, one must be familiar with the function of "upstream" and "downstream" valves. An upstream valve (Figure 4-2) is one that is forced closed by the high pressure gas in the cylinder. Conversely, the downstream valve (Figure 4-2a) is one that is forced open by the high pressure cylinder gas. As the pressure in the cylinders drops, less ambient pressure is required to open the upstream valve. The downstream valve is configured with springs, which can keep the valve closed at maximum cylinder pressure and is, therefore, more resistant to opening as cylinder pressure decreases.

Although several different types of demand regulators may still be in use, the one-stage regulator is no longer in common use. Several different types of two stage regulators are commercially available.

**Figure 4-3
Two-Stage Double
Hose Regulator**

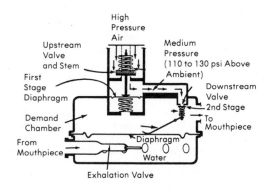

High
Pressure
Air

Upstream
Valve
and Stem

Medium
Pressure
(110 to 130 psi Above
Ambient)

First
Stage
Diaphragm

Downstream
Valve
2nd Stage

Demand
Chamber

To
Mouthpiece

From
Mouthpiece

Diaphragm

Water

Exhalation Valve

4.1.1.1 Two Stage Demand Regulator

Two stage regulators are designed to reduce the gas in a cylinder to ambient pressure in two stages. The first stage reduces the pressure to approximately 110 to 130 psi above ambient pressure. The second or demand stage further reduces the pressure to ambient pressure for diver breathing. The major advantage of this additional stage is that air is supplied to the demand stage at a nearly constant pressure, thus allowing a reduction in breathing resistance, and reduced fluctuations in breathing resistance resulting from changes in depth and decreasing cylinder pressure. Breathing resistance is further reduced because the demand valve is working against a controlled pressure (110 to 130 psi above ambient from the first stage).

Two stage regulators are available in two different styles, and with three different types of first stage reduction valves. The two styles of the two stage regulators are double and single hose models; the three types of first stage reduction valves are the standard, the balanced, and the piston types.

The double hose regulator combines both pressure reduction stages into one assembly mounted on the high pressure cylinder valve. A low pressure hose leads from the regulator valves to the mouthpiece, which contains two one-way valves. Another low pressure hose returns exhaled air to the regulator body where it is exhausted into the surrounding water (Figure 4–3).

The single hose regulator is configured with the first pressure reduction stage attached to the high pressure (HP) cylinder valve. The second pressure reduction stage is connected to the mouthpiece. Both first and second stages are connected by a

length of medium pressure hose. Exhaled air is exhausted from the second stage (mouthpiece connected) into the water (Figure 4–4).

The standard first stage valve (Figure 4–4a) is an upstream valve in which the high pressure cylinder acts to close the valve. A heavy spring applies force to compensate for the high cylinder pressure and acts on a flexible diaphragm. The flexible diaphragm is directly connected to a valve stem which unseats (opens) the high pressure valve. Water or air pressure on the flexible diaphragm compensates for pressure changes resulting from changes in depth. The heavy spring can be manually adjusted to maintain a constant medium pressure between the first and second stages. As this constant medium pressure between stages is reduced by respiration, the diaphragm flexes, unseats the high pressure valve, and restores the medium pressure to its desired level. The standard first stage is used with double hose as well as single hose regulators.

The balanced first stage valve (Figure 4–4b) was developed to eliminate the effects of HP cylinder gas pressure on seating the first stage valve. The balanced first stage eliminates the requirement for a small valve orifice, thereby increasing the maximum air flow capacity of the unit. The valve stem of the balanced first stage is exactly the same diameter as the valve orifice and extends through the high pressure chamber into the mid-pressure (MP) chamber opposite the flow orifice. As a result, the high pressure air does not exert a closing force on the valve stem, and the gas pressure in the mid-pressure chamber acts to balance the forces acting on the valve stem. If the valve stem were not of the same diameter as the orifice, an unbalanced surface area would be presented to the MP air at one end of the valve/valve stem assembly, and an opening or closing force would exist. With the effect of cylinder air pressure neutralized, only the mechanical force of the spring effects the operation of the valve. The springs can be adjusted to give exactly the desired medium pressure, and this will remain constant regardless of the pressure in the HP cylinder. As the valve is unaffected by fluctuations in cylinder pressure, large orifice diameters can be used to deliver large volumes of air flow with no increase in respiration effort.

The piston first stage valve (Figure 4–4c) represents an alternative to the balanced valve. The piston actuated first stage valve is opened and closed as a result of forces generated by the pres-

**Figure 4-4a-d
Diagrams of First
and Second Stages
of Two-Stage Regulators**

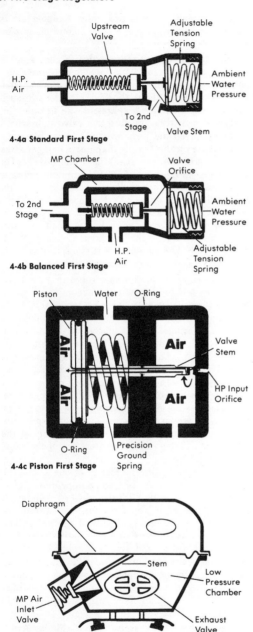

4-4a Standard First Stage

Upstream Valve

Adjustable Tension Spring

H.P. Air

Ambient Water Pressure

To 2nd Stage

Valve Stem

4-4b Balanced First Stage

MP Chamber

Valve Orifice

To 2nd Stage

Ambient Water Pressure

H.P. Air

Adjustable Tension Spring

4-4c Piston First Stage

Piston

Water

O-Ring

Air

Air

Air

Air

Valve Stem

HP Input Orifice

O-Ring

Precision Ground Spring

4-4d Second Stage

Diaphragm

Stem

Low Pressure Chamber

MP Air Inlet Valve

Exhaust Valve

Mouthpiece

sure in two mid-pressure chambers at either end of the valve stem. The pressure exerted within the two MP chambers is equalized by a hole bored through the valve stem. A closing force is generated due to the unequal valve assembly surface area presented within the two chambers. The surface area at the piston end is greater than at the valve seat end, resulting in a new closing force regardless of chamber pressure. The valve closing force is opposed by ambient pressure exerted within a centrally located, free flooding water chamber, and by a constant force exerted by a precision ground spring within the free flooding chamber. The free flooding chamber provides depth compensation, while the spring ensures a constant over ambient pressure against the demand valve. When a piston type first stage regulator is connected to an HP source, air enters the MP chamber under pressure. As the MP chamber pressure rises, the closing force applied to the valve stem by the piston increases until it overcomes the opening force provided by the spring and ambient pressure, closing the valve. As air in the MP chamber is reduced by a diver's inhalation, the pressure provided by the spring and ambient pressure on the free flooding side of the piston causes the valve to open. The first stage valve will remain open throughout inhalation, until the demand valve seats. The resultant increase in pressure in the MP chamber counteracts the spring and ambient pressure forces, and causes the valve to seat. The piston type first stage, employing only a single moving part, is simple and functional. However, two vital O-ring seals are subject to malfunction if damaged by sand or crystallized salt.

The second stage valve (Figure 4–4d), located in the mouthpiece, is connected to the first stage by a medium pressure hose. A constant medium pressure is supplied to a valve in the mouthpiece. The reduction in pressure in a low pressure chamber in the mouthpiece, caused by inhalation, results in distortion of a diaphragm in the valve. This distortion applies pressure to a stem or linkage which is directly connected to the MP air inlet valve, opening the valve and admitting air into the mouthpiece at ambient pressure. As long as a diver continues to inhale, air will continue to flow into the mouthpiece. Upon exhalation, the diaphragm returns to a neutral position, releasing pressure on the stem or linkage, which returns to its normal position, closing the MP valve. As pressure in the low pres-

Figure 4-5
Breathing Hoses

Figure 4-6
Mouthpieces

sure chamber builds up above ambient pressure due to exhalation, a one-way mushroom valve is unseated, allowing the exhaled gas to be exhausted into the surrounding water. A properly constructed second stage has a minimum of dead space, thereby limiting the air that will be rebreathed.

4.1.1.2 Breathing Hoses

In double hose scuba, the breathing hoses (Figure 4–5) are flexible, large diameter rubber ducts, which provide passageways for air from the cylinder to the diver. They are usually corrugated rubber hoses but may be rubberized fabric with metallic ring or spiral stiffening. In order to provide minimum resistance to breathing, the hose should have an inside diameter of at least 1 inch, and must be long enough, in the "relaxed" state, to allow full freedom of body movement. The hose must be capable of stretching to twice their relaxed length without collapsing or buckling.

Single hose scuba, with the second stage of the demand regulator mask-mounted or mouthpiece-mounted, does not require the large bore, ambient pressure breathing hose described above as the gas in the hose is at a medium pressure (110 to 130 psi above ambient) rather than ambient pressure. The second stage, or demand valve, is connected to a cylinder-mounted first stage regulator by a single, smooth base, medium pressure hose of relatively small diameter. Exhaled gases are discharged directly into the water through an exhaust valve in the mask or mouthpiece.

4.1.1.3 Mouthpiece

The mouthpiece (Figure 4–6) provides a relatively watertight channel for the flow of breathing gas

between the diver and his life support system. The size and design of the mouthpiece differs between various manufacturers, but it is generally molded of rubber, neoprene, or plastic. Typically, it consists of a flange which fits between the lips and teeth. Bits, one on either side of the mouthpiece opening, serve to space the teeth restfully apart. The mouthpiece should fit comfortably and should be held in place by a slight pressure exerted by the lips and teeth. The novice diver often forgets that the bits are spacers and are not to be used as grips under normal conditions. In an emergency, the bits will provide a reliable grip, but continuous force exerted through the teeth will weaken the bits and cause considerable fatigue to the muscles around the jaws.

The mouthpiece assembly incorporates a system of "one-way" check valves. Clamps are provided for a pair of breathing hoses in the case of the double hose scuba. The mouthpiece is incorporated into the second stage demand valve housing of the single hose scuba regulator. In unusual cases, the mouthpiece assembly may be replaced entirely by a full face mask. The use of the full face mask in place of the mouthpiece facilitates voice communications by freeing the diver's mouth.

4.1.1.4 Check Valves and Exhaust Valves

Check valves and exhaust valves (Figure 4–7) are designed to permit fluid flow in one direction only. Check valves direct the flow of inhaled and exhaled gases through the breathing system. During inhalation, the mouthpiece chamber experiences a decrease in pressure (now lower than ambient), which seats the exhalation check valve, but opens the inhalation check valve. During exhalation, the air is directed out through the mouthpiece and

Figure 4-7
Check and Exhaust Valves

exhalation tube to the exhaust valve. This pair of valves within the mouthpiece assembly minimizes "dead air space" within the system and thus minimizes rebreathing of exhaled gases. The inhalation check valve also prevents water from entering the demand regulator when the mouthpiece floods.

The exhaust valve is a special check valve which permits discharge of exhaled gas from the breathing system without permitting the entrance of water. The flapper valve (also called a flutter valve) is typically employed as an exhaust valve in the double hose regulator, while a mushroom valve generally fulfills the function in the single hose model. The flapper valve is simply a soft rubber tube collapsed at one end. When ambient water pressure is greater than the air pressure within the valve, it remains in the collapsed condition. During exhalation, the increase in pressure (over ambient pressure) forces the flapper open allowing the gas to escape. Water cannot enter the valve while the higher pressure gas escapes, and when the pressure equalizes, the flapper returns to the "relaxed" or closed position.

The mushroom valve of the single hose model is made of extremely soft, flexible rubber which renders it very sensitive to changes in pressure across the check valve. A wheel-shaped valve seat is fashioned to hold the rubber mushroom in place. Rigid "spokes" of the valve seat support the mushroom valve against a closing pressure, but permit the flow of air when pressure within the mouthpiece exceeds ambient pressure.

4.1.1.5 Preventative Maintenance Procedures

As one of the primary components of the life support system, the regulator will require careful maintenance. While all components of the regulator are constructed of corrosion resistant materials, the introduction of foreign matter into areas where close tolerances exist or where perfect seals are required can cause a malfunction. The primary entry point for foreign matter is the high pressure inlet in the first stage. For this reason the plastic dust cap should be kept in position covering the high pressure inlet whenever the regulator is not in use. Salt water, entering the HP inlet will leave deposits of salt, which can prevent proper operation or can pit valve surfaces.

The most important maintenance to be performed on the regulator is the fresh water rinse after each use. This will remove salt and other debris (sand, dirt, etc.) from the regulator and prevent deterioration. This should be accomplished within a few hours of the completion of the dive, regardless of whether the dive was conducted in fresh or salt water. Procedures for washing the single and double hose regulators vary significantly, and are discussed below.

With the dust cap sealed in place, the first stage of a single hose regulator should be held under a stream of warm, fresh water for a period of at least 2 minutes. The water should be allowed to flow freely through any open ports. This is especially important with piston type regulators as it prevents the buildup of salts on the piston tracks. Since dust caps provided with some regulators may not be water-tight, the diver must check this before rinsing the regulator.

When rinsing the second stage, allow the water to enter the mouthpiece and exit the exhaust. This is working in the direction of the nonreturn exhaust valve and will wash sand, dirt, etc. out of the mouthpiece. **Never push the purge button as this opens the air inlet valve, and could possibly allow water carrying other debris to pass through the MP hose to the HP stage.** If the regulator is to be stored for a long period of time, it may be desirable to remove the band holding the two sections of the second stage and the diaphragm in place, and to rinse each separately, allowing each piece to dry prior to reassembly.

Rinsing procedures for the double hose regulator are slightly more complicated than for the single hose model. As with the single hose regulator, rinsing should be conducted with the water-tight dust cap in place. The exhaust side of the regulator will have a series of holes, and water should be allowed to flow freely through this section.

Care must be taken when rinsing the hose and mouthpiece assembly. If water is forced under high pressure into the mouthpiece, it may bypass the soft rubber nonreturn valve and permit water to enter the intake side, resulting in corrosion. Hold the mouthpiece with the air inlet valve up, and allow water to enter the mouthpiece, flow through the exhaust valve and hose, exiting at the main body of the regulator. To remove water from the corrugations in the hose, stretch the hose slightly and blow through the mouthpiece, allowing excess water to pass out the exhaust. Never hang the regulator by the mouthpiece, as this will stretch and weaken the hose.

4.1.2 Compressed Gas Cylinders

The scuba cylinder assembly is secured to the diver's back through a combination of shoulder, chest, waist, and crotch straps, known as the harness assembly. There has been a more recent trend toward the more comfortable, form fitting back pack assembly. The back pack itself is a lightweight frame, molded to conform to a diver's back and hip contours, and secured to the diver by adjustable, nylon shoulder and waist straps. The back pack is equipped with a clamping mechanism which secures either a single scuba cylinder or a multiple cylinder unit. Regardless of which of the many available harness or back pack models is employed, all straps which secure the apparatus to the diver must be equipped with corrosion-resistant, quick release buckles to permit rapid opening under emergency conditions.

The scuba cylinders contain the compressed breathing gas to be used by a diver. Most cylinders are of steel or aluminum alloy construction, specially designed and manufactured to safely contain compressed gas at working pressures from 1800 psig to 3000 psig (211 kg/cm²) or greater. Regardless of cylinder type, data describing the cylinder should be clearly stamped into the shoulder of the cylinder (Figures 4–8 and 4–8a).

The internal volume of a cylinder is a function of its physical dimensions and may be expressed in cubic inches or cubic feet. Of more interest is the capacity of the cylinder, which is the quantity of gas at surface pressure, which can be compressed into the cylinder at its rated pressure. The capacity is usually expressed in cubic feet or liters of gas.

Cylinders of various capacities are commercially

**Figure 4-8
Stampings on
Steel Cylinder**

**Figure 4-8a
Stampings on
Aluminum Cylinder**

available. Commonly encountered steel scuba cylinders have a rated working pressure of 2250 psig (158 kg/cm²) (153 atm) and contain 64.7 cubic feet (1848 liters) of gas. When these cylinders meet certain Department of Transportation standards, they may be overfilled by 10 percent of the rated capacity. This additional capacity is indicated by a plus (+) symbol adjacent to the hydrostatic test date stamped on the cylinder. Cylinders with capacities from 26 cubic feet (742 liters) to over 100 cubic feet (2857 liters) are also available commercially.

The gas capacity of any cylinder is a function of the internal volume of the cylinder, and its rated pressure. It can be determined using the following formula:

$$C = V_1 \left(\frac{PR}{14.7} \right)$$

where

C = capacity in cu. ft.
V_1 = internal volume in cu. ft.
PR = rated pressure in psi.

The quantity of gas remaining in a partially filled cylinder is a function of the pressure remaining in the cylinder and its volume. It can be determined using the following formula:

$$V_1 = V_2 \left(\frac{P_1}{P_2} \right)$$

where

V_1 = volume of gas remaining in cylinder (in cu. ft.)
V_2 = rated capacity of cylinder (in cu. ft.)
P_1 = pressure remaining in the cylinder (in psi)
P_2 = rated pressure of the cylinder (in psi).

Because of the high stresses imposed on a scuba cylinder at working pressure, the cylinders must be manufactured in accordance with the precise specifications provided by the Department of Transportation. The diver must ensure that each cylinder he uses has been manufactured, tested and certified in accordance with these rigid specifications by checking the information stamped on the shoulder of each cylinder (Peyser 1970). He must further ensure that these cylinders are inspected internally on an annual basis and hydrostatically tested in accordance with DOT regulations. The information stamped on the shoulder of the cylinder includes:

DOT (or ICC) material specification,

Service working pressure,

Serial number assigned by manufacturer,

Identification mark of manufacturer or owner,

Inspector's stamp,

Month and year of initial hydrostatic test,

Allowable 10 percent over service pressure, +,

WARNING

Do Not Fill Aluminum Cylinders Beyond Their Rated Pressure.

Month and year of latest requalification test.

The enormous potential energy of a fully charged scuba cylinder necessitates that special stowage, maintenance and handling precautions be observed.

1. Do not fill HP cylinders if the inspection date has expired (5 years for steel cylinders, 3 years for aluminum).

2. Charge cylinder at a slow rate to prevent excessive heat buildup.

3. Never exceed the maximum allowable pressure for any particular cylinder (usually 2250 psi plus 10 percent on steel cylinders, and 2475 or 3000 psi whichever is indicated on the aluminum cylinders).

4. Never perform maintenance or repairs on a cylinder valve while the cylinder is charged.

5. Handle charged tanks carefully. Handling by the valve or body is preferred. Handling by straps or backpack can allow the cylinder to slip or drop.

6. Store charged cylinders in an upright position in a cool, shady place to prevent overheating.

7. Secure cylinders properly. This includes blocking them against rolling when stored horizontally, and strapping them into position if stored vertically.

8. Internal inspections, hydrostatic tests, and repair work should be accomplished only by those trained to do so.

9. Have cylinders inspected for interior deterioration annually.

10. Inspect cylinders externally before and after each dive for signs of deterioration, damage, corrosion, dents, cracks, or other damage. Never use a dented, welded, or scarred cylinder.

11. Remove cylinder boot periodically and inspect for corrosion and rusting. Boots which do not permit draining and drying should not be used as they may allow water to remain in contact with the cylinder forming rust.

12. Do not completely drain the tank of air. This prevents moisture from entering the tank.

The open-circuit scuba cylinders are worn on a diver's back with the manifold/valve assembly up. In this configuration, the demand valve of the double hose regulator "rides" at the back of the diver's neck. The demand valve of the single hose regulator is positioned at the diver's mouth, regardless of cylinder orientation. The demand valves of both types must be kept in close proximity to the diver's primary respiratory organs in order to ensure a minimum hydrostatic pressure differential between demand valve and respiratory organs, regardless of diver orientation. If this is not achieved, the respiratory system must work harder than necessary in order to overcome this differential during inhalation or exhalation, depending upon orientation. Thus, positioning of cylinders on the diver's back is especially important when a double hose regulator is employed.

4.1.3 Cylinder Manifold and Valve Assembly

If diver's air is to be supplied by two or more cylinders simultaneously, a manifold assembly is employed to join the cylinders and provide a common outlet. The manifold consists of sections of high pressure piping and appropriate fittings specially configured and threaded to incorporate two or more cylinders, a stop valve, a low air warning/reserve air device, and blow-out plugs, into a single functional unit.

The cylinder stop valve assembly is a simple, manually-operated on-off valve which controls the flow of high pressure gas from the scuba cylinder. It is also the point of attachment for the demand regulator. After the regulator has been clamped to the cylinder valve, and just prior to using the apparatus, the valve is opened fully, and then closed ¼ of a turn. It remains open throughout the dive. Upon completion of the dive, the cylinder stop valve should be securely closed. Air in the regulator can then be bled to atmospheric pressure preventing an O-ring blowout while removing the regulator.

When a single cylinder supplies diver's air, the cylinder valve unit is sealed directly into the neck of the cylinder by a straight threaded male connection containing a neoprene O-ring on the valve body. When a single cylinder is utilized the cylinder valve assembly houses a high pressure blow-out plug (or disc), as a safety feature, to prevent cylinder pressure from reaching a critical level during charging or under conditions of elevated temperature. When a pair of cylinders are employed, two blow-out plugs are installed in the manifold assembly. Blow-out plugs utilized with cylinders rated at 2250 psi working pressure are designed to blow out at 3400 psi. The plug rating is stamped on the face of the plug to prevent confusion, and plugs of different pressure ratings are not to be used interchangeably.

The standard cylinder valve assembly described above is known as the "K-valve." A cylinder valve which incorporates a "low air warning"/reserve air mechanism is known as a "J-valve."

4.1.4 Low Pressure Air Warning/Reserve Air Mechanism

There are several mechanisms employed in open circuit scuba, which, to varying degrees, perform the important dual function of warning a diver that his air supply is approaching a critically low level, and then providing him a reserve air supply that allows him to proceed safely to the surface. The device may be incorporated into the cylinder valve/manifold assembly or into the demand regulator, and generally consists of one of the following: J-valve, submersible tank pressure gauge, restricting orifice, or auditory warning device. Each of the various devices is discussed and the limitations of each is reviewed in the following paragraphs.

4.1.4.1 J-Valve (Reserve Valve)

The J-valve, illustrated in Figure 4–9 is a spring-loaded check valve which begins to close as cylinder pressure approaches a predetermined level, generally 300 or 500 psi. The J-valve always permits unrestricted flow of air to the regulator throughout

Figure 4-9
Valve Assemblies

K-Valve   J-Valve

the dive until this pressure is approached. At the predetermined pressure, a spring forces a flow check against the port orifice and restricts the air flow, causing increased breathing resistance. This is followed by total obstruction of air flow if the reserve air is not manually released. The remaining, or reserve air can be released by manually overriding the spring-loaded check valve.

NOTE:

Reserve Lever Must Be In Down Position When Charging Cylinders.

When the diver depresses the cylinder valve/manifold-mounted reserve lever, a plunger pin within the J-valve advances, forcing the flow check back off the orifice against the action of the spring. The remaining 300 or 500 psi is now available to the diver.

When planning a dive, a diver must be aware of the fact that the availability and duration of reserve air supplied through the J-valve is dependent upon the number of cylinders as well as the depth. The 300 psi reserve available in a single tank normally is gauge pressure, not 300 psi above ambient pressure. Depth compensated reserves are available. At a depth of 100 feet (ambient pressure of approximately 50 psi) only 250 psi will be available until the diver starts his ascent. Also, the J-valve mechanism retains a reserve air supply in only one cylinder of a twin or triple set of cylinders, while the other cylinder or cylinders are exhausted. When the reserve mechanism is activated, the reserve air distributes itself equally among both cylinders, and the reserve pressure is reduced by one-half, or one-third in the case of three cylinders. It is for this reason that the J-valve employed with twin

Figure 4-10
Combination Submersible
Cylinder Pressure Gauge
and Depth Gauge
(front and back view)

Photo: Farallon Industries

cylinders *must* be set up to provide a 500 psi reserve or a 750 psi reserve with a triple set of cylinders. Unfortunately, while generally quite reliable, the J-valve reserve mechanism is subject to physical damage or mechanical failure, and if moved as little as 1/8" to 1/4", can be inadvertently tripped early in the dive, allowing the reserve air to be exhausted without warning.

4.1.4.2 Submersible Cylinder Pressure Gauge

The submersible cylinder pressure gauge, providing a continuous cylinder pressure read-out, is an alternative to the J-valve reserve mechanism. However, it does not provide a reserve air supply in the strict sense. It is useless under conditions of zero visibility unless illuminated. Employing the J-valve reserve with the submersible cylinder pressure gauge provides the diver with a system which overcomes the individual limitations. The submersible pressure gauge, positioned at the end of a two to three foot length of hose increases the the chances of fouling on bottom debris or with other items of equipment when worn improperly. The submersible cylinder pressure gauge is illustrated in Figure 4-10.

The gauge assembly employs standard fittings, and can be secured to most high pressure fittings on the cylinder valve demand regulator.

WARNING

The Submersible Cylinder Pressure Gauge Is Vulnerable to a Great Degree of Inaccuracy if Water Gets Into It Prior to Its Use. It Should Not Be Used Until Repaired.

Do Not Look Directly Into the Face of a Submersible Pressure Gauge When Turning on the Cylinder Due to the Possibility of Blow Out.

4.1.4.3 Audible Low-Air Warning Device

The audible low-air warning device produces a sonic signal automatically when cylinder pressure reaches a predetermined level. The sound continues until the cylinder air is exhausted. These devices are usually incorporated into the first stage assembly.

4.1.4.4 Restricted (or Calibrated) Orifice

The restricted (or calibrated) orifice warning/reserve mechanism is now seldom used and is **not recommended.** It operates on the principle that the flow rate through an orifice of a given size is proportional to the pressure differential across the orifice. Inserting an orifice of a given size into the system can result in an insufficient flow rate when cylinder pressure decreases to the demand pressure over ambient pressure.

4.2 SEMI-CLOSED-CIRCUIT MIXED GAS SCUBA

Closed circuit oxygen scuba was developed to take advantage of the benefits of gas conservation but is extremely limited in dive depths and duration by oxygen toxicity effects. Open-circuit scuba provides greater depth flexibility, but is limited in dive duration, especially at deeper depths by the inefficiency of gas utilization. Because an entirely closed-circuit mixed gas scuba was not technically possible at the time, due to the problem involved with inert gas buildup, semi-closed-circuit mixed gas scuba was developed (Figure 4-11) to bridge this gap between duration and depth.

The semi-closed circuit scuba operates on the same basic principles as closed-circuit scuba, but requires a continuous or frequent purge to prevent a toxic buildup of inert gas. The high pressure gas cylinders are charged with a mixture of oxygen and an inert gas which corresponds to the safe oxygen level for the maximum depth to which the diver will descend. The gas flow from the cylinders into the breathing circuit is controlled by a regulator and nozzle which admits a continuous and constant mass of gas. The diver inhales the breathing medium from a breathing bag and exhales it into an exhalation bag. Pressure in the exhalation bag forces the gas through the scrubber where carbon dioxide is removed, and from the scrubber the gas again passes into the breathing bag for consumption by the

Figure 4-11
Semi-Closed-Circuit Scuba

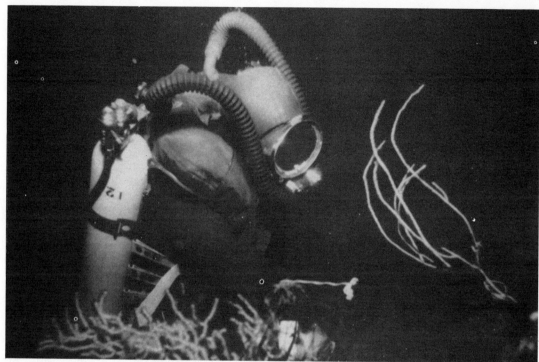

U.S. Navy Photo by Bill Bunton

diver. When the gas pressure in the breathing circuit reaches a pre-set level, a relief valve located in the exhalation bag lifts, purging excess gas into the surrounding water (See Paragraph 11.3).

4.3 CLOSED-CIRCUIT MIXED GAS SCUBA

All closed-circuit mixed gas scuba function on the same basic principle and have the same basic components. They are precision pieces of equipment, and safe operation is dependent on a thorough understanding of the system. Oxygen and an inert gas, referred to here as the diluent, are stored in separate high pressure cylinders. The addition of diluent gas is controlled by a regulator to maintain a constant volume. The oxygen content of the breathing gas is continually monitored by a series of sensors which automatically add oxygen to the breathing circuit as required (Figure 6–3). The mixed breathing gas of some systems is stored in a breathing bag from which the diver inhales directly. The exhaled gas is passed directly into the absorbent canister where

CO_2 is removed, and returned to the breathing bag to await rebreathing (See Paragraph 11.4).

4.4 CLOSED-CIRCUIT OXYGEN SCUBA

By employing carbon dioxide absorption, closed-circuit oxygen scuba permits essentially complete utilization of the available gas supply at a rate independent of depth. Most units consist of a mouthpiece, breathing valve assembly, breathing hoses, inhalation and exhalation breathing bags, a carbon dioxide absorption canister, an oxygen supply cylinder, and an adjustable gas-flow regulating assembly.

Compressed oxygen is delivered from the high-pressure oxygen cylinder into the inhalation breathing bag by the gas-flow regulating assembly at a rate at which the diver uses the oxygen. The diver inhales the gas from the inhalation breathing bag through the inhalation hose and exhales into the exhalation breathing bag through the exhalation hose. The exhaled gas displaces the gas from the exhalation breathing bag causing it to flow into the carbon

Figure 4-12
Umbilical Diver

Photo: Richard Cooper

dioxide absorption canister, where the carbon dioxide is removed. Gas within the canister, now freed of carbon dioxide, is displaced into the inhalation bag, where it remains until the next inhalation.

4.5 UMBILICAL DIVING

While the majority of diving situations will be under circumstances which dictate the use of open-circuit scuba equipment, umbilical diving has many important advantages which self-contained diving cannot provide (Figure 4–12).

One of the major limitations of self-contained diving is the quantity of breathing gas the diver can carry. With umbilical diving, the diver has a continous air supply, thus allowing extended bottom times. Because the diver is directly tethered, only one diver is required in the water at a time, thus conserving diver manhours.

Of significant importance is the increased safety factor possible with umbilical equipment. The diver is tethered and normally has direct voice communications; therefore, he can safely operate under conditions which may be considered too hazardous for

the self-contained diver such as zero visibility. Should the diver become fouled or disabled, his air supply is continuous and the standby diver can proceed directly to his assitance by following the entrapped diver's tether. Strong currents may present a significant problem to the tethered diver. If required, he can safely use additional weights to hold him on the bottom while working.

Umbilical diving may be conducted not only from the surface but from a habitat, a personnel transfer capsule, or a lock-out submersible. An umbilical from the gas storage cylinders of the habitat, capsule or submersible provides the diver's breathing gas, hot water, if required, and a communications link.

The major disadvantage associated with umbilical diving equipment is the increased requirement for support equipment and personnel.

A wide variety of diver's masks and helmets are commercially available. They are safe and efficient and most can be adapted for use with scuba. All will provide the diver with a continuous supply of breathing gas, and some models allow the diver to select between free-flow or demand breathing. A communications system is standard equipment in the majority of modern helmets.

4.5.1 Lightweight Diving Mask

Probably the oldest and simplest form of lightweight diving mask is the "Jack Browne" mask (Figure 4–13). This mask is easy to maintain and operate, and may be equipped with voice communications. It consists of a rubber seal molded to a copper frame and a large triangular faceplate. Air enters the mask through an air control valve on the right side, and is exhausted through a manually closeable one-way valve located on the left side. This helmet is compatible with scuba accessories or a weighted dry suit. The umbilical consists of the air supply hose, lifeline, and communications line, when installed.

4.5.2 Free-Flow/Demand Mask

The free-flow/demand mask (Figure 4–14) provides several features, such as variable air flow, communications and an emergency air bottle connection. This equipment is designed to be used tethered, or with scuba from the surface, from a personnel transfer capsule (PTC) or from a submerged habitat. It can be used to deep depths with either air or mixed gas as the breathing medium.

Photo: Lee Somers

Photo: Lee Somers

The body of the mask is constructed of fiberglass molded to fit the contours of the face. A faceplate and regulator are part of the mask. The faceplate is constructed of acrylic plastic. An adjustable nose pad is available to assist the diver in clearing his ears and sinus cavity during descent. All free-flow/demand masks are similar and may include a side valve assembly, demand regulator, oral-nasal mask, exhaust assembly, emergency air supply, and communications system.

The side valve assembly on some masks has two control valves. One valve, when closed, directs breathing gas into the regulator assembly and on to the oral-nasal cavity upon demand. When open, it additionally allows breathing gas to free flow across the face plate to prevent fogging. The second valve controls the source of the breathing gas which would either be primary or emergency.

The demand regulator is a modified second-stage scuba regulator. It will accept breathing gas at pressures between 50 to 200 psi above ambient pressure and has a control which allows the diver to manually adjust the breathing resistance. The regulator is secured to the fiberglass frame directly in front of the diver's mouth, and admits air into the oral-nasal cavity upon demand. Gas is supplied to the regulator from the side valve assembly. A manual purge button on the front of the regulator allows the diver to quickly switch to a free flow of air through the regulator.

An oral-nasal mask may be located inside the fiberglass frame and is used to create a partial seal around the diver's nose and mouth, thereby effec-

tively reducing dead space and the chances of a CO_2 buildup. Air enters the cavity directly from the regulator, and is exhausted through the regulator exhaust when the demand mode is in use. When the mask is set to free-flow, the gases enter the oral-nasal cavity directly from the side valve, through a check valve, and are exhausted through the regulator exhaust. The oral-nasal cavity is an important safety device and it is recommended that it be used.

WARNING

If the Oral-Nasal Mask Is Absent There Is a Danger of CO_2 Buildup. Therefore the Diver Must Ventilate at Frequent Intervals.

Free-flow/demand masks generally have two exhaust assemblies located near the bottom of the fiberglass frame, below the regulator. These one-way valves are constructed of neoprene rubber, are of the mushroom design and function automatically when the pressure inside the mask is greater than ambient pressure. Because of their location, the exhaust valves function as a purging system, automatically maintaining the water level in the mask below the oral-nasal cavity if the mask is in a relatively upright position.

A partially or completely flooded mask can be quickly purged by placing the exhaust valve in a downward position and opening the free-flow valve or depressing the manual purge button on the demand regulator.

Figure 4-15
Lightweight Helmet

Photo: General Aquadyne

A self-contained emergency gas supply system (or bailout unit) is used in conjunction with surface-supplied diving equipment for work in excess of a 60 foot depth or when working in tunnels, pipes, etc., or where there is specific danger of entanglement. The unit consists of a scuba cylinder assembly, a reduction regulator (first stage of a standard single-hose regulator), and a backpack-harness assembly. The capacity of the scuba cylinder assembly will vary from 10 ft^3 to 140 ft^3, depending on the diver and the situation. The self-contained emergency gas may be fed directly into the mask through a special attachment on the side valve or directly into the diver's air hose assembly. In the latter case, a check valve should be located between the intersection of the emergency gas supply hose and the primary surface supply hose. A completely separate bailout system may be used in which a scuba tank and regulator are carried. Upon loss of the umbilical air supply, the full face mask is removed and the diver ascends using the scuba tank and mouthpiece. If this system is selected, a face mask should also be carried. The advantage is complete independence. The disadvantage is loss of communication, difficulty in putting on the face mask and locating the regulator.

One of the primary advantages of the free-flow/demand mask is the availability of reliable voice communications. The microphone is located inside the oral-nasal cavity. The earphones are located in pockets in the hood or attached to an adjustable boom which can be placed over the ear.

Head protectors are used with the free-flow/demand mask to prevent injury to the diver's head. The helmet-style protector is generally constructed of fiberglass and designed to absorb shock either through internal padding or special attachment to the mask. Head protectors are recommended when working under boats or other types of obstructions.

4.5.3 Lightweight Helmets

Several lightweight helmets are commercially available. These helmets (Figure 4–15) are compatible with the variable volume dry suit, the standard wet suit and heated wet suits. Unbreakable faceplates and improved visibility are additional advantages. Many models are designed for use with an emergency air supply and for use with mixed gases.

The modern lightweight helmet is commonly constructed of copper, brass, or a tough, rigid fiberglass. Improved air control and exhaust valves are easy to operate and are corrosion and clog resistant. Most have a large primary viewport and a smaller port for looking upward. The majority of helmets incorporate a neck ring which can be connected to the neck seal of all types of dress.

The lightweight helmet is equipped with communications and may be the safest choice of equipment for conducting very strenuous underwater tasks.

4.5.4 Diver Umbilical

The umbilical is that combination of hoses and lines from the support platform or habitat required to support the diver. A scuba diver may have an umbilical consisting solely of a lifeline. Surface-support umbilicals usually have a minimum of two lines (gas hose and communications line), but may have as many as five (gas hose, communications line, pneumogauge hose, hot water hose, and lifeline).

4.5.4.1 Gas Supply Hose

The gas supply hose is the primary source of life support gas and is the most important part of the umbilical. A synthetic rubber, braid-reinforced hose with an inside diameter of $3/8$-inch is normally used. The hose must be extremely tough and durable; weather, abrasion, and oil resistant; and capable of withstanding a minimum internal pressure of 200 psi. The hose must be easy to handle, flexible and kink resistant. Only high quality hose insuring minimum shrinkage properties should be used.

If possible the hose should be of one-piece construction to reduce the chances of separation; however, if necessary, special connectors can be used. The hose itself should be frequently inspected for wear, cracking, abrasion, or other deterioration.

4.5.4.2 Communications Line

The communications line must be durable enough to prevent parting due to strain on the umbilical assembly, and have an outer jacket that is waterproof and oil and abrasion resistant. A two, three, or four size 16 or 18 conductor shield wire with a neoprene outer jacket is satisfactory. Although only two conductors are in service at one time, the extra conductors may be used for rapid field repairs in the event of one of the conductors breaking while in service. The wire-braid shielding adds considerable strength to the umbilical assembly. For example, spiral 4 communications line with four #18 plastic-coated conductors embedded in a vinyl filler surrounded by stainless-steel wire braid and synthetic cover has a breaking strength rating in excess of 1,460 pounds.

The wire is fitted with connectors compatible with those on the mask or helmet and the surface communicator. When joined together, the electrical pin connections are established and a watertight seal is formed, insulating the wire from the surrounding sea water. Many masks and helmets are equipped with post binders instead of socket-type connectors. As a backup, the conductor wires may be attached directly to these terminals; however, the quality of communications is lowered and the wires are easily pulled loose.

4.5.4.3 Lifeline

The use of a separate lifeline for umbilical diving is optional and at the discretion of the Dive Master. An umbilical assembly consisting of high quality hose (i.e., SAE100R3 or equivalent specification) and shielded communications wire is generally considered of sufficient strength for free-flow/demand mask and lightweight helmet diving. For those who wish to incorporate a lifeline into the umbilical assembly the use of limited stretch synthetic line or lightweight aircraft cable is recommended. Avoid

nylon or other similar synthetic materials which stretch under tension and put unnecessary strain on other components of the umbilical. Some divers use a combination communications wire-braided polypropylene synthetic line. The communications wire may be fed through the hollow core of the braided line to form a strong, compact single unit.

4.5.4.4 Pneumogauge Hose

The pneumogauge is used to accurately monitor the diver's depth. It consists of a durable, lightweight flexible hose attached to a low pressure air supply source on the surface, and open at the diver's end. The hose should be attached to the umbilical with the open end terminating at the diver's chest. Although the open tube is not subjected to high pressure, it should have a working pressure capacity of 200–250 pounds per square inch. Lightweight air hose (0.25 inch inside diameter), extruded seamless nylon tubing (0.17 inch inside diameter, 0.25 inch outside diameter, with a 250 pound per square inch maximum working pressure), or thermoplastic tubing with external open polyester braid (0.25 inch inside diameter, 0.456 inch outside diameter, with a 250 pound per square inch maximum working pressure) have been found satisfactory (Somers 1972).

4.5.4.5 Hot Water Hose

When diving with hot water wet suits, a specially insulated hose is required. This can be obtained in either 1/2 or 3/4 inch inside diameter depending upon the depth and volume of water to be supplied to the diver. The insulation reduces heat loss to the open sea allowing a lower boiler operating temperature. The hose should be equipped with a quick-disconnect female fitting compatible with the manifold attached to the suit. The hot water hose should be joined to the diver's gas and communications umbilical to prevent handling problems.

4.5.4.6 Assembly of the Umbilical

The various components of the umbilical are assembled and taped at approximately 1-foot intervals with 2-inch wide, polyethylene cloth, laminated tape (duct tape) or the equivalent. Prior to taping, the various components (gas hose, communications wire, lifeline if used, pneumohose, and hot water hose) are laid out adjacent to each other and inspected for damage or abnormalities. The gas supply hose is plugged at one end and pressurized to the

**Figure 4-16
Umbilical Attachment
Assembly**

Photo: Lee Somers

working pressure (generally 120–200 pounds per square inch) to ensure that the shrinkage factor will not cause "looping" when the umbilical is in use. When assembling the umbilical, take into account the length of gas hose whip, communications wire whip and the hot water hose connection location. Generally, the communications wire is longer than the rest of the assembly at the diver's end. This provides an extra length of wire in the event that repairs must be carried out. The excess is looped around the umbilical and secured with tape. The diver's end must be assembled first so as to prevent excess looping and bulk; the umbilical should not interfere with the diver's movements. It is best to start taping at the diver's end and work toward the surface end.

A quick-release type swivel snap shackle or special air hose clamp is secured to the umbilical to facilitate attachment to the diver's harness and prevent pull on the helmet or mask. The shackle may be tightly secured to the umbilical with several wraps of nylon line or a specially constructed cable saddle. Attachment location will depend on the harness assembly worn by the diver, but should never be attached to the weight belt in case it needs to be dropped (Figure 4–16).

4.5.4.7 Coiling and Storage of Umbilical Hose

After the umbilical hose is assembled, it should be stored and transported with protection provided for hose and communications fittings. The hose ends should be capped with plastic protectors or taped closed to keep out foreign matter and to protect threaded fittings. The umbilical hose may be coiled on take-up reel assemblies, "figure-eighted," or coiled on deck (Figure 4–17) with one loop over and one loop under. Incorrect coiling, all in the same direction, will cause twist and, subsequently, handling problems. The tender should check the umbilical assembly at the end of each dive to ensure that there are no twists. The coil should be secured with a number of ties to prevent uncoiling during handling. Placing the umbilical assembly in a large canvas bag or wrapping it in a tarp will prevent damage during transport.

4.5.4.8 Umbilical Maintenance

After a day's diving, the umbilical should be washed with fresh water, visually inspected for damage and carefully stored to prevent "kinks."

If the umbilical is to be stored for a long period of time, the hoses should be blown dry and the connectors capped, to prevent foreign matter from entering. Connectors should be lubricated with silicone spray after capping.

4.5.4.9 Harness

The diver should wear a harness assembly to facilitate attachment of the umbilical assembly. The harness should be designed to withstand a minimum of 1000-pound pull in any direction and must prevent strain from being placed on the diver's mask or helmet when a pull is taken on the hose assembly.

WARNING

Never Attach the Diver's Umbilical Directly to His Weight Belt. A Separate Belt or Harness Is Recommended

4.6 SUPPORT PLATFORM EQUIPMENT

The equipment installed on a support platform depends heavily on the type and duration of the diving activity and the physical limitations of the platform itself. Support platforms encompass surface ships

Figure 4-17
Properly Coiled
Umbilical

Photo: Lee Somers

and barges as well as underwater habitats and submersibles. The primary equipment in the support platform is that associated with the diver's breathing medium. Air compressors or banks of compressed gas cylinders constitute the major diver support items in all platforms. Saturation diving complexes and recompression chambers require a significant allotment of deck space when installed on diving barges or ships. A habitat, while requiring some surface support equipment, especially air compressors or mixed gas supplies, may, in an emergency, utilize internal compressed gas sources for maintenance of its atmosphere. Submersibles carry sufficient gas in cylinders to maintain their atmosphere for long periods of time as well as support divers who may make excursion dives from the submersible. This paragraph discusses various aspects of low pressure air compressor equipment as well as compressed gas cylinders, whether they support a diver directly, or are ancillary to the habitat or submersible. For a discussion of high pressure air compressors see Paragraph 5.1.3.

4.6.1 Air Compressors

The air compressor is the most common source for diver's breathing air. The compressor is generally backed up by a bank of high pressure gas storage cylinders to reduce the possibility of interrupting the diver's breathing gas supply due to loss of power or compressor malfunction.

The low pressure air compressor is the most frequently used source of breathing air for the umbilical supplied diver supported from the surface, a diving bell, or habitat. Of the several different designs of air compressors available, the reciprocating model is the primary type used for diving operations. These compressors are capable of compressing gases to the pressures required for scuba operations, or in the quantities required for low pressure surface supplied operations. The gas is compressed to the desired pressure by a series of pistons. Coolers are used to reduce the temperature of the compressed gas and the water vapor in the compressed gas.

The centrifugal compressor will provide a large volume of air, but compact size and high RPM complicate maintenance so that they are not readily adaptable to diving operations. Rotary compressors are compact units, but normally limited to one stage and an output of only 100 psi.

A compressor is rated at the pressure at which it will unload or the unloading switches will activate. A compressor must not only have the volumetric capacity to provide sufficient breathing medium, but must also provide the pressure above the range equivalent to the ambient pressure the diver will experience at his planned depth. A practical minimum allowable margin for dives less than 120 feet is 50 psi over bottom pressure. For dives over 120 feet, a compressor rating of 100 psi over bottom pressure is the accepted standard.

All air compressors used for diver's air supply must have an accumulator (volume tank) as an integral part of the system. The accumulator will provide a limited emergency supply of air should the compressor fail and will provide air for the diver while the surface crew switches to the backup air supply.

4.6.2 High Pressure Cylinders

Occasionally it is advantageous to use a series of large, high-pressure cylinders as the source of gas in lieu of a compressor. This is particularly advantageous in areas where convenient access to a high-pressure compressor for recharging is available. Using cylinders as the gas source will reduce the chances of losing the primary supply as the entire volume of gas required for a dive is compressed and stored prior to the dive. The cylinders can be stored out of the working area. Most lock-out submersibles carry the diver's gas supply in high-pressure cylinders built into the body of the submarine. It is important to note that cylinder banks may be used to store mixed gases for diving operations as well as compressed air. Mixed gas cylinders are usually taken to the dive site prior to the diving operation. The dive time is limited by the amount of compressed gas available. Compressed gas cylinders are usually built into a habitat to provide a backup gas supply in case of emergency and from which scuba tanks may be refilled. In general terms, high-pressure cylinders are an excellent means for storing diver's breathing gas as both a primary source as well as a backup for emergency use.

In some instances, it may be advantageous to manifold a number of scuba tanks together to supply a tethered diver. This system may be used to best advantage when both scuba and umbilical diving are being used on the same job. The advantage is elimination of the large high-pressure cylinders commonly used.

4.7 DIVER EQUIPMENT

The on-scene Dive Master will determine which items of equipment are required to accomplish the underwater task on a per case basis. Any equipment which is unnecessary for the anticipated dive should be disallowed. The overuse of equipment complicates the diver's task, and can become a hazard rather than an asset. This is particularly true when diving in a strong current, or under conditions of very limited visibility, or heavy surge, as each additional item of diving equipment, especially additional lines, increases the probability of fouling the diver. Diver equipment considered in this paragraph include the face mask, flotation devices, the weight belt, the knife, and swim fins.

4.7.1 Face Mask

The face mask (Figure 4–18) provides the diver with the ability to clearly observe his surroundings, and protects the eyes and face from a variety of underwater hazards.

The face mask is relatively simple in construction, consisting of a faceplate, body, retaining band, and headstrap. The primary safety feature to be considered when selecting a mask is the construction of the faceplate. All masks should have a faceplate made of shatterproof or tempered safety glass. Regular glass can be easily broken, and if cracked, could shatter into many sharp pieces which could result in severe and painful lacerations to the face. Shatterproof plastic is available which fulfills the safety criteria, but is subject to discoloration, is easily scratched, and tends to fog up easily. For divers with impaired vision, optically corrected

Figure 4-18
Face Masks

Photo: U.S. Divers

lenses in faceplates are available.

The body of the mask is constructed of a flexible rubber which must be firm enough to maintain its shape yet soft enough around the edge to provide a comfortable fit and waterproof seal around the face. The mask is held to the face by a combination of water pressure and a flexible rubber strap designed to run behind the head.

Face masks are available in a number of different styles and the diver should select one which fits him comfortably. The standard face mask is oval in shape. Large wrap-around face masks are available which provide the diver with some peripheral vision, although this is slightly distorted. Other models are small and light. A one-way valve is included in some models for purging water which enters the mask. Others are designed to allow the diver to pinch or block his nose to facilitate equalizing his ears. The edge of the face mask varies with different models.

Figure 4-19
Flotation Device

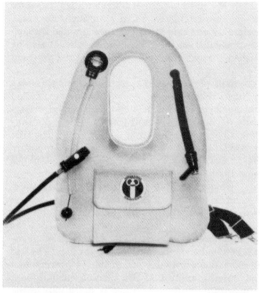

Photo: U.S. Divers

Some have a tapered neoprene edge while others have a soft, foamed neoprene edge. A face mask is available which contains the preferred combination of features for any individual.

A comfortable fit which forms an air tight seal on the face is important. The diver can determine if any particular mask will properly seal by putting the mask to the face without the benefit of the strap, and inhaling through the nose. If the mask fits properly the pressure in the mask will be reduced, a seal will be created and the mask will adhere to the face until the individual exhales.

Because of generally poor air circulation in the mask it is prone to fogging. The most common method of reducing fogging is to thoroughly smear the inside of the faceplate with saliva, and then rinse it lightly just prior to the dive. Commercial anti-fogging liquids can be purchased or a solution of mild liquid soap may be used. Should the faceplate fog up during a dive it can be easily cleared by partially flooding the mask, rolling the water around on the faceplate, then purging the water.

Relatively little care or maintenance is required to maintain the face mask in safe condition. After each dive it should be rinsed in fresh water and allowed to dry prior to storing. The faceplate should be frequently washed to remove any oils or film which could cause fogging. If the mask has a purge valve it should be thoroughly washed out to remove any sand which might prevent it from sealing properly. The mask should not be left in the sun for any extended period of time as this results in the head-strap and sealing edge becoming brittle and cracked. The headstrap can be easily and economically replaced. Deterioration of the sealing edge which prevents a proper seal renders the mask useless and it should be discarded.

4.7.2 Flotation Device

The flotation device (Figure 4–19) is one of the most important and yet most frequently ignored pieces of equipment. Many divers apparently feel they are not necessary, or are for use by beginning or weak divers. The flotation device is most frequently used to provide buoyancy for a diver on the surface who has become fatigued or is returning to the surface without air. Many experienced divers use them for fine buoyancy control while submerged. The use of a flotation device for an emergency ascent is extremely infrequent, however. Many of the commercially available products do not provide effective buoyancy until the diver ascends to within 30′ of the surface.

The flotation device should be designed so that a diver, even in an unconscious condition will float with his head out of the water. The inflating mechanism of the device should be constructed of a corrosion resistant metal. Some commercially available models have these critical mechanisms constructed of metal which corrodes rapidly when exposed to salt water, or of plastic which is subject to breakage and subsequent failure. These should be avoided. A relief valve should be part of the device when it is used for buoyancy compensation. The relief valve will normally be constructed of neoprene rubber with plastic seat. Most devices are designed to be inflated automatically when a CO_2 cartridge is punctured, or by a compressed air cylinder. All flotation devices should be equipped with an oral inflation tube regardless of their method of automatic inflation.

Selection of the proper flotation device is extremely important. Although the design of the vest is a prime factor, in general the buoyancy provided by a device which uses a single 12 or 16 gram CO_2 cartridge for inflation is not sufficient to support a fully equipped diver. A recent series of tests indicates that the commonly used 12 gram cartridge will not adequately support a diver with his head out of the water.* The single 16 gram cartridge will hold the diver's head out of the water in calm seas, but will allow his mouth to be submerged by waves over 6 inches in height.

Recent studies have determined that a minimum of 25 pounds positive buoyancy* are required to support a fully-outfitted diver in sea-state 1. To achieve this, a 19–25 gram CO_2 cartridge used with a properly-designed buoyancy compensator must be used. It should also be noted that U.S. Coast Guard regulations require life jackets to have a positive buoyance of 24.5 pounds to support a fully-clothed adult male. Flotation devices which use larger cartridges, multiple cartridges, and one or two inflation compartments are available. These models can be used as buoyancy compensators by partially inflating the device while submerged through the oral inflation tube. If the device does not have a relief valve, care must be taken while surfacing to prevent the expanding air from rupturing the flotation device.

Specially designed buoyancy compensators are commercially available. These have large oral inflation tubes easily reached by the diver and frequently have separate inflatable chambers. A large cylinder of compressed gas, which is chargeable from a standard scuba air cylinder is an integral part of some buoyancy compensators and allows for partial or complete inflation while submerged. Pressure relief valves are provided for each compartment to prevent overinflation.

If the device is not inflated during a dive the maintenance procedures are significantly reduced. The exterior should be thoroughly rinsed with fresh water after each use. Special attention should be given the CO_2 release mechanism, oral inflator, and other movable mechanical parts, to ensure they operate freely and easily. The CO_2 actuating lever should be worked up and down as the water is flushed through the mechanism. The mechanical parts should be allowed to dry, and then lubricated with a silicone lubricant. The threads on the CO_2 cartridge should be lubricated with Vaseline or a white, all-purpose grease to prevent them from being frozen in the mechanism by corrosion.

The most frequent causes of flotation device malfunction are the result of salt water entering the inflation compartments. The resulting salt residue can block the CO_2 passage and cause significant deterioration of the inflation release mechanism. If this occurs, the device should be filled approxi-

mately one-third full of warm fresh water. The water should be circulated rapidly through the vest, preferably one side at a time, then drained through the oral inflation tube. Fresh water should also be flushed through the passage between the vest and the CO_2 cartridge.

Certain periodic checks of the inflation devices are also required. The device should be inflated and hung up over night and/or submerged periodically to check for leaks. If leaks are observed they should be repaired before it is used again. The CO_2 cartridges should be frequently weighed to ensure they have not lost their charge. If their weight is more than 3 grams less than the weight printed on the cylinder, the cartridge should be discarded. Be certain the cartridge in the device is the one designed for use with that item. Many different capacity cylinders have the same threads. The use of a lower capacity cylinder can result in underinflation and a significant loss of buoyancy. The use of too large a cylinder can result in overinflation and possible rupture of the inflation compartment if an overpressure relief valve is not a part of the flotation device. When inflated, a well-designed flotation device should not ride above the head or choke the diver.

4.7.3 Weight Belt

The weight belt is used by the diver to achieve neutral buoyancy. Just enough weight should be carried so that the diver is slightly negative with a full tank, and becomes slightly positive as he consumes his air. The positive buoyancy provided by the wet suit is probably the largest contributing factor in determining weight requirements. Without a wet suit the diver will probably be able to achieve neutral buoyancy with less than 5 pounds of weight, whereas if a full wet suit is worn 10 to 20 pounds may be required depending on depth. The diver should accurately determine his weight requirements in shallow water prior to performing working dives. Failure to do this can result in a great deal of unnecessarily expended air and energy consumed by the diver trying to maintain depth. A test to determine the amount of weight required may be carried out. A full lung of air at the surface should support the diver at eye-level with the water. Exhalation will result in a slow sinking, while inhalation will cause a slow rising. As a general rule, the deeper the dive, the less weight will be required

---

*John McAniff, 1974: personal communication.

Figure 4-20
Divers' Knives

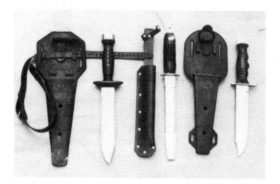

Figure 4-21
Fins

to achieve the desired buoyancy.

Except during saturation diving, all weight belts should be equipped with a quick-release mechanism. This is to allow the diver to discard the belt and its weights quickly, thus immediately gaining a degree of positive buoyancy. The quick-release buckle must be capable of being released with one quick motion of either hand. Should an emergency be encountered which requires additional positive buoyancy, the diver must not be required to untie knots or undo buckles. The common army cartridge belt does not have a quick-release buckle and should not be used as a weight belt.

The belt itself is normally made of 2 inch nylon, but the material may vary. Standard scuba weights made to accept a 2 inch belt, are made of lead and range in weight from 1 to 10 pounds. The design of scuba weights varies, and includes some which can be easily removed or added to the belt without removing other weights or equipment, and others which conform to the contour of the diver's waist. To be worn safely, the weight belt should be worn outside of all other equipment to allow it to fall clear when released. Maintenance of the belt is limited to a fresh water washing after use, and pre-dive checks of the quick-release mechanism to ensure it is corrosion free and operating properly.

4.7.4 Diver's Knife

The diver's knife (Figure 4–20) should always be carried for emergency use. Some models are designed as a combination pry bar and knife, and can be useful for removing coral, mollusks, or other marine life from the bottom.

The diver's knife should be constructed of a corrosion resistant metal, preferably stainless steel.

Handles must provide a good, firm grip and be resistant to deterioration. Plastic, hard rubber, or wood handles are satisfactory. A convenient blade size will be 5 to 7 inches long and approximately $1\frac{1}{4}$ inches wide, one edge being sharp, and the other having serrations.

The location of the knife is a matter of individual preference, subject to certain limitations. It must be worn where it is easily accessible in an emergency, but should never be worn on a piece of equipment which would be discarded under such circumstances. The knife is frequently placed around the waist or on the inside of the calf of the leg. Carrying the knife on the inside of the calf is becoming increasingly popular as it tends to prevent fouling and is readily accessible to both hands. This also provides a clear drop-path for the weight belt.

Because the knife is essentially an emergency piece of equipment it must be properly maintained. Improper maintenance can result in it being virtually useless in an emergency. After each use the knife should be rinsed with fresh water, dried and coated with a layer of light oil prior to storage. It must be frequently checked to ensure the blade is sharp. The material used in most diving knives will retain a good cutting edge for a long period of time if properly maintained. If abused during a job by prying or cutting a hard substance, the edge should be checked after the dive.

4.7.5 Swim Fins

Swim fins (Figure 4–21) increase the propulsive force of the legs. Used properly, swim fins conserve the diver's energy and facilitate underwater movements. Swim fins are available in a variety of sizes and designs. Variations in characteristics in-

4-21

clude size and shape of foot pocket; size, shape, angle, and degree of stiffness of the blade. Selection of fins is a matter of individual preference, mission requirements, fit, and physical condition. Performance is dependent upon fin design, the style of diver's kick, and the force in which this style is applied to the water.

In general there are two styles of fins: swimming and power. Swimming-fins are smaller, lighter weight, and slightly more flexible than the power style, and are used with a wider, more rapid kick of less thrust. The blade may have a greater angle. Some utilize an open vent or overlapping blade principle which gives the swimmer maximum thrust with minimum energy requirements. This style uses approximately as much force on the up-kick as on the downward kick. The swimming-style fin is less fatiguing for extensive surface swimming, less demanding on leg muscles, and more comfortable. This type of fin is recommended for trainees. Power-style fins are longer, heavier, and more rigid than swimming fins. They are used with a slower, shorter kicking stroke with emphasis on the down kick. This style fin is designed for maximum power thrust of short duration with a sacrifice in comparative comfort, and is desirable for working divers who are required to swim while encumbered with multiple-cylinder scuba and heavy equipment. Many divers own both swimming-style and power-style fins. Buoyant and nonbuoyant models are available in both styles; this factor doesn't generally affect the quality or performance of the fin.

Swim fins are available in open- or enclosed-heel models. Open-heel models are recommended for use with coral shoes or rubber boots. They are much easier to don and fit more comfortably. The open-heel models have either an adjustable strap or a one-piece nonadjustable strap. Adjustable strap models are designed to accommodate a wide range of foot sizes; however, they are less comfortable when worn without foot protection.

The strap buckle must be sturdy and designed to hold the strap securely in place. Since open-heel fins have a closed toe section, the fin must be properly sized to prevent cramping of the toes. Open-heel fins are generally larger and stiffer than closed-heel models. Closed-heel fins are often used for diving in warmer climates where exposure suits and boots are not required. Even in warmer waters some divers prefer some sort of foot protection (socks or boots) to prevent chafing and blisters, especially if they wear fins for long periods of time.

Basically, the fin must fit comfortably. It must be properly sized to prevent cramping or chafing. The fin must match the individual's physical condition (Somers 1972).

4.8 DIVER'S PROTECTIVE CLOTHING

When a diver enters the water he is subjected to an environment entirely different from the one to which he is accustomed. In addition to the life support and standard diving equipment already discussed, the diver frequently will require some form of protective clothing. This clothing affords protection from cold water and from possible abrasions and minor bites. Protective clothing is available in a wide variety of types, styles and materials. A thorough understanding of the conditions under which the diver will be operating is necessary when selecting the dress to be used. The types of divers dress most frequently employed are the wet suit and the dry suit.

4.8.1 Wet Suit

The neoprene wet suit is undoubtedly the most common form of protective clothing in use today. In its various configurations it will provide thermal protection to a diver over the wide range of temperatures encountered under normal diving conditions. It will also provide adequate protection from coral, stinging coelenterates and other marine hazards. If damaged it is quickly and easily repaired when the diver returns to the surface. The basic wet suit consists of neoprene pants and jacket, with boots, gloves, hood, and vest being optional (Figure 4–22). They are available in a variety of sizes and configurations, or can be constructed to the individual diver's preference. For warm water diving, a brief vest is available which covers only the body trunk. Full length styles which cover the entire body including the hands, feet, and head, with the exception of the face, are available for use in colder waters.

Wet suits are constructed from closed-cell foamed neoprene, normally of $3/16$ or $1/4$ inch thickness, although suits as thin as $1/8$ inch and as thick as $3/8$ or $1/2$ inch are available if desired. The thinner suits will provide for more freedom of movement, with the thicker material providing better thermal protection. Most suits use a nylon liner on the inside surface of the neoprene to limit tearing and facilitate easy entry. Models are available with nylon on both the inner and outer surfaces to decrease tears and abrasions; however, the added layer of nylon fur-

**Figure 4-22
Standard Wet Suit**

Photo: Parkways

**Figure 4-23
Effects of
Water Temperature**

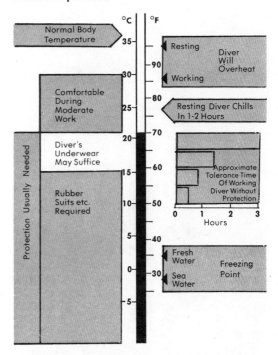

ther restricts the diver's movements as do elbow and knee pads. The sections of the suit are joined by using a neoprene glue. On the better models the seams are sewn together to prevent separation. Neoprene glue is available in small cans for quick and easy wet suit repair. However, double surface nylon does not repair well with ordinary cement so tears should be sewn. The wet suit might have as many as five zippers, one in each ankle and sleeve, and one in the front of the jacket. A good quality suit is flexible and strong enough to be constructed without need for ankle and sleeve zippers. A suit should be flexible enough to enable the diver to don it without aggravation either to himself or to the material.

When water temperatures approach 60° F, the hands, feet and head lose heat at a rate which makes diving without protective gloves, boots, and a hood, impractical. Even in tropical climates the diver may elect to wear some form of boots and gloves for abrasion protection. In colder waters, loss of body heat in these areas may significantly affect diver performance unless some form of thermal protection is worn (Figure 4–23).

Thermal protection of the hands is extremely important, as the loss in dexterity which accompanies thermal reduction can significantly reduce the diver's effectiveness. However, the loss in dexterity inherent in most gloves also reduces diver performance. Most divers prefer to avoid their use as long as possible, utilizing cotton gloves or other forms which do not severely restrict finger movement and feeling. Five-fingered foamed neoprene gloves are available in 1/8 or 3/16 inch thickness which, while restricting the diver's sense of touch, still permit a satisfactory degree of finger movement. Three fingered "mitts," often extending nearly to the elbow, are used in extremely cold water. A proper fit is important, as too tight a fit will restrict blood circulation, advancing the rate of heat loss.

Failure to wear a hood in cold water can result not only in a numbing of the facial areas, but a feeling of extreme pain in the forehead area immediately upon entering the water, persisting until the head becomes acclimated. The hood should have an adequate skirt, which extends down at least midway onto the shoulders, to prevent the admission of cold water down the spine. In extremely cold waters,

4-23

Figure 4-24
Hot Water Wet Suit

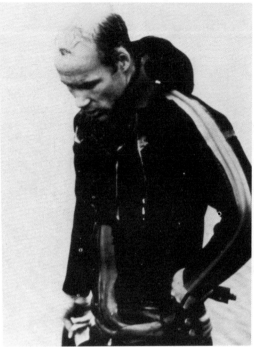

Photo: Laurence Bussey

a one-piece hooded vest is recommended. Fit is important when selecting a hood, and too tight a fit can result in jaw fatigue, choking, headache, dizziness, and thermal reduction.

When using a wet suit, the diver will normally require additional weight to compensate for wet suit buoyancy. The exact amount of buoyancy provided by a wet suit will vary, and is dependent upon such factors as suit thickness, suit size, age, and condition. As the suit is compressed with an increase in depth it will lose some of its buoyancy, possibly as much as 10 pounds at 100 feet (See Paragraph 4.7.3).

Proper care and maintenance of the wet suit is necessary if it is to last for a reasonable length of time. After each use the suit should be thoroughly washed with fresh water, and allowed to dry prior to storage. It should be carefully inspected for rips and tears, and repaired to prevent their spreading, prior to the suit being used again. A suit can be used approximately 10 minutes after it has been repaired, but for best results it should be left unused for several hours. Zippers and metal snaps should be frequently inspected and maintained corrosion free.

Vaseline is satisfactory and will not adversely affect the neoprene. If the suit is not going to be used for a long period of time it should be hung or laid flat or rolled, not folded. Prolonged folding can cause creasing and deterioration of the rubber at the fold. Suits should be hung on wide specially-padded hangers to prevent tearing on sharp corners. Care should be taken to avoid getting petroleum products such as oil or gas on the neoprene as it will cause deterioration. Finally, the suit should be stored out of the sunlight. Prolonged exposure to sunlight will cause the neoprene to rot, become brittle and crack.

4.8.2 Open-Circuit Hot Water Wet Suit

A special type of wet suit has been designed for use in extremely cold waters (Figure 4–24). This suit is similar to the standard wet suit, but is designed to accept hot water supplied from an external source, and thus maintain body heat. This suit is constructed of $3/16$- or $1/4$-inch thick neoprene with nylon on both sides, and is of one-piece construction with a single front entry zipper. A system of tubes cemented to the outside of the suit allows hot water to be distributed evenly through holes within the suit. A valve mounted on the side of the suit allows the diver to control the flow of hot water and therefore the temperature inside the suit. Care must be taken to ensure the flow of hot water to the diver is not interrupted, as the suit does not fit the body nearly as closely as a standard wet suit, and the insulating layer of hot water would be rapidly dispersed resulting in a rapid cooling of the diver. Under extremely cold conditions, a $1/8$-inch vest will assist in retaining body heat.

The supply of hot water may originate on the surface, and be pumped directly to the diver, or passed to the diver from a diving bell, submersible, or habitat. To maintain body heat a continuous flow of 1.5 to 2.0 gallons per minute of 95° F to 105° F water is required by the diver, depending on the ambient water temperature and the length of the hose. A heater pumping system similar to a swimming pool heater, using either propane or diesel fuel, is commonly used for this purpose. The size of the heater/pump unit required is dependent on the water temperature, depth, and number of divers to be supplied. A 40 to 50 pound per square inch pressure head is sufficient for most operations. The system does not recirculate the warm water, but dumps it into the sea through appropriate valving.

There are some disadvantages with the hot water

Figure 4-25
Closed-Circuit Hot
Water Suit Undergarment

Figure 4-26
Variable-Volume
Dry Suit

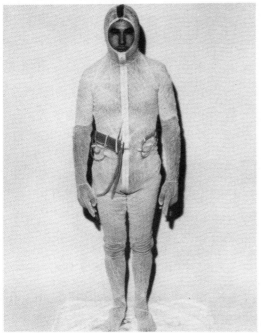

Photo: Bill Douthit, U.S. Navy

Photo: Aqua-Sport

wet suit. Heat is lost to the sea between the heat source and the diver and extra surface support is required for the heating unit and pump. Despite these minor disadvantages the open-circuit hot water wet suit is dependable and effective at retaining body heat in extremely cold waters.

4.8.3 Closed-Circuit Hot Water Suit

This suit consists of the dry suit and a special set of underwear through which heated water is circulated (Figure 4–25). The water is pumped from a heater, through a series of loops in the underwear, and back to the heat source. The hot water can originate either from a heater carried by the diver, or from a surface heater. Primary advantages of this system are that the diver is dry upon his return to the surface or habitat and, should the hot water source be lost or fail, the suit will retain its insulating ability for a moderate period of time. The major disadvantage of this suit is that the tubulated underwear severely restricts diver movement. A water refill is periodically required if the self-contained heater is utilized, and a surface heater increases the

requirements for surface support.

4.8.4 Variable-Volume Dry Suit

The variable-volume dry suit is a one-piece dress made of closed-cell foamed neoprene, and will effectively conserve body heat in extremely cold water over an extended period of time (Figure 4–26). The suit is light and requires no surface support, making it ideal for use at remote locations. It is simple and reliable thus greatly reducing maintenance and repair requirements. Operations have been conducted in arctic regions using this dress for long duration dives (2 hours) under ice in 28.5° F to 30° F water.

The suit itself is constructed of $3/16$ or $1/4$ inch closed-cell foamed neoprene with a nylon interior and exterior lining. It is designed to be worn with thermal underwear, is of one-piece construction and is entered through a water and pressure-proof zipper. The hood and boots are an integral part of the suit while the gloves are separate. To prevent separation all seams are sewn. As the knees are the point of most frequent abuse, knee pads are per-

Figure 4-27
Snorkel

manently attached to reduce the likelihood of leaks in that area.

The suit can be inflated via an inlet valve which is connected to the diver's air supply at the low pressure fitting on his regulator. Air inside the suit can be exhausted by a valve on the opposite side of the chest from the inlet valve. By manipulating these two valves, a properly weighted diver can maintain complete buoyancy control at any depth.

This dry suit provides superior thermal protection to the diver while in the water and during pre- and post-dive periods. As he is dry and his suit acts as a windbreaker, the diver in this suit is much more comfortable while on the surface than he would be in any other type exposure suit.

Care must be taken to avoid icing of the inlet and exhaust valves when diving in cold weather. This icing will make the valves inoperable until they have warmed to the ambient seawater temperature and the ice melts. Icing of the inlet valve in the open position can be caused by using long bursts of expanding air instead of several short bursts to inflate the suit. When the inlet valve freezes in the open position, the diver faces the danger of suit overexpansion and loss of buoyancy control.

If overexpansion surpasses the exhaust valve's capability to let air out, the diver can hold up one arm allowing excess air to escape under the suit wrist seal into the mitten. The fist must be tightly balled, grasping the palm of the mitten so that the air from the suit can escape under the mitten wrist seal without pulling the mitten off the hand.

This type of suit requires some diver familiarization before use and an awareness of its limitations. These include:

(1) Horizontal swims are fatiguing due to the suit bulk.

(2) Air can migrate into the foot area if the diver is horizontal or head down, causing overinflation, loss of fins, and loss of buoyancy control.

(3) Inlet and exhaust valves can malfunction.

(4) A parting seam, zipper or perforation could result in sudden and drastic loss of buoyancy as well as increasing thermal stress.

Any diver planning to use this suit in polar waters should be thoroughly familiar with the manufacturer's operational literature, and should conduct training dives in less strenuous conditions.

Maintenance on the variable-volume dry suit is only slightly more complicated than that required for a regular wet suit. After every use the exterior of the suit should be washed thoroughly with fresh

Photo: Scuba-Pro

water, and inspected for punctures, tears, and seam separation, all of which must be repaired prior to the next use. The zipper should be closed, washed clear of any grit and lubricated. After every fifth use, the zipper should be coated with waterproof grease. The inlet and outlet valves must be thoroughly washed with fresh water, and lubricated prior to and after each dive. Cuffs, collar, and face seals also require lubrication with pure silicone spray prior to, and after, each dive. The inflation hose must be visually inspected prior to each dive. For a discussion of the buoyancy control of a variable-volume dry suit, see Paragraph 7.2.6.2.

4.9 DIVERS' ACCESSORY EQUIPMENT

There are numerous items of equipment which have special uses and are valuable to a diver in accomplishing underwater tasks.

4.9.1 Snorkel

The snorkel (Figure 4–27) is simply a breathing tube which allows the diver to swim comfortably on the surface without the requirement for turning his head to the side to breathe. It will allow the scuba diver to search or survey the bottom in shallow water

Figure 4-28
Digital Depth Gauge

without expending any of his valuable air supply and to comfortably swim to the dive platform while carrying his scuba equipment at completion of a dive.

Snorkels are available in a wide variety of designs, and selection is a matter of individual preference. The most commonly used snorkel is simply a curved piece of plastic or rubber tubing with a 180° bend and mouthpiece at one end. Other models are bent to conform to the configuration of the head, or have a flexible length of hose at the breathing end which allows the mouthpiece to drop away when not in use. Ideally the inside diameter of the snorkel should be ⅝ to ¾ inch and not more than 15 inches in length.

Whenever the diver goes under water the snorkel will flood, but is easily cleared by exhaling forcefully through the tube. With some snorkels, especially those with flexible tubing near the mouthpiece, it is difficult to completely clear the snorkel, and small amounts of water may remain in the curve or corrugations of the tube. This can be easily cleared upon surfacing by bending the head back slightly so the end of the snorkel is pointing down, and exhaling.

4.9.2 Watch

The diver's watch is an important piece of equipment when decompression is expected during a dive, and is of particular value to the diver in staying within the no-decompression limits. The watch must be water- and pressure-proof, and reliable. It should be equipped with a counterclockwise-only rotating bezel

to assist the diver in keeping track of his bottom time, and should be easily readable in murky, low-visibility waters. The band should be one-piece construction to prevent loss of the watch should one of the retaining pins be dislodged. Prior to every dive the diver should check his watch stem to ensure it is firmly in place. A loose stem can result in internal flooding and a ruined watch. A flat scratch-proof crystal and a screw-down and lock stem are recommended features for a diving watch.

4.9.3 Depth Gauge

The depth gauge (Figure 4–28) is a small, portable pressure-sensitive meter calibrated in feet which allows a diver to determine his depth while submerged. The watch and depth gauge should be worn on the same wrist where they can be used in tandem to decompress.

The depth gauge is a delicate instrument and must be treated as such or decalibration can result. Accuracy is an extremely important factor, and the gauge should be recalibrated if it is dropped or suffers a sharp blow, and at periodic intervals varying with the amount of use, but not exceeding 12 months. The need for recalibration can be determined by submerging it to a known depth, or pressurizing it to a specified depth in a hyperbaric chamber. After each use the depth gauge should be thoroughly washed in warm fresh water and stored.

The majority of depth gauges commercially available operate on either a capillary, diaphragm, or bourdon tube principle. The capillary depth gauge consists of a plastic tube, open to the water at one end and attached to a background calibrated in feet. As the depth increases the pocket of air trapped in the tube decreases, and depth is read from the water level in the tube. The diaphragm model type has a sealed case, one side of which is a flexible diaphragm. As pressure increases the diaphragm is distorted, resulting in the movement of a needle to which it is linked. The bourdon tube depth gauges are the most fragile models and will require more frequent recalibration. The bourdon tube type operates on the principle that water pressure will cause a distortion of a bourdon tube, which in turn is linked to a needle which indicates depth. Both the bourdon tube and diaphragm type depth gauges are available in sealed, oil filled models for smooth, reliable operation.

Figure 4-29
Compass Mounted on
an Underwater Slate

Figure 4-30
Cylinder
Pressure Gauges

should be worn on the opposite wrist as the watch and depth gauge to limit magnetic interference. It may also be mounted on a slate board (Figure 4-29).

Models are available which will allow the diver to read the compass while holding it horizontally in front of the face when swimming. Recalibration is not necessary and maintenance is limited to a fresh water rinse after use.

4.9.5 Cylinder Pressure Gauges

There are two styles of pressure gauges used to determine the amount of air in a scuba tank. The surface cylinder pressure gauge (Figure 4-30) is used to check the amount of air in a tank while on the surface. It fits over the cylinder manifold outlet and attaches in the same manner as a regulator and provides a one-time check of the pressure in the tank. A pressure release valve is installed so that the air trapped in the gauge after the valve on the tank has been secured can be released and the gauge removed. The submersible cylinder pressure gauge (Figure 4-10) attaches directly into the first stage of the regulator by a length of high-pressure rubber hose and provides the diver with a continual readout of the air remaining in his tanks. The length of hose allows the diver to attach the pressure gauge to his waist or wrist by means of a rubber strap which is provided. These gauges are normally not calibrated nor are they extremely accurate at low pressures.

Maintenance of the submersible pressure gauge is limited to a fresh water rinse after use. To prevent internal deterioration and corrosion of the surface gauge, care must be taken that the plastic plug which covers the high-pressure inlet is firmly in

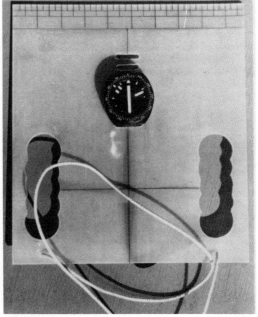

Photo: Lee Somers

Bourdon tube models will retain salt water in the tube and cause corrosion. To prevent this, the tube should be sucked free of water and the gauge stored in a jar of distilled water. A more expensive model depth gauge is battery operated, extremely accurate and presents a digital readout. Helium filled depth gauges will leak and become inaccurate if not kept completely submerged in water while exposed to high pressure conditions as would be encountered in decompression chambers or habitats.

4.9.4 Wrist Compass

The underwater compass consists of a small magnetic compass housed in a waterproof and pressure-proof case, and is attached to the wrist by a band similar to those used for watches.

The underwater compass can be useful for underwater navigation, especially in conditions of reduced visibility. It can also be useful when swimming back to a boat while submerged, as it frees the diver from the requirement of surfacing frequently to obtain bearings. A typical compass will not produce precise bearings, but is primarily used to provide a convenient, reliable directional reference point. When used, it

Figure 4-31
Light

place. These gauges should be handled with care and securely stored when not in use.

4.9.6 Underwater Slate

A slate can be a useful piece of equipment when observations are to be recorded or it is expected that the divers may require a means of communication beyond the limits of hand signals. A simple, handy slate can be constructed from a $^1/_8$ or $^1/_4$ inch thick piece of acrylic plastic, lightly sandpapered on both sides and used with an ordinary pencil. More elaborate models resemble a clipboard with several recording slates and a compass, depth gauge, watch, etc., mounted across the top. The slate itself should have a loop or lanyard made of sturdy line to prevent its loss.

4.9.7 Diving Light

The waterproof, pressure-proof diving light (Figure 4–31) is an important, if not mandatory, item of equipment when operating in areas where visibility is restricted by the absence of light. They are most frequently used when night diving, cave diving, wreck diving, exploring holes and crevices, or diving under ice. An underwater light, regardless of how powerful will be of limited value in murky, dirty waters where visibility is restricted by suspended matter, and light reflected back off of this matter may in fact further reduce visibility.

Many lights commercially available are constructed with one-piece plastic bodies, an integral handle, a light and reflector (frequently a sealed-beam head-

light), an O-ring and front piece. When the front piece is screwed onto the body, the O-ring is compressed and a waterproof seal created. The electrical circuit is essentially the same as any flashlight with current flowing from the negative pole of the battery, through a waterproof switch and light (in either order), and back to the positive pole of the battery. The switch is either a common toggle switch with a rubber, waterproof cover, or, on the more expensive models, a waterproof magnetic switch. Power is frequently provided by a standard 6-volt lantern battery or a series of $1^1/_2$ volt "D" batteries. To provide for longer life nickel cadmium batteries are frequently used. Rechargeable lights in a wide variety of configurations are also available. Other models are available which have bodies constructed of brass or aluminum and which have the front piece attached by a series of screws. The selection of a light is dependent on cost, the task for which it is going to be used, and the individual diver's preference.

Diving lights are designed to be held in a number of different ways. The most frequently seen are the pistol grip and the bar grip which consists of a handle running parallel to the axis of the light for its entire length, approximately $1^1/_2$ to 2 inches above the light. Most smaller diving lights are designed similar to, and held in the same manner as, the common two-cell flashlight. Regardless of the grip, a lanyard should be provided to attach the light to the diver and prevent its loss.

Because a high degree of dependability is necessary, and the diving light is more complex than many of the other types of accessory equipment, it will require more maintenance. As required with all other pieces of diving equipment it should be washed with warm fresh water after every use. When not in use the batteries should be removed from the light and stored separately. Before the light is used it must be thoroughly checked for proper operation. The batteries should be replaced if they show any signs of running low, and spare light bulbs and a battery should be available at the dive site. The O-ring should be lubricated with a silicone grease and checked for any debris which could prevent a proper seal, every time the light is assembled. If proper maintenance procedures are followed the light will be a dependable piece of equipment.

4.9.8 Signal Devices

The various forms of signaling devices constitute

Figure 4-32
Flare

Figure 4-33
Strobe Light

Photo: Lee Somers

one of the important, yet most frequently ignored safety devices available to the diver. Signal devices can be of great value should the diver surface a great distance from his surface support platform, or should he be forced to the surface prematurely by an emergency. They are particularly useful in areas of fog, rain squalls, or when sudden weather changes are likely. There are several types of effective signaling devices available to the scuba diver.

The whistle is the simplest means of signaling available, and because of its simplicity is reliable. Under normal circumstances its range is limited to a few hundred yards, although under unusual wind conditions the range can be greatly extended. They can be useful in periods of reduced visibility. The whistle will not pinpoint a diver's location but will let the surface support personnel know the diver is on the surface and in which general direction he is located. Whistles are constructed of either plastic or metal; however, a plastic model should be selected as they are not subject to corrosion. Because the whistle is of limited range additional signaling devices should be carried.

The flare is another useful signaling device (Figure 4–32). They are long-ranged and will

effectively and quickly pinpoint a diver's location. Any flare which will remain watertight under pressure, and can be safely carried and ignited by the diver is satisfactory, although a smoke/flare for day/night use is preferred. Most flares are of short duration, usually about 90 seconds. Once ignited, the diver should hold the flare over his head and downwind from himself. Most flares can not be ignited under water, but once lit will function whether wet or submerged. If a flare does not ignite immediately when the ring is pulled it may ignite if shaken for a few seconds. Small fountain-pen size aerial flare launchers are available from several manufacturers. Although not designed to be carried submerged at great depths, most are water resistant. These flares and launchers can be purchased at marine hardware or sporting goods stores. This type of flare is designed to rise about 300 feet into the air and burn from 6 to 8 seconds. The flares and launcher can be carried in a watertight accessory case manufactured by some photo accessory dealers.

An additional means of signaling is the strobe light (Figure 4–33). A small, model used by aircraft crewmen is commercially available. This is waterproof and provides a high-intensity, pulsating light signal visible for 10–15 miles from an aircraft at 1,500 feet and has a duration of up to 9 hours of continuous use. It is powered by a mercury battery and intermittent use will extend its effective life well beyond 9 hours.

Any signaling device should be carried where it is easily accessible and will not be lost should any equipment be discarded. A built-in ring is frequently found on life jackets which will accommodate a whistle or strobe light. The flare is commonly taped to the knife scabbard with friction tape, but may be carried wherever desired as long as it is not attached by the ignition ring. The strobe light can be attached to the diver's life jacket, but should be visible when the diver is floating without requiring him to hold it out of the water.

The signaling device requires only limited maintenance, most being either sealed or of such simple construction as to require only a fresh water rinse. Flares should be replaced if they show any signs of corrosion or damage.

4.9.9 Line

A diver's line or safety line will not be necessary for every dive, but when required is an important piece of safety equipment. The use of the line varies, but will fall into three major categories. When a scuba diver is operating under hazardous conditions such as when cave diving, working under ice, or in strong currents he should have contact with an ascending line to the surface.

A line to both divers from a single float will provide a common reference and rendezvous point. Diver to diver lines should be used when the divers could become separated while working under hazardous conditions. This will provide the divers with a quick and effective, although limited, means of communication.

The safest and most commonly used type of line is made of nylon, dacron, or polypropolene. This material is strong, of nearly neutral or slightly positive buoyancy, and corrosion resistant. A snap can be spliced into each end to facilitate easy attachment to a float or around the diver's weight belt.

Maintenance consists of inspecting and lubricating the snaps. A reel and line, frequently used in cave diving, must be dependable and will require additional maintenance and careful inspection. The line should be replaced if it shows any signs of weakness or abrasion. The reel must be maintained corrosion free, well lubricated, and in perfect working condition (See Paragraph 9.3.1).

4.9.10 Float

A float with the diver's flag should be used when the diver is operating from the beach or when operating in an area frequented by small boats. A float will also provide the Dive Master with quick and accurate information as to the location of the divers, and provides the diver with a point of positive buoyancy in an emergency. Floats can consist of just a buoy and flag, or may be as large as a small raft. The most frequently used type is an automobile innertube with the center portion lined with net. The float should be brightly colored and have a diver's flag on a staff, attached. The bright color will make the raft easily noticeable while the flag will inform boatmen that a diver is in the water. Be cautious of an unattended float as curious boatmen may attempt to pull it up. A line attached to the float will allow the diver to keep the float with him, and a small anchor, hook or snap attached to the line will enable him to attach it to the bottom while working. Floats can be constructed from wood, a plastic bottle or innertube, or commercially manufactured floats can be purchased. Maintenance consists of a fresh water rinse after use and inspection of the air chambers for leaks.

4.9.11 Shark Defense Devices

In areas where sharks are frequently encountered many divers elect to carry some form of shark defense, a variety of which are available and have been proven effective. These devices are designed as defense mechanisms and are not intended to allow the diver to pursue offensive attacks on a shark.

Probably the oldest anti-shark device is a 3- to 4-foot-long wooden club with a short nail in one end, which is counterweighted to facilitate effective use under water, and commonly called a "Shark Billy." It is used to fend off or strike the shark, preferably on the nose. Years of experience have proven this device in discouraging annoying sharks.

A power head can be used if the diver desires not only to discourage a shark, but to eliminate him altogether as a threat. This device, commonly called a "bang stick," consists of a specially constructed chamber designed to accommodate a powerful pistol cartridge or a shotgun shell. It is attached to the end of a pole and shot or pushed against the shark, the shell firing upon impact. This device is effective against marine life other than sharks. Although it has a built-in positive safety, it should be handled with extreme caution.

A device known as a "shark dart" is commercially available which is designed to instantly disable or kill a shark by the injection of a burst of compressed gas. This device consists of a hollow stainless steel needle approximately 5 inches long which is connected to a small carbon dioxide cylinder or extra scuba tank, and is available in dagger or spear form. The dart is thrust against the shark's abdominal cavity, penetrating into the body cavity and discharging the contents of the CO_2 cartridge. The gas expanding into the shark creates a nearly instantaneous embolism and forces the shark toward the surface.

Hitting the shark in a vulnerable area and killing it quickly is of great importance. Different model shark darts will accept different sized CO_2 cartridges, and the larger the cartridge, the greater the effective depth. Like the power head, a positive safety is provided, but the shark dart can still be dangerous and must be handled with care.

4.9.12 Decompression Meter

The decompression meter illustrated in Figure 4–34 automatically computes decompression by simulating nitrogen absorption and elimination in the human body. Despite the complicated function it performs, this decompression meter is relatively simple in construction. It consists of a stainless steel outer housing, a flexible gas filled bag, a ceramic gas flow restricting filter, a rigid housing, a sealed bourdon tube inside the rigid housing, and an indicating meter. The flexible gas filled bag is attached around the rigid bourdon tube housing with the ceramic filter connecting the two. Holes in the outer case allow the gas filled bag to be affected by pressure.

Immediately upon entering the water, water enters the outer case through the holes and exerts pressure upon the gas filled bag. The ceramic filter restricts the flow of gas from the bag into the rigid bourdon tube housing at a rate approximating that of the absorption of nitrogen by mid-level tissues of the human body. As the diver proceeds deeper or remains longer at a specific depth more gas is forced from the bag into the bourdon tube housing, causing a distortion of the bourdon tube and a resultant deflection of the meter needle to which it is connected. When

Figure 4-34
Decompression Meter

the diver has remained submerged long enough to require decompression the meter needle will be deflected far enough to indicate such. As the diver's depth decreases during ascent the pressure differential is reversed and the gas begins to flow from the bourdon tube housing through the ceramic filter back into the gas filled bag, with a resultant deflection of the decompression needle in the opposite direction. The gas is passed back through the ceramic filter at a rate approximately the same as nitrogen is exhausted from mid-level body tissues. To decompress the diver simply follows the needle to the surface, remaining at the depth indicated until the needle moves into the next depth range, and surfacing when the needle moves out of the required decompression zone.

The air trapped in the bourdon tube housing after surfacing effectively substitutes as residual nitrogen time and allows the meter to be used for repetitive dives for up to 6 hours after the original use. The gas pressure differential is completely equalized after that period of time and the meter should not be used for repetitive dives with a surface interval of greater than 6 hours. Once the meter has been used by one diver it cannot accurately be used by another diver until the gas trapped in the bourdon housing has completely equalized with external pressure.

The decompression meter is subject to a gradual deterioration of accuracy, or may be jarred out of calibration if dropped or damaged. A diver will be able to tell if a decompression meter is seriously out of calibration by following the manufacturers test procedures. As the diver's health is dependent on the meter, repair or recalibration should not be attempted by the individual but left up to a qualified technician. After each use the meter should be rinsed in warm fresh water, dried and securely stowed. Do not try and disassemble the instrument or clean the holes as serious damage or decalibration could result.

When using this decompression meter a number of restrictions must be observed. The meter should not be used for repetitive dives if the surface interval exceeds 6 hours. Decompression meters reach saturation after approximately 2 hours of bottom time and should not be used for dives which exceed that limit. Finally, the meter cannot consider the diver's physical condition, the severity of the work the diver is accomplishing or other factors which affect the nitrogen content of the body. It can only be used when diving with compressed air.

NOTE:

There Are a Number of New Meters Currently Under Development Which Show Promise. However, Until Tests Have Been Completed, These Meters Must Not Be Blindly Relied Upon.

WARNING

Use of a Decompression Meter Is Not Recommended When Decompression Can Be Computed Using Proven Tables.

4.9.13 Hazardous Accessory Equipment

There are several pieces of equipment commercially available which can cause injury to the diver or convert a routine situation into an emergency. Earplugs should never be used while diving. They create a seal of the outer ear thereby preventing pressure equalization, and can result in a serious ear squeeze, a ruptured eardrum, and possibly total loss of hearing, should the plug be forced deeply into the ear cavity.

Goggles are another piece of equipment which should not be used. They do not cover the nose and therefore cannot be equalized. The increase of pressure as depth increases can cause the rim to cut deeply into the face, and/or the eyes to be forced against the glass plates, resulting in severe and painful tissue damage or eye squeeze.

Another piece of equipment which has proven itself hazardous is the regulator neckstrap. Experience has proven these to be difficult and often impossible to remove in an emergency. Most single-hosed regulators come with these straps as standard equipment. They should be removed and discarded.

Any equipment which is not necessary for a dive may be hazardous. Extra equipment, even if normally considered safe, will only get in the way, increase the diver's chances of fouling, and result in an advanced rate of fatigue. Excess gear should be left on the surface.

4.10 UNDERWATER COMMUNICATION SYSTEMS

A number of underwater communication systems have been developed and are available for general purchase. These systems vary in effectiveness due to inherent deficiencies or due to environmental effects. Studies have shown that regardless of the efficiency of these systems, the intelligibility of messages transmitted through any type of diver communication system can be improved significantly by training divers to be better talkers in the underwater environment (Hollien and Rothman, in press).

4.10.1 General Description

Basically, there are three approaches available for diver communications. The first consists of acoustic systems. An "acoustic" system includes a microphone, amplifier, power supply and transducer; it characteristically transduces speech directly into the water by means of the projector (underwater loudspeaker). The signal produced can be received by a hydrophone placed in the water, or by divers without any special receiving equipment. Several acoustic systems have been studied in detail (Hollien et al. 1970, 1971).

These systems were evaluated under diver-to-surface (near field), diver-to-surface over distance in salt water, and diver-to-diver conditions.

The second type of communicator consists of amplitude modulated (AM) systems. Figure 4–35 shows an AM type system adapted for a single hose regulator. The receiving unit is shown on the head strap. The power pack worn by the diver is not shown. Several units within this category have been studied under various conditions. In an AM system, a carrier wave is utilized and is modulated by the speech signal. Such a system ordinarily consists of a microphone, power supply, amplifier, modulator and underwater transducer. Speech pro-

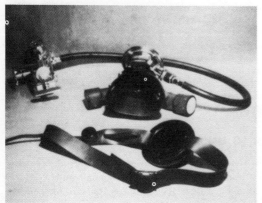

Photo: Harry Hollien

duced in this manner can be understood only by a diver or a surface observer having an appropriate receiver and modulator. In one such unit, for example, a 42 kHz carrier signal is transduced into the water after being modulated by the speech signal and the mixed signal is picked up by a receiving coil, demodulated, and heard in the normal speech mode. Other carrier signals may be used depending on the system design.

The third type of communication system, the "hardwire" approach, employs a closed loop comparable to a telephone, including: (a) a microphone, (b) a cable over which the signal is transmitted, and (c) a receiver. These units require a physical connection; i.e., umbilical, between the talker and the listener. The hardwire system used for surface-supplied diver communications represents the greatest potential for intelligible communications. The amplifier case is the heart of the system and contains the amplifier, the tender's reproducer, the control switches, the volume control, the power switch, and the diver's jacks. These components are contained in a weatherproof wood, plastic, or metal case for protection. Most units are powered by internal, 6- or 12-volt, lantern-type batteries, which provide continuous operation on moderate volume output for 25 hours or more. Some units feature connections for external power supply. Other units incorporate redundant batteries so that there is always a spare in case of emergency.

4.10.2 Operating Procedures

For hardwire systems, the tender's reproducer,

mounted in the amplifier case, serves as a loud speaker when the diver is talking and as a microphone when the tender is talking. In most units the tender must depress a spring-return "tender-to-diver" switch to communicate. When the switch is in a normal position, the tender hears all divers connected to the unit. Amplifiers are available in one-, two-, or three-diver models.

On multiple-diver units, separate spring-return control switches marked "diver-to-diver" are used for diver-to-diver communications. By pressing a switch, a designated diver may communicate with another diver. The control-switch configuration will depend on the make of the unit. Effective use of this feature requires a certain amount of circuit discipline. All switching is done by the tender.

A microphone is located in the diver's helmet or oral-nasal mask assembly, and earphones are placed next to the diver's ears to eliminate noise to the diver and acoustic feedback to the microphone. The diver has no switches or keys to activate. Volume and tone are controlled by the tender. The diver may call for adjustment in volume or tone during the dive.

The diver communication system is designed to be as rugged as possible; however, it fundamentally remains a piece of electronic equipment and must be protected from shock and moisture. Many mask and helmet components may be only water resistant and *not waterproof*. They must be especially protected from salt water. The unit should be maintained and repaired in accordance with the manufacturer's instructions.

4.10.3 Speech Intelligibility

The speech intelligibility of several systems has been evaluated and the systems placed in a rank order (Hollien et al. 1970). Potential users should familiarize themselves with these data before obtaining a system, as speech intelligibility scores can range from 1 percent to 90 percent depending on the system, the distance, the depth, and the experience of the user. The modulated systems appear to provide greatest intelligibility in a variety of situations and distances.

Microphones can affect a communication link in various ways. For example, if the frequency response of a particular microphone drops sharply at approximately 3500 Hz, it would not be effective in a helium/oxygen atmosphere. Further, the

Table 4-1
International
Morse Code

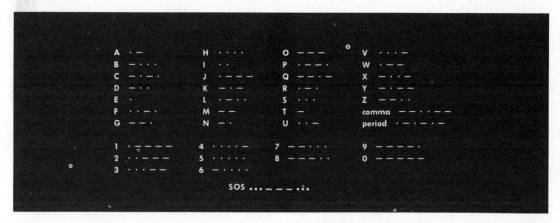

A	· —	H	· · · ·	O	— — —	V	· · · —
B	— · · ·	I	· ·	P	· — — ·	W	· — —
C	— · — ·	J	· — — —	Q	— — · —	X	— · · —
D	— · ·	K	— · —	R	· — ·	Y	— · — —
E	·	L	· — · ·	S	· · ·	Z	— — · ·
F	· · — ·	M	— —	T	—	comma	— — · · — —
G	— — ·	N	— ·	U	· · —	period	· — · — · —

1	· — — — —	4	· · · · —	7	— — · · ·	9	— — — — ·
2	· · — — —	5	· · · · ·	8	— — — · ·	0	— — — — —
3	· · · — —	6	— · · · ·				

SOS · · · — — — · · ·

addition of cavities (e.g., helmets and muzzles) to the vocal tract has an effect on speech intelligibility. Therefore, particular care must be taken when selecting a microphone/muzzle or helmet combination. For example, if a microphone's output peaks strongly in the frequency ranges where there are large cavity resonances, the response function of the cavity plus microphone will exhibit dramatic variations which can degrade speech intelligibility significantly. Evaluations of microphone and muzzle helmet configurations have shown certain combinations to be most effective (Coleman and Krasik 1971).

Although none of the communication systems can be regarded as completely satisfactory some of them begin to approach levels which allow for intelligible voice communication between divers and between divers and the surface. The problems of underwater communication are most acute when the communicator himself is in the water or in a helium/oxygen pressure environment. Problems of a much lesser magnitude exist when an individual is communicating from a habitat or chamber to a diver in the water or the surface. Hardwire systems are clearly most effective from a reliability and intelligibility standpoint. In any case, certain precautions can be taken to enhance the effectiveness of the total communication link. The following will serve as examples:

1. In order to ensure adequate surface-to-diver communications, a diver's tender should be located away from areas of high ambient noise (e.g., winches, compressors, etc.). If possible, he should be housed in a portable acoustical isolation booth and use a noise cancelling microphone. If space considerations preclude a proper environment, at the least, a small enclosure of acoustic absorbent material can be constructed and placed around the microphone and the surface tender's head.

2. Divers should pay particular attention to the proper fitting of masks, muzzles and/or helmets.

3. Proper communication procedures should be developed and utilized. This is particularly necessary when initiating communications. For example, a repeated attention device, e.g., "Hello Diver, Hello Diver" can alert the diver to hold his breath and will allow bubble noise to dissipate so that the message can be heard. A standardized end-of-transaction code will ensure completion of a message before a second diver begins communicating.

4. For acoustic units and for some amplitude modulated systems, it is necessary for the diver to orient the transducer toward the receiver (either another diver, or a hydrophone or a surface pick-up unit). Further, divers should orient themselves so that there are no major obstructions in the path of transmission and to ensure that the transmitter is free of bottom mud and/or sand.

5. Divers should be trained to speak with a low fundamental frequency, high intensity and slow (i.e., overarticulated) type of speech.

6. A basic form of communications is the International Morse Code (Table 4-1). When diving in foreign waters, or becoming trapped in an area where voice communications may not be possible, a knowledge of Morse Code could be of vital importance. Taps with a knife handle on a scuba tank can be heard for long distances in the water.

4.11 UNDERWATER TOOLS

A fundamental aspect of accomplishing work underwater is the selection of proper tools and equipment for the task to be performed. In all operations the relative advantage or disadvantage of power tools versus hand tools must be considered. Expenditure of effort is an important consideration in underwater work and it is evident that power tools can reduce physical exertion. However, the complications of power supply and transportation of the tools may be a disadvantage.

The diver's capability to perform tasks under water is degraded by several factors. These include water resistance, diver buoyancy, equipment bulk, confined space, time limitations, visibility restrictions, and uncontrolled movement of the object being worked on. There may be a significant decrease in performance of an underwater task as compared to the same task on land. Certain tasks may be easier to accomplish underwater due to three-dimensional mobility, and the ability to adjust buoyancy.

Since diver safety is a primary consideration in any underwater operation, such hazards as electric shocks, excessive noise, and the possibility of injury must be taken into account when selecting underwater tools.

Table 4–2 lists some common tools used underwater, along with their source of power and available accessories. Most pneumatic and hydraulic tools can be adapted for underwater use. Refer to various major tool manufacturers for specifications in detail.

4.11.1 Hand Tools

Almost all standard hand tools can be used under water. A few are discussed in the following paragraphs along with their characteristics.

The screwdriver is generally available in three configurations: the machine (or straight slotted) type, the phillips type and the allen type. Of the three, the allen type is easiest for the diver to use. This is primarily due to the grip characteristics of the allen screw and the positive alignment of the screwdriver to the screw. The other types have a tendency to slip out of the screw head or damage the screw by twisting motion.

A single multi-purpose tool can be made by welding a screwdriver blade and a pair of pliers to an adjustable wrench.

Sawing, using a hand saw is a difficult underwater task. The diver finds it difficult to follow a straight

Table 4-2
Diver Power Tools

Tool	Type	Description
Impact wrench	Pneumatic	1/4–4-in. square drives available, 4-in. drive weighs 600 lb handles 7/32–12-in. bolt, torque corresponds to drill size.
	Hydraulic	3/4–2 1/2-in. square drive 10,000 ft lb on 3-in. bolt.
(Angle wrench)	Electric	250 ft lb on 3/4-bolt.
Drill	Pneumatic	Metal bits to 3-in. dia. Wood bores to 4-in. dia. Star drill to 1-in. dia. Accessories available.
	Hydraulic	Metal and wood bits to 1-in. dia.
	Electric	Motor 5/8 hp. 1/4 hp develops 250 ft lb on 3/4-in. bolt.
Hammer	Pneumatic	Paving breaker.
Jackhammer	Pneumatic	Turns and reciprocates, drills holes 1–3 in.
Riveter	Pneumatic	1/8-in. aircraft to 1 1/8-in. structural steel.
	Hydraulic	Up to 1-in. dia.
Screwdriver nut runner	Pneumatic	Wood screws 2 to 14. Machine screw 1/4–5/16-in.
Hacksaw	Pneumatic	14-in. cut for wood; shorter for metal. Pipe cutting special cuts 60-in. pipe with 2-in. wall.
Hacksaw	Hydraulic	8 1/2-in. cut for wood; shorter for metal; pipe cutters available.
Rotary saw	Pneumatic	4 1/8-in. cut.
	Hydraulic	4-in. cut.
Chain saw	Hydraulic	15-in. cut—wood.
Grinders	Pneumatic	8-in. dia.
	Hydraulic	9-in. dia.
Stud drivers	Power velocity	To 1/4-in. dia.
Hole cutters	Pneumatic and hydraulic Power velocity	Attachments to drill holes over 3–4 in.
	Explosive	Any size with shaped charge.
Cable cutters	Power velocity	Up to 3/4 in.
	Explosive	Any size.

Figure 4-36
Pneumatic Drill

Figure 4-37
Hydraulic Impact Wrench

Photo: Ackley Tool Company

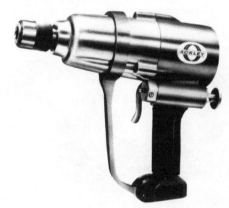

Photo: Ackley Tool Company

line. An added complication is the tendency of the blade of a hacksaw to flex, increasing the possibility of breaking the brittle blade and decreasing the chances of achieving a straight cut. The most useful type of saw has the teeth pointed toward the diver so that the cut is made on the draw.

The ordinary hand hammer is probably used under water more than any other hammering implement; however, a sledge hammer is preferred in many cases. Since considerably more effort is required to swing a hammer under water than on land, it is easier to develop force by pounding with the heavy weight of a sledge hammer than by a swinging motion necessary with the lighter hand hammer.

Tasks involving grinding, chipping, pounding, polishing and reaming with hand equipment are all arduous and time consuming. The use of hand tools for these tasks is not practical if the task is of any magnitude.

On all hand tools used under water, a protective coating of grease, epoxy paint, or chromium plate will retard corrosion.

4.11.2 Pneumatic Tools

These tools though rarely designed specifically for

use under water need little, if any, alterations in order to perform the required tasks (Figure 4–36). Most pneumatic tools require 90 psig of air pressure and usually exhaust into the water. The exhaust bubbles may create problems. It is possible to exhaust 10 to 20 feet from the work or at the surface; however, the tool must be adapted to provide a hose attachment to the air exhaust. The use of pneumatic power has proven itself both depth-limited (100 to 150 feet) and excessive in maintenance and costs.

4.11.3 Hydraulic Tools

Underwater hydraulic tools, such as impact wrenches (Figure 4–37), chain saws, disc grinders (Figure 4–38), cable and pipe cutters, are essentially modified versions of hydraulic tools designed for land use. There are two basic problems associated with the hydraulic tools for diver use. The first is that of providing a hydraulic power supply to the tool in the diver's hand and the second is that of providing the diver with a tool and associated hardware that is safe and easy to operate. The various methods of providing hydraulic power to the diver's tools are: (1) surface support systems that require an umbilical from the support ship to the work site; and (2) bottom supported systems where the total hydraulic system is submerged.

In choosing a hydraulic tool, it is necessary to provide a device that does not result in excessive diver fatigue or discomfort. Tools must be designed to get the job done quickly as the diver's muscles have an increased tendency to become cramped and painful if the trigger and handles are difficult to hold, or if

Figure 4-38
Hydraulic Disc Grinder

Photo: Ackley Tool Company

the tools produce excessive torque or vibrations. Stiff hoses or cables and the drag of currents on hydraulic power supply lines increase the diver's difficulties.

An advantage of hydraulic tools is that they create no bubbles to block the diver's vision.

4.11.4 Electric Tools

Electrically operated tools are seldom used under water, but some do exist. Experimental designs for drills and nut drivers have been developed, but few have proven totally reliable in all situations.

Although electrically operated tools offer no depth limitations, there exists the various hazards of shock, and the difficulties involved in breaking an electric connection in a conductive medium such as saltwater.

4.11.5 Power Velocity Tools

Power velocity tools are actuated by a cartridge which fires a high pressure charge against a piston. The piston drives a pin or rivet into an underwater structure. Power velocity tools are generally well suited to underwater work. They must be reloaded with each shot, which is a slow process under water, but they are comparatively light and require no umbilicals or power lines. Power velocity tools do present a safety hazard and should be used only by divers trained in their use and under circumstances where safety precautions are carefully planned.

4.11.6 Cutting and Welding Tools

The Oxy-Acetylene cutting torch is the most widely used gas tool. The Oxy-Arc torch, using a jet of oxygen with electricity, cuts through metal up to 2 inches thick, but is more expensive and hazardous to operate.

Electric arc-welding is a proven method of welding under water. This again takes special equipment and training.

Two important aspects of underwater welding are:
- Underwater welds are generally not as strong as surface welds.
- The diver must be protected from the shock hazard of the arc welder. Metal helmets must be insulated.

Regardless of the type of tool the diver uses, he must resist the reaction caused by the tool. This reaction may tend to twist the diver or push him away from his work area. Therefore, it is important to find a means to counteract these forces. A common method is to utilize a handhold in the work area, the diver working the tool with one hand and gripping the handhold with the other. The diver may also grip with his legs using a pipe or other structure to stabilize himself. A technique adopted by working divers to counteract tool reaction is "leading" the tool. Using this method, the diver starts his body in motion prior to engaging the tool, using the tool reaction to stop his body motion. An example of this method is torquing or tightening a nut. The diver starts his body in motion in the direction he wishes the wrench to move, then tightens his grip on the wrench imparting an impact force to the wrench. The reaction to the impact stops his body motion.

Another method of reducing tool reaction is to use a long lever arm on the tool, which tends to reduce the forces acting on the diver. In each work situation, the reaction of tools on the diver must be considered and appropriate preparations or training conducted to reduce or eliminate them.

4.12 EXPLOSIVES

Explosives and shaped charges can be used to perform some types of work under water, including demolition, sheet cutting, cable cutting, and making holes (Figure 4-39). Explosives suitable for underwater work include primacord, various gela-

**Figure 4-39
Explosives
(see separate captions)**

Model of chain cutter.

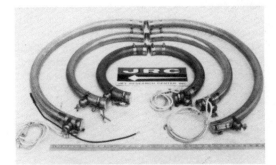
Assortment of outside circular cutters.

"Quick Ditch"™ charges placed on bottom.

Detonation of underwater charges.   Photos: Jet Research Center, Inc.

tins, plastic blocks, and some liquids. Such explosives are relatively safe because the diver can set the charges, return to the surface and detonate them by remote firing.

WARNING

Handling of Explosives Should Only Be Done by Properly Trained Personnel.

The following discussion of safety precautions is presented so that a diver who is involved in a project that includes the use of underwater demolition, will be aware of the general safety precautions that should be used.

General. Use safety precautions that pertain to each type of explosive in accordance with the manufacturer's recommendations.

Transporting and Storing. Know and obey all Federal, State, and local laws and regulations applicable to transporting and storing of explosives. All explosives stored on board ship should be in Coast Guard approved magazines with blasting caps and primers separated from bulk explosives.

Responsibility. One individual must be responsible for the preparation, placement, and firing of all explosives.

Premature Detonation of Caps. All radio transmitters must be secured prior to capping in of electrical firing assemblies and must remain secured until the charge has been fired.

All blasting activities (electric and nonelectric) must be suspended during electrical storms.

Smoking. No smoking should be permitted at any time in the vicinity of explosives.

Firing System. Depending on the size of the demolition task, the firing system may consist of a main charge, a primer, a detonator, and a firing assembly.

Main Charge. The main charge should be water resistant and insensitive to shock and friction. It can be primed at the surface and placed by a diver or submersible on the blast site.

Primer. The primer should be water resistant and insensitive to shock and friction, like the main charge, only somewhat lesser. Even so, using proper procedures, it can be primed with a detonator at the surface and placed by a diver on the blast site.

Detonator. The detonator most often used will be an explosive cord referred to as primacord. Primacord is a relatively insensitive, strong, flexible explosive cord. It can be led from the blast site to the surface where it is primed with a firing assembly *after all divers are out of the water* (See Paragraph 1–10). All kinks and bends must be removed from the primacord. If not, a misfire will be likely.

Firing Assembly. The firing assembly can be electric or nonelectric with electric being the preferred method, because it allows for more positive control. It should be connected to the detonator at the surface and by the one individual responsible for the demolition operation. Do not use blasting caps under water, as they become unreliable and crush with depth causing misfires.

Electric Firing Assembly. This assembly consists of an electric blasting cap, connected to a length of firing wire, connected to a blasting machine. Electric blasting caps are extremely sensitive and must be protected from shock and extreme heat. The cap must be shunted until the firing wire is connected. The cap should be connected to the detonator first and then the firing wire can be connected to the cap. The firing wire must be shunted.

After moving away from the blast site and firing assembly, the firing circuit should be tested using a galvanometer with a silver chloride cell. Just prior to firing, after making certain that all personnel and equipment are in a place of safety, the blasting machine is connected. The blasting machine should be carried only by the individual responsible for the demolition operation.

Misfires. Misfires are the most dangerous part of any demolition operation and should be treated with extreme caution.

Misfires – Electric.
1. Check the firing wire connection at the blasting machine.
2. Make 2 or 3 attempts to refire.
3. Refire with another blasting machine.
4. Attempt to initiate the cap with a shotgun blast.
5. Shunt the firing wires at the blasting machine and check the entire circuit.

6. Disconnect the firing wires from the cap and shunt the cap.
7. Place a countermine and fire.
Misfires – Nonelectric.
1. Wait thirty minutes, plus the delay time of the fuse.
2. Attempt to initiate the cap with a shotgun blast.
3. Place a countermine and fire.
Nonelectric Firing Assembly. This assembly consists of a nonelectric blasting cap, crimped to a length of time fuse, connected to a fuse lighter. Nonelectric blasting caps are extremely sensitive and must be protected from shock and extreme heat. Dirt or foreign matter should be removed from the cap only by tapping the open end down against an open hand. The time fuse should be timed using a 3 foot length after discarding a 6 inch length from the free end. The length of fuse used in the firing assembly should be long enough to permit all personnel to reach a safe distance at a normal pace before the explosion. The cap should be slipped gently down over a square cut end of the time fuse with no twisting or forcing. The cap should be crimped with a pair of cap crimpers $1/8$ to $1/4$ inch from the open end, pointing the cap away from the body. A fuse lighter can then be attached to the time fuse and the firing assembly can be attached to the detonator.

Firing. The charge should be fired only by the individual responsible for the demolition operation after making certain that all personnel and equipment are in a place of safety on the surface.

4.13 AIR LIFTS

When the task requires removal of a large area of bottom material, one of the most effective tools is the air lift (See Paragraphs 8.3.3 and 8.9.3).

An air lift can be constructed of 3″–4″ pipe of various lengths. Other sizes can be used as required by the job. Attached to the pipe is a 1″ air line (Figure 8–25). A 100–300 cu ft per minute air compressor will be required for adequate lift.

This device is lowered to the bottom and the air compressor started. The diver should keep well clear of the suction end until actual suction has begun, as there is a tendency for the hose to kick initially. The suction end is then slowly passed over the bottom allowing all loose matter to be drawn up the hose onto the deck of the surface support craft.

SECTION 5
BREATHING
MEDIA

BREATHING MEDIA 5

5.0 GENERAL

In other sections divers' breathing media are discussed in terms of composition and applicability to a particular diving technique or apparatus. The physiological aspects of breathing media were reviewed in Section 2. This section discusses breathing media from several other aspects: the purity of the gas itself; the grades and types of gases available that are suitable for breathing; the sources of breathing gases; and the techniques used to determine the acceptability of a gas for breathing.

This section is divided into three areas: compressed air; oxygen; and the various gases that can be used as diluents with oxygen.

5.1 COMPRESSED AIR

Compressed air is the most frequently used diver's breathing medium. In its natural state at sea level pressures it consists of nitrogen, oxygen, argon, carbon dioxide and trace amounts of other gases. Table 5–1 gives the composition of air as it occurs naturally.

Unfortunately, all ambient air does not meet the required standards for use as a diver's breathing medium. For example, in urban areas carbon monoxide may be present in free air at rather high levels, in some cases as high as 50–100 parts per million (ppm). Other impurities such as dust and oxides of sulfur are also present in the atmosphere. These contaminants come from such sources as industrial and automotive exhausts and must be avoided. In addition to the contaminants that may be present in free air, air compressor machinery may also add contaminants. These include oil vapor, hydrocarbons from the compressor motor exhausts, and oil breakdown products from the compressor lubricant. All of these must be avoided or removed before compressed air is suitable for diver use.

To avoid the contaminants that are sometimes found in free air it is essential that the air compressor intake is not exposed to the contaminating effects of internal combustion engine exhaust, ship engine or ventilator exhausts, ship's engines, unventilated rooms or ship's compartments, areas of high dust levels, or areas where excessive moisture is present. It is not advisable to fill scuba tanks when an air pollution alert is in effect. The methods of avoiding contamination caused by air compressor machinery are given in Paragraph 5.1.3.1.

5.1.1 Limitations of Compressed Air Diving

Section 10 discusses in detail the limitations of compressed air as a diver's breathing medium.

5.1.2 General Safety Precautions for Compressed Air

There are three primary areas of safety associated with compressed air or any compressed gas. These are:

1. Purity and acceptability for its intended use (See Paragraph 5.1.5).

2. Identification and handling of the compressed gas cylinders or storage tanks.

3. Special precautions for avoidance of fire or other hazards.

Compressed air is readily available from many sources. Most of it however is produced for industrial purposes and is below the standards of purity for use as a diver's breathing medium. When compressed air is purchased from a manufacturer, it is essential that the gas is certified by the manufacturer to be of high purity, free of oil contaminants, and suitable for breathing. Compressed air suspected of being contaminated should not be used for diving until tested.

**Table 5-1
Composition
of Air in Its
Natural State**

Gas	Percent by volume
Nitrogen	78.084
Oxygen	20.946
Argon	.934
Carbon dioxide	.033
Rare gases	.003

**Table 5-2
Color Coding
for Gas Cylinders**

Gas	U.S. Navy color code	Bureau of Standards color code
Oxygen	Green	Green.
Helium	Buff	Brown.
Air	Black	Black.
Helium and oxygen	Orange	Brown and green.
Nitrogen	Light gray	
Exhaust	Silver	

Proper identification and handling of compressed gas cylinders is essential. All compressed gas cylinders used to transport gas under pressure are subject to Department of Transportation regulations. These regulations include design, material, inspection procedures, and marking requirements. Compressed gas cylinders can be extremely hazardous if mishandled. They should be securely stored in a rack in either the upright position or on their sides.

Compressed gas cylinders are protected against overpressure by a rupture disc on the back side of the valve.

The failure of regulators or gauges can occur when a cylinder valve is opened to check pressure. Do not stand in the line of discharge but at the side of the cylinder to avoid the blast effect in case of failure.

WARNING

Do Not Stand in the Line of Discharge When Opening a High Pressure Cylinder.

If a cylinder has a neck leak, don't try to repair it. Sometimes a leak in a high pressure gas system will be noticed from the frost which may form from gas expansion. Do not try to tighten threads that are cold. This may result in stripping them and blowing down the whole system.

When being transported, cylinders should be secured against rolling. Standing a cylinder on end, unsecured, or allowing it to roll unsecured, could result in the cylinder rupturing. The resultant rapid expansion of gas is equivalent to an explosion of a high order. The cylinder can be a deadly missile capable of penetrating a wall, the side of a car, or propelling itself through the air at great speeds over long distances.

Scuba tanks are often fitted with a rubber or plastic boot which should have holes to permit draining. These boots fit over the tank base and facilitate holding the tank in an upright position. Tanks equipped with this boot should not be left unsecured in an upright position, as they are subject to the same accidental rupture as tanks not so equipped.

Scuba tanks are not generally color coded or labeled as to the type of gas contained. However, large gas cylinders are color coded and labeled. Compressed air cylinders are color coded *black* and have a black label. The label is the primary means of identifying the content of a large gas cylinder. Color coding of gas cylinders is given in Table 5–2.

Several special safety precautions to be observed when using compressed gas are noted on the gas cylinder label. In general, these precautions concern the flammability of the gas and its ability to support combustion. Compressed air, while not in itself flammable, does support combustion and should not be used or stored in an area where open flames, burning, or highly flammable gases are present.

5.1.3 Air Compressors

Air compressors commonly used to provide diver breathing air may be categorized into the following groups:

1. Low-Pressure Air Compressors. Large stationary low-pressure air compressors are often used in surface-supplied diving operations. These compressors are fitted with auxiliary devices to clean, filter, and dehumidify the compressed air. Compressors of this type vary in pressure rating and capacity and are used to provide air to a diver through storage cylinders. They are generally found at sites where large-scale diving operations are being conducted or aboard surface platforms fitted out as diving platforms (See Paragraph 4.6.1).

2. Portable High-Pressure Compressors. These compressors are available for filling scuba tanks. Portable models should deliver a minimum of 2 cubic feet per minute (cfm) of air at 2,000 psi and operate at a low rpm and temperature to avoid the possibility of breakdown of compressor lubricants and the subsequent contamination of air during compression.

3. Stationary High-Pressure Compressors. Permanently installed high-pressure compressors are available for filling scuba tanks. These stationary models should be rated to deliver a minimum of 8 cfm of air at pressures in the 3000- to 5000-psi range.

Air compressors may be driven by an electric motor or internal combustion engine. Electric-motor-driven compressors have the advantage of eliminating the possibility of contamination of the compressed air from the internal combustion engine exhaust and are preferred.

The lubricants used in compressors providing breathing air must be of the quality and type designated by the equipment manufacturer. Substituting of lubricants is not a safe practice and should be avoided. Chlorinate lubricants, phosphate ester (either pure or in a mixture), or tetrafluoroethylene piston rings must not be used. Water-lubricated and dry-lubricated compressors are available that have the advantage of precluding the production of carbon monoxide or other contaminants resulting from the chemical breakdown of compressor lubricants.

The primary factor causing the breakdown of lubricants and contamination of the compressed air is high temperature in the compressor cylinders. Cylinder heads may be cooled by air blowers or water spray systems or cooling systems integral to the compressor machinery. A cylinder head temperature controller is valuable in eliminating the possibility of excessive cylinder temperatures.

5.1.3.1 Filtering Systems

Air leaving a compressor must be cleaned and filtered prior to storage or immediate use. In some compressor systems the compressed gas is passed through an oil and moisture separator to remove entrained oil, mist, and excessive moisture. This is followed by passage through a filter system to remove excess water, oil particulate matter, and odor.

Recently developed systems are on the market that more effectively remove contaminants (National Safety Council 1973). They are designed to remove carbon monoxide, oil vapor, nitrogen dioxide, odor and taste contaminants. One such system does this by the oxidation of carbon monoxide to carbon dioxide through chemisorption and catalysis with a material called Hopcalite. Hopcalite is a true catalyst in this reaction and is neither consumed nor exhausted in the process until it is deactivated by water vapor. The amount of carbon dioxide produced by the catalytic action is so small as to be physiologically insignificant.

The amount of oxygen used up is approximately 0.5 part per million per part per million of carbon monoxide and has no appreciable effect on the air produced. Nitrogen dioxide is also removed from the air by a combination of adsorption and chemical reaction. Activated carbon is used to adsorb odor and taste.

The location of the compressor intake with respect to possible sources of contamination is fully as important as any single factor in assuring satisfactory air quality. Compressors should not be operated near the exhausts of internal combustion engines, sewer manholes, sandblasting, painting, electric arcs, or sources of smoke. Intakes must be provided with filters for removing dust and other particles in the respirable size range. Proper orientation to wind direction is also a critical factor in setting up air compressor systems.

Both the compressor and the filter system must be properly maintained. Compressors and filters are usually given routine maintenance on an hours-of-operation basis. Filters should be examined each 24 hours of operation and replaced in accordance with the manufacturer's specifications. The compressor lubricant and mechanical parts should be replaced on a rigorous schedule based upon the manufacturer's recommendation or the results of an air analysis. A carefully kept log should be maintained for each air compressor indicating all time in service, maintenance actions, and data on any analysis made of product air from the compressor.

For some diving operations, air is supplied by the manufacturer in banks of high-pressure cylinders. These cylinder banks are fitted with valves and manifolds and may be used to provide breathing air in surface-support diving operations and for filling scuba tanks.

5.1.4 Gas Analysis

Instruments for testing the composition and purity of gases fall into two categories: those for laboratory use, and those for field use. Laboratory instruments are complex, highly accurate, and include the mass spectrometer, the gas chromatograph, and chemical analysis devices. These instruments are not generally available at a diving site because they require specialists trained in their use, operation, calibration, and interpretation of the data.

Instruments are available for field use that provide sufficiently accurate data to determine the safety of a gas to be used as a breathing medium. Portable instrumentation is used to determine the percentage of oxygen in the gas, gross percentages of carbon dioxide, and the amount of carbon monoxide present but is not capable of precise analysis of the total gas composition. A brief description of available portable gas analysis equipment follows.

1. Oxygen Analyzers. Several portable oxygen analyzers are available for measuring the percentage of oxygen in a gas. Calibration of these instruments is important, and instructions are usually included with the equipment.

Oxygen content can be determined by using a gas chromatograph, a standard volumetric gas analyzer, electrometric analyzer, thermal conductivity analyzer, or color-indicating tubes.

2. Carbon Dioxide Analyzers. Analysis conducted in the field can detect only gross amounts of carbon dioxide in a breathing medium. Field use CO_2 analyzers are capable of detecting CO_2 in quantities of less than one percent. Any diver's gas containing gross amounts of CO_2 is not safe to use (See Table 5–3).

Carbon dioxide content can be determined by using a gas chromatograph, titrimetric analysis, standard volumetric gas analyzer, or color-indicating tubes.

3. Carbon Monoxide Analyzers. Small, portable analyzers, sensitive in the range of trace to 0.002 percent by volume are available. These analyzers use chemicals that change color in relationship to the percentage of carbon monoxide present.

Carbon monoxide testing can be accomplished using either the portable units or laboratory equipment as follows:

1. Laboratory analysis using the iodine pentoxide method or infrared spectrophotometry.

2. Field testing using NBS colorimetric tubes.

As a general rule, unpolluted air compressed in a well-maintained compressor designed for compressing breathing gas is considered to meet oxygen and carbon dioxide requirements without testing. However, a simple test for water, oil, or particulate matter can be performed. The gas cylinder is inverted in the valve-down position for at least 5 minutes. The valve is then opened slightly, and air is allowed to flow into a clean glass container. Oil, water, or particulate matter can be observed on the glass. Laboratory methods for testing for water in breathing gas include electrolyte monitor, the piezoelectric hydrometer, standard dew point apparatus, or electrical conductivity test. Ultraviolet spectroscopy is used to test for oil contamination.

A useful field test for oil, water, or dust is to pass a 5000-cc sample of air through a white-sieve membrane filter. If no visible material appears on the filter, the air meets requirements for water, oil, and dust.

Hydrocarbons present in air can be determined in a laboratory using a total hydrocarbon analyzer.

Objectionable odors may be detected by smelling the gas prior to use.

For further information on gas analysis equipment see the U.S. Navy Diving Manual 1973.

5.1.5 Compressed Air Purity

There are at present no Federal standards governing the purity of compressed air. However, the standards given in Table 5–3 are considered as safe for air to be used as divers' breathing media.

The Compressed Gas Association, Inc., has defined a number of grades and types of compressed air in a highly detailed specification (Compressed Gas Association, Inc. Pamphlet G–7.1, 1973).

5.2 OXYGEN

Oxygen is a colorless, odorless, and tasteless gas. It is one of the most common elements found in nature, and is the most essential gas in the respiratory and metabolic processes of the body.

The use of pure oxygen as a breathing gas for divers is limited to the closed-circuit oxygen scuba. Oxygen and mixed gas diving are discussed in detail in Section 11.

Oxygen may be mixed with nitrogen, helium,

Table 5-3
Air Purity Standards

Element	Purity
Oxygen..............................	20 to 22 percent by volume.
Maximum carbon dioxide............	0.050 percent by volume (500 ppm).
Maximum carbon monoxide.........	0.001 percent by volume (10 ppm)*.
Maximum total volatile hydrocarbons.	0.001 percent by volume (10 ppm).
Maximum total oxidants............	0.000005 percent by volume (0.05 ppm).
Dust and water.......................	Lack of any residue on membrane after passing 5000 cc of air through filter (See Note).
Oil vapor..............................	Not more than 5 mg/m³.
Odor...................................	Not objectionable.

NOTE: Maximum moisture content for compressed air used for scuba at temperatures below 20° C is 0.02 mg/liter. Particulants, including oil, in gas over 2 atmospheres must not exceed 1 mg/cubic meter; below 2 atmospheres, they must not exceed 5 mg/cubic meter.

Rare gases such as helium, neon, krypton, hydrogen, and xenon represent only 0.003 percent of the atmosphere, and, as they occur in a natural state present no hazard to a diver, even at the partial pressures experienced at the maximum depths permissible during an air dive.

*Compressed Gas Association.

or other gases for use as a breathing medium.

5.2.1 Limitations of Oxygen

Oxygen may become toxic to the body when breathed at high partial pressures. A partial pressure of between 0.2 and 0.5 atmosphere is considered optimum. Partial pressures of 0.5 to 1.2 atmospheres can be tolerated for short periods of time, generally less than 4 hours.

5.2.2 General Safety Precautions for Oxygen

Oxygen is the most hazardous gas divers handle because it lowers the ignition temperature of flammable substances and greatly accelerates combustion. Hydrocarbons ignite almost spontaneously in the presence of oxygen, and oxygen fires instantly create intense heat. When materials burn in oxygen the flame temperatures are higher than in air because the nitrogen content of the air is not being heated.

To start a fire, an oxidizer, a fuel and a source of heat are needed. Since the oxidizer is ever present in an oxygen storage system, the fuels and sources of heat must be eliminated. Fuels may appear in oxygen systems in the form of combustible lubricants, gaskets, plastics, cleaning solvents, sealants, threading compounds, diaphragm materials and insulation. Even common fabricating metals may react with oxygen under proper temperature and pressure conditions. In addition to limiting material which can act as fuel, the system must be assembled free of organic contaminants and loose particles, which is known as "Clean For Oxygen Service." However, even with the most careful precautions some dirt can eventually get into an oxygen system which increases the importance of eliminating sources of heat (Gilardi 1974).

Oxygen cylinders should never be completely emptied, but should be maintained with a minimum of 25 psi cylinder pressure to prevent contamination from entering the cylinder.

5.2.3 Oxygen Equipment

Oxygen of the purity required for diving is generally refined by cryogenic separation from air. This is a complex process, and cannot be done at an operational site.

Oxygen is shipped in gas cylinders that are color coded *green*. The label on the cylinder, also color coded green, provides exact data as to the grade of oxygen in the cylinder.

5.2.4 Oxygen Purity

The purity standards for oxygen are detailed in Federal Specification BB-0-925 (U.S. Navy Diving Manual 1973). This specification categorizes oxygen into three grades as follows:

Grade A	Aviator's oxygen.
Grade B	Industrial, medical oxygen.
Grade C	Technical oxygen.

The difference between Grades A and B is the moisture content. Grade A, used by aviators, must be extremely dry to prevent freezing at the low temperatures associated with high altitudes. Grade B is allowed a maximum of 5 ml free water per cylinder. Grades A and B oxygen are suitable as a breathing medium for divers. Both Grades A and

B are required to be 99.5 percent pure oxygen, and must pass tests for acidity or alkalinity, carbon dioxide, carbon monoxide, halogens, and other oxidizing substances as specified in U.S. Pharmacopia (XIV Revision). Grade C, technical oxygen, is not suitable as a diver's breathing medium.

5.3 DILUENT GASES

Mixed gas breathing media are controlled mixtures of oxygen with one or more diluent gases. Nitrogen and helium are commonly used. Argon, neon, and hydrogen have been investigated as diluents but are not commonly used.

5.3.1 Limitations of Diluent Gases

Nitrogen, the most commonly used diluent, is limited because of its tendency to produce narcosis plus the fact that adding it to an air mixture affects bottom time and decompression. When increased nitrogen partial pressures are used, the resultant air-equivalent depths must be calculated prior to diving (See Paragraph 11.4.3). Helium shows no narcotic effect on a diver over a wide range of depths, but is limited by its high cost, its relative scarcity, high thermal conductivity, and the difficulty of voice communication associated with speech distortion in a helium-oxygen mixture. This latter limitation has been largely eliminated by special helium voice communication equipment, which utilizes electronic filtering and special frequency modulation techniques.

The major limitation with mixed gas diving is economic rather than operational. The costs of pure gas, the controlled mixing of the gases, and the diving apparatus itself limit this type of diving to those depths where air diving cannot be conducted. Training divers in mixed gas equipment use, and associated maintenance and logistic requirements, combine to place the cost of mixed gas diving much higher than air diving.

The thermal conductivity of helium is six times that of nitrogen, resulting in a more rapid heat loss from the body. While during a short dive in very cold water (15 minutes or less), the heat loss is not significant, a prolonged dive can greatly reduce diver efficiency.

Neon is sometimes used as a diver's breathing gas, but is far too expensive to use in the pure state. Neon offers some advantages over helium. Most notably, because of its higher density, it produces

lower thermal conductivity, and a reduced speech distortion problem. A mixture of neon and helium (about 75 percent neon and 25 percent helium) is a byproduct of cryogenic oxygen and nitrogen production. This mixture is available commercially and is suitable for use as diluent in divers' breathing gas. Neon does not appear to have a narcotic effect. It is inert, and tests indicate that decompression requirements are similar to those of helium. Neon, however, does create more breathing resistance at greater depths.

Hydrogen is generally not used as a diver's breathing gas because of its propensity to explode. Hydrogen-oxygen mixtures are readily ignited by static electricity discharges unless the oxygen concentrations are below the combustible limit, which is about 6 percent oxygen at 1 atmosphere pressure. Explosive limits of hydrogen-oxygen mixtures have not been investigated at high pressures and are not known, but would be below the 6 percent oxygen level.

Hydrogen causes more speech distortion than helium and its thermal conductivity is higher resulting in a high rate of body heat loss. Hydrogen is, however, easier to breathe at great depths, because of its low density. The effects of hydrogen on body tissue at high pressure have not as yet been fully explored.

5.3.2 General Safety Precautions for Diluent Gases

Helium, nitrogen, and neon are inert and do not represent a special safety hazard. Hydrogen is explosive around oxygen and air, and must be handled carefully to prevent explosions.

The principal safety precaution associated with mixed gas breathing media is to assure that the partial pressures of the oxygen and diluent gas are in the proper ratio. The partial pressure of oxygen should be maintained in the 0.2 to 0.5 atmosphere range for normal operations. Under unique circumstances, an oxygen partial pressure of from 0.5 to 1.2 atmospheres may be required by the operational condition of the dive. The presence of carbon dioxide and carbon monoxide should be monitored to ensure they are below toxic levels.

5.3.3 Equipment for Diluent Gases

Mixed gases are used only with mixed gas scuba

or with surface-supplied equipment using helmets designed specifically for mixed gas (See Section 4).

5.3.4 Diluent Gas Purity Specifications

Helium is generally produced as a byproduct of natural gas production, where it coexists with hydrocarbon gases in a natural state.

Helium is produced by the Federal Government under Public Law 86–777, Sept. 1960, in four grades, A through D. Presently only grades A and D are in production. Grade A is approximately 99.999 percent pure, is free of oil and moisture, and is suitable for use in diving. Grade D is equally pure, but oil pumped. Grade D helium is unsuitable as a breathing gas. Several private manufacturers produce helium of grades and purities equivalent to that produced by the Federal Government; however, low purity helium is available commercially for use in welding. This grade is only 50 to 85 percent pure and is designated as crude helium. Crude helium is not acceptable for use in diving operations.

Helium in cylinders is color-coded *buff* under U.S. Navy color coding standards and *brown* under Department of Commerce (Bureau of Standards) standards. The label affixed to the cylinder provides data as to its grade.

Nitrogen, oxygen, and neon are produced by cryogenic fractioning of air. Hydrogen is produced as a byproduct of a number of chemical processes or from the electrolysis of water.

Nitrogen purity is defined in Federal Specification BB–N–411a. This specification describes three grades of Type 1 (gaseous), Class 1 (oil free) nitrogen.

Grade A is 99.95 percent pure, maximum moisture content is 0.02 mg/liter.

Grade B is 99.5 percent pure, maximum moisture content is 0.02 mg/liter.

Grade C is 99.5 percent pure, maximum free water of 5 ml per cylinder.

Nitrogen of Class 1 in Grades A, B, and C may be used for diving operations, providing the trace contaminants, 0.5 percent by volume, consist of oxygen and carbon dioxide.

A high percentage of CO_2 contamination in Grades B or C may preclude their use.

Nitrogen in cylinders is color-coded *light gray*. The label on the cylinder provides data as to the class and grade.

The individual gases used in preparing various breathing mixtures are available in a highly pure state. Trace contaminants have been observed, but these are usually from the residue of the cleaning agent used to prepare the gas containers.

The reader is referred to the Compressed Gas Association's *Handbook of Compressed Gases* and R. C. Gilardi's *Safe Handling of Diving Gases* (1974).

GENERAL DIVING PROCEDURES 6

6.0 GENERAL

Diving operations, simple or complex, require adherence to proven diving procedures. These procedures have been established after countless hours of diving experience in many diving environments. To ensure safe and efficient diving operations, all diving personnel should have a thorough understanding of the procedures presented in this section. This must be reinforced with local procedures, familiarity with the area, and regulations dealing with the immediate situation. Poor procedures not only result in unnecessary and costly delays, but also affect the success of a project and increase susceptibility to accidents.

6.1 PLANNING THE DIVING OPERATION

6.1.1 Definition of Mission and Goals

A clear definition of the mission and its goals is an imperative first step in planning a diving operation. Diving procedures, selected in consonance with the mission and goals, are of primary importance in successful underwater projects.

In establishing an operational plan all parties engaged in the project should participate, including those who will be actively diving as well as those engaged in nondiving roles. The role diving will play in the overall project should be defined. Resources, including qualified divers, diving equipment, surface or underwater support platforms, and support equipment must be determined. Logistics to get the diving operation to a site on time at a minimum cost must be assigned. A clear definition of the goals to be achieved and the responsibility of the divers must be specified. The data or samples to be gathered, work to be performed, or observations to be made, must be determined, and bottom time to achieve these goals estimated as closely as possible.

Also, the instrumentation, equipment, and underwater techniques to be used to accomplish the goals must be decided upon.

As in all endeavors, the defined missions and goals of a diving operation must be regularly examined and, as required, updated and altered to reflect the oftentimes changing tone of a project.

6.1.2 Selection of Diving Equipment

Selection of the type of equipment best suited for a diving operation is dependent, generally, upon the environmental conditions to be encountered at the dive site, as well as the dive's mission and goals. More specifically, the equipment must:

1. Allow the diver to ascend and descend in the underwater environment safely and in relative comfort.

2. Allow the diver the ability to accomplish required tasks.

Divers will use, during the majority of their diving operations, one of the following types of diving equipment systems:

- Open-Circuit Scuba (Figure 6–1)
- Umbilical-Supplied Systems (Figure 6–2)
- Closed-Circuit Scuba (Figure 6–3)

The majority of dives conducted by divers will be to depths of 130 feet and less, using open-circuit air scuba. However, because of the variety of environmental conditions that divers encounter, and the varying mission requirements imposed by different projects, other types of diving equipment may be required and must be considered. Depth and duration of the dive; type of work to be accomplished (heavy work, light work, silent work); temperature of the water; amount of current at the dive site; all these influence the selection of diving equipment. Detailed descriptions of the various types of diving equipment are given in Section 4. For plan-

**Figure 6-1
Open-Circuit
Scuba Cylinders**

**Figure 6-2
Umbilical-Supplied
Equipment**

ning purposes, the following general guidelines can be used in selecting diving equipment:

Open-Circuit Scuba

Generally Used For
> Scientific observation
> Light underwater work and recovery
> Sample gathering
> Shallow water search
> Ship inspection and light repair

Major Advantages
> Underwater mobility
> Accessibility and economy of equipment and breathing medium
> Portability and minimum support
> Reliability

Major Disadvantages
> Lack of efficient voice communication
> Limited depth and duration

Umbilical-Supplied Systems

Generally Used For
> General scientific investigation
> Heavy ship repair and inspection
> Heavy salvage
> Long duration scientific observation and data gathering
> Harsh environments (low visibility, currents)

**Figure 6-3
Closed-Circuit
Scuba Equipment**

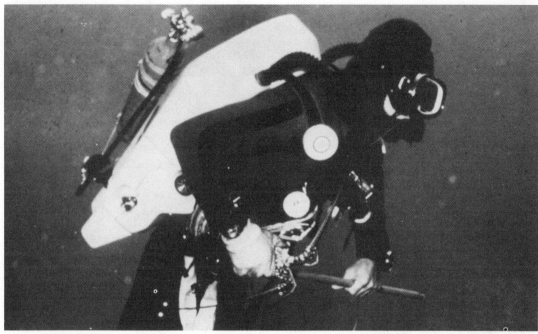

Photo: General Electric Corporation

Major Advantages
> Heat can be supplied for suit and breathing medium
> Not limited by breathing medium supply duration
> Voice communication
> Not limited to air as the breathing medium

Major Disadvantages
> Limited mobility
> Significant support requirements

Closed-Circuit Scuba
Generally Used For
> Missions requiring quiet, long duration observations

Major Advantages
> Mixed gas capability
> Noiseless operation
> Conservation of breathing medium
> Long duration

Major Disadvantages
> Complicated maintenance
> Extensive diver training requirements
> Lack of efficient voice communication.

6.1.3 Dive Team Organization

6.1.3.1 Dive Master

The selection of personnel for a diving operation begins with the selection of the Dive Master. Total responsibility for safe and efficient conduct of the diving operation rests with the Dive Master. He must be an experienced diver, qualified to at least the requirements of the proposed dive. Once designated, he is the only person in charge of the diving operation. No diving will be conducted when he is not on the scene. The Dive Master's responsibilities are many and include, but may not be limited to, the following:

1. Overall charge of the diving operation
2. Safe execution of all diving
3. Preparation of a basic plan of operations
4. Liaison with other organizations
5. Determination and selection of equipment
6. Proper maintenance, repair, and stowage of equipment
7. Selection, evaluation, and briefing of divers and other personnel

8. Monitoring the progress of the operation and updating requirements as necessary

9. Tabulation and submission of results and required records

10. Monitoring of decompression (when required).

The Dive Master is responsible for the assignment of all divers to an operation and for ensuring that their qualifications are equal to or exceed the requirements of the dive. The Dive Master shall ensure that all divers are thoroughly briefed as to the missions and goals of the operation. Individual responsibilities will be assigned each diver by the Dive Master. Where special tools or techniques are being used, the Dive Master shall ensure that each diver is familiar with their application and use. Practice and refresher dives shall be made as necessary to ensure safe and efficient operations at the designated dive site. Although the Dive Master must be a knowledgeable diver, it is recommended that in operations involving a large number of divers or very complex dives the Dive Master perform no actual diving but devote his entire time to directing the operations of other divers.

6.1.3.2 Diving Medical Officer/Medical Technician

The advantage of a qualified Diving Medical Officer on site cannot be discounted. It is recognized however, that this may not always be practical. A Dive Master should not discount the possibility of obtaining a Diving Physician for the program, particularly if the operation will be at some distance from emergency assistance; if any decompression diving is planned; or if the operation involves a large number of divers and dives.

As an alternative to a Diving Medical Officer, a Diving Medical Technician should be considered for major programs. The technician, although not a physician, is experienced in determining diving-related accidents, and, under the direct advice of a physician, administering temporary first aid until the services of a physician can be reached. Most Diving Medical Technicians are also qualified chamber operators.

If a Diving Medical Officer or a Diving Medical Technician cannot be obtained for full time on-site assistance, the Dive Master should consider the use of a medical officer on shore who is on 24-hour-a-day call throughout the operation. Should an emergency arise, the medical officer can be in direct radio contact with the ship and provide consultation.

6.1.3.3 Science Coordinator

On missions where diving is performed in support of scientific programs, a Science Coordinator should be designated. The Science Coordinator is the prime point of contact in the operation for all scientific aspects of the program. Scientific equipment, its use, calibration, and maintenance, fall under his purview. Working with the Dive Master, the Science Coordinator briefs divers on upcoming missions, and supervises the debriefing and sample or data accumulation following a dive.

6.1.3.4 Divers

Although the Dive Master is ultimately responsible for the overall diving operation, each individual diver has his own responsibilities. He is responsible for maintaining himself in proper physical condition and for the checkout of his equipment prior to a dive. He must ensure that he thoroughly understands the tasks(s) he is going to perform prior to entering the water. He is required to obey all signals from the surface. Finally, he is responsible for the successful completion of his assigned tasks.

6.1.3.5 Support Divers and Other Support Personnel

In most diving operations the number and types of support divers depend upon the size of the operation and the type of diving equipment being used. As a general rule, those surface support personnel working directly with the diver should also be qualified divers. The use of nonqualified personnel who do not understand diving techniques and terminology can result in confusion and unnecessary complications. Persons not qualified as divers can be used when the need arises only after they have demonstrated an understanding of diving procedures to a standard acceptable to the Dive Master.

6.1.3.6 Small-Scale Operations

For self-contained diving operations, a minimum of two divers should be used. In a small-scale operation where the complexity of the assigned task is minimal the Dive Master may dive, and no surface support is required. For an operation of increased scope, or as the tasks to be performed under water increase in complexity, standby divers and even tenders may be required.

Figure 6-4
Large Vessel Sometimes
Used for Diving

When surface-supplied equipment is used, a minimum crew of three topside personnel is desirable. The topside crew consists of the Dive Master, a tender, and a standby diver who can double as a timekeeper/recorder. If the standby diver is required to enter the water, the Dive Master can double as timekeeper/recorder. However, in most operations of this nature the team leader commonly assumes the responsibility of Dive Master and Science Coordinator.

6.1.4 Selection of Surface Support Platform

Divers will, during the course of operations, enter the water from many platforms of various sizes and descriptions, ranging from small, inflatable rubber boats to large research vessels. Barges, specially outfitted for diving, may also be used.

Generally, the operational requirements, the type of diving equipment, the magnitude of the diving task, and prevailing and predicted environmental conditions will dictate the surface support platform most desirable to use. For example, near-shore diving using self-contained equipment in relatively calm water may be accomplished without

much difficulty from a good quality boat. More extensive offshore diving operations using self-contained or umbilical-supplied equipment would be undertaken from a large vessel with adequate deck space (Figure 6–4) or a suitable barge. A complete discussion on surface support platforms is given in Section 14.

6.1.5 Environmental Conditions

Environmental conditions at a dive site play a vital role in planning a diving operation. Generally, environmental conditions can be divided into surface environmental conditions and underwater environmental conditions. Surface conditions include weather, sea state, and ship traffic. Underwater conditions include depth, bottom type, currents, water temperatures, and visibility. Regional and special diving conditions are discussed in Section 9.

6.1.5.1 Surface Environmental Conditions

Weather conditions will be a factor to consider in planning a dive. Whenever possible, diving

Table 6-1
Sea State Chart
Wind and Sea Scale for Fully Arisen Sea (U.S. Navy Diving Operations Handbook 1971)

Sea-General		Wind				Sea						
Sea State	Description	(Beaufort) Wind Force	Description	Range (Knots)	Wind Velocity (Knots)	Wave Height Feet — Average	Wave Height Feet — Average 1/10 Highest	Significant Range of Periods (Seconds)	T (Average Period)	l (Average Wave Length)	Minimum Fetch (Nautical Miles)	Minimum Duration (Hours)
0	Sea like a mirror.	U	Calm	Less than 1	0	0	0	—	—	—	—	—
	Ripples with the appearance of scales are formed, but without foam crests.	1	Light Airs	1-3	2	0.05	0.10	up to 1.2 sec.	0.5	10 in.	5	18 min.
1	Small wavelets, still short but more pronounced; crests have a glassy appearance, but do not break.	2	Light Breeze	4-6	5	0.18	0.37	0.4-2.8	1.4	6.7 ft.	8	39 min.
	Large wavelets, crests begin to break. Foam of glassy appearance. Perhaps scattered white horses.	3	Gentle Breeze	7-10	8.5 10	0.6 0.88	1.2 1.8	0.8-5.0 1.0-6.0	2.4 2.9	20 27	9.8 10	1.7 2.4
2 3	Small waves, becoming larger; fairly frequent white horses.	4	Moderate Breeze	11-16	12 13.5 14 16	1.4 1.8 2.0 2.9	2.8 3.7 4.2 5.8	1.0-7.0 1.4-7.6 1.5-7.8 2.0-8.8	3.4 3.9 4.0 4.6	40 52 59 71	18 24 28 40	3.8 4.8 5.2 6.6
4	Moderate waves, taking a more pronounced long form; many white horses are formed. (Chance of some spray).	5	Fresh Breeze	17-21	18 19 20	3.8 4.3 5.0	7.8 8.7 10	2.5-10.0 2.8-10.6 3.0-11.1	5.1 5.4 5.7	90 99 111	55 65 75	8.3 9.2 10
5	Large waves begin to form; the white foam crests are more extensive everywhere. (Probably some spray).	6	Strong Breeze	22-27	22 24 24.5 26	6.4 7.9 8.2 9.6	13 16 17 20	3.4-12.2 3.7-13.5 3.8-13.6 4.0-14.5	6.3 6.8 7.0 7.4	134 160 164 188	100 130 140 180	12 14 15 17
6	Sea heaps up and white foam from breaking waves begins to be blown in streaks along the direction of the wind. (Spindrift begins to be seen).	7	Moderate Gale	28-33	28 30 30.5 32	11 14 14 16	23 28 29 33	4.5-15.5 4.7-16.7 4.8-17.0 5.0-17.5	7.9 8.6 8.7 9.1	212 250 258 285	230 280 290 340	20 23 24 27

Sea State	Description	(Beaufort) Wind Force	Description	Range (Knots)	Wind Velocity (Knots)	Wave Height Feet Average	Wave Height Feet Average 1/10 Highest	Significant Range of Periods (Seconds)	T (Average Period)	I (Average Wave Length)	Minimum Fetch (Nautical Miles)	Minimum Duration (Hours)
7	Moderately high waves of greater length; edges of crests break into spindrift. The foam is blown in well marked streaks along the direction of the wind. Spray affects visibility.	8	Fresh Gale	34-40	34	19	38	5.5-18.5	9.7	322	420	30
					36	21	44	5.8-19.7	10.3	363	500	34
					37	23	46.7	6-20.5	10.5	376	530	37
					38	25	50	6.2-20.8	10.7	392	600	38
					40	28	58	6.5-21.7	11.4	444	710	42
8	High waves. Dense streaks of foam along the direction of the wind. Sea begins to roll. Visibility affected.	9	Strong Gale	41-47	42	31	64	7-23	12.0	492	830	47
					44	36	73	7-24.2	12.5	534	960	52
					46	40	81	7-25	13.1	590	1110	57
	Very high waves with long overhanging crests. The resulting foam is in great patches and is blown in dense white streaks along the direction of the wind. On the whole the surface of the sea takes a white appearance. The rolling of the sea becomes heavy and shocklike. Visibility is affected.	10	Whole Gale	48-55	48	44	90	7.5-26	13.8	650	1250	63
					50	49	99	7.5-27	14.3	700	1420	69
					51.5	52	106	8-28.2	14.7	736	1560	73
					52	54	110	8-28.5	14.8	750	1610	75
					54	59	121	8-29.5	15.4	810	1800	81
9	Exceptionally high waves (Small and medium-sized ships might for a long time be lost to view behind the waves.) The sea is completely covered with long white patches of foam lying along the direction of the wind. Everywhere the edges of the wave crests are blown into froth. Visibility affected.	11	Storm	56-63	56	64	130	8.5-31	16.3	910	2100	88
					59.5	73	148	10-32	17.0	985	2500	101
	Air filled with foam and spray. Sea completely white with driving spray; visibility very seriously affected.	12	Hurricane	64-71	>64	>80	>164	10-(35)	(18)			

operations should be cancelled or delayed during bad weather. Current and historical weather data should be reviewed to determine if proper weather conditions are prevalent or predictable for a sufficient amount of time to complete the mission. Critical weather changes and a wind shift can jeopardize safety of personnel and platforms.

Diving operations conducted during periods of low visibility (fog, snow, rain, etc.) require special planning. Scuba divers are particularly vulnerable during periods of low visibility as they may lose orientation and be unable to relocate the surface platform.

Diving, standby, and support personnel must be protected from excessive exposure to adverse surface weather conditions. When working in tropical areas, the staging area should be shaded to prevent over-exposure to sun. During cold weather, divers and surface personnel must be protected from cold air temperatures and wind. Divers should not be expected to don or remove diving dress in an open, unprotected area. When working from small boats, divers should dress prior to entering the boat.

If under-ice dives are required, divers should dress in heated shore facilities or heated portable structures on the ice. Do not submit divers to excessive cold-temperature exposure prior to the dive. Heated quarters and warm showers should be available immediately after surfacing.

Surface weather conditions can, in some instances, influence selection of diving equipment. For instance, even though water temperatures may permit the use of wet suits, cold air temperature and wind would dictate a variable-volume dry suit (or equivalent) when diving from an open or unheated platform.

When possible, avoid or limit diving in rough seas (See Table 6-1). Naturally, sea-state limitations will be dependent to a large degree on the type and size of diving platform. Diving operations may be conducted in rougher seas from properly moored, larger platforms such as diving barges, oceangoing ships, or fixed structures. Divers using self-contained equipment should avoid entering the ocean in heavy surf.

In the event that bad weather sets in after a diving operation has commenced, appropriate recall signals should be employed (See Paragraph 6.2.3).

Ship traffic in the dive area must be a planning consideration as it can constitute a hazard to divers, particularly those using self-contained equipment.

It is necessary to display proper visual signals in a prominent location on the diving platform during operations to notify approaching vessels that divers are in the water. Signals are described in Table 6-4.

6.1.5.2 Underwater Environmental Conditions

Dive depth is a basic consideration in the selection of personnel, equipment, and techniques. When possible, determine the depth as accurately as possible in the planning phases, and plan the dive duration, air requirements, and decompression schedule (when required) accordingly.

The type of bottom affects a diver's ability to work and also is a factor in determining visibility. Consequently, this must be considered in the preliminary planning stages and certain precautionary measures may be necessary to ensure the diver's safety and efficiency.

Mud (silt and clay) bottoms are generally the most restrictive for divers. The slightest movement will stir sediment into suspension and restrict visibility. The diver must orient himself so that the current, if any, will carry the suspended sediment away from the work area.

Sand bottoms present little problem for divers. Visibility restrictions from suspended sediment are less, and footing is firm.

Coral reefs are solid but contain many sharp protrusions. A diver should wear gloves and coveralls or a wet suit for protection if the mission requires considerable contact with the coral.

Currents are essentially flowing masses of water within a body of water caused by gravity, surface winds, tides, earth rotation, and by internal waves. Divers must always account for currents when planning and executing a dive, particularly a scuba dive. Attempts to swim against currents exceeding one knot may result in severe fatigue. When anchored in a current, a buoyed safety line at least 100 feet in length should be trailed over the stern of the boat during diving operations. Upon entering the water, a diver who is swept away from the boat by the current can use this line to keep from being carried far down current.

Descent into water with currents should be made down a weighted line. Free swimming descents in currents should be avoided. Ascent should also be made up a line.

When currents exceed one knot, scuba diving

should be avoided unless adequate provisions are made for a diver pickup boat to operate down current. Also, divers should carry signal devices. Divers, heavily weighted, using umbilical-supplied equipment are frequently required for work in currents. Tidal currents may prohibit diving at some locations except during periods of tidal current direction change. Divers may occasionally drift along with a current as little or no exertion is required and long distances can be covered. Careful observation of changing tidal currents often permits a diver to drift down current and return to the starting point on the return current. Expert local knowledge permits effective use of back eddies. Consult tide tables when necessary and determine the magnitude of tidal currents prior to diving.

When bottom currents are encountered, the diver should always swim into the current at the beginning of the dive, not with the current. This will facilitate easy return to the boat at the end of the dive. He should stay close to the bottom and use rocks if necessary to pull himself along in order to avoid overexertion. If the diver wants to maintain position he should grasp a rock, or stop behind a rock, and not attempt to swim. Because air is used up much faster when currents are encountered, a submersible pressure gauge should be used and constantly checked.

Water temperature is a major factor to be considered in planning a diving operation as it will have a significant effect on the type of equipment selected and, in some cases, the practical duration of a dive.

Diving in *thermoclines* (layers of water having different temperatures) poses no hazard to a diver, but does require some preplanning when known thermoclines exist at a dive site, or replanning if they are discovered at the site.

Thermoclines can occur at various levels, close to the surface as well as deep in the water. Temperatures can vary as much as 20° F between temperature at the water's surface and within layers below the surface. Also, temperatures vary from layer to layer. Divers entering the water dressed and equipped for temperatures at the surface may find drastic changes in temperature at various depths below the surface which could cause, because of diver heat loss, early termination of a dive. Attempts should be made to predict the presence of thermoclines at a planned dive site and equip divers accordingly so that, even with drops in water temperature, diver comfort can be maintained.

Scientists diving in thermoclines, taking measurements and gathering samples, should be aware of the temperature differences and adjust instrumentation and techniques accordingly.

Equipment especially suited for operating in cold water is discussed in detail in Section 4.

Underwater visibility depends on time of day, locality, water conditions, season, bottom type, weather, and currents.

Divers will frequently be required to dive in water where visibility is minimal, sometimes down to zero. Diving in these conditions requires experience and competence.

Diving in low visibility is best performed using surface-supplied equipment. The diver has communication with the surface, communication with the diver(s), and a direct physical contact with the surface.

WARNING

Diving Using Self-Contained Equipment Should Be Avoided When Possible Where Visibility Is at Zero or Severely Limited. If Scuba Must Be Used a Buddy Line and Float Are Recommended.

The sense of feel is extremely important to a working diver or scientist in low or zero visibility. Learning to feel tools, work areas, and instruments, is valuable to a diver who must perform in the dark. Oftentimes divers will "rehearse" work functions while blindfolded on the surface.

Underwater hand-held low light level closed circuit television has been used successfully in low visibility situations, as it has been found that a television camera "sees" more in these conditions than does the human eye. This is true mainly where the reduced visibility is due to the absence of light (in cases where the problem is caused by high turbidity, the TV camera does not offer a significant advantage). The diver holds the camera, which transmits a picture to the surface. The surface, in turn, directs him in the performance of the work.

6.2 DIVING SIGNALS

6.2.1 Hand Signals

Hand signals are used under water by divers to convey information. The signals are shown in Figure 6-5.

It should be noted that there are various hand

Table 6-2
Line Pull, Audio,
and Visual Signals
for Diver-to-Diver
Communication

Signal Title and Meaning	Hand Squeeze/ Line Pull/ Light Flash/ Tank Tap	Answer
OK? or OK	One	Same
Go	Two	Same
Stop	Three	Same
Surface	Four	Same
Emergency or Come Here Quickly	Five or More	Go Quickly to Signaller

All signals, except the emergency signal, should be answered when received.

signal systems presently in use that have been developed by different organizations. Divers in different parts of the country and the world use different signals or variations of signals for the same message. Prior to a dive, the Dive Master should review with all divers the signals shown in Figure 6–5. This review is particularly important when divers from different diving areas constitute a dive team, or when divers are cooperating in a dive with other organizations.

6.2.2 Line Signals

Line signals are used by divers using surface-supplied equipment, either as a backup to voice communications to the surface, or as a primary communications means. Line signals can also be used by divers using self-contained equipment as a means of communication with the surface or, in restricted visibility, for diver-to-diver communication. Tables 6–2 and 6–3 contain line signals used by divers.

NOTE:

Hand or Line Signals May Vary by Geographical Areas or Between Organizations. Divers Should Review Signals Before Diving With New Buddies or Support Personnel.

Table 6-3
Line Pull Signals
for Surface-to-Diver
Communication

Emergency Signals
2-2-2 Pulls "I am fouled and need the assistance of another diver"
3-3-3 Pulls "I am fouled but can clear myself"
4-4-4 Pulls "Haul me up immediately"
All signals will be answered as given except for emergency signal 4-4-4

From tender to diver
1 Pull "Are you all right?"
    When diver is descending, one pull means "stop."
2 Pulls "Going down"
    During ascent, 2 pulls mean you have come up too far, go back down until we stop you."
3 Pulls "Stand by to come up"
4 Pulls "Come up"
2-1 Pulls "I understand," or "answer the telephone"

From diver to tender
1 Pull "I am all right" or "I am on the bottom"
2 Pulls "Lower" or "give me slack"
3 Pulls "Take up my slack"
4 Pulls "Haul me up"
2-1 Pulls "I understand" or "answer the telephone"
3-2 Pulls "More air"
4-3 Pulls "Less air"
Special signals from the diver to the tender should be devised as required by the situation

Searching Signals	Without circling line	With circling line
7 Pulls	"Go on (or off) searching signals"	Same
1 Pull	"Stop and search where you are."	Same
2 Pulls	"Move directly away from the tender if given slack, move toward the tender if strain is taken on the life line"	"Move away from the weight"
3 Pulls	"Go to your right"	"Face the weight and go right"
4 Pulls	"Go to your left"	"Face the weight and go left"

Table 6-4
Diver Signals

Signal	Use	Meaning
Red / White **U. S. Divers Flag**	Displayed by civilian divers in the United States. The flag should be flown at a sufficient height above the water so as to be easily visible.	Divers are below. Boats should not operate within 100 feet. (Varies in accordance with individual state laws)
White / Blue **International Code Flag "A"[1]**	Displayed by all vessels and divers in international and foreign waters and by the United States Navy.	"I have a diver down; keep well clear at slow speed."
"I" — Yellow, Black "R" — Yellow, Red **International Code Flags "I R"[1]**	Displayed by all vessels in international and foreign waters.	"I am engaged in submarine survey work (under water operations). Keep clear of me and go slow."
International Day Shapes and Lights[2] Shapes/Day: Red Ball, White Diamond, Red Ball Lights/Night: Red, White, Red	Displayed by all vessels in international and foreign waters engaged in under-water operations.	This vessel is engaged in underwater operations and is unable to get out of the way of approaching vessels.

[1]U.S. Navy, *International Code of Signals*, United States Edition, 1969.
[2]U.S. Coast Guard, *Rules of the Road: International—Inland*, August 1, 1972.

**Figure 6-5
Hand Signals Used
by Scuba Divers**

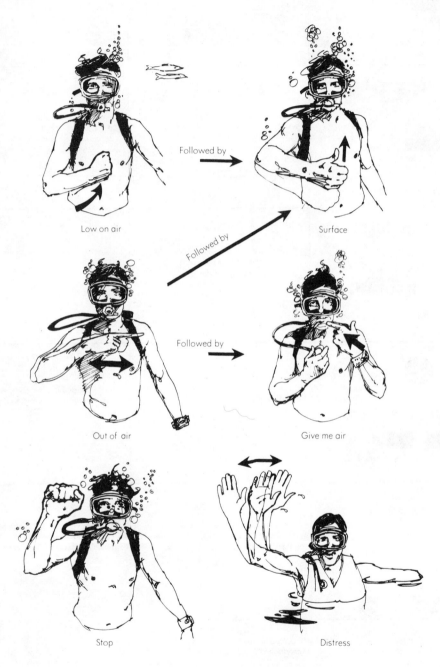

Low on air

Followed by

Surface

Followed by

Out of air

Followed by

Give me air

Stop

Distress

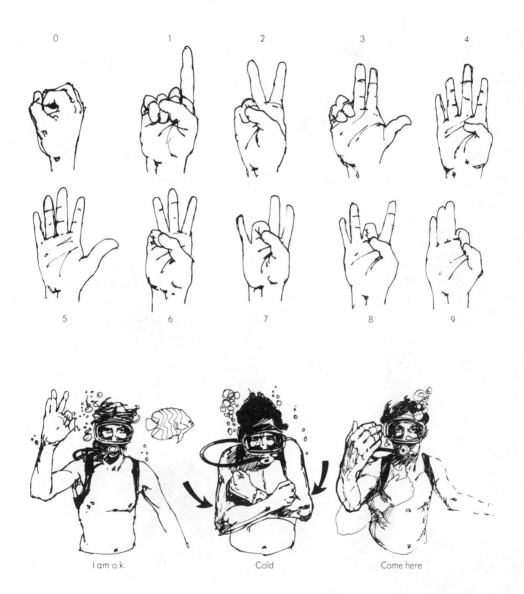

| 0 | 1 | 2 | 3 | 4 |

| 5 | 6 | 7 | 8 | 9 |

I am o.k.

Cold

Come here

**Figure 6-5 continued
Hand Signals Used
by Scuba Divers**

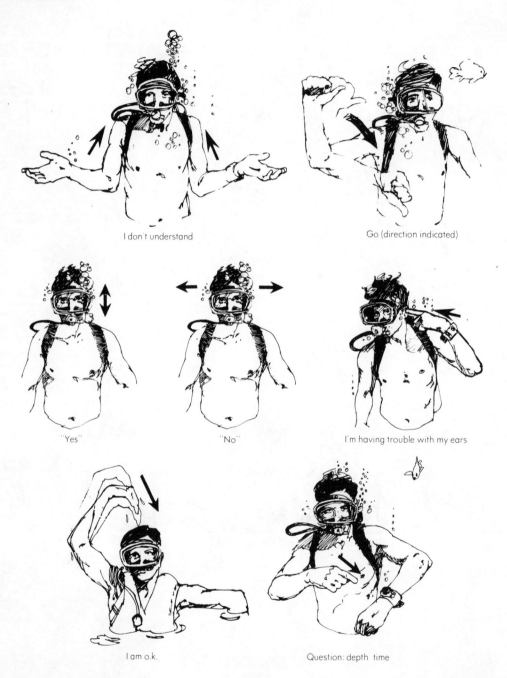

I don't understand

Go (direction indicated)

"Yes"

"No"

I'm having trouble with my ears

I am o.k.

Question: depth time

Figure 6-6
Buddy Breathing

6.2.3 Surface to Diver Recall Signals

Unexpected situations often arise that require divers to be called from the water. When voice communications are not employed the following methods should be considered:

- Acoustic Detonator—A small device ignited by a flame and thrown into the water
- Hammer—Rapping four times on a steel hull or metal plate
- Bell—Held under water and struck four times
- Hydrophone—Underwater speaker
- Strobe—Used at night, flashed four times

6.2.4 Surface Signals

If a diver needs to attract attention upon surfacing, and is beyond voice range, the following signaling devices may be used:

- Police Whistle
- Flare
- Flashing Strobe
  (See Paragraph 4.9.8)
- Flags (See Table 6-4)

6.3 EMERGENCY PROCEDURES

No matter how well-planned the diving operation or how well-trained the diver, emergency situations occasionally arise, usually the result of a failure to observe some safety precaution. The single most important rule to observe in any underwater emergency is "DON'T PANIC!" In most instances, taking a few seconds to make an accurate assessment of the situation and determine the actions necessary to alleviate the problem can keep the emergency from becoming an accident.

6.3.1 Loss of Air Supply and Buddy Breathing

The loss of a diver's air supply is a serious emergency. If the loss is gradual and the diver is using self-contained equipment with a reserve supply, simply opening the air reserve mechanism and ascending to the surface may alleviate the situation. If the loss of air is sudden and unexpected "buddy breathing" can be used. The most efficient method of buddy breathing is for the two divers to face each other, each alternately breathing from the same mouthpiece while ascending (Figure 6–6). During exchange the exhaust valve on single hose regulators must be below the mouthpiece or a failure to eliminate water from the second stage can occur. The

Figure 6-7
Clearing a Face Mask

donor controls the air, and both divers must exhale between exchanges. Contact should be maintained by holding the straps or belt of the other diver.

If it is necessary to cover a horizontal distance while buddy breathing, a number of different methods can be used. The two most common are for the divers to swim side by side about halfway on their sides, facing each other, or to swim one above the other, the diver with the good air supply on the bottom. In this manner, the mouthpiece can be easily passed back and forth between divers.

WARNING

When One Diver Runs Out of Air the Buddy Usually Is Very Low. At Double Consumption, Available Air Can Be Depleted in Seconds. Buddy Breathing Ascent Should Therefore Be Prompt.

Scuba tanks can be equipped with an "octopus" or double regulator for emergency buddy breathing or failure of the primary regulator. This is a valuable safety item that should be considered when new equipment is purchased.

A scuba tank that is apparently empty on the bottom, will supply air as the diver ascends, if he relaxes and breathes shallow.

WARNING

Discarding Self-contained Equipment and Making a Free Ascent Should Be Considered a Last Resort. When This Procedure Is Used, Exhale All the Way to the Surface. (See Paragraph 2.2.2)

A diver using umbilical-supplied equipment who experiences a loss of air supply will most likely have a limited amount of usable air in his helmet or his constant-volume suit. If a resumption of air supply to the mask does not resume again quickly, the diver should signal his tenders (See Paragraph 6.2) to bring him to the surface, or make a controlled ascent to the surface. The diver should not discard his equipment unless it is hopelessly fouled.

6.3.2 Loss or Flooding of Equipment

Flooding of a face mask can be caused by another diver inadvertently kicking the mask loose with a fin, by high currents, or by a diver turning his head into a rock or other obstruction. The mask can be cleared by tilting the head back, pressing the top of the mask against the forehead, and blowing into the mask through the nose (Figure 6-7). The air will displace the water forcing it out the bottom of the mask. When the mask is equipped with a purge valve, the diver should position his head so the purge valve is in the lowest position relative to the mask and exhale through the nose. If the mask is completely lost the diver will still retain his air supply, but is left with a limited amount of visibility. If a nearby diver can be distinguished, the stricken diver should swim to him and have him assist in locating the mask. If the mask cannot be found, the diver should proceed to the surface in a controlled ascent.

When a single hose regulator mouthpiece is lost, the hose will normally be lying over the right shoulder. If it is not, it can be located by reaching back with the right hand over the right shoulder, grasping the first stage of the regulator at the tank's neck and locating the hose where it joins the first stage, then following the hose out to the mouthpiece. The mouthpiece will probably be flooded, but can be cleared by pushing the purge button.

With a double hose regulator, the mouthpiece and hose will float. One method of recovery is for the diver to roll onto his back. The hose and mouthpiece will then be floating over the diver's face. When the mouthpiece of a double hose regulator is above the level of the tank neck it will free-flow air; the hose and mouthpiece can be cleared of water by holding the mouthpiece above the head. If the exhaust hose is flooded, it can be cleared after the mouthpiece is back in his mouth by the diver exhaling or rolling over longitudinally to the left, allowing the water to flow the length of the exhaust hose, and be forced out the air exhaust valve.

6.3.3 Fouling and Entanglement

When a diver becomes trapped, entangled, or fouled, it is important that his first step be a calm assessment of the situation. Struggling to free himself immediately will probably only result in even deeper entanglement, and damage to or loss of, diving equipment.

The diver using self-contained equipment is most concerned with entanglement, as his air supply is limited and verbal communication to the surface is usually not possible. His best assets at this time are calmness and common sense, another nearby diver, and his diving knife. Using controlled movements he, or an assisting diver, should be able to cut obstructions and maneuver out of entanglements.

Emergency free ascent should be used only as a last resort.

When umbilical-supplied equipment is used, a diver should notify the surface immediately upon becoming fouled or entangled. If he cannot free himself, he should request assistance from a standby diver.

6.3.4 Drowning

The most common antecedent to drowning is panic, induced when a diver finds himself in a position for which he is not prepared mentally or physically. The majority of drownings can be avoided if the diver is properly trained, is in good physical condition, and is using reliable well-maintained equipment. He must stay with his buddy diver and dive within the limits of his experience.

The most important step in the immediate treatment of a drowning victim is to restore breathing. The most effective means of artificial respiration when used by trained personnel is a mechanical resuscitator. If one is not available, artificial respiration will be required, the most effective means being mouth to mouth. This method is simple and can be administered to the victim while still in the water. Complete information on mouth-to-mouth resuscitation is given in Section 17.

6.3.5 Emergency Controlled Ascent

Unless the breathing apparatus is entangled, a diver should not abandon it. The reduction of ambient pressure as the diver rises to the surface increases the pressure differential, resulting in additional air for breathing allowing the diver to make a controlled ascent.

WARNING

The Weight Belt Should Be Immediately Released If the Diver Is Having Difficulty Ascending. Before Dropping Weight Belt Make Sure No Divers Are Below.

When using constant volume dry suits or large buoyancy compensators extra caution should be taken to prevent uncontrolled ascent. Spreading the arms and legs will increase drag and stability, thus slowing the rate of ascent.

The diver must continue to exhale throughout the ascent. The head should be extended back. This allows maximum opening of the throat area and a good overhead view. The diver should swim to the surface, constantly being aware of possible entanglements or obstructions, and of consequences of holding his breath. The mouthpiece should be left in place.

6.3.6 Emergency Buoyant Ascent

In desperate emergency situations when a diver feels that he may lose consciousness, it may become necessary to make an emergency buoyant ascent and risk entanglement, injury, and air embolism. This is accomplished by dropping the weight belt and inflating an emergency flotation device (only high-capacity buoyancy compensators provide the desired amount of buoyancy). The ascent will be slow at first and will become more rapid as the wet suit or compensator expands, especially near the surface. A few kicks may be necessary to initiate the ascent. Remember, in all emergency ascents, exhale continuously throughout the ascent. The possibility of air embolism is always present in an emergency ascent (See Paragraph 2.2.2.4).

WARNING

An Emergency Buoyant Ascent Should Only Be Used as a Last Resort to Resolve an Emergency Situation. It Is Hazardous and Difficult to Accomplish Safely in Situations of Stress.

Upon reaching the surface after an emergency ascent, or when in trouble at the surface following normal ascent (rough water, exhaustion, etc.), inflate the buoyancy compensator, and signal for pickup. When a long distance from assistance, it may be necessary to use a signal flare to attract attention. The surface crew should be alert for divers in trouble at all times.

When not in difficulty, swim for the diving platform or shore. If the breathing apparatus interferes with swimming, a diver should remove the equipment and tow it while swimming on his back (jacket inflated or deflated) or on his front with a snorkel. The diver may have to discard his equipment if he faces a long swim to safety.

6.4 FLYING AFTER DIVING AT SEA LEVEL

Elimination of inert gas from body tissues following an exposure to pressure continues for a period of 24 hours or more before equilibration to the ambient partial pressure of nitrogen in air at the surface is completed. During this period, further reduction of ambient pressure will create a condition the same as that which occurs during decompression following a dive. Caution must be exercised when travelling in mountainous terrain as well as in flying after diving. Cabin atmosphere in modern pressurized aircraft is usually maintained at an altitude of 8,000 feet (0.74 atmosphere) (Edel et al. 1969). This reduction in pressure may be sufficient to cause inert gas dissolved in tissues to come out in the form of bubbles, thus causing decompression sickness. This has occurred in divers flying after diving with severe symptoms. It is a recognized hazard to be avoided. Termination of the flight with increase in ambient pressure to 1 atmosphere will not necessarily result in gas bubbles formed being recompressed sufficiently to become asymptomatic. Recompression treatment may be required to produce relief of symptoms.

Since a diver may have left the site of a recompression chamber, great difficulty may be occasioned in finding a chamber in which treatment can be instituted. The delay that results is likely to cause permanent tissue damage and require prolonged treatment to obtain a satisfactory outcome.

If it becomes necessary to fly immediately after a decompression dive or a series of repetitive dives, or after recompression treatment, such as in the case of injury which requires medical treatment not available at the dive site, the diver could be transported at low altitude by helicopter or aircraft, or in a pressurized aircraft which does not exceed a cabin atmosphere of 800 feet of altitude. If it is necessary to transport, by air, a diver suffering from decompression sickness, the flight should be conducted at the lowest safe altitude possible or in a pressurized aircraft in which the cabin atmosphere does not exceed 800 feet of altitude. In addition, the victim should breathe pure oxygen until he arrives at a recompression chamber.*

WARNING

The Following Procedures Are Not Applicable for Flying After Saturation (See Paragraph 12.6.4)

*Robert D. Workman, M.D., 1973: personal communication.

Before flying in an aircraft in which the cabin atmosphere will be less than 8000 feet (usually the case for most flights), a diver who has completed any number of dives on air, and decompressed following the U.S. Navy Standard Air Decompression Tables, should wait at sea level breathing air for the computed surface interval that allows him to be classified as a Group D diver in the U.S. Navy Repetitive Diving Table.

This procedure is illustrated by the following example:

0800   Dive to 50' on air for 60 minutes.

0900   Surface. (The U.S. Navy Residual Nitrogen Time Table for Repetitive Air Dives indicates diver is in repetitive Group H) Remain at sea level for 5 hours.

1400   U.S. Navy Residual Nitrogen Time Table for Repetitive Air Dives indicates the diver has moved to Group B. Dive to 60' on air for maximum no-decompression time of 49 minutes. This is found by subtracting the residual nitrogen time of 11 minutes for Group B at 60' (U.S. Navy Residual Nitrogen Time Table for Repetitive Air Dives), from the maximum no-decompression time of 60 minutes at 60' (U.S. Navy No-Decompression Limits and Repetitive Group Designation Table for No-Decompression Air Dives).

1449   Surface. (U.S. Navy No-Decompression Limits and Repetitive Group Designation Table for No-Decompression Air Dives indicates the diver is in Group J) Diver must wait 185 minutes to move into Group D.

1754   Diver can now fly to a maximum cabin altitude of 8000'.

Before flying, the diver should check with the flight engineer to verify the maximum planned cabin altitude and to inform him that divers are aboard. When flying in small or older aircraft, this is especially applicable.

In order to shorten the necessary surface interval before flying, oxygen may be breathed instead of air. The following table lists the length of oxygen breathing time necessary before flying for the various Repetitive Dive Group classifications.

Repetitive dive groups	Oxygen time before flying
	(Hr:Min)
Groups M through Z	1:30
Groups H through L	1:00
Groups E through G	0:30
Groups A through D	0:00

SECTION 7
WORKING
DIVING
PROCEDURES

WORKING DIVING PROCEDURES 7

7.0 GENERAL

The preceding section described the general procedures necessary for conducting safe diving operations. This section outlines specific techniques which may be used by the working diver. In the context of this section, the working diver is defined as any diver, trainee, student, professional, or scientist, who enters the water for the purpose of doing useful work.

7.1 WORKING TECHNIQUES

Underwater tasks require techniques different from those used on the surface to complete a similar task. Most working dives will utilize one or more of the following techniques:
- Search and Recovery
- Underwater Navigation
- Maintenance and Repair
- Instrument Implantation
- Salvage
- Photography.

7.1.1 Search and Recovery

Search techniques all rely on one common element: the adoption and rigid execution of a defined search pattern. The pattern should commence at a known point, cover a known area, and terminate at a known end point.

Search patterns must be selected to fully utilize the capabilities of the search equipment, whether it be sonar, visual search, or diver hand-held sonar. Search patterns are conducted by carrying out search sweeps that overlap. To be efficient, the overlap should be minimal. The initial step in a search is to define the general area and the limits to be searched. If the search is being conducted to locate a specific object, the last known position of the object is the starting point for defining the search

area. The drift in the open sea resulting from sea and wind currents, the local wind condition at the time the object was lost, and the leeway, or movement through the water from the force of the wind, should be studied. The sea currents can be estimated for a particular area using NOAA Tidal Current Tables and Tidal Current Charts and the U.S. Navy's Atlas of Surface Currents (1944, 1947, 1953). Wind currents can be estimated using the following table:

Wind speed (knots)	Wind current (miles/day)
1–3	2
4–6	4
7–10	7
11–16	11
17–21	16
22–27	21
28–33	26

The leeway is generally calculated at 0 to 10 percent of the wind speed depending upon the area of the object exposed to the wind and the relative resistance of the object to sinking. The direction of leeway is downwind, except for boats that have a tendency to drift up to 40 percent off the wind vector. The calculation of a value and direction of leeway is highly subjective for objects that will float or resist sinking; however, if the average wind velocity is relatively low (under 5 knots), or the object is of a nature to sink rapidly, the leeway has little or no effect on the calculation of a probable location.

Once the vectors of water current, wind current, and leeway are added vectorially and applied to the last known position of the object, a datum point is defined. *The datum point is the most probable position of the object.*

Once the datum point is defined, the search radius around the datum point is selected. The search

Table 7-1
Comparison of
Search Techniques

Search	Brief Description	Advantages	Disadvantages
Circular	Involves search in a circular area defined by the tethered radius of the diver.	Easiest and fastest method available. Requires only one search line. Can utilize any number of divers.	Difficulty establishing overlapping circular perimeters to prevent segments of incomplete search . . . hence, most inefficient of the three methods.
Jackstay	Uses a rectangular search area laid down by a diver. Two divers traverse parallel paths back and forth across the width using a pair of search lines.	More efficient than circular method. Methodical elimination of area already searched.	Requires two divers who must be separated by up to 100 feet. Hence, the need for buddy lines. Requires more preparation, equipment, and execution time than the circular search.
'Z'	Also uses a rectangular search area. Diver(s) search across width of area and return diagonally.	Most thorough search. Adaptable for one or two divers. If more than one diver is used, they remain in contact.	Slowest method of the three. A single diver must be tethered.

radius, R, is equal to the total probable error of position plus a safety factor, as defined by the following formula.

$$R = (1 + k)C$$

where

R = radius
k = safety factor (between 0.1 and 1.5)
C = total probable error

The total probable error is a mathematical combination of the initial error of the object position (x), the navigation error of the search craft (y), and the drift error (d_e). The drift error is assumed to be one-eighth of the total drift. The total probable error "C" is:

$$C = (d_e^2 + x^2 + y^2)^{\frac{1}{2}}$$

Each factor included in the total probable error is somewhat subjective. Selecting conservative values has the effect of enlarging the search radius. Therefore, a small search radius is sometimes selected with repeated expansions around the datum point continued until the object is located. Searching around the datum point can be carried out in a variety of patterns depending on the search equipment, visibility, or number of search vehicles involved. Systematic searching techniques are the key to success (U.S. Navy, Deep Water Search Procedures Report 1972). A good search technique must assure complete coverage of the probable area, clearly define areas already searched, and identify areas to be searched.

Some standard search techniques, are summarized in Table 7–1 and discussed in subsequent paragraphs.

The visibility, bottom topography, number of available divers, and size of the object(s) to be located are prime factors in selecting the best method for a particular search.

In favorable conditions (bottom is free of projections, the visibility is good, and the object(s) to be found is (are) reasonably large), and where the area to be searched is small, the Circular Search is probably the best. In areas larger than the tethered range of the diver, however, either the 'Z' or Jackstay should be used to eliminate segments of incomplete search.

For large areas in which visibility is good and time is of the essence, the Jackstay is usually the most desirable method.

The 'Z' Search is most efficient, however, and is more likely to locate very small objects, especially in low visibility or where conditions exist that prevent visual coverage. Because much of the search is conducted by touch and feel, and because it covers most of the area twice, the 'Z' search is the slowest of the three.

Figure 7-1
Circular Search

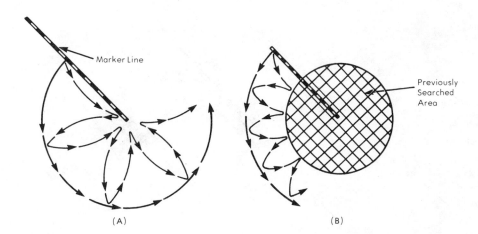

Marker Line

Previously
Searched
Area

(A)   (B)

7.1.1.1 Circular Search

A search line is anchored to the bottom or tied with a bowline around the bottom of the descent line and used to sweep the area. In order to determine when a 360-degree circle has been made, a marker line should also be laid out from the same anchor as the search line. This marker line should be highly visible and numbered with the radial distance from the anchor.

Where current is noticeable, this marker should be placed in the down current position such that the diver always commences his search from the position where the possibility of entanglement is decreased. When more than one circle is to be made with tethered diver(s), the direction of travel should be changed at the end of each rotation to prevent the possibility of fouling lines.

The circular search has many modifications depending on the number of divers and the thoroughness of the search required.

The standard technique is to station one or more divers along the search line close to the center of the desired search area. The marker line can be used to assign precise distances. The divers swim a circle while maintaining taut holds with one hand on the search line until they return to the marker line and are certain that 360 degrees have been covered. The divers increase the radius for the next search, moving out a distance that will permit good visual coverage. This procedure is continued until the outermost perimeter is reached.

When two divers are used . . .

Effectiveness can be increased as shown in Figures 7–1 (a) and (b), by having one diver hold the circling line taut and swim the outside perimeter of the area to be searched while another diver sweeps back and forth along the taut circling line. As shown in Figure 7–1(a), the first search will cover a full circle bounded by the outside diver's path. The search starts and finishes at the marker line. The search may be extended by the pattern shown in Figure 7–1(b). In this case, the circling line is marked where the outside diver was previously stationed. The outside diver then moves to a new position, farther out on the circling line, and the inside diver sweeps back and forth between the marker and the outside diver's new position. The outside diver covers a considerably greater distance than those on the inside and therefore must swim faster. Positions may be changed at regular intervals if fatigue becomes a factor. This can be done at the end of each sweep by having the outside diver hold his position after moving out one visibility length. The other diver(s) move outside taking up positions for the next sweep.

7.1.1.2 Jackstay Search

Both the Jackstay Search and the 'Z' Search require a rectangular boundary. The layout procedure described below is recommended for use with both searches.

Step 1. A weight is lowered near the center of the search area.

Figure 7-2
Jackstay Search

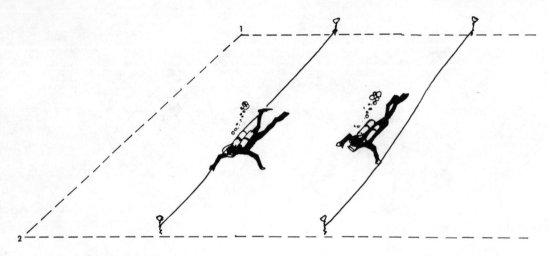

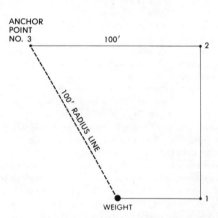

Step 2. The diver swims from the weight with a 50' distance line to establish anchor point No. 1. An anchor is implanted.

Step 3. An 87' boundary side line is connected to anchor point No. 1 and a 100' radius line is connected to the weight. These two lines are drawn taut to form anchor point No. 2. The boundary line is left in place.

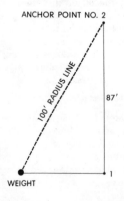

Step 4. A 100' search line is connected to anchor point No. 2 and extended with the radius line of step 3 until both become taut, forming anchor point No. 3.

Step 5. The second 87' boundary side line is connected to anchor point No. 3 and a second 50' distance line is connected to the weight. These are drawn taut to establish anchor point No. 4 and complete the rectangular boundary.

Figure 7-3
Jackstay Leapfrog

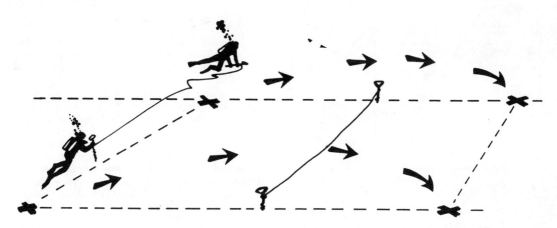

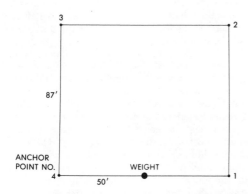

NOTE: Steps 3, 4, and 5 are more easily a-chieved using two divers. With one diver, the procedure is the same except that the diver must be able to locate the free ends of the two lines.

The search commences by laying two 87' Jack-stay lines parallel to the boundary line of points 1 and 2 (Figure 7–2). The first line should be laid only as far from the boundary line as visibility permits. The second Jackstay line should then be placed the same distance as the first (to the limit of visibility). The divers then search between the boundary line and the first Jackstay line. As soon as they complete that area, the first Jackstay line can be leap frogged over the second line to the limit of visibility (Figure 7–3).

When the search is completed in the 87' × 100' area it is only necessary to shift anchor points Nos. 2 and 3 to establish points Nos. 5 and 6, using

the same technique as shown in step 3. A new search area cornered by points Nos. 1, 4, 5, and 6 is now formed.

If the area to be searched extends beyond the combined area of the two halves (100' × 174' total), the weight must be moved to the positions illustrated (Figure 7–4), and the search continued from step 2.

7.1.1.3 'Z' Search

The layout of the 'Z' Search boundary lines is done exactly as the Jackstay Search. The search is conducted by both divers traveling on the same anchored search line. Each diver maintains one hand on the line with the free hand searching to the extent of the arm reach, while slowly moving along the search line. At the end of the traverse, the anchor is shifted with the opposite end remaining unchanged. Upon searching in the opposite direction and reaching the opposite distance line, the same procedure is followed. The search pattern resolves itself into a 'Z' pattern on each sweep (Figures 7–5 and 7–6). This results in almost all of the search area having double coverage. The remainder of the search continues until the area has been covered.

7.1.1.4 Searching Without Lines

When conditions are such that it would be unfeasible to use search lines, a search can be conducted using an underwater compass. Many patterns may be developed which will ensure

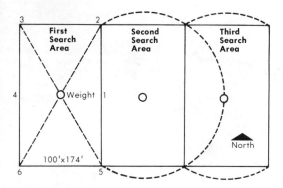

Figure 7-4
Rectangular Search Plan
for Jackstay
and 'Z' Searches

maximum coverage. However, simplicity is of major importance. Use the cardinal points—N, E, S, W; the length of side—one minute intervals or, say, 50 kicks; and turning the same way each time.

In addition to normal safe diving practices, it should be helpful to consider the following when conducting searches:

1. When ⅛" plastic coated steel wire is used, a small pair of wire cutters should be carried to prevent entanglement. They should be carried by each diver in a plastic or leather sheath in addition to the normal diving knife.

2. Where two tethered divers are used in search patterns, one should be designated as inside diver so that he always remains under and inside the other tethered diver to prevent hose fouling.

3. Where nontethered divers are used, it may be advisable to use lines of contrasting materials for radius, boundary, and distance lines, to decrease the possibility of a diver becoming lost. Polyethylene line provides a good contrast to the plastic coated stainless steel wire and is suggested for use in boundary lines.

7.1.1.5 Recovery

Recovery of a lost object depends on its size and weight. Small items can be carried directly to the surface by the diver. Larger items require lift devices that are suited to the object being lifted. The diver will be required to attach lifting straps and equipment to the item being recovered. A line longer than the depth of water being searched with a small buoy attached should be carried to mark the located object (See Paragraph 7.1.5).

7.1.2 Underwater Navigation

At present, there is no general underseas navigation or positioning system that does not rely upon a surface position for its origin. Thus, the navigational or geodetic position undersea must be extrapolated and, therefore, is subject to additional error. Underwater navigation today is chiefly by dead reckoning, and operations suffer from the inadequacy of this method.

Divers are restricted as to the navigational equipment that can be carried. On most jobs it is impractical to carry and operate cumbersome and complex navigation equipment. Therefore, for the vast majority of undersea work, the diver's navigational ability is limited by his basic tools—a watch, compass, and depth gauge.

Sonar is an effective method of achieving underwater "visibility." The diver may benefit by carrying a compact active sonar for the purpose of obstacle avoidance.

The U.S. Navy for years has used underwater diver-held sonar with some success (Figure 7–7). However, the success of these operations is directly related to the quality of training offered to the diver. Many hours of listening to audio tones in a headset are required before the diver can "read" the tones.

Commercial diver held sonars are available through local dive shops (Figure 7–8). The diver positions himself vertically or horizontally on the bottom, and makes a slow 360 degree rotation until the object he seeks produces an audible tone in the headset. He then notes the compass heading. As the diver swims toward the object, the tone will diminish in frequency until contact is made. The active range of most diver held sonars is about 200 yards. In the passive or listening mode, pingers or beacons can sometimes be detected as far away as 1000 yards.

Acoustic beacons or pingers are battery operated devices which emit a high-frequency signal when activated. Beacons are the companion units to hand-held sonars and require the sonar to be operated in the passive mode (Figure 7–9).

Beacons can be attached to any underwater structure such as:

■ Habitats
■ Submersibles
■ Pipelines
■ Well heads
■ Hydrophone arrays

Figure 7-5
'Z' Search

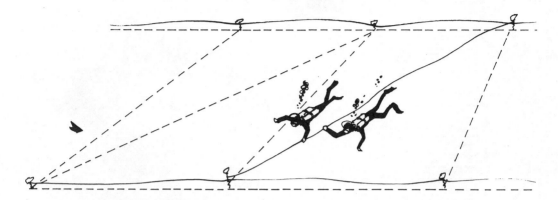

- Wrecks
- Scientific instruments.

Location of the signal is done the same way by the diver as with active sonar. When the signal is strong, a compass bearing is noted and the diver proceeds in a line along the bearing until the object is located visually.

The *compass*, *watch*, and *depth gauge* are for relatively short underwater excursions, the simplest navigation devices available. Once a compass bearing is ascertained, the diver swims along the line of bearing, holding the compass in as nearly a horizontal position as possible in front. He times his progress with the watch, and notes the depth as he proceeds. In order to swim a good compass course, the axis of the compass must be parallel to the direction of travel. A simple and reliable method is to fully extend the arm without the compass in front and grasp the elbow joint of the extended arm with the arm containing the compass. Swimming with the arms in this position will greatly aid the diver in following the desired course and in low visibility prevents the diver from colliding with unexpected objects. The compass will be affected by steel tanks. Thus it is advisable to determine the deviation in a pool with a second diver swimming alongside varying his course. The depth gauge and watch should not be worn on the same arm as the compass because they can cause a deviation in heading.

By checking the depth over the prescribed course on a chart and measuring the distance to be traveled, the diver can estimate his transit time using the following formula:

$$T = \frac{D}{S}$$

T = transit time in minutes
D = distance to be covered in feet
S = speed of advance in feet per minute.

The diver can estimate speed by swimming at a pace easily maintained over a known distance and slightly modifying the formula.

$$S = \frac{D}{T}$$

For example, if the diver can cover a 1000-foot course in 10 minutes, he can swim at a speed of 100 feet per minute or approximately one nautical mile per hour.

Some underwater topographical navigation aids that can be used are landmarks (and turns made with respect to them), the direction of wave ripples in the sand, and the direction of the current (if it is known that it will not change during the dive). Some areas will require the use of a transect line because of the lack of distinct bottom features. Increasing pressure on the ears and mask or the change of the sound of exhaust bubbles are commonly used to detect changes in depth.

7.1.3 Maintenance and Repair

Activities that involve the maintenance and repair of equipment, structures, and instruments in the underwater environment require an understanding of the skill of the diver, the scope of the work, the requirements for mechanical manipulations, and

**Figure 7-6
'Z' Search Layout**

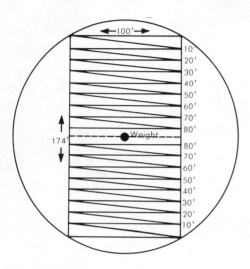

**Figure 7-7
U.S. Navy
Diver-Held Sonar**

the environmental conditions incident to the work area.

If practical, a diver should practice an underwater task in shallow water prior to attempting it in deep water. The timing associated with accomplishment of the task must be worked out so that a diver can accomplish the entire task or portions of the task within the time constraints of his air supply. For strenuous tasks the work should be divided into subtasks, with one diver replacing another at various stages. If only one diver is available, he should be given periods of rest between the work stages.

To accomplish any underwater work, four diving phases are usually involved. The first phase is an inspection of the work site and the condition of the item upon which maintenance or repair is to be performed. The second phase encompasses the selection of tools (See Paragraph 4.11). The third is the actual repair or maintenance action. The fourth phase is a reinspection to ensure that the work has been accomplished. For simple tasks, using well-understood techniques and experienced divers, all phases may be combined into one dive. Conversely, for complex tasks, the phases may necessitate an extended series of dives by a number of divers.

Of the many underwater maintenance and repair tasks that a diver may be asked to perform, the majority are associated with the inspection and repair of a ship's rudder, propeller, sea chest, and

cathodic protection system. When a diver is working over the side of a ship performing a maintenance task it is recommended that the ship's propeller be locked, the rudder held in static position, and no material thrown over the side. The appropriate international code flag should be hoisted.

The above tasks can be more easily accomplished if a restraining system is used. This could be a simple line attached to a convenient point for the diver to hold onto, or as elaborate as a jacket with magnets or suction cups to attach to a shear plate.

7.1.4 Instrument Implantation

The proper implantation of scientific instruments may be fundamental to the success of an underwater scientific investigation. Instruments implanted on the sea bottom may include lights, cameras, positioning stakes, radiometers, recording current meters, thermistors, oxygen sensors, and acoustical devices. Factors affecting instrument implantation are:

- The size and weight, mounting dimensions, fragility, and hard points that can be used to lift or anchor
- Power supply and instrument readout cables; or, if self-contained, the frequency with which batteries must be changed, the instrument serviced, or replaced
- The alignment of the instrument when in position, its height above the bottom, and its sensitivity to misalignment

**Figure 7-8
Commercial
Diver-Held Sonar**

Photo: Robert Dill

**Figure 7-9
General Purpose Pingers**

Photo: Burnett Electronics Lab, Inc.

- The bottom conditions, the bearing strength of the bottom, anticipated currents, and marine life that may affect the instrument or its implantation
- The precise marking of instrument location and the methods used for recovery at completion of the mission.

The size and weight of the instrument, its physical dimensions and fragility affect the type of anchor to be used and the techniques used to move the instrument to the site. For small instruments a concrete block may be used as an appropriate anchor. The blocks may be predrilled and fitted with fasteners while on the surface, and the entire assembly moved to the site and positioned. In other cases, the concrete block and instrument may be moved to the site separately, with the instrument positioned and aligned by a diver in the water. A concrete block anchor may be positioned by direct lowering from the surface using a winch, or may be fitted with flotation devices and guided to position by the diver, who removes the flotation device when the anchor is in position.

For large instrument packages anchors are constructed of metal piles, which are driven into the bottom by a diver using a sledge-hammer or pneumatic impact hammer. Steel pilings create magnetic anomalies that can affect the instrument reading and should only be used after calibrating the effect on the instrument. Pilings may be grouted in place with concrete supplied from the surface. Embedment anchors may be used to stabilize an instrument installation, and are driven into the bottom for securing lines. Chains or wires equipped with turnbuckles may be run over the instrument package between anchors to further secure an installation.

A foundation should be designed to easily accept an instrument package and make the attachment as simple as possible for a diver. When the foundation is complete, a line or lines should be run to the surface to assist in lowering and guiding the instrument in place.

Many underwater instruments require outside power to operate and transmit data through cables to outside receivers. During installation of instrument cables a diver is usually required to anchor the cable at various points along the cable run. The first point of anchor should be near the instrument package. The diver should allow a loop, or bight, of extra cable between the first anchor and the instrument to reduce the possibility of the cable toppling the instrument or movement of the cable or instrument from breaking the cable connection. The diver should guide the instrument cable around rocks or bottom debris that might abrade the cable covering. Anchors should be placed frequently along the cable length, wherever the cable turns, and on each side of a cable run over an outcropping or rise in the bottom. Cable anchors may be simple weights attached to the cable or special embedment anchors.

The alignment of a foundation may be critical to the successful implantation of an instrument. A simple technique for alignment is for a diver to drive a nonferrous stake into the bottom, the stake having a nonferrous wire or line attached. A compass is hung from the line or wire. A second nonferrous stake is driven when the compass indicates the proper alignment. The two stakes and attached line act as the reference point for alignment of the foundation or instrument. A tape is used to translate measurements from the reference stakes and line to the foundation or the instrument.

Prior to selecting the location for an instrument, the bottom conditions should be analyzed to determine the type and suitability of a foundation. The instrument site should be reinspected by a diver at frequent intervals to ascertain the condition of the instrument and clear away sediment or marine growths that may affect instrument readings.

Once an instrument package is implanted, its location should be carefully noted on a topographical chart of the area. A buoy, either surface or subsurface, should be used to mark the location for recovery or maintenance dives.

7.1.5 Salvage

Salvage of a ship or craft, its cargo, or its equipment involves not only the technical aspects of recovery but the legal aspects of ownership of the salved items and claims for salvage. A salvor who recovers a ship or craft, or its cargo, without prior agreement with the owner must file a claim in the United States District Court nearest to the port in which the salved items are landed.

Salvage techniques vary considerably with the size and condition of the item to be salved, the value of the time, the depth and sea floor condition, and the equipment available to conduct the salvage. The techniques used may include direct lift using a crane, flotation devices to compensate for negative buoyancy of the ship or craft, or techniques that repair and restore the inherent buoyancy of the craft itself.

Of interest to the individual diver, is the salvage of instruments or instrument arrays, anchors, or small structures used in an operation. In the majority of these, the item is simply carried to the surface by the diver. In others, the diver attaches a flotation device or, for heavy items such as an anchor, the diver may attach a line or wire to the item to facilitate a direct lift to the surface using a surface-mounted winch or crane.

In some salvage operations it will be necessary to clear bottom sediment from around the item prior to its recovery. This is necessary to ensure that the item is free and not entangled in structure or bottom debris that would prevent its movement. A water jet or air hose is commonly used to clear away debris. The reaction of such a jet, tends to push the diver away from the area he is clearing.

When working with heavy items or items overhead, and cables, lines, or chains under tension, a diver must develop a "sixth" sense for safety. He must avoid positioning himself or his umbilical under heavy objects that might fall, or placing himself over lines that are under considerable tension where failure could cause injury by the whipping of the parted line or release of a buoyant object. The buoyancy or the weight of water displaced from a container by compressed air necessary to raise an object is equal to the weight of the object in water plus the weight of the container. One should remember:

- That the container should be vented to prevent excess air from rupturing it.

- If the object is raised from the bottom before all the water has been displaced from the container, the air will expand, displacing more water, possibly increasing the speed of ascent to an uncontrollable rate.

- The weight of the object in water is reduced by an amount equal to the weight of water it displaces.

Objects that can be used as lifting devices include, a trash can or bucket inverted and tied to the object, a plastic bag placed in a net bag, or 55 gallon oil drums. If the object is lying on a soft bottom, it may be necessary to break the suction effect of the mud by using high pressure hoses or by rocking the object back and forth.

Raising and lowering can be accomplished with commercially available plastic "lift bags" of various sizes and lifting abilities, or with ordinary automobile tire inner tubes. One regular-sized tube will lift about 100 pounds. The tube or tubes are rigged with a short loop or rope holding them together at one point, with the values at the bottom. The valve caps and cores are removed. This rope loop is attached to the object to be lifted, and pulled down as close to it as possible, as the tubes have a tendency to stretch to about twice their original length before lifting starts. An ordinary shop air nozzle with a spring-loaded trigger is attached to a short length of low-pressure air hose and plugged into the low-pressure port on a single-hose regulator first stage mechanism. This is attached to a separate air cylinder and carried to the work site. The end of the nozzle is inserted into the tire valve opening and pushed so air will not escape. The tube fills and the object rises to the surface. Care must be taken to leave the valve open, as the expanding air on surfacing could burst a closed system. With practice, objects can be raised part-way to the surface and moved under kelp canopies, etc., into clear water where they can be surfaced and towed. Divers using this technique should try to accompany the object to the surface, and should not stay on the bottom or in any way expose themselves to the drop or ascent path of the object if the lift should fail. This technique is especially useful to biologists in lifting heavy bags of specimens.

If the object cannot be lifted to the surface directly by winching or lift devices, the rise of the tide can be used if a large vessel or pontoon is available. Lines are tautly connected to the object and the surface platform at low tide. As the tide rises, the load is also raised and can then be towed to shallower water until grounding occurs. This process is repeated until the object can be towed to a location to be lifted from the water.

Each diving project must be individually planned and executed. Tool requirements must be planned accordingly (See Paragraph 4.11). Novice divers should not attempt underwater salvage tasks for which they are not properly trained or equipped.

7.2 UMBILICAL DIVING PROCEDURES

When underwater tasks require the diver to work in a specified area for an extended period of time, it may be safer and more efficient to plan the dive using umbilical diving techniques. The following advantages can be gained:
- Continuous Air Supply
- Communications
- Heat if Required
- Comfort for Extended Duration
- Safety.

Special procedures must be followed when diving with an umbilical. The assembly of the equipment is discussed in Section 4, whereas the procedures to be used are discussed below.

7.2.1 Tending

Ideally, surface umbilical diving tenders should also be experienced divers. The most effective assistance can be given only by a tender who is familiar with the equipment, procedures, safety precautions, conditions and difficulties inherent in diving. It is the tender's responsibility to see that the diver receives proper care while both topside and under water. He must check all equipment

before sending the diver down, and aid the diver in dressing and computing decompression requirements. While the diver is submerged, the tender handles the umbilical and maintains communications, keeps time, and monitors the air supply system, unless other personnel are designated these responsibilities.

The following procedures should be carried out prior to the dive:
- Assemble air supply system, including compressor and/or high-pressure cylinders and umbilical assembly, and pressure test for leaks.
- When using high-pressure cylinders, gauge and mark each cylinder to ensure that all personnel know which cylinders are full and are to be used for the dive.
- Check air regulation or control system including emergency switching to secondary air supply and back-up regulator (if so equipped).
- Mask or helmet should be prepared.
- Notify nearest chamber so it is ready for immediate use in the event of an emergency and have personnel available to operate the chamber.
- Assemble all equipment for final check by *tender, diver,* and *Dive Master.*
- The tender and/or Dive Master will enter necessary information into the "rough" diving log.

In tending the diver's umbilical assembly, or lines, the tender must not hold the diver's line so taut as to interfere with the work. The diver should be given 2–3 feet of slack when he is on the bottom, but not so much that he cannot be felt from time to time. Signals cannot be received on a slack line; consequently, the diver's lines must be kept in hand with proper tension at all times.

Line-pull signals (See Paragraph 6.2.2) consist of a series of sharp, distinct pulls, strong enough for the diver or tender to feel but not so strong as to pull the diver away from his work. When sending signals, take all of the slack out of the line first. Repeat signal until answered. The only signal not answered when received is the emergency "haul me up," and "come up" is delayed until the diver is ready. Continued failure to respond to signals may indicate that there is too much slack in the line, the line is fouled, or the diver is incapacitated. If *contact with the diver is lost,* the following procedures should be followed:
- If intercom communications are lost, the tender should attempt line-pull communications immediately.

- Depending upon diving conditions and previous arrangements made during planning, the dive may be terminated or continued to completion with line-pull signals. Generally, in research diving, it is best to terminate the dive to resolve the problem or reorganize the dive plan.
- If the tender receives no immediate line-pull signal reply from the diver, he should take a greater strain on the line and signal again. Considerable resistance to the tender's pull may indicate that the umbilical line is fouled. A standby diver should be dispatched as soon as possible.
- If the tender feels sufficient tension on the line to conclude that it is still attached to the diver, yet receives no signals, he must assume that the diver is unconscious. In this event, he should dispatch a standby diver immediately.
- If a standby diver is unavailable, or it is considered unwise to use one, the diver must be pulled to the surface at a rate not exceeding 60 feet per minute. Prepare to administer first aid and recompression. Note: If the diver is wearing a closed-dress or variable-volume dry suit, this procedure is used only as a last resort. Subsequent blowup is almost unavoidable without the assistance of another diver. Therefore, when using a variable-volume dry suit a standby diver must always be ready to enter the water.

The tender should continuously monitor the diver's depth and underwater time. He should inform the diver several minutes before the expiration of bottom time so that the diver can make necessary preparations for ascent. In addition, he must continually monitor the diver's activity. For example, the tender can frequently evaluate the diver's exertion by counting the number of breaths per minute. Experienced tenders will learn the diver's normal breathing rate. Significant increase in breathing rate may indicate potential over-exertion situations. The tender may ask the diver to stop work, rest, and ventilate his helmet or mask.

The tender may also have to serve as timekeeper. This job includes keeping an accurate record of the dive time and details of the dive. When possible, a separate timekeeper should be used or the timekeeper duties handled by the Dive Master.

7.2.2 Dressing

The dressing procedures will depend upon the type of diving dress or suit and helmet or mask used. Specific instructions or special manuals are supplied by the suit manufacturer. Prior to starting dressing procedures, the air supply system should be operational and the mask or helmet completely prepared for diving. The following is a generalized dressing procedure applicable to most surface-supplied diving systems:

- Don diving dress or suit with assistance from the tender(s) if necessary.
- Don diver's harness, secure, and adjust.
- If weighted diving shoes or ankle weights are used, they are placed on the diver by the tender and secured. If fins are used, they may be donned later with the assistance of the tender.
- Don neckring and secure if helmet is to be used.
- Don and adjust weight belt.
- Secure knife to belt, leg, or arm (diver's preference).
- With the diver or a second tender holding the mask or helmet, secure emergency gas cylinder.
- Don mask or helmet and secure mask harness or helmet clamp.
- Secure the umbilical assembly to harness.
- The tender ensures that the diver is properly dressed, that all equipment is functioning properly, and informs the Dive Master that the diver is ready.

7.2.3 Weighting

The amount of weight used by the umbilical diver will depend on the environmental conditions, mission requirements, and equipment used. In some cases the umbilical diver, like the scuba diver, may prefer to retain a state of neutral buoyancy. This is achieved in the same fashion as for the scuba diver with a buoyancy compensator being used to compensate for wet suit compression. The diver properly trimmed has a mobility capability, within the range of his umbilical, comparable to that of a scuba diver. Depending on the diving dress used and the mission requirements, the diver may choose to weight himself in a negatively buoyant mode. For working in currents or using some tools under water the diver may choose to use 20 or 30 pounds of extra weight on his belt or in the form of weighted diving shoes (or ankle weights). Naturally in this mode he will be working on the bottom.

Working in a negative mode is most desirable when using a variable-volume dry suit which enables the diver to inflate his suit in order to aid in bottom movement and ascent. Negative buoyancy is very important in live boating, and when taking decompression stops on a line in strong currents.

The standard scuba divers weight belt is satisfactory for handling no more than 25 pounds of weight. Some divers add a shoulder harness assembly to the weight belt in order to provide added comfort. One must be certain that belts equipped with shoulder harnesses can be readily jettisoned in an emergency and not foul on the umbilical assembly or emergency air system. The wider heavy duty commercial type weight belt is more desirable for weights in excess of 25 pounds.

7.2.4 Free-Flow/Demand Mask

The following procedures are recommended when preparing the *mask* for diving:
- Inspect the mask for any damage or loose fittings.
- Open free-flow valve, blow through the check valve, and then suck back to ensure that the check (nonreturn) valve is functioning.
- Check free-flow valve and regulator adjustment for free movement.
- Check exhaust valves to ensure that they are properly seated and free from foreign matter.
- Connect communications wire and test communications.
- Purge gas supply hose to ensure that it is free from foreign matter.
- When using emergency manifold block, attach to gas supply hose and purge prior to attachment to mask.
- Verify that the emergency gas cylinder is filled to capacity, attach regulator, and connect to manifold block.
- Prior to connecting the primary gas supply hose, open the emergency cylinder valve and activate emergency system to verify proper function. Check for leaks and close emergency system valve.
- Connect primary gas supply hose and verify free flow and demand system operation. Adjust the demand regulator to slight free flow and then close until free flow stops. Readjustments may be required at depth.
- Apply a thin film of antifogging solution to the interior of the face port to prevent fogging during the dive. Liquid dishwashing soap is highly satisfactory.

- Place the mask on and test both breathing systems.
- Secure the head harness as low as possible on the neck so that pressure is put on the base of the skull by the lower legs of the harness. The amount of tension will vary with individual preference.
- Secure the umbilical hose to the diver's harness (not to his weight belt).

7.2.5 Helmet

The procedures recommended when preparing the *helmet* for diving are the same as for a free-flow/demand mask with the following additions:
- Open free-flow valve, blow through the check valve, and then suck back to ensure that the check (nonreturn) valve is functioning. Another method of ensuring that the internal nonreturn valve is operating satisfactorily is to close the free-flow valve, connect an air supply to the helmet, and flow some air into the helmet. Without opening the free-flow valve, bleed and remove the air supply line. Submerge the helmet air hose connection in water; if no bubbles emerge, the valve is functioning properly.
- Ensure that neck-ring seats and locks properly.

7.2.6 The Dive

When all personnel have completed dressing, checking equipment, and final briefings, the captain (if diving from a vessel) is notified that the divers are ready to enter the water. He must give clearance before the diving operation can commence. Entry technique will depend upon staging area or type of vessel. Upon entering the water, the diver should stop at the surface to make a final equipment check. The dive procedure is as follows:
- Adjust buoyancy if necessary. Whether the diver is weighted neutral or negative will depend on the mission requirements.
- Ensure that air supply system, helmet or mask, and communications are functioning properly. If not, corrections must be made prior to descent. *Never* dive with malfunctioning equipment.
- The tender should also verify that all equipment is functioning satisfactorily.
- The diver is given permission to descend by the Dive Master.
- The diver descends down a descent line. The descent line should be heavily weighted at

bottom and should not be greased or oiled. A timer is started when the diver begins his descent. Descent rate will depend on the diver; however, it should generally not exceed 75 feet per minute.

- The diver must equalize pressure in his ears and sinuses during descent. If equalization is not possible, the dive must be terminated.
- When descending in a tideway or current, the diver should keep his back to the current so he will be forced against the descent line.
- When the diver reaches the bottom, he should inform the tender of his status.
- Regulate buoyancy and regulate air flow if necessary before releasing descent line.
- Attach distance line, if used, and proceed to work area. A distance line should be used when visibility is extremely poor and the diver cannot see his descent line from a distance.
- Upon leaving the descent line, proceed slowly to conserve energy. It is advisable to carry one turn of the umbilical hose in your hand.
- Pass over, not under, wreckage and obstructions.
- If moving against a current, it may be necessary to assume a crawling position.
- If the diver is required to enter wreckage, tunnels, etc., a second diver should be present to tend the umbilical hose at the entrance.
- Avoid excessive exertion. The tender should monitor breathing rate and call for the diver to "*stop, rest, and ventilate*" as required. Also, avoid excessive excitement. This can enhance the onset of fatigue. Slow methodical efforts are always best in an emergency.
- The tender must keep the diver *constantly* informed of his bottom time. Always notify the diver a few minutes in advance of termination time so he can complete his task and prepare for ascent.

7.2.6.1 Fouling

A surface-supplied diver's umbilical line may become fouled in mooring lines, wreckage, or underwater structures, or the diver may be trapped by the cave-in of a tunnel or shifting of heavy objects. The surface-supplied diver is in a much better situation to survive since he has a virtually unlimited air supply and generally the ability to communicate, thus facilitating rescue operations. Consequences of fouling may result in fatigue, exposure, and prolonged submergence, with sub-sequent prolonged decompression. If the diver becomes fouled, he should:

- Remain calm
- Think
- Describe the situation to his tender
- Systematically attempt to determine the cause and to clear himself
- Use a knife cautiously to avoid cutting portions of the umbilical assembly.

If efforts to clear himself prove futile, he should call for a standby diver, and calmly wait. Struggling and panic can only make the situation worse.

Divers should proceed cautiously under water and attempt to recognize obstructions, etc. which might cause fouling. Pass over or around if possible, not under. Proper precautions can usually avert fouling.

7.2.6.2 Blowup

Blowup is a hazard for the diver using a closed-dress (deep-sea or lightweight helmet connected to dry suit) or variable-volume dry suit (UNISUIT or equivalent). Blowup is caused by overinflation of the dress or suit, too strong or rapid pull by the tender, or by the drag of the current causing the diver to lose hold of the bottom or descending line thus sweeping him to the surface. Accidental inversion of the diver, with subsequent filling of the legs with large amounts of air, may result in an uncontrolled blowup. This hazard even exists for the scuba diver when using a variable-volume suit.

WARNING

The Buoyancy Characteristics of Variable-Volume Dry Suits Should Not Be Used as a Substitute for Lift Devices to Carry Objects to the Surface.

Accidental blowup may result in injuries such as:
- Air embolism
- Decompression sickness
- Physical injury from head striking on some object such as the bottom of the ship.

The diver must be certain that all exhaust valves are functioning properly before descending. The diving suit or dress should be of proper size (especially length) to avoid excessive space in the legs for accumulation of air should the diver become inverted. This is especially true for divers wearing variable-volume suits. Divers must be trained under controlled conditions, preferably in a swimming pool, in the use of all closed-type diving suits, regardless of previous experience with other types. "Controlled" blowups employed by some divers for ascent are discouraged.

A blowup victim should not be allowed to continue the dive. If the diver appears to have no ill effects and is still within the no-decompression range as prescribed by the tables, he should return to 10 feet and decompress for the amount of time that would normally be required for ascent from his working depth. He should then be surfaced, dressed, and observed for signs of air embolism and decompression sickness.

If the victim is near or within the decompression requirements, he should be recompressed in a chamber and decompressed in accordance with surface decompression procedures if it appears that surface decompression tables offer an immediate solution. If not, the victim should be recompressed in a chamber to depth as appropriate for U.S. Navy Treatment Tables 1A or 5. If no ill effects appear, treat the victim in accordance with the treatment table selected. If no chamber is available and the victim is conscious, he should be treated in accordance with procedures for interrupted or omitted decompression. If the victim is unconscious, the procedures for handling victims of air embolism and decompression sickness should be followed.

7.2.6.3 Normal Ascent

When bottom time is up or the mission is completed, the diver will return to his ascent line and signal his tender that he is ready for ascent. The ascent procedure is as follows:

- The tender will pull in excess umbilical line and take a slight strain on the umbilical line. He will pull slowly and steadily at the prescribed rate (generally 60 ft/min).
- A timer is started at the beginning of ascent and the tender will watch the timer and pneumo-fathometer (if used) to control ascent rate.
- The diver will regulate his buoyancy, if using a closed- or variable-volume suit, to aid the tender. Be cautious to avoid overinflation of dress and subsequent "blowup."
- The diver should never let go of his line, and may "climb" the line to aid the tender. A 3 to 4 foot line, with a slip ring around the descent line, may be required in strong currents.
- The tender or Dive Master must inform the diver well in advance of his decompression re-

quirements. A diving stage may be required for long decompressions.
- When decompression is completed, the diver is taken on board via the ladder or diving stage.

7.2.6.4 Emergency Ascent

An emergency gas supply or "bailout" unit is a great asset in any type of diving, especially where direct ascent is prohibited. Upon failure of the primary gas supply, the emergency gas valve is opened, and the diver proceeds directly to the surface or first decompression stop. The free-flow valve should be closed and the demand circuit used to conserve gas. Should the diver's hose be fouled to the degree of preventing ascent, and the primary gas supply is inoperative (not allowing sufficient time for the standby diver to descend), the diver should alert the surface crew of his situation and notify them that he is cutting or releasing the umbilical hose to make an emergency ascent. Some divers wear a small scuba tank with a separate single-hose regulator. In the event of primary gas supply failure, they simply jettison the mask and breathe from scuba while ascending. In this case, a scuba face mask should also be carried. If this situation occurs in waters of limited visibility, the umbilical should be followed to the surface.

Should gas failure occur when diving without self-contained emergency supply, the diver may drop his weight belt and ascend without removing the mask (exhaling throughout the ascent to prevent air embolism). In the event that the diver's hose is fouled, preventing him from surfacing with the mask on, the weight belt and harness (or harness attachment) should be released. The diver then removes the mask by grasping the main body and pulling the mask forward, up, and over the head.

7.2.6.5 Postdive Procedures

The divers should be helped from the water and aided with removal of equipment by surface personnel. The divers should be observed for signs of sickness or injury resulting from the dive and warming procedures should be commenced as soon as possible. Preventive maintenance on equipment should be undertaken as soon as possible after the dive. The divers and tenders should report any defects noted during or after the dive and the defective equipment should be tagged for corrective maintenance. Divers should be debriefed and the log completed.

7.2.7 Diving From Small Boats

Although most surface based umbilical diving is conducted from larger vessels or fixed platforms, the system may be readily adapted to small boat operations. Generally, when working from small boats, i.e. 16 to 30 feet, a bank of high-pressure cylinders is used to supply air, thus enabling the group to operate without the excessive noise of an air compressor's motor during diving operations. This enhances communications considerably and provides more pleasant conditions for surface personnel. The number and size of cylinders used will, of course, depend on the size of the boat. For small boats, two or more sets of standard twin-cylinder scuba may be connected by a specially constructed manifold which is, in turn, connected to a high-pressure reduction regulator or small gas control panel. The umbilical is then connected to the pressure side of the pressure reduction unit. In larger boats air may be carried in a series of 240 or 300 cubic foot high-pressure cylinders. Regardless of the cylinder configuration used, all cylinders must be properly secured and the valves, manifold, and regulator protected to prevent damage to equipment and prevent personal injury. The umbilical may be coiled on top of the air cylinders or in the bottom of the boat. The communicator is generally placed on a seat or platform for the convenience of the tender. Communications equipment must be protected from weather and spray.

Since small boats are generally used for only shallow water work, the umbilical is normally only 100 to 150 feet in length. Longer umbilicals are bulky and cumbersome in small boats. It is generally wise to limit diving depths to less than 100 feet when working from a small boat and the boat may be readily moved to facilitate the lateral movements of the diver. Otherwise, normal surface supplied diving procedures and lightweight equipment are recommended.

The small boat umbilical diving team will normally consist of a diver, tender and standby diver. If properly qualified, all personnel may alternate tasks for maximum operational efficiency. The standby diver may be equipped with a second umbilical and mask or, as frequently the case, equipped with scuba. He should be completely dressed and capable of donning his scuba and entering the water in less than a minute. If he is using scuba, it is wise for him to be fitted with a quick-release lifeline (readily releasable in the event of entanglement). Some use a heavy duty communication cable as a lifeline enabling maintenance of hardwire communication between the standby diver and tender. This line is also constructed so it may be readily released in event of entanglement.

Many divers consider the use of a high pressure cylinder air supply system safer and more dependable than systems incorporating a small compressor and volume or receiver tank. Some desire that a small volume tank be incorporated into the system so the diver will have air for surfacing in the event of a malfunction, others find this unnecessary. Most agree that the diver should carry a small self-contained emergency scuba for use in event of primary system failure. This is mandatory when working around obstructions where entanglement is possible or inside submerged natural or man-made structures.

"Live Boating" is a relatively common practice for surveying with an umbilical system. In this situation, the boat will follow the diver as he swims ahead or the diver will be slowly towed behind the boat on a weighted line or "tow-plane." The speed of the boat must be slow (0.5–1.5 k), and carefully controlled, depending on the experience of the divers. Precautions must be taken to avoid fouling the diver's umbilical in the propeller. Generally, the propeller is covered by a specially constructed wire or metal rod cage, and the umbilical is "buoyed" so it floats clear of the stern. When live boating from a large vessel, it may be desirable to tow a small boat behind the vessel and tend the towed diver from the smaller boat. The tender must be especially cautious to keep the umbilical clear and positive communications must be maintained between the bridge on the large vessel and the tender. The bridge may also wish to incorporate a system that allows monitoring the divers communication. If diver to surface communication is interrupted for any reason, the engines must be stopped.

7.3 UNDERWATER PHOTOGRAPHY

NOTE:

No Attempt to Cover the Details of Underwater Photography Has Been Made in This Manual. The Reader Is Referred to Appendices A and B for Publications Giving More Exhaustive Treatments.

Scientific underwater photography divides itself into two categories: photography with a diver-held camera and with a camera operated remotely. In the first category, the diver and his photographic instruments are an integral package. In the second category, the photographer need not even wet his feet. Diving skill and experience allow the photographer a degree of mobility and precise positioning in relation to the subject that cannot be achieved remotely. On the other hand, the remote camera disturbs shy subjects less than the threatening bulk of a diver, and functions at depths the diver cannot reach or can only reach with complex surface support.

Aside from diving skill, scientific recording under water poses its own set of problems. There is less room for error than in photography on land. Objectives must be extremely clear and the scientist must carefully choose his equipment to record those objectives with minimal distortion and maximum information. Too often, the limited equipment from a laboratory's diving locker dictates the method of approach to a job. With ingenuity and commercially available equipment, the scientist need not be so restrained.

7.3.1 Still Photography

7.3.1.1 Lenses and Housings

Consider the 35 mm camera as a basic platform — a starting point that must be modified for task requirements. Two approaches are possible in the selection of the camera: an instrument specifically designed to operate in the sea with watertight sealing, such as the Nikonos (Figure 7–10), or a camera designed for air use housed in a water-tight casing (Figure 7–11). The first is extremely portable and easy to use. The second is more versatile in lending itself to modification to fit specific requirements beyond the capabilities of the Nikonos.

Choice of lens for either the free or housed camera is dictated by the required field of view and by the clarity of water. Since the distance from camera to subject must be short compared to air (Figure 1–5), the photographer requiring a broad expanse must use a lens with a wide degree of coverage. A rule of thumb is that photographic visibility is only about one-third of eye visibility, so the wide angle becomes an important tool even in clear water.

Wide angle lenses, when used under water, create their own optical problems. When used through a plane parallel port facing the water, several objectionable qualities are evident in the resulting photograph. Distortion and lack of sharpness in the periphery, color aberrations, and narrowing of the angle of view, all rob the under water photo of image quality it would have if the same focal length lens were used in air. The optical characteristics of water are such that wide angle lenses *must* be corrected for water use. This is possible by designing water correction into the lens formula (expensive but effective), or using corrective ports of varying sophistication and price in front of wide angle lenses designed for use in air. A plexiglass dome (part of a hemisphere), coupled with provision for closer focusing of the lens than is necessary in air, solves the problem with the least cost. Several commercial underwater housings have corrective capabilities.

When close-up photography of small objects is required the plane parallel port coupled with lenses of longer focal length, becomes a viable tool. Desirable requisites for this type of photography include ground glass focusing for precise framing, whisker sharpness of the image, a lens which can focus closely on the object, and at least one light source coupled to the camera. The plane parallel port that is so destructive to a wide angle image becomes an aid, when using a longer lens, enhancing the telephoto effect without noticeable destruction of the sharpness or color quality of the picture.

The "off-the-shelf" underwater cameras or simpler housings for air cameras, if unmodified, allow the scientist to work only in the middle distance range. Although this permits the collection of much useful data, invariably distant and closeup shots will be necessary. A well-designed and engineered housing is heavier and bulkier, and requires more maintenance than an in-water camera. It is, however, a more flexible instrument in the range of wide angle and closeup work than the in-water instrument. An in-water camera does not have ground glass focusing. Its extreme wide angle lenses are expensive and limited to a few focal lengths. Its provision for closeup modification demands that the diver work within rigid distances between camera and subject and shoot blindly, relying on mechanical extensions from the lens to determine the distance. Few small fish will tolerate the close proximity of a metal framing rod extending into their immediate territory. At the very least, the rod will induce by its presence unnatural behavior in fish and other

**Figure 7-10
Nikonos Underwater Camera
With Electronic Flash
and Wide Angle Lens**

**Figure 7-11
35mm Camera in
Underwater Housing**

Photo: Lee Somers

Photo: U.S. Navy

marine life. With ground glass focusing of the housed camera, this problem does not exist. Longer lenses allow the photographer to work far enough from his subject so as not to interfere with behavior, much less frighten away his subject.

7.3.1.2 Light and Color

Light and color go hand-in-hand under water (Figure 7-12). Color films balanced for either daylight or tungsten light are relatively blind to the color subtleties which our eye can distinguish within the blue or green spectra of water. In shallow depths, filtration offers some compensation. A color correction filter (Table 7-2) over a lens will break the blue up enough to restore a certain amount of color that the diver's eye sees and the unfiltered film cannot. The color red however disappears at about 40 feet of water and no filtration can restore it.

Artificial light not only illuminates situations too dim for film exposure, but also brings out color inherent in the subject. To be effective, artificial

light in water must be used much closer to the subject than in air. The closer and more powerful the light, the more it will compensate for the excessive blue of seawater. By varying distance and power, different balances can be obtained. A water-blue background with a slight hint of color can be accomplished as easily as brilliantly illuminating the subject, completely obliterating the water quality.

Several good electronic flash units are made for underwater use. Some offer an under water wide beam for use with wide angle lenses; others a narrow beam which penetrates the water column more effectively (Table 7-3). Small electronic flash units designed for air use can be housed effectively for water use in simple plexiglass containers. Connectors are available for unplugging the units under water without danger.

Tests should be made to establish correct exposures with any unit with various speed films prior to the principal assignment (Table 7-4). Guide numbers, a quick and easy method of determining exposures in air, are virtually useless in water.

Flash bulbs can be used effectively under water in units designed for water work (Table 7-5); clear bulbs for distance and blue bulbs for closeups. The longer water column effectively filters the clear bulbs with blue so that the light balances for the daylight film. Beware of bulb implosion at great depths—nasty cuts on hands have occurred when changing bulbs in deep water.

Incandescent light powered by battery or by a topside generator (a must for motion picture work) has application in still photography also. It does not penetrate the water as well however, and is clumsier to use than electronic or bulb flash.

Lighting arms and brackets, or extension cords for off-camera light allow for a variety of positioning. Care must be taken not to place a light on the

**Figure 7-12
Diurnal Variation
of Light Under Water**

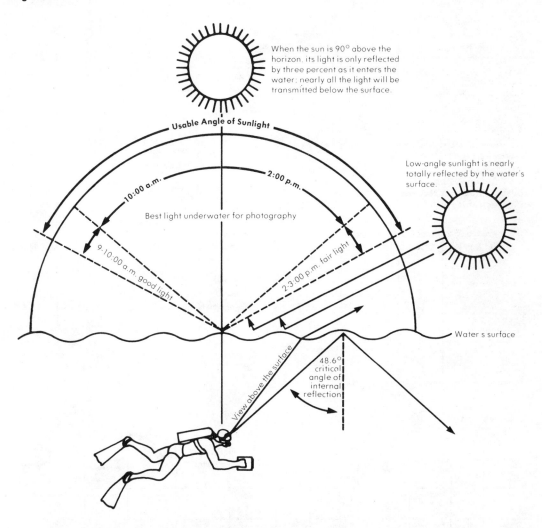

When the sun is 90° above the horizon, its light is only reflected by three percent as it enters the water; nearly all the light will be transmitted below the surface.

Usable Angle of Sunlight

10:00 a.m.

2:00 p.m.

Best light underwater for photography

9-10:00 a.m. good light

2-3:00 p.m. fair light

Low-angle sunlight is nearly totally reflected by the water's surface.

Water s surface

View above the surface

48.6° critical angle of internal reflection

camera lens axis. Such direct lighting of suspended particles in the water can curtain off the subject matter. Exposure meters with selenium cells have a more accurate response in the blue spectrum under water than the CDS (cadmium sulphide) battery operated meters that are so accurate in air. Both reflected and incident light measuring meters properly housed are effective under water. Choose a meter with larger numbers on its scale, or carry a magnifying glass (just as effective under water as above).

7.3.1.3 Selection of Film

Depending upon the quality of documentation required by the scientist, a wide variety of both black and white and color films are available from which to choose (Table 7–6).

A fast film, such as High Speed Ektachrome with an ASA value of 160, will produce very acceptable results with good depth of field at moderate light levels. In low light conditions, the effective ASA value may be increased four times to ASA 640

Table 7-2 Color Correction Filters

Underwater path length of the light (feet)	Filter	Exposure increase in stops
1	CC 05R	1/3
2	CC 10R	1/3
5	CC 20R	1/3
8	CC 30R	2/3
12	CC 40R	2/3
15	CC 50R	1

For distances of greater than 15 feet a composite filter with the appropriate number of filter units can be used.

Table 7-3 Suggested Exposure Guide for Narrow Beam Electronic Flash *

Distance to subject (feet)	ASA rating		
	25	64	160
1	f16	f22	f32
2	f8	f16	f22
3	f5.6	f8	f11–16
4	f4	f5.6	f11
5	f2.5	f4.5	f8
6	—	f3.5	f5.6
7	—	f2.5	f4
8	—	—	f3.5

*Exposure guides furnished by Subsea Products.

Table 7-4 Approximate Exposures for Underwater Photography

KODAK Film Bright Sunlight — Light Bottom*	Depth	
	2 to 5 feet	10 to 20 feet
VERICHROME Pan and PLUS–X Pan Stills at 1/50 or 1/60 sec	f/8	f/2.8
TRI–X Pan Stills at 1/50 or 1/60 sec	f/16	f/5.6
TRI–X Reversal Movie Film at 16 or 18 F.P.S	f/11	f/4
KODACHROME II for Daylight Stills at 1/25 or 1/30 sec Movies at 16 or 18 F.P.S	f/8	f/2.8
KODACHROME–X, EKTACHROME–X, or KODACOLOR–X Stills at 1/25 or 1/30 sec	f/8	f/4
High Speed EKTACHROME, Daylight Type Stills at 1/50 or 1/60 sec	f/11	f/5.6

*A dark bottom may require one or two more lens openings; even so, it may cause poorly lighted subjects. Hazy sunlight will usually require at least 1/2 a lens opening larger.

Table 7-5 Underwater Photographic Light Sources

Type of Lighting	Depth Limit (ft)	Factors Limiting Visibility	Accuracy of Color Rendition	Ability to Light Subject for the Human Eye as Camera Will See It	Control of Effects From Light Scattering	Duration (sec)	Intensity	Means of Determining Exposure	Power Requirement	Extent of Use	Remarks
Natural	50 to 100	absorptivity, scattering	poor (predominantly green)	very good	fair to good	continuous	good at surface, but decreases with depth	meter	none	general	—
Flood	none	absorptivity, scattering	fairly good	very good	very good	continuous	relatively low	guide number determined by experiment	high (1/2 to 2 kw)	general, especially at greater depths	—
Flash bulbs	none	absorptivity, scattering	fairly good	poor	fair	1/50 to 1/100	high	guide numbers	self-contained battery	general	Diver must replace bulbs
Electronic flash	none	absorptivity, scattering	fairly good	poor	fair	1/1,000 to 1/2,000 or faster	very high	guide numbers	self-contained battery	general	Electronic flash is probably better than regular flash for use under water.

Table 7-6
Films Best Suited
for Under Water Use

Film type	ASA	Contrast	Latitude grain	Resolving power	Color balance
Black-and-white films:					
Panatomic–X	32	Low	± 1 Stop very fine..................	Excellent	—
Tri–X	400	High	± 2 Stops moderate to heavy ...	Fair	—
Color films:					
Kodachrome II	25	Moderate	± ½ Stop finest....................	Excellent	Best.
Kodachrome–X	64	Moderate to high	± 1 Stop fine.......................	Excellent	Slightly brown.
Ektachrome–X......................	64	Moderate	± 1 Stop moderate	Moderate ...	Slightly blue.
High Speed Ektachrome..........	160	Low	± 1½ Stop poor	Poor...........	Good.
Kodacolor	80–100	Moderate to low	+ 3, − 1 Stops moderate	Good	Good.
Movie films:					
Kodachrome II	25	Moderate	± ½ Stop finest....................	Excellent	Best.
E.X.H.S. 7242,41..................	100–160	Low	± 1½ Stop poor	Poor...........	Good.
E.X. Commercial 7252	16 day 25 tungsten	Moderate	± 1 Stop fine.......................	Good	Excellent.
E.X. Medium speed................	64	Moderate	± 1 Stop moderate	Good	Excellent.

(Table 7–7). Other color film is available which, with special processing, can be exposed up to ASA 1000. Black and white films are available at speeds up to ASA 3200.

Infrared film opens up new avenues of interest in underwater photography. However, due to the drastic color changes, the film is not suitable for scientific color documentation. Kodak recommends starting at ASA 100, but underwater tests have shown that ASA 50 exposed at $1/60$ sec at f5.6 on a sunny day, in 20 feet of water, will give proper exposure. A yellow filter should be used to exclude excessive blue saturation.

7.3.2 Motion Picture Photography

Nearly any motion picture camera can be adapted for under water use. Cameras must be confined in rugged, reliable underwater housings that will withstand rough handling. All camera controls should be outside the housing and kept as simple as possible. The camera must be properly balanced, and as near neutral as possible under water. The cinematographer becomes his own crane and dolly, and must be able to swim in and out of scenes with as little unnecessary camera movement as possible.

Plan to make several dives to cover one subject adequately in a film. An average for topside shooting in good amateur work is 1:5 (1 foot used for every

5 feet exposed). Consider the use of a tripod if the documentation is generally in one area.

Artificial lighting is critical for motion picture work deeper than 30 feet (Figure 7–13). Surface powered lights are cumbersome, but more reliable and longer-lasting than battery-powered types. The latter, however, are compact and much easier to swim with. Ideally, one should plan for a buddy diver to handle the lights, freeing the cameraman to concentrate on filming techniques.

The specific techniques that are always a good practice to follow, regardless of the scene, are summarized below:

- Be as steady as possible.
- Overshoot at the beginning and end of each scene to establish the scene and for editing purposes.
- Vary the length of scenes (some short, some long). This is mostly accomplished in editing, but you can save film if you know the value and length of each scene while you are shooting.
- Shoot different distances, angles, and exposures of each scene when these are not known precisely.
- Don't rush scenes. The ease and beauty of the sea can be destroyed photographically if the photographer is hurried.
- Use a minimum of special effects and only when they can be exceptional and are of intrinsic value to the film.

Figure 7-13
Luminous Efficiencies
of Several Light Sources

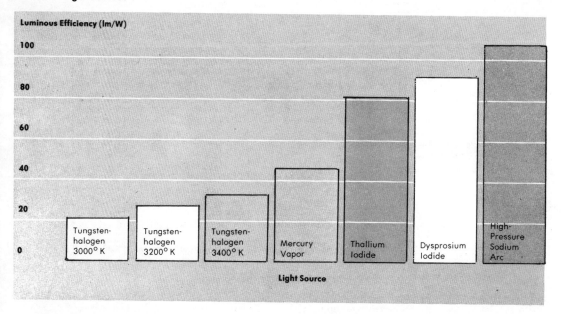

- Don't shoot something just because it is there; have a purpose for the footage unless it is extremely unusual. Then it is always valuable footage to have.
- Follow your shooting script but deviate as the situation dictates. Don't allow the script to handicap the effectiveness of the scenes under water.
- Know your camera so you can use it and the lights effectively.
- Cooperate with your diving associates so you will be able to acquire complete coverage. Undersea filming is not your best if done alone. Teamwork is just about mandatory.

7.3.3 Special Procedures

The photographer may find the following helpful hints beneficial:

- Overweighting with plenty of lead makes a diver a much steadier photographic platform. A buoyancy compensator gives him back his mobility.
- A wet suit protects against rock and coral even when not needed for thermal protection. Getting the pictures inevitably slices up naked limbs in such situations.

- Do not suspend photographic equipment from lines on boats in a rough sea unless a shock absorber is incorporated in the line.
- Plan photography before the dive as much as possible.
- Take a camera down to a habitat open unless there is a relief valve on the housing. Pressure will effectively prevent opening it below. Take the camera housing back up open regardless of relief valves. It can flood with the release of external pressure.
- Establish a basic tool kit for maintenance. Bring spare parts whenever possible; i.e., plenty of O-ring grease, WD40 or equivalent, towels, etc. Be prepared to fight a never-ending maintenance war against salt water.
- A wool watch cap can keep water drips from wet hair out of the camera when reloading.
- Protective shock absorbing cases, lined with foam rubber, are essential for boat transportation of photo gear.
- Rely on your own experience and experiments far more than on books written on underwater photography, where many basic errors have been passed from author to author.
- Upon flooding a camera in salt water, the best immediate action is to pack the equipment in

**Table 7-7
Modification of
First Developer
Time in the Kodak E-4
Process to Achieve
Various Film Speeds**

Camera exposure	Effective exposure index desired			First developer time [a]
	Ektachrome–X	High-speed Ektachrome Daylight type	High-speed Ektachrome Type B	
2 stops under..............................	250	640	500	Increase by 75 percent.
1 1/3 stops under	160	400	320	Increase by 50 percent.
1 stop under..............................	125	320	250	Increase by 35 percent.
Normal	64	160	125	Use normal time.[b]
1 stop over................................	32	80	64	Decrease by 30 percent.
2 stops over	16	40	32	Decrease by 50 percent.

[a] Approximate.

[b] See Kodak process instruction sheet E–4.

ice and keep it frozen until delivery to a repair facility can be made. If ice is not available, flush thoroughly by immersing in fresh water or alcohol.

■ At the end of the day's work, all camera equipment should be washed with fresh water.

■ When the camera and housing are removed from the water, they should immediately be placed in the shade. This is especially true in the tropics where even a minimal exposure to the sun can cause heat inside the camera housing to damage the film.

**SECTION 8
SCIENTIFIC
DIVING
PROCEDURES**

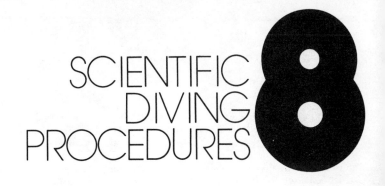

SCIENTIFIC DIVING PROCEDURES 8

8.0 GENERAL

Over the past two and one-half decades, the acquisition of scientific data by diving has become widespread, and has resulted in many new and highly significant discoveries in the marine sciences. In many of today's detailed studies of the marine environment, the use of scuba is the only means by which valid observations and measurements can be made. Using specialized equipment and techniques to take advantage of this new tool, the diving scientist has selectively sampled, recorded, photographed, and made field observations that are as significant to marine research as those made by his "dry-land" colleagues, or those who must remotely probe the sea from its surface.

New approaches needed to solve unanswered questions have been provided by placing scientists in the environment they want to measure and observe. This intimate contact has shown that in some research, such as observations of fish behavior, ecological surveys and benthic inventories, the entire study can be done using diving techniques. In many cases, the studies cannot be made by means other than diving. In other studies, diving investigations may only be needed to supplement commonly used remote sensing methods or surface ship surveys. Regardless of the project or the role that diving plays in a study, it is obvious from the published record in scientific journals, that marine research, utilizing diving as a scientific tool, has been of considerable importance in developing an understanding of the ocean, its organisms, and the processes that govern its existence.

The purpose of this section is to present examples of procedures that have been used in diver-oriented science projects. The methods should serve as guidelines and should not be construed as being the only way a survey, study, or set of observations can be conducted. There are definite limitations as to what a scientist can do, utilizing scuba as a tool.

As in all scientific research, the investigator should use the most efficient and least expensive means to obtain data. Scuba is only one way to do the job.

Unlike the "dry-land" scientist, the diving scientist or technician, unless saturated, must usually work against time measured in minutes versus hours. For 10 minutes working time, on the bottom at 50 meters, he must decompress for 2 minutes. If bottom working time is extended to 40 minutes, decompression time on ascent is 82 minutes. Longer periods of work, therefore, may increase decompression times to periods double the work time. It can be readily seen that the economics of scientific diving projects depend almost entirely on how efficiently and fast scientists can perform their tasks.

Maximum efficiency under water requires good tools and rugged instruments that can be set up rapidly. In most instances, these instruments and tools are made by individual scientists to meet the specific needs of their experimentation. Almost no standardization exists for scientific equipment and methods. Through necessity, scientists who dive must not only be proficient in their discipline, but be a diver, inventor, and mechanic. A resistance to sea sickness helps immeasurably.

8.1 SURVEYING AND RECORDING PROCEDURES

To systematically and accurately study any region, it is necessary to precisely plot the location of obtained data on a base map. This is especially important if there is need to return to the same location several times during a study. The scale of the base map will depend on the detail of the study and the size of the area to be investigated. In geological mapping of the seafloor, a scale of 1-inch equals 200 yards is adequate for reconnaissance surveys; in archeological or some biological studies, a much more detailed base map, with a scale of 1-inch equals 30 feet, may be required. In general, if existing charts do not contain the proper scale or sounding density, it may be necessary to construct a bottom bathymetric map prior to diving, utilizing echosounder survey techniques. Gross features can be delineated, and more efficient utilization of bottom time can be planned, if the diver has a good bathymetric map of the study area. If published topographic charts are inadequate, the sounding plotted on original survey boat sheets of a region (made by the Coast and Geodetic Survey now the National Ocean Survey) can be contoured and will usually provide an adequate bathymetric control for a diver survey of a region. If the survey plan requires bottom traverses, it will be necessary to provide some means of locating the position of the diver's samples and observations on the base chart.

The great majority of diving is carried out in near-shore waters where surface markers, fixed by divers over strategic points in the working site, may be surveyed from the shore using well-established land techniques including the theodolite, plane table, and alidade, or from the sea, using bearings from a magnetic compass, or preferably, measuring horizontal angles between known points with a sextant (Shepard 1973). With the exception of the compass, these methods allow one to establish the locations of a number of major features in the working area to an accuracy of 3 feet or better. If buoys are used for location, particular care is needed to ensure that the surface floats used during the initial survey lie directly over the weights anchoring them to the selected underwater features; the best plan is to wait for a calm day at slack tide. The seabed markers remaining after the floats have been cut away should be clearly labeled and coated with fluorescent paint to enhance their visibility.

Having established a basic grid on the seafloor, fixed relative to permanent features on the shore, the diver now proceeds to record the position of individual features within the working area relative to the grid.

8.1.1 Underwater Surveying

With the exception of long distance visual triangulation, many of the methods used in land surveying can be used under water. A review of a standard college text on "Surveying" will provide the scientist with much of the basic information needed to conduct such a survey. Woods and Lythgoe (1971) give an excellent description and review of methods that have been used under various diving conditions. A special consideration for diving surveys is that most distances must be measured by a calibrated line or a metal surveyor's tape. If long distances are required, these lines must be on reels or severe fouling and tangling will occur. In clear waters, optical instruments can and have been used to measure both distance (range finder) and angles between objects for triangulation. Warton describes his successful use of a standard surveyor's theodolite in the Mediterranean. He prevented corrosion by dismantling his instrument each night and soaking the component parts in kerosene (Woods and Lythgoe 1971).

Small transistorized echosounders, encased in underwater housings, have also been used to measure distances between acoustic or natural reflectors on the seafloor. This method is extremely useful in turbid waters of harbors, or in the measuring of distances across the heads of near-shore submarine canyons. The echosounder pointed up at the surface also gives an accurate depth reading. If a compass is incorporated into this package and a narrow-beamed sound source is used, bearing angles can also be measured.

The first step in surveying any area is to establish a horizontal and vertical control network of accurately located stations (bench marks) in the region to be mapped. Horizontal control is the framework on which a map of features (topography, biology, or geology) are to be constructed. Its purpose is to provide a means of locating the detail that makes up the map. Vertical control gives the relief of the region and may be obtained by stadia distance and vertical angles or by spirit leveling. Rough measurements can be made by comparing differences in depth using a diver's depth gauge, but these can be inaccurate if the reference point is the irregular sea surface.

The detail to appear on the finished map is located from the control networks (bench marks) by measurement of distance and angles to the features which are to appear on the finished map. On some surveys, the control is located first and the detail is located as a separate operation after the control survey has been completed. On other surveys, the control and the detail are located at the same time. The former method is preferable if long-term observations in an area are contemplated, such as a region around a permanently established habitat. The latter is preferable if reconnaissance studies are being made in remote regions or in areas that will not require reestablishment of stations.

8.1.2 Underwater Photogrammetry

The science and art of obtaining reliable measurements from photography "photogrammetry" while not as advanced under water as on land, is a tool that is being utilized with increasing frequency. Limited visibility is one of the major drawbacks in its application.

Photographs with appropriate scales in the field of view can be useful in measuring objects on the sea floor, and recording changes with time. Subtle changes are often recorded on sequentially obtained exposures of the same area or station that would be missed by relying on a diver's memory alone. Whenever possible, photographs should be taken of environmental features described in sea floor studies. These photographs are useful in conveying word pictures and dimensions to persons who do not dive and who lack a "common vocabulary" with persons who work under water.

Photographic transects are useful in showing variations over an area or with depth. Unfortunately very little "true" photogrammetry has been accomplished to date because of the technical difficulties in producing corrected lenses, maintaining altitude and constant depth, and high relative relief of many bottom features. To date, a system capable of obtaining accurate photogrammetric pictures equivalent to those obtained on land does not exist. Mertens (1970) discusses the problems of underwater photogrammetry and outlines several systems used in simple measurements from photographs. Woods and Lythgoe (1971) have presented a number of photogrammetric methods for measuring microoceanographic features, archeological sites, and seafloor features. The fundamental optics of underwater photographic measurements are well described in McNeil (1972) and would be valuable to anyone wishing to develop an underwater photogrammetric system for sea floor mapping.

Discussions of underwater photography methods and equipment used by diving scientists are given in Section 7.3.

8.1.3 Bottom Survey Methods

In most instances, the diver's position on the bottom can be determined by locating the surface-tending boat over the bubbles and shooting angles on shore stations previously located on the base map. A three-arm protractor is an extremely valuable tool to plot the position of the diver on the base map. A simple means for the diver to request a location from the surface tender is to send a small buoy to the surface. An inexpensive buoy can be made by cutting a broom handle into 1-inch lengths. A small balloon can also be used. If a sample is to be retrieved, the buoy can be wrapped with a light line to which a sample sack is attached. A diver can easily carry four to six of these small buoys and continue bottom traverses after each sample station without having to take the time to surface. Each sample station should be recorded by the divers on a writing slate along with the time of its retrieval for correlating with the times their position was determined and plotted by the surface tender. Field notes should also be correlated with time for later location on the base map of the survey area.

It is more efficient in nonsaturation diving surveys for the traverse to start in deep water and move toward shallower areas. If several divers are involved, it will often be necessary to change partners after the first dive to utilize the maximum bottom time available to the group. For instance, diver "A" starts with diver "B" on the first dive of the day to 150 feet for 5 minutes. Diver "A" then dives to 150 feet with diver "C" for 5 minutes on another outer traverse line. The group would then move into shallower water and divers "B" and "C" would dive together utilizing the repetitive dive tables to determine their maximum no-decompression time for the next dive (See Appendix D). Utilizing this method, a team of three men can easily make up to nine dives per day, if cold water is not a restriction to the survey work. For long traverse-swimming with hard work, it is usually not practical to spend over 3 hours total per day under water. Presurvey planning is required if efficient utilization of bottom time is to be expected. For practical purposes, a maximum depth of 150 feet has been determined as the point where traverse surveying becomes too time-consuming and inefficient to be considered a useful nonsaturation diving tool. Useful deeper dives can and should be made, especially in regions of steep slope. These dives,

Figure 8-1
A Simple Aquaplane
for Towing Divers

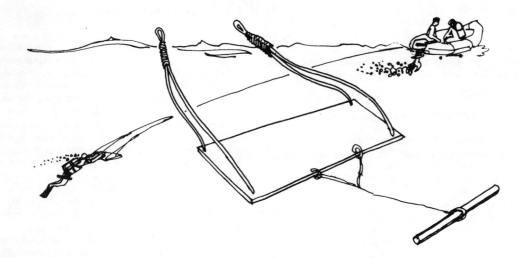

however, should be for special purposes and not for routine and systematic surveys.

8.1.4 Diver Towing

In many traverses across the bottom, a diver may wish to be towed, either to conserve energy or to cover a greater distance for the same expenditure of bottom time. Several methods have been used for towing a diver. One simple, inexpensive, and practical method of towing is to attach a tow bar or grapnel at the end of a long parachute shroud line (breaking strength 800 lbs.). The divers hold on to the tow bar or grapnel, and use their bodies to plane up or down as they are towed at about 1 to 2 knots.

Another towing method uses the aquaplane (Figure 8-1). The simplest version is a board, which, when tilted downwards or sideways, provides a dynamic thrust to counter the corresponding pull on the towing cable. The addition of a broom-handle seat and proper balancing of the towing points permit one-handed control of the flight path. With this aquaplane, which can be made in a few hours from materials available in the field, a diver may be towed at speeds of two or three knots by a small boat, the maximum speed being limited by the hydrodynamic forces that tend to tear off the diver's mask.

As in the swimming traverse, a diver keys ob-servation to time. At the same time, a surface at-tendant "shoots in" surface locations as the tow boat or escort boat moves along the traverse with horizontal sextant angles marking locations versus time. Later, the position of the diver at times of recorded observations can be determined by sub-tracting the length of the tow line from the position of the surface boat at the time of the observation. Practical experience has shown that tows of about 15 minutes will usually obtain as much information as a diver can record prior to returning to the sur-face for interrogation and recording of data.

In areas where entanglement is not a problem, it may be necessary at times for divers to drop off a tow line during traverses to investigate objects of interest. The tow sled can be improved by adding a trailing line of 30 to 40 feet. This will permit the diver who drops off the sled to grasp the line and return to the sled. Hand signals can also be sent along the tow line to instruct the boat to speed up, slow down, or stop. Divers should carry flares (smoke and light) on long traverses in rough water or in areas of strong current. The scope of the tow line may be up to 10 to 1, and in deep water this could place a diver far behind the tow boat. In such cases, a safety boat may be used to follow behind the towed divers to assist in the event that they become separated from the tow line.

If after the divers drop off a tow, their bubbles cannot be seen from the tow boat, there is the

Figure 8-2
Field Computer Card Punch
(Port-A-Punch)

chance of their becoming temporarily lost. A standby buoy with an adequate anchor should be carried, ready to drop overboard should this occur. Search to relocate the divers should be from this buoy. This technique prevents the surface boat from being carried from the survey area by current or wind.

Another technique to ensure straight line traverses is to use range lines to keep the tow boat on position. This technique is especially useful in regions where the shoreline has high relief.

In relatively shallow, clear waters, reasonably accurate surveys of large seafloor areas can be conducted without the use of scuba by towing snorkel divers on a sled behind a boat. Kumpf and Randall (1961) did such a study in the Virgin Islands, and covered close to 100 miles of coastline to depths of 40–60 feet, using this method and correlating their observations with aerial photographs.

8.1.5 Recording Methods

The simplest method for recording observations under the sea is to write or draw with a graphite or wax pencil on a white, double-sided board made of some plastic laminate. These records will be sufficiently permanent to withstand normal handling during a dive, but they should be transcribed into a notebook directly after surfacing. Any delay before

transcription increases the risk of misinterpreting the often rather erratic notes made under water, where mental efficiency decreases rapidly with increasing depth, cold, and fatigue. The principal symptom of this drop in mental performance is a striking loss of memory. During routine dives, it is possible to overcome this tendency by preparing beforehand a list of tasks to be undertaken and tables for the clear entry of all measurements required during the dive. These lists and tables may be inscribed on the plastic pads. In some cases it is desirable to retain the original records (particularly important in the case of archeological drawings, for instance); drawings are then made with wax crayons, such as Chinagraph, on a waterproof paper, such as Permatrace or Draftex, attached to the plastic board by screws or rubber bands. There are several types of underwater paper, including a fluorescent orange paper. Standard formats can be duplicated ahead of time to facilitate recording during a dive.

Where precise measurements are to be made, it should be common practice for two observers to take independent measurements, and then check them with each other for agreement *prior to* returning to the surface. If there is disagreement, the measurements should be repeated until agreement is reached.

When a long series of preselected observations is anticipated, a technique involving the direct punching of computer cards can be used. This method requires setting up a template containing categorized observations, e.g., fish counts, bottom types, etc. A waterproof computer card is placed under the template. The diver simply punches the card with a standard pencil-like metal punch to record observations. This technique reduces the amount of writing necessary and allows more time for observation (Figure 8–2).

In cases where extensive data recording is required, a tape recorder may be used. Fager et al. (1966) report that this technique is extremely useful. The position of the microphone and the way in which it is waterproofed are the most critical factors determining the usefulness of an underwater tape recorder. Microphones in contact with the airspace in front of the mouth are most satisfactory. Even though this is a region of high noise level, particularly during inhalation, such noise can be eliminated from the recording by judicious use of the switch. The switch is either held in the hand or is attached to the diver's harness where it can be easily located. One or two auditions of their own recordings are sufficient training to enable divers to record intelligible data even with a standard scuba mouthpiece in the mouth. Fifteen minutes of tape are generally considered to be adequate for most dives. There are still problems because of regulator noise and the design of the oral cavity in the mask. Photographic documentation is discussed in Section 7.

8.2 BIOLOGICAL SURVEYS

In general, biological surveys have the same requirements and utilize the same techniques as described in Paragraph 8.1. There are, however, some specific approaches that should be mentioned.

Important uses of biological surveys include the determination of the environmental impact of placing man-made objects on the seafloor, and the effects of ocean dumping on marine resources. In most areas of the marine environment, there are insufficient detailed data in existence to assess the impact of man-made changes without making special studies. Such studies are called "base line surveys" and are designed to obtain specific information about the biota, plants, and the physical environment that will be affected by man's intrusions. To be effective, such studies must be made prior to the building of structures or to the discharge of material into the marine environment. However, in many instances this is not possible because the structure or dumping may exist or be underway before the biologist has the opportunity to assess existing conditions. In such instances, "base line studies" may only be useable as determining changes that take place after the time of the initial study.

Base line studies must be in such detail and with such methodology that the survey can be repeated as a *monitoring* study at prescribed time intervals, to allow accurate assessment of the changes which occur with time. Control stations are necessary, outside the sphere of influence of the structure or discharge, to provide data on the environmental changes which occur naturally and on a seasonal basis. Only with such data, collected and analyzed systematically, can statements be made about the impact of a man-made structure or discharge on the environment. An example of such a study is one by Turner, Ebert, and Given at Point Loma, San Diego County, California, in 1968.

During this study, a standardized methodology was established to make the results of a biological survey quantitatively meaningful and ecologically acceptable. This was done by modifying conventional principles of terrestrial quadrat-transect sampling for use in underwater environments. At each station, chosen at a specific depth interval along a transect line, the anchor was dropped and used as the center of a circle of study. Quantitative observations were made within the circle, while outside its boundaries only more obvious bottom topography or biological features were noted.

When using this technique, the amount of bottom area covered need not be the same for every station, because the effectiveness depends upon water clarity and the complexity of the biota. The poorer the visibility, the more restricted the amount of bottom that can be surveyed. Typically for West Coast regions, sand stations having a limited macrobiota, a 3.1 meter line was used to give a 30 square meter area of study. In rocky areas, where the biota is more diverse, a 2.2 meter line is used to give a 15 square meter area of study. The technique cannot be used in turbid water of very low visibility. Sampling conducted and data obtained at each diving station included:

- A vertical plankton tow, using a standard 18 cm diameter oblong plankton net with 62 micron mesh
- A bottom sediment core (when possible)
- Sample of bottom sediment for infauna such as polychaeta and foraminifera
- Depth
- Temperature
- Water clarity
- A general description of the bottom
- Enumeration by estimate, the larger plants and animals
- Quantitative sampling (by actual removal) of growth within a quadrat 0.25 m²; and
- Making a photographic record of general bottom conditions and each quadrat prior to sampling.

The investigator should strive to set up the sampling program so that it can be reproduced and be quantitatively accurate, and where possible be related to previous work in the region.

Environmental factors that must be considered when surveying the establishment and growth of underwater plant communities include exposure to wave or swell action, type and slope of substrata, water temperature, availability of dissolved oxygen and nutrients, and grazing. It is often necessary to

Figure 8-3
Underwater
Spectroradiometer

Photo: Morgan Wells

determine these factors accurately within a given community, and observation or measurement by divers may be indispensable.

Variations in intensity and spectral composition of light under water, have a significant effect on plant communities, but it is often difficult to obtain accurate light measurements.

Drew (1971) indicates that the illumination at or within a given plant community can be obtained with accuracy only by actual measurement *in situ*. The use of photographic light meters for this purpose is considered generally unsatisfactory. Instruments for underwater light measurement have been devised by Kitching (1941) and Boden et al. (1960), however, Drew (1971), and Burr and Duncan (1972), describe underwater spectroradiometers, which are probably the most effective means of measuring light in the sea. Submersible spectroradiometers have been used in studies of photosynthesis and calcification rates of corals (American Institute of Biological Sciences 1972) (Figure 8-3.). Duncan (1973) also used a spectroradiometer during kelp bed studies. North (1966–67) used a series of photocells with colored filters to measure light intensities in kelp beds.

Most underwater investigators have used transect or simple quadrat methods for the analysis of benthic communities. A reasonable description of the change in biota, relative to depth and other factors, can be obtained by measuring the area of cover with a grid and collecting representative samples for biomass determinations. Some investigators have made subjective assessments of the percentage cover along a strip transect. Accurate quantitative data on standing crops can best be obtained by collecting the entire ground cover

from a quadrat, and sorting this into component species in the laboratory for subsequent analysis. Larkum et al. (1967) developed a suitable implement for quadrat sampling.

8.2.1 Estimating Population Densities

When estimating the biological content or density of a given region, it frequently is necessary to take surface area into account. An irregular surface can greatly increase the area present, and to the extent the surfaces sampled depart from the horizontal they will be underrepresented or density will be exaggerated. This becomes particularly important as the scale of the surface variation approaches the scale of the distribution being measured. Dahl (1973) describes a technique designed to quantify the estimation of irregular surfaces in the marine environment. Briefly, the technique consists of making some simple height, frequency, and surface length measurements, and then applying a surface index formula to determine the surface area. The technique has been applied to coral reefs, benthic algal substratum, Thalassia, sand and rubble zones, reef crests, and patch reefs.

A simple method for estimating populations of sessile organisms is described by Salsman and Tolbert (1965), who were surveying and collecting sand dollars (Figure 8–4). At each location sampled, the authors spent 10 to 15 minutes on the sea bottom, making observations, taking photographs, and sampling population density. To facilitate counting and to ensure a random sample, a counting cell was constructed by bending an aluminum rod into a square 30 cm on each side. As a diver approached the seafloor, he would release the square allowing it to fall to the bottom. The organisms within this square were then counted and collected for later size determination. This procedure was repeated at least two more times at each location sampled. This same method can be used for any sessile organism where a random sample is desirable.

A device used for surveying epifauna is the diver operated fishrake (Figure 8–5). It has been used to obtain information on the small-scale distribution patterns and estimates of population densities of demersal fishes and invertebrates (Fager et al. 1966). The apparatus consists of a metal tubular frame fitted with a handle, a roller of rigid polyvinyl chloride tube into which stainless steel wire "staples" are fixed, and an odometer made of a

**Figure 8-4
Counting Square
for Determining Sand
Dollar Density**

Photo: U.S. Navy

**Figure 8-5
Diver Operated Fishrake**

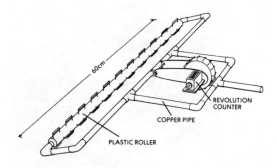

60cm

REVOLUTION
COUNTER

COPPER PIPE

PLASTIC ROLLER

plastic tracking wheel and removable direct-drive revolution counter. It is pushed along the bottom by a diver who makes visual counts, size estimates, and other observations on animals that occur within the path traversed by the roller.

In some underwater situations involving observations of animal behavior, it is necessary to remain a reasonable distance from the subject so as not to interfere with normal behavioral patterns. Emery (1968) developed an underwater telescope for such situations by housing a rifle scope in a polyvinyl chloride tube with acrylic plastic ends. The underwater scope described by Emery functioned satisfactorily to at least a 55-meter depth. An underwater telephoto camera lens was used during the Tektite II experiments (VanDerwalker and Littlehales 1971).

Diving has been used extensively to study the behavior and ecology of reef fish. Myrberg et al. (1967), report on the field observations of reproduction and general behavior of the damselfish made during more than 440 hours of underwater studies. Starck and Davis (1966) also studied the night habits of reef fishes using scuba diving techniques. Clarke (1970) used diving techniques extensively in his studies of the territorial behavior of the garibaldi off Southern California.

Ray and Lavallee (1964) and Kooyman (1968) used diving techniques to study the physiology, behavior, and ecology of the *Weddell seal* under Antarctic ice. These studies involved working under ice varying in thickness from 2.0 to 3.5 meters, and in water temperature as low as $-1.9°$ C. Kooyman et al. (1971) have also observed the diving behavior of Emperor Penguins under similar conditions.

8.3 BIOLOGICAL SAMPLING

As clearly stated by Fager et al. (1966) "Underwater operations have several advantages for ecological studies involving quantitative sampling or observations of behavior. Probably the most important practical one is the ability to observe the sampling apparatus in operation, to make estimates of its effectiveness, and to improve the design or procedure *in situ*. In some cases, such as with small demersal fish, underwater sampling is considerably more effective than from the surface. Direct observation gives one a feeling for the types and magnitudes of the errors associated with the sampling and allows one to decide whether the sampling site is unusual or representative of a larger area. With the less common species, it may be particularly important to be able to make repeated population estimates without imposing unnatural mortality by the removal of individuals.

"In addition to observations on the reactions of organisms to sampling gear, a diver can observe such behavior as feeding, interaction with other species and with other individuals of the same species, and reaction to various physical properties of the enviornment. As most of the species that we have worked with are apparently not seriously bothered by the presence of a diver and as the latter, if careful, disturbs the bottom very little while moving over it, we were able to observe behavior under relatively natural conditions. Interpretation of the behavior may often require a general knowledge of the environment that can best be obtained by having been in and over it repeatedly. Being subject to many of the same physical stresses gives the diver at least an anthropomorphic concept

**Figure 8-6
Hensen Egg Nets
Mounted on a Single
Diver Propulsion Vehicle**

Photo: William High

**Figure 8-7
A Circle Template
for Determining
Benthic Population Density**

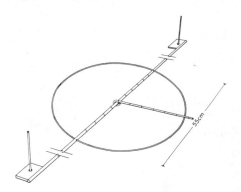

of the conditions under which the species he is
studying are living."

Because a diver, using marker buoys or stakes,
can return repeatedly to exactly the same location, changes in both environment and the biota
can be followed for considerable periods of time.
In addition, changes can be imposed on the environment by selective removal of species, by
alteration of the substrata, and so on, and the
effects of these experimental manipulations can be
followed in detail.

8.3.1 Plankton Sampling

Planktonic organisms that live within 1 meter
of the bottom can be sampled with a skid-mounted
multilevel net apparatus, which is pushed by a diver
over a predetermined distance. Hand-operated
butterfly valves are used to isolate the cod end
collection bottles.

Plankton sampling nets (30 cm in diameter, 2 to
3 mm mesh) are used for selective collecting of
plankton in reef areas. Air-filled bottles can also be
inverted in appropriate areas to suck up plankton
and water samples.

Several methods of sampling plankton have been
developed (Fager et al. 1966; Schroeder 1974).
Ennis (1972) has employed a method using two
diver propulsion vehicles on which a 50 cm plankton
net was mounted. A similar method was used by
Schroeder during a saturated dive at Grand Bahama
Island. Schroeder used two 1.0 m long Hensen
egg nets mounted on a single diver propulsion
vehicle at a speed of about 2–3 knots (Figure 8–6).
At the end of each run, one net at a time should be
washed and the sample concentrated into the
cod end by holding the net up inside a trapped

bubble of air under an 18-inch radius plastic hemisphere. The cod end should then be removed and
the contents poured into a glass jar. The jar should
be filled with filtered seawater except for a small
volume at the top and a piece of plastic wrap placed
over the top of the jar. This traps a small bubble of
air. The jar is then removed from the hemisphere
and carried to a work area on the base of the
habitat, if being carried out in a saturated mode.
The work area should be deeper than the hemisphere so hydrostatic pressure helps keep the air
bubble from escaping. The syringe needle filled
with 100 percent formalin is then pushed through
the plastic wrap, the jar is capped, immediately
secured, and labeled. When this procedure is
properly carried out, there is no sample loss.
Before a net is reused it should be turned inside out
and back-flushed. Schroeder describes other
techniques for sampling plankton in his review
paper previously referenced.

8.3.2 Benthic Organism Sampling

Quantitative sampling of the epifauna can be accomplished by counting the animals within a randomly located circle of a 0.25 square meter area
(Fager et al. 1966). A circle template, fixed center
rod, and movable arm may be constructed of brass,
with the center rod and movable arm marked with
grooves at 1 cm intervals (Figure 8–7). The position
of an animal within the circle can be defined by
three numbers: the distance along the center rod
from a standard end; the distance from the center
rod along the movable arm, and the half of the
circle within which the animal was observed. To

Figure 8-8
Coring Device
With Widemouth Container

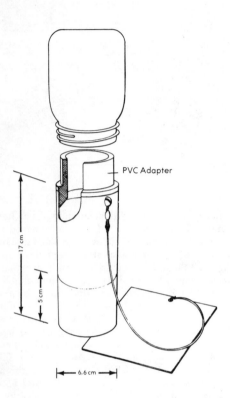

PVC Adapter

17 cm

5 cm

6.6 cm

Figure 8-9
Air Lift for
Sampling Enfauna

Photo: Robert Dill

study details of the pattern of distribution of individuals of sedentary species, the "distance of the nearest neighbor" technique can be used (Clark and Evans 1954). A large lightweight, metal square is preassembled and dropped on an appropriate location. Within the square, divers place short brass or plastic rods with fabric flags on them at predetermined positions in relation to individual species being examined. After the positions of all individuals have been marked, distances to nearest neighbors are measured, and reflexives counted.

Samples of the substrate and infauna can be collected with no observable loss of sediment or organisms using a simple coring device with a widemouth sample container (a jar) attached to the top (Figure 8–8). The corer is pushed a given distance into the sand (i.e., 5 centimeters), tipped slightly, and an aluminum plate is slid through the sand under it. The apparatus is inverted and the

sediment is allowed to settle into the jar. Once all sediment and organisms have settled into the jar, the coring attachment is removed, and the jar is capped.

A multilevel corer is used for studying the depth distribution of infauna. This corer samples an area of about 45 square centimeters to a depth of 6 centimeters. It consists of a square brass box fitted with a funnel adapter at the top to accept widemouth sample containers. The front side of the corer is slotted to permit thin metal slide plates to be inserted for separating the sample into five separate layers, which can be transferred under water to separate sample containers. Details for the construction and use of this apparatus are given by Fager et al. (1966).

8.3.3 Airlift Sampling

The airlift consists of a long plastic pipe equipped with an air device at the lower end, which carries sediment and organisms in a stream of air and water to the top of the pipe, where it is emptied into a mesh bag of a certain size (Figure 8–9). Large areas of soft bottom can be collected in a very short time with this device, and the samples can be screened through the bag in the process. When used with a diver-held scraping device, it is also useful on hard substrates, especially to collect the small organisms that tend to escape when attempts are made to "scrape and grab."

The occurrence and distribution of both attached and free-living benthic organisms is intimately dependent on the character and composition of the substrate on which they live. Some knowledge of geological techniques is helpful when sampling. For example, on rocky substrates it is important to know how to measure angles of inclines on overhangs or shelves, as this influences the orientation of many organisms. Composition of the rock is important in determining whether or not organisms can bore into it or merely attach to it, as well as determining its resistance to erosion over long periods of time. In soft bottoms, general descriptions based on sediment grain size and bottom configurations are useful. Accurate determinations of grain size, chemical composition, and other physical characteristics are best done by well-equipped geologists. Situations vary and it may be helpful to consult with geologists for recommendations on obtaining appropriate geological data.

8.4 CAPTURE AND TAGGING OF SHELLFISH

The use of diving as a research tool to study lobsters, crabs, scallops, and other types of shellfish has become increasingly common to the marine biologist. This has resulted partly because of the commercial importance of these living resources, and partly because they are oriented to or within the ocean bottom in a semimobile fashion, and are difficult to effectively sample with conventional surface oriented hardware (otter trawls, dredge, grab, trap, etc.). In general, such studies have been directed towards: (1) the ecology of the organism, (2) its behavior relative to sampling gear and artificially implanted tags, (3) the efficiency of the sampling gear for capturing the organism, (4) direct sampling of organisms that are virtually impossible to sample by other means and, (5) assessing the probable effect of conventional sampling techniques on the bottom environment and its fauna.

Perhaps more underwater studies have been conducted on the American lobster of the New England coast than any other single species of shellfish.

Direct, *in situ* observations of lobsters, using both scuba and surface supplied air systems are recognized by the scientific community as being the most effective way to study lobster ecology and behavior. Comparative studies of lobsters in the laboratory-aquarium environment have shown that their behavior is significantly altered when they are in captivity. For example, lobsters held in captivity are highly cannibalistic; in their natural

Figure 8-10
**Benthic Environment
of the American Lobster**

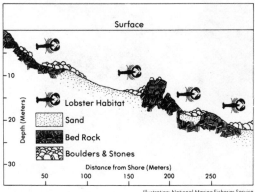

Illustration: National Marine Fisheries Service

environment cannibalism has rarely been observed. Furthermore, lobsters less than one-half pound in size are generally not nocturnally active in their natural environment but are in the confines of an aquarium tank. Lobsters spend most of their first 3 years of life in a labyrinth of tunnels projecting as much as three feet into the boulder-rock substrate of the ocean bottom. Replicating this substrate in an aquarium is difficult.

8.4.1 Capture Techniques

The conventional gear used to sample lobsters is the otter trawl and lobster trap. The *otter trawl* cannot be used over a boulder-rock bottom without incurring frequent and extensive damage resulting in a biased catch of lobsters or no catch at all. On smooth bottoms, the otter trawl generally skips over the lobster that occupies the usual bowl-shaped depression in the bottom substrate. *The trap* is highly selective in what it captures. Lobsters are attracted to the trap through the smell (taste) of bait. Small lobsters, in general, will not leave their tunnel complex for the baited trap. Thus, the trap is selective by size and by the lobsters' degree of hunger. Direct sampling by the diver on the relatively slow moving American lobster provides the biologist with representative samples with which he can calibrate the sampling efficiency of conventional gear. The careful dismantling of the rocky bottom with a detailed examination of tunnels, burrows, and crevices has been documented as the most effective and accurate way to assess the density and population structure of lobsters (Cooper 1974 in press). Figure 8-10 illustrates the typical

Figure 8-11
Tagging a Spiny Lobster

Figure 8-12
Algal Cover
of Rock Substrate

Photo: Bill Bunton

bottom environment of the American lobster and the obvious problems inherent in nondirect sampling.

A certain amount of "trial and error" is necessary in learning the correct procedure for capturing and handling lobsters in their environment to minimize damage to the lobster and to the diver. An 8 to 10 pound lobster can crush a coke bottle with his relatively slow-moving crusher claw. Even a small 1 pound lobster can badly bruise a diver's finger. The ripper claw, the quickest claw to be brought into action, can do only limited damage to a gloved hand. Lobsters should be grabbed behind the large claws over the back and held firmly. If a frontal approach is required for capturing the lobster, grab it by the ripper claw and hold on only for 1–2 seconds; don't give the lobster time to bring the crusher claw into action. A trained diver can reach into a burrow and extricate a live and kicking lobster if he is quick and makes good use of his sense of touch. Standard lobster snares can also be used.

Collecting lobsters in a catch bag must be preceded by banding or inactivating the claws. When disturbed, lobsters will rip and crush anything within their reach, including each other. If healthy specimens are desired at the end of the dive, special precautions are required during the collection process. During winter months when water temperatures range between 28.5° and 34.0° F lobsters will readily autotomize (drop) their claws when handled roughly. This is an apparent escape

mechanism used when attacked by certain predators.

8.4.2 Tagging Techniques

Lobsters have been tagged with short-term (lost at shedding) and long-term (retained at shedding) tags and marks within their natural environments. Lobster dens may be marked using styrofoam floats numbered carefully to note specific locations. Color coded tags may be inserted into the dorsal musculature between the abdomen and thorax of the lobster with the aid of a No. 20 syringe needle (Figure 8–11). A secondary mark may be made by punching a small hole (4 mm) into one of the five tail fan sections. This latter mark will be retained through at least one molt and will permit recognition of a lobster that has lost the primary tag. Movements and location of lobsters at night may be determined by using small sonic tags (pingers). These tags are small (about $3 \times 5 \times 1$ cm) and weigh only a few grams. Several types are available commercially. They operate in the general frequency range of 70 kHz and may be picked up as far away as 900–1200 feet on an open bottom and 30–60 feet when the tagged lobster is in a crevice. The detailed methods of these studies are given by Cooper (1970), Scarratt (1968), and Dybern et al. (1967).

When conducting a survey of lobsters, it should

be kept in mind that the very presence of the diver and the tagging procedures may affect overall behavior. In one study, a significant alteration of the population distribution was noted during the course of several weeks of capturing and tagging (Miller et al. 1971).

Fortunately, for the marine scientist, the American lobster is relatively slow moving, inquisitive, and can be accurately sampled. Its behavior can be studied and photographically documented using techniques that only diving can provide. Most other species of shellfish also lend themselves to the same research techniques.

8.5 BOTANICAL SAMPLING

Three percent of the ocean water mass and only one percent of the seafloor is illuminated sufficiently enough for plants to grow. Nevertheless, plants in this euphotic zone are the primary producers of organic matter on which all other marine organisms in both this and the vast aphotic zone depend for energy sources and body-building materials.

Much of what is known about benthic marine plants has resulted from collections and observations made in the intertidal zone, or, in deeper water, from material obtained by using dredges and trawls, or from beach drift. Only with the advent of modern diving techniques has it been possible to obtain accurate ecological information about the great majority of attached plants that live subtidally (Figure 8–12.). Some attached vegetation occurs in depths greater than 200 m, but most algae and vascular seagrasses live in the well-lighted part of the ocean, less than 33 m deep, and are thus accessible using conventional scuba equipment.

Saturation diving further extends the access to study areas day and night, prolongs stays in deep water, and provides a "resident perspective" that comes when living under water instead of visiting.

To date, however, ocean floor laboratories have not been designed to handle noxious chemicals such as formaldehyde. Consequently, it is more practical to have surface support divers collaborating with saturated divers to deal with this problem. Samples can be tied to a line and lifted to the surface for preservation or special treatment. During one saturation dive, divers obtained samples of

rare, deep water plants that were isolated and sent to the surface for live culture and pigment analysis. General collections that documented the kinds of plants in the area were also sent to the surface and preserved there, thus eliminating the need for handling formaldehyde and glacial acetic acid under water.

8.5.1 Basic Survey Techniques

Although techniques will vary depending on the objectives of the study the terrain, climate, and equipment available, generally, the methods described for biological sampling can be used for studying marine plants. Special methods suitable for sessile animals may be particularly appropriate for investigating marine plants.

To obtain quantitative information, most investigators have used transect or simple quadrat methods. A description of the change in vegetation with depth or other factors can readily be obtained by subjective assessment of percentage cover along a strip transect, while at the same time noting other relevant features. Modifications of the transect method for use in turbid and turbulent waters are described in recent literature in which representative samples are collected for analysis on the surface.

Such methods are particularly useful for the differentiation and classification of plant communities, as well as for the analysis of changes in floristic composition over extended periods. Accurate quantitative data on standing crop, vital for estimates of natural resources can best be obtained by collecting the entire vegetation from a quadrat and sorting this into component species in the laboratory. These specimens can then be weighed wet, or preferably dry. It is important to make allowance for the weight of calcifying material present in samples containing a considerable proportion of calcareous species, since this does not represent organic plant matter. Techniques for determining ash-free dry weight or calorific content are described in recent literature.

While there is no exact agreement on the size of quadrat to use in obtaining a representative sample, quadrats of $1/4$ to 1 square meter are recommended.

A useful preliminary test for selection of a quadrat suitable for representative sampling of a given community is to establish the "minimal area" which includes most of the species present. This is found by taking a number of quadrats and plotting number of species against area sampled. A suitable point to select as the minimal area is that at which a 100 percent increase in area yields only 10 or perhaps 5 percent more species.

It is advisable to use an area somewhat larger than the minimal for actual sampling. Larkum et al. (1967) showed that samples over 1 m square were necessary to establish statistically significant differences between the standing crops of dominant species in similar vegetation at 30 and 45 m depth (Woods and Lythgoe 1971).

Seasonal variations in the diversity and abundance of plants is very conspicuous in certain parts of the world. Although temperature is the most important and obvious cause of seasonal changes, other factors, such as biological cycles, seasonal storms, and seasonal tidal variations may produce changes. To get complete coverage of events in an area, and to gain understanding of the natural cycles, it is necessary to sample repeatedly throughout the year. It is best to return to the same station to monitor and perceive changes over time.

Some plants have a narrow temperature tolerance. These plants may be especially important as indicator species, as their presence or absence suggests certain environmental characteristics. Kelps, for example, do not live in warm water, and are not found in tropical latitudes except where cold currents or deep cold water provide suitable circumstances. Certain kelps thus live in deep cold water in the Mediterranean Sea (otherwise populated by warm temperature or tropical species) and in the equatorial Galapagos Islands, bathed by the cold Humboldt current.

Prior to beginning a collection program the investigator should survey the local environmental conditions. This is essential in order to know where and how to sample. Most algae require a hard substrate to begin growing, and the diversity of plants on rock surfaces is usually far greater than in soft or sandy areas. Pilings, shells, dead coral, barnacles, ship wrecks, and mangrove roots are among the places algae are likely to attach. Marine vascular plants or seagrasses follow the reverse pattern, with most species growing on soft or sandy substrates, with some exceptions such as *Phyllospadix*, common on rocky shores of the western United States. Frequently, seagrasses and larger algae themselves provide substrate for a great array of smaller epiphytic plants.

To get a good representation of plants, collections from diverse substrates should be sampled. Moreover, some plants live only in intertidal or shallow water, while others live only in deep water. Collections should therefore be made over a broad depth range. Wave action may also be a limiting factor, necessary for the survival of some species, but inappropriate for others. Grazing pressure is another factor that should be considered in sampling. Where herbivores are abundant, as on coral reefs, attached vegetation may be scarce, partly because of heavy grazing. Careful searching in crevices and other protected areas is required in such circumstances. To assess the impact of grazers, simple wire cages may be constructed to exclude herbivores, and growth measured over a period of time. Studies using this technique with specific methods described have been published by Randall et al. (1964), and Earle (1972).

8.5.2 Collecting Techniques

Although the methods described for geological and general biological surveys apply to marine plants, the following techniques are recommended for collecting plants.

Marine algae can be collected in much the same manner as invertebrates, as most are attached to a solid substrate. Small putty knives or thin knife blades are of use in lifting the algal holdfasts from the substrate. The entire holdfast should be removed from the substrate as it is important in identification.

Large plants, such as the kelp, *Macrocystis* (Figure 8–13), may be 100 feet in length, with holdfasts 3 feet in diameter and as many as 400 or 500 stipes. Holdfasts may be removed by cutting in from the outer edge and lifting upward. The center of the holdfast is usually rotten and not attached. These plants should be raised holdfast first, as the many individual stipes will become hopelessly entangled if raised from the top end. Plants such as the elk kelp, *Pelagophycus*, which have a single rope like stipe, perhaps 100 feet long, and blades 4 feet wide, and 15 feet long, should be also brought up holdfast first.

Small filamentous forms may be scraped from rocks and stored in plastic vials. These plants may float out of the container if reopened. Care should be exercised when placing several types of marine plants in a common container. There are plants

Figure 8-13
Diver in Giant Brown
Kelp *(Macrocystis)* **Bed**

Photo: Robert Dill

plant community can only be obtained by measurement *in situ*. Small, self-contained light meters can be positioned and read by a diver. It is important to understand certain principles before embarking on underwater light measurement of this kind.

The use of photographic light meters, incorporating selenium photocells, is unsatisfactory unless restricted spectral regions, isolated with colored filters, are measured. This is because a sensing system which responds differently to different wavelengths is being used to measure light which is becoming increasingly monochromatic with depth. The introduction of colored filters in front of the meter greatly reduces its sensitivity. If an opal cosine collector is added to make the system absorb light more as the plant surface does, then it is of use only in shallow, brightly lit waters.

A detailed description of the apparatus necessary to make such measurements is found in Paragraph 7.3. Generally it incorporates a selenium photocell of increased surface area, thereby ensuring increased current output per unit of illumination, a system for easily changing the colored filters, and a sensitive ammeter, the range of which can be altered by current attenuation circuitry.

8.5.3 Specimen Preparation and Preservation

It is helpful to examine and make notes on collections while they are still fresh to determine the kinds of macroscopic plants present, especially delicate species. Preparation of herbarium and voucher specimens from fresh material is preferred by many botanists, but this is often not possible in the field. Plants prepared soon after collection tend to retain their natural color better than those that have been preserved.

There are standard herbarium methods for pressing plants (Knudsen 1972), with some special variations for marine algae. The usual approach is to float specimens in large, flat trays, and to carefully slide them onto sheets of heavy weight herbarium paper (University of California type, 100 percent rag content, is best). Using water, the plants are arranged on the paper, then the paper is placed on a sheet of blotting paper, topped with a square of muslin or other plain cloth or a piece of waxed paper. This is topped with another blotter, and a corrugated cardboard "ventilator" placed on top. Another layer of blotter—paper—plant—cloth—blotter—cardboard is stacked on top, and

which have extremely high acidic content and will cause a breakdown in other forms of algae.

A clipboard should be used with waterproof paper and pencil for notes and a field notebook to record data immediately after diving.

Diving observations should be recorded as soon as possible, preferably while the diver is still on the bottom.

Field data should include notes on depth, substrate, terrain, water temperature, current, visibility (clarity), conspicuous sessile animals, herbivores, the date, time, methods used, and the collecting party. If possible, information on available light, salinity, and other environmental factors should be obtained.

An assessment of the conspicuous species of plants and the abundance of each should be noted—whether common, occasional, or rare; whether attached to certain substrates, or other peculiarities. In many instances, more than half of the species present are not conspicuous, and require careful microscopic examination. This is usually impossible under field circumstances because of the optical equipment, library facilities, reference collection, and time necessary to make an accurate systematic analysis.

Accurate light measurements within a given

so on. When 20 or 30 have been stacked, the pile should be compressed, using a weight or pressure from straps wrapped around the plant press. The top and bottom pieces should be stiff, usually boards slightly larger than the herbarium paper and blotters. After several hours (or overnight), the stack should be taken apart and the damp blotters replaced with dry ones. Many small algae dry in one day using this technique, but some, such as the large brown algae, may take a full week to dry completely.

A few small filamentous and gelatinous species can be successfully air dried without pressing if they are arranged on a $3'' \times 5''$ card. In all cases, it is essential that every sheet be labeled, at least with an identifying station number.

The usual method for preserving specimens for later detailed examination and herbarium preparation is simple and effective. For each station, one or more large plastic bags can be used to hold samples of larger plants. Small bags or vials should be used for selected fragile or rare plants. The best general preservative is a buffered solution of 5 percent seawater formalin (commercial liquid formaldehyde diluted with seawater). Specimens will keep successfully, thus preserved, for many years if kept in a cool, dark place. Exposure to light causes preserved plants to fade. Samples from many stations in separate bags can be kept in a single large storage drum that can be sealed tightly to prevent formalin from leaking out. For shipping, most of the preservative can be drained off, as the plants, once preserved, remain in good condition for several weeks if they are damp.

Kelps may require special handling because of their large size. Small plants can be preserved in 5 percent seawater formalin, but an alternative method for whole large plants involves soaking them for several hours or days in a solution consisting of 10 percent carbolic acid and 30 percent each of water, alcohol, and glycerin. Specimens thus preserved may be dried and then rolled up for storage. The glycerin helps to keep the plants flexible indefinitely. Another technique suggested by Dawson (1956) involves partially air drying giant kelps on newspaper (in the shade) and rolling the plants, beginning with the holdfast. Rolls are tied, labeled, and wrapped in paper, then left to complete drying. Specimens so prepared can later be resoaked for examination.

Coralline algae and rock-encrusting species also require special attention. Air drying specimens in shade, then storing samples in boxes, has proven a satisfactory technique for many large brittle and fragile species. Some small plants can be preserved with general collections, but delicate specimens should be isolated. Retaining small pieces of rock with coralline and encrusting algae attached helps to keep the plants intact.

Plants collected for histological study should be preserved in a solution of 90 parts 70 percent ethyl alcohol, 5 parts glacial acetic acid, and 5 parts formalin. In all cases, preserved specimens should be kept as dark as possible.

8.6 MARINE ARTIFICIAL REEFS

Artificial reefs are man-made or natural objects intentionally placed in selected areas of the marine environment to duplicate those conditions that cause concentrations of fishes and invertebrates on natural reefs and rough bottom areas. By increasing the amount of reef habitat, artificial reefs provide the potential for increasing stock sizes of fishes. The main features that appear to attract marine animals to these habitats are shelter, areas of calm water, visual reference points, and food. Artificial reefs also provide access to new feeding grounds, and open new tracts for territorial fishes.

Population estimates of reef fishes are made by direct counts of the number and species at the reef sites. These counts are made by two or more swimmers when visibility is 4 or more feet. Each observer makes counts by species for sections of the reef that are then totaled for the entire reef count. The totals of all observers are averaged for a mean count of each species of territorial and schooling fishes, such as black sea bass, Atlantic spadefish, grunts, and most porgies. For seclusive fishes, such as Carolina hake, morays, groupers, and flounders, the highest count obtained by any one observer is used. Although the accuracy of fish population estimates vary with visibility, species, and time of day, it is assumed that if these conditions remain the same the counts represent population density.

Artificial reefs can be used in all kinds of water, and can be made in many ways, e.g., old cars, cement, and miscellaneous debris. One of the easiest methods involves the use of old tires (Figure 8–14). Such reefs have been used for over 15 years to improve fishing in normally barren waters (Steimle and Stone 1973). In a recent study, the

Figure 8-14
Artificial Reef
Made From Old Tires

Figure 8-15
Underwater Equivalent of
a Geologist's Brunton Compass
Used for Measuring the Dip
and Strike of Underwater
Rock Outcrops

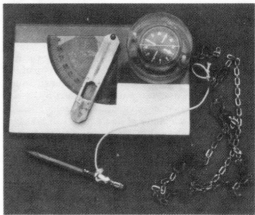

Photo: Robert Dill

tires were scattered and piled in the selected area in 20 stacks of four to eight tires, and fastened together with steel rods run through the stacks (Stone and Buchanan 1970). Each stack was weighted causing it to come to rest in an upright position on the bottom. Stacks were arranged in heaps, giving a naturally irregular appearance, in 45 feet of water, with a few single tires randomly distributed. This type of structure has proved highly successful in a number of experiments in other areas. The worn-out tires are cheap, almost indestructible, and make excellent bases on which marine life can grow. The hard, convoluted surfaces are ideal for concentrations of algae and encrusting organisms, and for small fish that find food and shelter in the many holes and crevices in and around the stacks. Larger predatory fish gather around the newly formed "fish havens," as do crustaceans and mollusks.

8.7 GEOLOGY

The use of diving has enhanced the geologist's ability to conduct underwater research by giving him direct access to the seafloor. *In situ* measurements and observations have become a necessary part of the study of the processes of sedimentation and erosion that mold the sea floor in nearshore regions. The initial phase of any offshore geological study is to compile data on the geology of the adjacent shore area, including surficial features and sediments; bore hole data; seismic data; and geological mapping and survey reports. One of the first uses of scuba was the study of the transport of sediment along the seafloor off southern California,

(Fisher and Mills 1952). The systematic mapping of seafloor geology began in 1952 during the expansion of offshore oil exploration (Menard et al. 1954). Dill and Shumway (1954) were among the first to document the significance of scuba diving in geological investigations, and presented drawings and photographs of instruments developed to support early studies. Such tools as an underwater equivalent of the Brunton compass (Figure 8–15), the basic instrument that geologists use for geological mapping, were developed by commercial divers and reported by Shumway (1955). This unit was later refined into an instrumented observation board, which included writing board, depth indicator, compass, inclinometer, protractor, ruled edges, bubble levels, pencil holders, accessory straps, and a belt clip. Menard et al. (1954) further utilized diving techniques for underwater geological reconnaissance mapping of the Continental Shelf areas off southern California.

The physical measurement of the bottom may utilize techniques previously described; however, a diver may use an accurate compass, an inclinometer, and a tape to acquire physical measurements of sufficient precision for most geological studies. The physical measurement of changing conditions on the seafloor or the creep of the strata of the ocean bottom is another matter, however, requiring measurements of some precision. Dill (1964) describes the use of accurately located and measured stakes to determine the amount of gravity creep and active slumping in submarine canyon sediments.

On-site evaluation of topographic data is another important role of the diving geologist. The techniques used for acquisition of topographic data, such as echo ranging and side scan sonar, are not capable of differentiating many topographical features of interest to the geologist. The makeup of the strata in outcroppings, and the direction in which the outcrop slopes, can only be verified by on-site visual observation or photographic techniques. A diver, with a minimum of equipment can measure and record geological features of this type. A diver using a camera can record the strata and sediment conditions in the natural state that cannot be acquired by other methods.

The limitation of visibility places severe restraints on the planning of geological and geomorphological work. Most species of animal or algae, a wreck or an amphora, are all sufficiently small for their form and orientation to be readily identifiable in good visibility, and usually identifiable in 2–10 m visibility. However, a cliff, large stack, sand ribbon, or sand wave, cannot be seen all at once even in good visibility. The diver, on first contacting the feature, may not realize what he has found, and will have to swim a ways before he can be sure that the crest of a sand wave is continuous, or the foot of a cliff is horizontal. In this sense the diver's vision, combined with the ability to recognize and integrate the parts of large features with his knowledge of position, becomes a real technique.

To aid the search and identification of features divers may swim on a fixed course, or alter course in a programmed way. If a feature is suspected of being in a certain locality the diver should be dropped well to one side so that a traverse in one direction is bound to take him across it. If the features are linear the divers should search on a line normal to the trend until they intersect a trend line. Search techniques are described in detail in Section 7. In this stage of work an aquaplane may be used (Figure 8–1). If the water is deep it is safer to lay a bottom line between buoyed shot weights, marked at intervals to aid position fixing. The buoys can be fixed by sextant or radar. In deep water, it helps to have a shot line for the diver to descend even if he is only giving a visual report on the bottom material or collecting a single sample, especially if there is a current (Woods and Lythgoe 1971).

In currents over 1 knot divers have difficulty maintaining their position by swimming during a search. They can be towed on an aquaplane with a screen to protect them from the water flow, or they can work on a fixed bottom line. If the fixed line leads up to the surface vessel, the vertical component of the tension will tend to lift the diver off the bottom. The best method is to attach a light line to the anchor before dropping it, keeping the free end on deck.

The diver descends using the combined cable. When reaching the anchor, he streams back on the light line, while the free end is held by an attendant. In this manner, the diver can swim from side to side downstream of the anchor, searching a wide area. He is also in continuous contact with the boat, and can be pulled back to it when he ascends. This system can be worked in 2–3 knots, after which the face mask is pulled off by the current.

Observations can include identification, recognition, delineation, the observation of processes, and the detection of change. It is immediately apparent to a diver if: there is size-sorting between crest and trough of ripples; the particles at the crest of ripples are discolored by biological growth while those in the troughs are not; bevelled recesses in a cliff line up to form a continuous notch; sand moves over ripples as a wave passes; or if dead shells on sand are more or less quickly broken up than those on gravel.

There are many useful aids to visualization of processes, such as dumping colored sand or gravel, or releasing dyes or neutral density floats into the water to reveal the movement. The best way to prepare a marked sample which will have the same hydraulic characteristics as the natural bottom material is to take a bottom sample, wash it, dry it, spray with aerosol paint, dry again, sieve it to break up agglomerates, and replace it on the sea bed at the point where it was removed. There is the inevitable risk that many of the smallest particles will remain stuck together by paint. This method, however, introduces less error than when dumping completely unnatural or artificial materials, and the method is simple to work in the field. The above techniques are discussed in further detail by Woods and Lythgoe (1971).

8.7.1 Geological Mapping

In general, a geologist mapping the seafloor must obtain the same information under water as on land. This usually includes the *dip* (the angle at which a stratum or any planar feature is inclined from the horizontal) and the *strike* (the course or

**Figure 8-16
Geologist Measuring
the Inclination
of a Rock Outcrop**

Photo: Laurence Bussey

**Figure 8-17
Coring a Large Coral Head
With a Submersible Drill**

Photo: Ian Macintyre

bearing of the outcrop of an inclined bed or stratum on a level surface) of bedrock outcrops. A representative rock sample is also taken to describe the rock type and fossil age of the formation being mapped. The location and information are placed on the regional map for later translation into stratigraphic cross-sections and a geological map of the region. Fault contacts can be followed as much as they can on land. The use of aerial photography may save much time and provide an overall context into which the results of underwater geological mapping can be placed. Pictures of bottom topography can often be obtained from aircraft at altitudes up to 12,000 feet.

One of the difficulties of geological mapping under water is finding rock outcrops. A thin cover of overburden can make mapping difficult. However, it is often possible for a geologist to use biological indicators as a means of reaching rock exposures. In many regions sessile organisms such as gorgonian corals and sea fans will extend up through the overburden, showing that a hard substrate is buried beneath a thin cover. Fanning away the sediment with the hand will expose the underlying rock surfaces and permit geological measurements.

It is often possible to follow small rockfish to rock exposures after they flee from a diver and seek protection in rock structures. Kelp beds often (but not always) give a surface indication of rocky

bottom. The geologist working under water must learn to "read" the environment—it will give many clues about where to find rock outcrops needed to complete geological maps.

In many instances, rock outcrops can be anticipated before the dive by looking for bottom irregularities with an echo sounder. Fish associated with rocky areas will also show up as distinct echos above the bottom return and are valuable as indirect indicators of rock bottom. Snapping shrimp that live in rocky areas can be heard as a "crackly" sound when a boat stops over rocky areas.

Grapnels towed from outrigger poles over the bottom can also be used as snags for finding isolated rock outcrops. It is advisable to have some breakaway system with a surface buoy to prevent excessive loss of gear.

Once a rock outcrop is found, the geologist should swim around the dive site to ensure that the rock to be measured is in place. (In many instances where differential erosion has undercut resistant beds, they will topple and give erroneous readings.) A useful instrument is a writing slate to which is attached an inclinometer and compass (referred to earlier). The dip of rock strata should be determined by measuring the dip bearing (the direction towards which the bed dips) of the outcrop. This value can be later converted into strike by subtracting 90 degrees from the dip bearing value. This method prevents confusion as to which direction the outcrop was facing. The actual dip is measured by placing the straight edge of the writing board on the bedding plain and determining its angle from the horizontal (Figure 8–16). A typical bottom notation would read:

dip bearing 95°, dip 13°

Other quantitative determinations might consist of direct measurement of ripple amplitude, orientation, wave length, crest length, and sinuosity. Divers are particularly valuable in estimating whether a sample came from a typical area, or from the immediate neighborhood of a rock outcrop or sediment boundary.

If a study is being made of the rate of movement of material, then a fixed point on the bottom is needed. This may either be a steel bar driven several feet into the bottom, or a concrete block.

Secondary points can be marked on the seafloor with painted or numbered stones, plastic sheets or boards, or tapes pegged to the bottom. If sediment movement is to be detected by dumping colored materials, then a search must be made on a grid around the dumping point, usually with the aid of a flashlight. If radioactive tracers are used to mark fine sand, greased plates can be used to pick up the samples. These are placed against photographic plates to reveal the number of marked grains per unit area.

When there is net transport of material into or out of an area, the level of the surface must alter accordingly. Stakes driven into the floor can be marked so that such change is detected (Woods and Lythgoe 1971).

8.7.2 Geological Sampling

Geological sampling consists of obtaining sediment and rock from known locations for subsequent analysis. As in geological sampling on land, the characteristics of the sediment and rocks present a picture of the conditions that were present during the formation of the sample. Using prior experience, a geologist can predict the general conditions of an area using the information of the sample composition, its location, and the layering.

Samples of unconsolidated sediment can be collected with a small scoop and immediately transferred to a plastic bag or plastic jar. Some geologists use the plastic jar for both collection and storage of samples, eliminating the scoop.

8.7.2.1 Rock Samples

Rock or coral samples may be taken using a pry-

bar, sledge hammer, explosives, or drill (Figure 8-17). The standard geological hammer is an excellent tool for obtaining rock samples. Several different types of explosives are commonly employed under water, and extreme care must be exercised when they are used (See Paragraphs 1.10 and 4.12).

Samples, whether sediment, rock, or coral, may be extremely heavy and the diver may need additional buoyancy to move them across the bottom, or to lift them to the surface. Methods of lifting heavy objects to the surface are described in Paragraph 4.13. Nylon net bags or wire baskets are convenient for lifting small amounts of rock or coral in that they offer little water resistance themselves. Samples may also be transported from one collecting site to another by adding air to some lift devices.

Labels on samples collected should give depth, time, location, and date. Upon returning to the surface, divers should be thoroughly debriefed, and all data recorded and plotted on the base chart. It is desirable to clean all organisms from the samples to reduce foul odors, and to make subsequent analysis easier.

8.7.2.2 Sediment Samples

Hamilton and Menard (1956) collected sediment samples for determination of *in situ* density values by carefully inserting a thin-walled brass ring, 1 inch in diameter and 1 inch high, into the sediment until the top was flush with the seafloor surface. Plastic discs were used to seal both ends before removing the ring, thus trapping a known volume of water-saturated sediment for subsequent laboratory determination of density and porosity.

Nearshore depositional structure samples. To understand the complex nearshore processes in topographically high energy areas, it may be necessary to obtain sediment samples of wave generated depositional structures. The techniques for obtaining such samples are described in detail by Clifton et al. (1971). The following summarizes these techniques. In these studies nearshore was defined as "a relatively narrow zone extending seaward of the shoreline and somewhat beyond the breaker zone. The zone of wave-induced nearshore currents."

Because the samples are obtained near shore, horizontal distance and location can be obtained by using a line attached to a fixed shore station which then extends over the selected bottom pro-

**Figure 8-18
Senckenberg Box Cores
for Determining Internal
Structure of Sand**

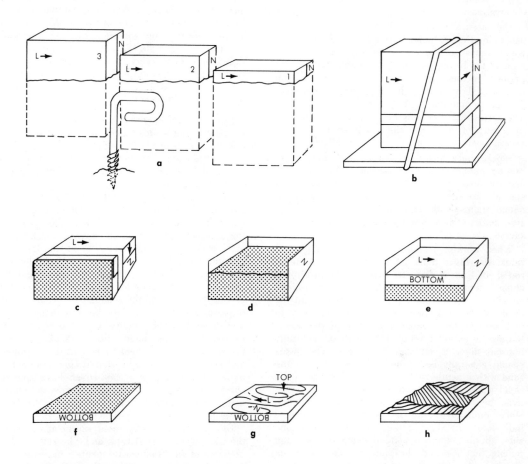

Taking and processing of sand box cores to identify internal structure: **a** — Senckenberg boxes, aligned in a series, shown here as normal to a northtrending shoreline (L). Box #1 is nearly completely emplaced, boxes #2 and 3 partly emplaced. Spiral anchor screwed in sand behind boxes provides stability and leverage for diver. **b** — Box filled with sand, bottom plate secured with elastic band. Box sides were taped together prior to sampling to prevent their spreading apart during emplacement. **c** — Box on side in laboratory, bottom plate removed. **d** — Upper side of box detached and uppermost 2 to 3 cm of sand removed by careful troweling. **e** — Metal tray inverted and pushed into sand surface. Orientation data transferred to tray. **f** — Tray removed and sand leveled and dried. Orientation data on underside of tray. **g** — Sand within tray impregnated with about 120 cc of epoxy resin. When resin has set, orientation data is transferred to the sand slab. **h** — Sand slab removed from tray, internal structure outlined by surface relief provided by preferential penetration of resin through individual beds. Orientation data on underside of slab.

file. Water depths may be obtained using a stadia rod with the average wave trough as the reference depth. Wave data are obtained from shore based observations.

The internal structure of the sediment may be ascertained using Senckenberg boxes (Figure 8–18) which measure about $20 \times 16 \times 8$ cm. Emplacement of the boxes 2–3 cm apart in an aligned series permits reconstruction of a section of internal structures 1 m or more in length and 20 cm high, an area comparable to that seen in many outcrops. The series of boxes may be aligned either normal to or parallel to the shoreline, or if a 3-dimensional view is desirable, in a "T" or "L" configuration.

Senckenberg boxes are, in general, difficult to use for subaqueous sand sampling (Bouma 1969) and sampling within the turbulent surf zone requires special care and technique. The boxes should be bound tightly with tape, numbered sequentially, and marked with orientation data prior to the sampling.

When working in the surf zone, or in high currents, the diver must be overweighted. A metal rod about 1 cm in diameter twisted to form a spiral about 75 cm long and 10 cm in diameter can make an effective hand anchor when screwed into the sand. Such an anchor is necessary not only to maintain position against the surge of the waves but also to supply leverage for the almost neutrally buoyant diver to emplace the boxes. The boxes should generally be pushed all the way into the sand with a gentle rocking motion. Because of the rapid wave scour around each box, all the boxes must be at least partly emplaced very quickly. Once embedded, the boxes may be removed individually by digging the sand away from one side, slipping a metal plate beneath the box and pulling the box and the plate upward. A strong elastic band is then placed around the box and the bottom plate and the secured box placed in a rigid plastic container and carried to the beach. If the box is not protected by the container, the strong currents generated by the waves will readily erode much of the sample along the seam between the box and the bottom plate. Small holes in the bottom of the containers permit a gradual draining of the water and prevent sample loss due to flushing.

The boxes should be opened only in the laboratory, and the central 20 mm of sand within the box placed in a metal tray inscribed with the orientation data and dried. Maintenance of the orientation of the sample at every step of the processing is vital. Use of only the central portion of the box reduces the structural distortion which occurs at the sides of the box. After the sample is dried, sufficient (about 120 cc) epoxy resin should be poured over the sand surface of the tray to partially penetrate the sample. Partial penetration provides sufficient surface relief on the cemented block to define much of the internal structure.

8.7.2.3 Core Samples

Simple diver-operated apparatus for sampling nearshore sands described in detail by Sanders (1968), consists of plastic sampling tubes, steel hammering cap and hammering sleeve, an aluminum extracting handle, and metal and rubber sealing plugs. For coring, the hammering cap is placed on the one end of the plastic tube and positioned vertically on the surface of the sediment. The driving hammer is repeatedly raised and driven against the hammering plate; numerous short-stroke blows yield most rapid penetration. When the desired or maximum depth of penetration is reached, the hammering cap and sleeve are removed, core orientation marked, the extracting handle fitted over the upper end of the tube, and the sealing plug secured in the upper end of the tube. The tube is extracted by pulling upward on the handles. It is imperative that a complete seal be made with the sealing plug to prevent loss of sediment; a second diver immediately seals the lower end when it clears the bottom by inserting a stopper or cap. Divers have collected cores of firmly packed nearshore sands up to 6 feet using this apparatus. See Paragraph 8.9.1 for a description of an archeological coring device.

Dill and Moore (1965), report on the adaptation of the vane-shear test (Evans and Sherratt 1948) to underwater *in situ* measurements where the vane can be inserted directly into the sediments (Figure 8–19). Knowledge of the sediment's resistance to shear is, for example, necessary for calculating submarine slope stability. The vane-shear apparatus developed by Dill and Moore is based on the modification of a commercially available 24-inch-ounce torque screwdriver; the measurement range between 0 and 24 inch-ounces appears to be adequate for most shear strengths encountered in the upper 6 inches of marine sediments for a vane having a dimension of $\frac{3}{4} \times \frac{3}{4}$ inch. When used by a diver, the vane is carefully pushed into the sediment to a predetermined depth. After the instrument has been

Photo: Lee Somers

inserted to the desired depth, force is applied by twisting the apparatus in the sediment. Torque is increased gradually and constantly over a period of time of no less than 2 minutes to obtain significant values. This vane-shear apparatus was used in determining the stability of sedimentary slopes (Dill 1969).

Numerous types of geological sampling devices are available on the commercial market. An underwater air lift may be used to remove sediment or sand. This method is described in Paragraph 4.13. A large array of corers, dredges, grabs, and sediment lift devices have been made available to meet specific requirements of a particular investigation. Bouma (1969) provides technical details of various geological sampling devices.

8.7.2.4 Drilling Samples

A portable submersible drill was developed that will enable diver scientists to obtain cores $2\frac{1}{8}$ inches in diameter to penetration depths of 50 feet or more (Macintyre 1974). This hydraulically powered drill unit was developed by adapting an "Ackley" hydraulic impact wrench to accommodate drill pipe and double-tube core barrels that are standard equipment manufactured commercially.

This tool has been successfully field tested in coral reef areas both from a boat and from land off Panama, where carbide drill bits were found to be more effective and economical than diamond bits. This technique can produce a core representing a sequence of accumulated reef structure without undue disturbance to the local environment.

The drill unit together with the short 2-foot core barrel weighs about 150 pounds, and can be handled readily by two divers (Figure 8–17). The drill can be operated freely for shallow penetration (e.g., drilling 5–10 feet into a coral head), but a winch and tripod were required for retrieving cores from greater penetrations. Field tests indicated that a three-man team is required for optimum efficiency; one is needed to operate the drill, a second to operate the winch and tripod, and a third to assist in adding and removing drill pipe. Submerged coring using this technique can probably be carried out to depths of 150 feet.

8.8 MICRO-PHYSICAL OCEANOGRAPHY

Probably the most under-exploited use of diving techniques lies in the field of micro-oceanography. For some unknown reason the physical oceanographers have not widely utilized *in situ* measurements and observations of the water mass processes. This is a relatively new and promising part of diving science. The study of turbulent cells, boundary layers, and flow regimes at the scale, seen and felt by every diver, has received only minimal attention. Yet because the physical oceanographic conditions are such an important part of each dive they have become known as a folklore around diving scientists. Notable among published accounts are the studies of visual indications of the thermocline, the use of dye tracers to reveal flow patterns (Woods and Lythgoe 1971), and the study of internal waves and the formation of bubbles in sound attenuation (LaFond and Dill 1957). Work by Schroeder (1974) in Hydro-Lab has shown that the diver has more of a contribution to make than the emplacement, tending and recovery of oceanographic instruments. He is the best means by which the scale of measurements of the physical nature of the water column can be ascertained. The day of blindly lowering instruments into the sea to predetermined depths, and hoping to find out the true oceanographic conditions that prevail in a region are far behind us. The oceanographic scientist today must dive to implant his instruments

Table 8-1
Micro-Oceanographic
Techniques

Parameter	Technique	Diving Mode*	Placement	Problems	Remarks
Temperature	Thermometer array	C,S	Taut-line buoy pier, piling, oil rig.	Where to position thermometers. Pre and post use calibration. Requires repetitive observation.	Limited by bottom time.
	Recording thermograph	C,S	Same as above but secure to bottom.	Equipment flooding. Electronic failure. Only one data point unless multiple units used.	Relocation of units.
	Remote readout	C,S	Same as above.	Same as above.	Excellent for use in habitat.
Salinity	Water samples	C,S	Bottle rack carried by diver.	Number of samples. Processing procedures.	Limited by bottom time.
	Recording salinometer	Same as Temperature ·			
	Remote readout	Same as Temperature ·			
Dissolved Oxygen	Water samples	C,S	Bottle rack carried by divers.	Outgassing when brought to surface.	Best used from a habitat.
	Remote readout	Same as Temperature			
Multiple Sensor Unit	Recording	Same as Temperature			
	Remote readout	C,S	Reverse vertical profiling using floats and pulley system.	Fouling of cables. Interface at surface.	Excellent for habitat operations.
Currents	Recording	Same as Temperature ·			
	Remote readout	Same as Temperature ·			
	Dye studies	Refer to Woods Underwater Science			
Tides	Recording (waves)	Same as Temperature ·			
	Ambient pressure gauge inside habitat	S	Gauge inside habitat.		

*C = conventional diving
 S = saturation diving

**Figure 8-20
Measuring Dissolved Oxygen
in the Exhaled Water
of a Sponge**

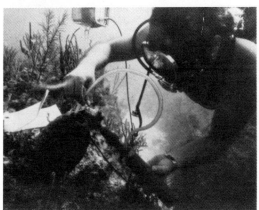

Photo: Laurence Bussey

**Figure 8-21
Underwater
Instrument Chamber**

Photo: Morgan Wells

in those parts of the water column that are active, he must observe their response to determine if they are measuring the "real world," and he must use his eyes and sense of touch to plan future long term measurements that cannot be done by an *in situ* approach.

Table 8–1 summarizes some of the micro-oceanographic parameters and problems which involve the use of divers in data collection. As methodology is developed, the diver's role in micro-oceanography will expand.

8.8.1 Emplacement of Instruments

The implantation, reading, and maintenance of instruments and instrument arrays, and the recovery of samples and data, are important roles of the diver in oceanographic surveys. Instruments implanted on a site to measure current flow or direction or other phenomena may become damaged or inoperative as a result of marine growths or buildup of sand or bottom debris. If the instruments are read remotely, these conditions may, unknown to the investigator, alter the validity of data measured by the instrument. A diver may routinely check the operating condition of implanted instruments to ensure that the instrument is operating correctly.

Diving techniques have long been an integral part of *in situ* experiments concerning the effects of controlled nutrient enrichment of phytoplankton populations in Lake Michigan (Somers 1972). In these studies divers placed large plastic bags at

various depths. This required placement of a screw-type anchor or other anchoring device in the lake bottom, and attachment of a collapsed bag held in a vertical position by a submerged float. Divers could then insert a hose into each bag to facilitate filling with lake water and nutrient solutions. After the filling process was completed, the divers disconnected the hoses and secured the filling tubes. Water samples were taken periodically by divers utilizing a hose and pump.

In situ recording respirometers have been used

8-25

**Figure 8-22
Dye-Tagged Water Being
Moved by Bottom Current**

Photo: U.S. Navy

to determine respiration and photosynthesis of benthic organisms (Figure 8-20) and communities in undisturbed, natural states by McCloskey and Chesher (Miller et al. 1971), Wells, Wells, and VanDerwalker (1973), Johannes et al. (AIBS 1972), and Wells (1974). The biochemical oxygen demand of domestic sludge beds has been determined using plexiglass domes equipped with oxygen electrodes and mixing devices. Undersea laboratories are of great advantage in experimental studies requiring large quantities of instrumentation and long dives. The *U*ndersea *I*nstrument *C*hamber (USIC) provides a stable underwater housing for instrumentation which records oxygen, temperature, light, pH, conductivity, redox potential, and sound. USIC can be entered by divers for data retrieval, calibration of equipment, and maintenance (Figure 8-21).

8.8.2 Use of Dye Tracers

In addition to the emplacement and monitoring of instruments, divers have measured currents, internal waves, thermoclines, and various turbulent components of the water column, using dye tracing techniques (Woods and Lythgoe 1971).

Water masses tagged with fluorescein dye can be followed and photographed so as to provide an accurate measurement of current speed and direction. If a point source of dye (a bottle full of dyed water) is released into the current, accurate measurements can be made at speeds lower than most current meters commonly employed (Figure 8-22).

In order to understand the generation of turbulence inside a thermocline and within the water column it is necessary to know both the density gradient and the *velocity shear.* The most convenient technique for laying a shear streak is to drop a tiny pellet of congealed fluorescein through the layer under study. Disc-shaped pellets, 3 mm in diameter and 1.5 mm thick, are particularly useful. These pellets are attached to a light line and dropped through a thermocline. The dispersion of the dye by the ambient flow can then be photographed.

The only disturbence to the existing flow caused by the pellet's passage through the water column is in the formation of a small vortex wake, whose individual vortices rapidly lose their own motion and proceed to follow the ambient flow. The pellets are sealed in waterproof polythene strips until needed. Three sizes, each with the same aspect ratio, are used: the smallest, described above, gives the most regular wake, but only lasts for about 5 minutes. The largest (6 mm diameter by 2.3 mm thick) can lay a streak through the whole thermocline. Speeds of these pellets are comparable with the differences in horizontal velocity encountered along any streak, their drop path is often quite complex, so the velocity profile cannot be obtained from a single photograph. Instead, the mean shear across any given layer is obtained in successive frames of a timed sequence of still photographs or using motion pictures.

The general procedure for the diver is as follows: after identifying the area of interest by dropping a trial pellet, the photographer positions himself at the chosen level and signals to an assistant, floating some 3–4 m above and upstream, to release a second pellet. As the pellet begins to fall the assistant increases buoyancy which allows him to rise gently away from the dye streak without disturbing it by turbulence from his fins. Whenever possible the assistant positions himself above the sheet overlaying the layer being filmed; this sheet isolates his movements from the dye. The photographer films the dye streak (keeping the sun behind the camera to increase contrast).

Current can also be measured near the bottom by using dye tagging techniques (Figure 8–22).

Figure 8-23
Diver Using
Water Sample Bottle

Figure 8-24
Water Sample Bottle Backpack

Care must be taken not to kick up sediment or to create artificial vortices by swimming in the area during such studies.

8.8.3 Water Samples

When taking measurements in the water column extra care should be exerted to minimize the amount of diver activity around study sites in order to avoid mixing of the water column caused by vertical water currents from exhaled bubbles. This bubble problem can also occur around habitat operations. Instruments should be placed well away and "upstream" of all bubble activity.

Considerable effort has been directed towards obtaining accurate measures of dissolved oxygen in seawater. A major concern is that the changes in pressure to which a sample of seawater is subjected as it is brought to the surface will affect the chemical nature of the "solution." While some of the effects will be negligible due to the relative insensitivity of liquids and solids to pressure variation; other effects will be significant if dissolved gases are of concern, since these substances exhibit a great dependence on pressure. Even if it were possible to isolate the container completely from its surroundings so that the sample would be unaffected as it is raised through the water column, once it is opened at the surface dissolved gases may escape quickly and irreversibly. Recognition of this shortcoming in conventional methodology led to the development of a sampler, which is portable, versatile, and inexpensive (Cratin et al. 1973). This sampler and technique are equally effective for operations from the surface or from an ocean

floor laboratory.

The sample bottles (Figure 8–23) are constructed from polyvinyl chloride (PVC) tubing 60 mm O.D., 48 mm I.D., and 12 cm long. (This provides a volume of about 225 ml.) Screw caps made of plastic and fitted with PVC inner linings and rubber O-rings effectively seal both ends of the sample bottle from their surroundings. A hole, 15 mm in diameter, is drilled into the side of each sampler and a piece of PVC tubing 15 mm long is sealed into it. Finally, a rubber septum is fitted into and over the small PVC tubing. When taking large numbers of samples, a backpack designed to fit over double scuba tanks is a useful accessory (Figure 8–24).

A sample collection is as follows: the open bottle (i.e., without the screw caps) is moved to the desired underwater location, tapped several times to ensure complete removal of all trapped air, and one of the caps is screwed on. A marble is placed into the sample bottle and the second cap is then screwed firmly into place.

To prevent dissolved oxygen from escaping when the sample is brought to the surface, two chemical "fixing" solutions are added in the following manner: a venting (hypodermic) needle is placed into the septum, and 2 ml of solutions of manganese (II) sulfate and alkaline potassium iodide are injected into the bottle via hypodermic syringes. (Special care must be taken to make certain that no bubbles of air are present in any of the hypodermic syringes.) The bottle is shaken several times to ensure complete mixing. (The dissolved oxygen gas is converted through a series of chemical reactions into a white insoluble solid, manganese III hydroxide.) When the samplers are taken to the laboratory, they must be kept under water as added insurance against leakage.

Once in the laboratory (with the bottle still under water) a venting needle is inserted into the septum and 2 ml of concentrated sulfuric acid are added via a hypodermic syringe. The bottle is shaken several times to ensure complete reaction. The sampler is then removed from under the water, one of the caps carefully unscrewed, and known volumes of solution are withdrawn. A knowledge of the volumes, concentrations of reacting chemicals, and other pertinent data, enables the analyst to calculate quantitatively the oxygen content in seawater. Details of this procedure are described in "Standard Methods for the Examination of Water and Wastewater," 12th Edition, pp. 406–410, 1965.

This sampling technique is limited only by the depth at which a diver may safely work. Oxygen analysis of samples taken from much greater depths requires considerably more complicated and expensive equipment that can be operated remotely.

8.9 ARCHEOLOGICAL DIVING

The application of diving to archeology has become increasingly important and widespread in the last 5 to 10 years. Not only are professional archeologists utilizing diving more, but thousands of amateurs are constantly exploring new "finds" and searching for historical artifacts.

Diving archeologists are now successfully diving to depths of 150 feet to locate, chart, excavate, make accurate three-dimensional plan drawings, and retrieve objects of great historical significance. Dumas (1962) and Bass (1966) have written the most complete publications on techniques of underwater archeology.

8.9.1 Locating Underwater Sites

Techniques used to search for underwater sites fall into two general categories: visual search techniques and electronic search techniques. The results from the latter must be verified by divers once an archeological find is made.

Visual search techniques utilize divers, observers in a boat, or observations from aircraft to locate the area of interest. Several techniques are of interest to divers in the detailed visual search and survey of an archeological site. These are: (1) the circling

line technique in which the diver descends to the bottom and systematically circles around the anchor or a weight; (2) the guideline method, where divers swim along a series of weighted, parallel guidelines on the bottom; and (3) the use of diver-held sonar where reflected signals may lead the diver to a sunken artifact. Details of these techniques are described by Bass (1966).

Clues to the existence of archeological sites range from purposeful research on historical events to accidental findings of fishermen and amateur and commercial divers.

Prior to excavation, it is essential to determine the general character of the environment, which will help to make the operation more efficient, and avoid unnecessary expenditures, accidents, and mistakes. The kinds of information found to be most useful include:

1. Measure the rates of sedimentation and bottom topography to determine size of air lift and excavation equipment needed.

2. Conduct subbottom profiling to determine sediment layers relative to wreck or site; and/or coring requirements.

3. Determine potential number of work days and best time of year to work on site and the type of weather conditions to be expected.

4. Determine movement of suspended materials, underwater visibility, wave action, current, and temperature.

5. If near shore, determine use of shore area as land base, work area, and living area.

Prior to excavation, all possible information about the attitude and extent of a shipwreck and its cargo must be known. Dumas (1962) discusses wreck analysis excavation in detail. His primary solution to determine the extent of the site is by systematic core sampling. The core sampler used to investigate archeological sites is usually a tube (10 to 12 feet long, 2 inches in diameter), with a cutting edge at one end that is driven into the bottom by its own momentum, by an explosive charge, or by some form of power generated by mechanical means. Once the preliminary survey is completed, a site excavation plan is formulated, and systematic layer by layer surveying and artifact removal is begun. Extreme care must be exercised to avoid unnecessary damage or removal of artifacts without documentation of position. Excavation requires knowledge of technique and equipment and a great deal of patience.

8.9.2 Surveying and Mapping

Archeologists have devised several methods for precision mapping of small areas under water (500 square yards). These methods are described in some detail because the same techniques can be used for small scale surveying in general. The following are among the most useful:

8.9.2.1 Peterson's Wheel-Meter Tape Triangulation Method

This method requires a wheel, with the rim marked in degrees, mounted on a vertical shaft. The shaft is driven into the bottom at selected locations. The 0-degree mark on the rim is aligned with magnetic north. A meter tape, pulled out from the top of the shaft, measures the distance to any point, with the direction read on the wheel rim where it is crossed by the tape. A slightly larger wheel, mounted over and perpendicular to the first so that it can pivot around it, allows elevations to be calculated from simultaneous readings of upward or downward angles. This is a simple method of making measurements under limited visibility conditions by two divers equipped with voice communication.

8.9.2.2 Meter Tape Triangulation Method

This method is considered more desirable than the Peterson's wheel method for application to small areas having reasonable visibility. Although it is time consuming, it is inexpensive, requires little equipment, a limited number of divers, and is especially adaptable to level and uncomplicated sites. Control points at known distances from each other are selected and marked on the seafloor around the site. Horizontal measurements with a meter tape made from two of these control points to any object or point on the site provide the necessary information for plotting the position on a plane.

8.9.2.3 Plane Table Triangulation Method

Bass (1966), Ryan and Bass (1962), and Milne (1972). This method may be used in clear water as on land, both for position triangulation and for taking elevations. Simple plane tables are necessary. They consist of a wooden table, three movable legs, and a weight. A simple alidade is constructed by combining a sighting device, a tube with cross hairs at each end, and a straightedge on a weighted base. Sheets of frosted plastic are then tacked to the table tops with the alidades set on these. Two plane tables are placed on the bottom, one on each side of the site, and leveled. Initial sightings are made on a previously selected reference or primary fixed control point and across the site from one table to the other. Lines are inscribed on each plastic drawing surface with ordinary lead pencils and respectively labeled. The resultant vectors, plus a measurement of the distance between the two points, establish the position of both tables on a horizontal plane. If the tables are not at the same elevation, the relationship is determined by placing a 20-foot-long calibrated range pole, weighted at the lower end and buoyed at the top with a float, on the lower table. A sighting is made from the upper plane, and the distance between the sighted point on the length of the pole and the lower table provides the vertical elevation relationship.

A diver mans each of the two plane tables. A third diver moves the range pole from point to point on the site, and sightings are taken from each table and labeled consecutively. Elevations are measured by the third diver moving a marker up or down the pole until he receives a signal from one table to stop; he then measures the distance from that point to the object being positioned and records the distance. The plane table diver uses the horizontal element of the cross hairs for this measurement. The efficiency of this method is limited by the clarity of the water and the requirement for three divers to record each point.

8.9.2.4 Dumas' Measuring Frame Method

This method of precision mapping for small areas has been successfully used by archeologists (Bass 1966, Ryan and Bass 1962, and Dumas 1962). A 5-meter square metal frame is fitted with four telescopic legs and extension couplings. The telescopic legs enable the frame to be leveled a few meters above a sloping site, and the extension couplings allow the size to be indefinitely doubled by fitting new 5-meter sections in place. Using two sides of the frame as tracks, a horizontal crossbar, mounted on wheels, can be moved from one side of the frame to the other. This crossbar is, in turn, traversed by a yoke holding a vertical pole. The mobile crossbar, the vertical pole, and the frame

Figure 8-25
Heavy Overburden Airlift

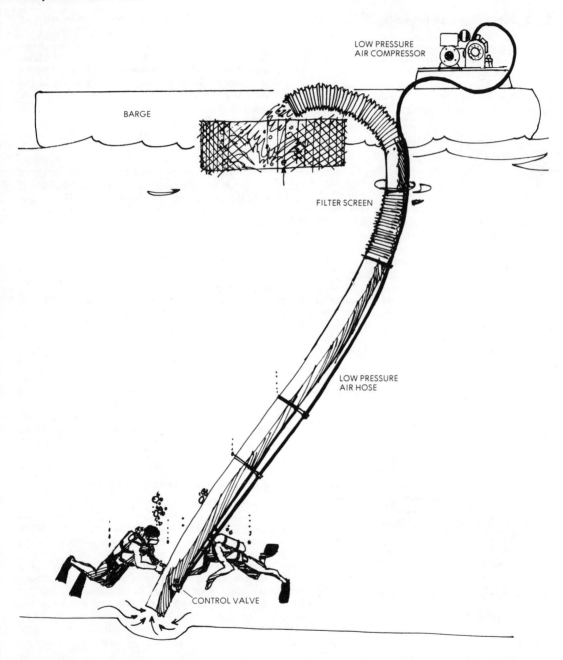

LOW PRESSURE
AIR COMPRESSOR

BARGE

FILTER SCREEN

LOW PRESSURE
AIR HOSE

CONTROL VALVE

are calibrated in centimeters. The vertical pole is adjusted to touch any object within the frame.

The coordinates of the point are recorded from three measurements read on the frame, the beam, and the elevation pole. The details around the point must be drawn by a diver hovering over portable 2-meter grids placed directly on the site materials. The simple 2-meter grids are divided into 20-centimeter squares, which are designated by numbers and letters marked on the sides of the grids. The measuring frame is used to fix the positions of the corners of the 2-meter grid.

8.9.2.5 Merifield Rosencrantz Method

A simple method for surveying a small area under water to measure ground control points has been developed and tested by Merifield and Rosencrantz (1966). The method is simple, rapid, and minimizes the requirements on divers. Three divers are required to complete the survey. The survey procedure consists of the following operations:

1. Two guide lines spaced 4 meters apart are stretched over the site to facilitate placement, spacing, and rapid relocation of numbered control point marker stakes (weight markers for rock bottoms). For an area 15 meters by 30 meters, 11 markers are placed.

2. Distances between control point marker stakes are measured by tape and recorded on a plan of the approximate locations drawn on a plastic sheet mounted on a clipboard. Measurement of a complete triangular net (three sides of all triangles) eliminates the necessity of angular determinations.

3. Relative elevations are determined with a range pole and leveling device. The leveling device consists of a transparent plastic tube 1 centimeter in diameter and 10 meters long. A diver induces air into one end of the tube until it is almost filled. The air-water interface within the hose is held at the marker stake's highest elevation. Buoyed by the entrapped air, the hose forms a convex-upward arc. A second diver holds the opposite end of the hose against the range pole, which rests vertically atop an adjacent marker stake. The position of the air-water interface on the range pole indicates the difference in elevation between the two marker stakes. A third diver records the measurements and directs the movements of the other divers.

8.9.2.6 Photographic Method

To improve mapping for detailed archeological studies, photographic towers may be utilized (Bass 1964, 1966, 1968; and Ryan and Bass 1962). The progress of excavation in each area can, therefore, be recorded with grid photographs taken through a hole in the top of the tower. Before objects can be traced onto the overall plan photographs taken by this method must be corrected for (1) difference in scale relative to elevations; (2) position of objects relative to their distance below the grids and lateral distance from the center of the grids; and (3) "pillowing" effect.

Series of stereophoto pairs may be taken of sites for three-dimensional viewing under a stereo-viewer. More important, the parallax in the pairs can be measured with a micrometer, and the elevations of any object then calculated by the simple formula:

$$\frac{f \times b}{p} = H$$

where

f = focal length of lens
b = distance between cameras (base)
p = parallax
H = distance from camera to object (height)

A water-corrected lens must be used on the camera.

Current solutions to the underwater surveying of large areas still depend on simplicity and, at least in shallow water, a coordination with basic surface surveying techniques.

8.9.3 Archeological Sampling

Archeological sampling requires considerable care and patience in the removal and recording of artifacts. The equipment necessary for the removal of heavy overburdens of mud and silt around an archeological site is large and cumbersome.

The air lift, the "shovel" of underwater archeology, has been used on virtually every major excavation under water (Bass 1966). The air lift is a simple instrument (Figure 8–25), consisting of a rigid, or part rigid and part flexible tube, into which air is introduced at the lower end. Consequently, the air breaks into small bubbles and mixes with the water. The result is a gas-liquid mixture of less density than the liquid outside the pipe. Since the density of the mixture inside the pipe is less than the density of the liquid outside the pipe, the air-water mixture will rise until the pressure of

Figure 8-26
Fish Trap

the column of the mixture equals at its base the pressure of the water at the same level. The suction created at the lower end of the air displaces unconsolidated materials and carries them to the surface.

Lifted matter is discharged at the surface for screening and inspection through a reinforced flexible rubber section of tubing onto a barge or nearby land, or directly into the water down current from the work site. In the latter case, a wire screen container fitted with a small cloth bag at its lower portion is used to prevent loss of artifacts (Bass 1966).

The air lift, if used without discretion, can damage or lose important artifacts. Details of air lifts and excavation techniques are given by Dumas (1962), and Bass (1966).

The success or failure of air lifting directly on the site is relative to a diver's ability to change the size of the mouth (footpiece) and vary the lift's power. With a small, 2-inch lift at low power, extremely delicate work can be undertaken.

In some areas, to avoid the dumping of airlifted materials back onto the site, it is necessary to transport this material away from the area. A long horizontal pipe floated on the surface will accomplish this task. To facilitate movement of material in the horizontal portion of the pipe, it may be necessary to attach a water jet pump.

A versatile instrument for removing muck and other overburden from a site is the *underwater suction dredge.* Similar to that used to recover gold, it uses the reverse injection method in which water, pumped under considerable pressure through a hose from above, is injected a few inches behind the mouth of a pipe (2 to 12 inches in diameter). A strong suction is created in the opening, and a current is forced along the pipe. A hose is attached to the pipe, and the sucked material is pumped to the surface for screening. The mouth of the dredge can be screened to prohibit the entrance of heavy bulky objects that might clog the hose. Although not as effective as the air lift in some ways, the dredge is apparently a more gentle technique and permits a fairly systematic excavation (Jewell 1964).

An *underwater dredge and surface sluice machine* for screening materials and retrieval of artifacts, with sufficient power, can be used for shallow water work to depths of 30 feet to remove large amounts of overburden. A small water jet can also be incorporated into these units. Modifications of existing equipment would make the dredge and surface sluice machine highly adaptable for saturation diving operations with sluicing and screening being accomplished either in a dry compartment similar to that used for inert gas welding on submerged pipelines, or directly under water. Depth would not be a limiting factor.

A *high pressure water jet* can be used to cut through unconsolidated overburden and force it away from the site. The system consists of a hose, pump, and nozzle. The recoilless nozzle, which sends a water jet backward as well as forward, is recommended. A standard fire hoze nozzle may be used if a diver compensates for the backward push of the water jet.

The use of *flotation gear* is an inexpensive and effective method of lifting. Lifting bags are available in different sizes and forms ranging from large rubberized bags and metal tanks capable of lifting several tons to small plastic and rubberized nylon bags for lifting 50 to 500 pounds. Larger bags should be equipped with an air relief valve at the top. For archeological work, the smaller rubberized nylon bags are recommended; these self-venting bags with a lifting capacity of 100 pounds are useful in all underwater operations. Lifting devices are described further in Paragraph 7.1.5.

8.10 CAPTURE TECHNIQUES

A wide variety of devices are utilized by scientists and commercial fishermen to aggregate, concentrate, or confine aquatic animals. Trawls, seines, traps, grabs, and dredges have been successfully observed by scuba-equipped scientists concerned with animal and gear behavior. High (1971) points out that divers can frequently play a critical role in the design and evaluation of trawls and related gear. This role may be in the form of basic design,

**Figure 8-27
Divers Inspecting the Cod
End of a Cobb
Pelagic Trawl**

Photo: National Marine Fisheries Service

operational observation in shallow water, or by the observation of animal behavior within the gear's influence.

High and Beardsley participating in the Tektite II undersea program were able to directly observe fish near stationary traps 25 to 80 feet below the surface for up to eight hours per day (Figure 8–26) (Miller et al. 1971). Methods were found to alter catch rates and species captured. Divers from the National Marine Fisheries Service accurately estimated fish populations attracted to experimental submerged structures during studies to develop automated fishing platforms. These and other diver studies conducted near passive fishing gear usually posed few unique or unexpected problems.

8.10.1 Nets

Nets vary as to size, purpose, materials, and methods fished. Size is a major concern as divers desiring to make direct observations of an active net (one which is being towed) can readily alter or distort small nets by swimming near or touching net components. Any net is considered large if direct diver contact does not appreciably influence its configuration or operation. Plankton nets typify small nets both in physical size and the light-weight web required to retain microorganisms. At the larger extreme, high seas tuna seines often are 3,600 feet long with 4½ inch long meshes stretching 200 or more feet down into the water. Gill nets are designed to entangle fish attempting to push through the meshes. Webbing mesh and thread size varies as does the net length and depth, depending upon the size and species of fish sought. Gill nets use fine twine meshes hung vertically in the water

between a corkline and leadline. The net may be suspended at the surface, below the surface, or be weighted to fish just above bottom across the expected path of migratory fish. Divers and their equipment readily tangle in gill net web which is difficult to see in the water.

8.10.2 Seines

Seines are similar to gill nets in that a wall of web is held open vertically in the water by opposing forces of a corkline and leadline. However, the seine is set in a circle to confine fish schools within the web rather than entangle the fish. Seines often have rings along the leadline through which a line or cable can be pulled to draw the bottom closed, sealing off the fishes' escape route.

8.10.3 Trawls

Trawls are nets constructed like flattened cones or wind socks and are towed by one or two vessels. The net may be operated at the surface, in midwater, or across the seafloor. Specific designs vary widely depending upon the species sought. A 10 foot long plankton net having a ½ meter mouth opening may be towed at speeds up to 5 knots whereas a 200 foot long pelagic trawl opening 40 by 70 feet may filter water at 1 knot (Figure 8–27). Trawls may be opened horizontally by towing each wingtip from a separate vessel, by spreading the net with a rigid wooden or metal beam or with paired otterboards suspended in the water to shear out away from each other horizontally when towed.

8.10.4 Diving When Underway

Diving on stationary gear such as traps, gill nets, and some seines presents only a few unique problems to the experienced diver. He can dive either inside or outside the net to observe animal behavior or carry out work assignments. A diver must be alert to the probability of loose diving gear including pull rods, valves, mask rims, knives, vest inflator mechanisms, and weight belt buckles becoming fouled in the web. Loose undulating web not under strain is a likely source of entanglement. Such entanglements can usually be cleared more readily by the buddy than by the fouled diver. Unless the fouled diver turns or spins around, he is not likely to be wrapped in the web. Sometimes a fouled diver must remove the tank, disengage the caught mesh, replace the tank assembly and continue the assignment.

Hazards and diver difficulties increase with the speed of active nets or their components. During early retrieval of purse seines, web, purse rings, and the purseline move slowly. Toward the end of the pursing and net retrieving sequence, these components move quickly through the water. Since divers usually lack communication with surface winch and line hauler operators, the divers must stay out of the bight of the line or the immediate path of the gear.

Diving within the influence of a trawl or other devices towed from vessels underway does present unique hazards to divers. These include entrapment within the net, fouling, and being forced against bottom obstructions. If the device is moving slowly (under 1½ knots), the diver may be able to swim alongside for short periods. At speeds up to about 2.5 knots he may hold onto large nets without seriously distorting them and be pulled through the water. Both of these methods require the diver to be in excellent physical condition and to be trained in this special form of research diving.

High (1967) has described the methods used by divers to study trawls. Generally divers operating on large midwater or bottom trawls descend to the trawl by entering the water from the towing vessel and moving down the towing cables. Care must be exercised to avoid jamming broken cable strands into the diver's hand. This descent technique provides a direct route to the net with a minimum of energy and compressed air expended. Caution must be observed as the divers approach the turbulent water behind the otterboards, especially when the boards are in contact with the bottom. Clouds of sediment stirred up by the otterboard obscure portions of the bridles between the otterboard and the net so the diver must feel his way along the bridle. As an alternative, when visibility is good (25 feet horizontal), experienced divers may swim inboard of the otterboard just within the path of the oncoming trawl and wait for the bridles to clear the mud cloud or for the net to appear.

Divers can make their observations while hanging directly onto the trawl and conveniently move hand over hand to all parts of the net. However, trawls having a stretched mesh size of less than 2 inches (each side of the aperture 1 inch long) are difficult to hang onto. Distances between two points on the trawl can be estimated by pulling low stretch polypropylene twine taut between the points then cutting the line (Figure 8-28). The tied end will remain with

Photo: William High

the trawl until retrieval when the line can be removed and measured.

Small trawls and other moving gear can be observed without direct contact which may affect the system by using a separate tow line for the divers. A sea sled with a current deflecting shield can be towed parallel to the gear providing protection for divers who can then observe the gear at much greater speed than divers hanging directly on the gear. Under these conditions one diver is the pilot and his buddy the observer. The divers must be particularly careful to maintain proper breathing rhythms to prevent embolism in the event of sudden rising of the sea sled. The pilot should have a depth gauge mounted to be easily read at all times. He should continually monitor the gauge maintaining a constant depth or making necessary changes slowly. The use of a sea sled facilitates the use of a hard wire communications system between divers and the surface.

Each diver must be alert to possible dangers in a bottom trawl's path. Some obstructions encountered will cause the trawl to stop momentarily then

**Table 8-2
Levels of Anesthesia
for Fish**

Stage	Description	Behavior
0	Unanesthetized	Normal for the species.
1	Sedation	Decreased reaction to visual stimuli and/or tapping on the tank; opercular rate reduced; locomotor activity reduced; color usually darker.
2	Partial loss of equilibrium	Fish has difficulty remaining in normal swimming position; opercular rate usually higher; swimming disrupted.
3	Total loss of equilibrium	Plane 1—Fish usually on side or back; can still propel itself; responds to tap on tank or other vibrations; opercular rate rapid. Plane 2—Locomotion ceases; fins may still move but ineffectively; responds to squeeze of peduncle or tail; opercular rate decreased.
4	Loss of reflex	Does not respond to peduncle squeeze; opercular rate slow—often may be erratic. This is the surgical level.
5	Respiratory collapse	Operculum ceases to move; cardiac arrest (death) will occur within one to several minutes unless fish revived in untreated water.

surge ahead with great force. Logs may be lifted and carried into or over the net. Turbulence behind the otterboards may lift sharp spined animals up off bottom into the path of divers.

Imminent danger exists whenever any part of a diver is ahead of a bottom trawl. Severe injury would result from being pinned between parts of the net and an obstruction.

In the event a diver is carried into a trawl from which he can not readily extricate himself, he must cut an exit through the web. Usually trawls have heavier web in the aft portion (cod end). Therefore, if possible cut an escape opening forward in the top of the trawl body. Make a 3 foot long diagonal slit in the trawl. Make another similar slit at 90° to and beginning at the upstream end of the first slit. The water current should then fold a triangular flap of webbing back out of the way leaving a triangular escape hole. The diver's buddy should assist the trapped diver through the opening to free any gear which snags on meshes.

WARNING

Trawl Divers Must Carry a Sharp Knife Strapped to the Inside of the Calf of the Leg to Prevent Its Catching on the Web.

Often a small single blade knife is carried in the wet suit wrist cuff as a spare. An electrician's skinning knife is ideal for this purpose as its wide, curved blade is easily opened with heavy gloves on and it resembles a linoleum knife when open.

Vessel course or speed changes normally pose no hazard to working divers. Often, changing speed can be used as a simple signal between divers and vessel personnel. As speeds rise above 2½ knots, divers will have difficulty holding mouthpieces in and keeping facemasks on. At higher speeds they may lose their grips and be forced off the net. When stopped, the net does not normally collapse, but rather slowly settles and becomes slack. Under this condition the divers should be cautious of a sudden start which may tangle them in a line or web. Divers working from a sea sled adjacent to a trawl may be forced against the trawl during a turn. As pointed out by High (1967), trawl divers should be well-trained gear experts so they will know where they are in relation to any part of the trawl at all times, even when only a small portion of the net is visible in turbid waters.

When trawl dives are conducted, a safety pickup boat is required. The boat is operated on a parallel course adjacent to the estimated position of the trawl and divers. At the termination of the dive, the buddy team makes a normal ascent and is picked up by the boat.

8.10.4.1 Diving Equipment When Diving While Underway

Special attention must be given to diving equipment used during dives on moving gear.

WARNING

Double-Hose Regulators Are Unsatisfactory When Diving While Underway Because Water Flow Causes Hoses to Vibrate and Collapse, Shutting Off the Air Supply.

Single-hose regulators with large diameter purge buttons occasionally free flow, because of strong water current against the button face.

Reserve valve pull rods are the single greatest source of diver entanglement in webbing. Often, they are removed from the tanks. A diver's reserve valve is then actuated by the buddy, providing positive notice that both should terminate the dive. When a pull rod is used, the pull-ring should be brazed shut or taped to prevent webbing from slipping into the loop. Direct pressure gauges permit team members to moniter each other's air supply and depart the net while ample air reserve remains. The strap on the pressure gauge hose should be fastened to a strap of the *backpack* only! The gauge should not be left dangling at the diver's side as it will often become caught in the net.

Adjustable straps on face masks and fins are an occasional source of difficulty for trawl divers. The loose ends of the fin straps should be on the inside of the strap next to the ankle to prevent the flopping strap or buckle from entangling in the net. Straps should be adjusted until comfortable then securely taped in place to prevent pulling out.

Towed divers must have exposure suits with warmth qualities superior to those necessary during regular dives. Rapid movement through cold waters will quickly chill a diver, reducing his effectiveness and exposing him to the dangers of hypothermia (See Paragraph 2–4). Variable volume dry suits are excellent for use in cold water (below 60° F). However, additional drag on a towed diver may preclude their use when high mobility is desired.

Snorkels should not be attached to a towed diver's mask. Normally, snorkels are omitted from the gear complement due to their tendency to catch on webbing, and they are not normally needed since the diver floats at the surface until picked up by the safety boat.

Scientists who plan to dive near capturing systems should undertake special training dives which simulate conditions likely to be encountered.

8.10.5 The Use of Anesthetics in Capturing and Handling Marine Fishes

Anesthesia has been defined as a state of reversible insensitivity of the cell, tissue, or organism. In discussing fish, narcosis and anesthesia are often used interchangeably and not all chemicals characterized as fish anesthetics act as analgesics. Obviously nonanalgesics should not be used for surgical

intervention or other painful manipulations. Fish anesthetics have been used in conjunction with a multitude of operations including capture, transport, tagging, artificial spawning, blood sampling, moving fish in aquaria, surgical intervention, and photography. There is a wealth of published information in the popular aquarium literature as well as in scientific papers and textbooks concerning a wide variety of chemicals and their application. The following paragraphs discuss several anesthetics commonly used or potentially useful in handling fish. Important reviews with additional information have been published by McFarland (1960), Bell (1967), Klontz and Smith (1968), and McFarland and Klontz (1969). An important source of recent and continuing research information is the series of reports "Investigations in Fish Control" published by the U.S. Department of the Interior, Bureau of Sport Fisheries and Wildlife.

8.10.5.1 Response to Anesthetics

Fish anesthetics are most commonly administered by adding them to the water which is taken up by the gills. As the fish proceeds into anesthesia, it usually follows a series of definable stages which are useful in evaluating the depth of anesthesia.

A simplified scheme modified in part from McFarland (1959) and in part from Schoettger and Julin (1967) is presented in Table 8–2.

The response to an anesthetic depends upon a number of factors including the species and size of fish, water temperature, salinity or hardness, pH, and state of excitability of the fish as well as the dosage and type of anesthetic. With some anesthetics, not all of the stages mentioned in Table 8–2 are observable. For example, with quinaldine there is generally no definitive sedation stage.

Recovery generally begins when the fish is removed from the anesthetic bath to untreated water and usually proceeds through the stages in reverse order.

8.10.5.2 Selecting an Anesthetic

Factors to consider in choosing an anesthetic are purpose, toxicity, repellant action, ease of application, and cost. Reference to the literature may be helpful in choosing a suitable anesthetic for the species and purpose concerned. In the absence of applicable data, it is often advisable to conduct a preliminary experiment since even closely related species may not respond in the same manner. Species specific intolerance has been demonstrated with some anesthetics (Marking 1967).

Many chemicals exhibit toxic effects not related to their anesthetic action. These may be transitory or sustained. Some which exhibit toxic effects during long term exposure may be satisfactory for short term anesthesia.

The therapeutic ratio $TR = \dfrac{LC_{50}}{EC}$ is sometimes used in evaluating an anesthetic.

where

LC_{50} = concentration at which 50 percent of the specimens die.

EC = concentration necessary to provide the desired anesthesia.

Generally, a TR of 2 or more is considered desirable but as it varies with time of exposure and a variety of other factors, its usefulness is somewhat limited.

Toxicity to humans must also be considered. A given anesthetic may be dangerous to handle because of its acute toxicity or carcinogenicity or it may toxify fish flesh rendering it dangerous or fatal to eat.

Specific responses to an anesthetic may be important. The stages can vary with the anesthetic. For example, as mentioned above, quinaldine cannot generally be utilized to produce the sedation stage. Some chemicals are much more repellant to fish than others.

Several anesthetics have low solubility in water and must be first mixed with a carrier such as acetone or alcohol. This may cause considerable inconvenience particularly in field work.

Cost is a further factor which must be considered, especially where large field collections are concerned.

8.10.5.3 Application of Anesthetics

Rapid Immobilization. Fishes may be rapidly immobilized for capture or handling if the anesthetic is administered in high enough dosages. The fish is then removed from the influence of the anesthetic to untreated water for recovery. The chemical may be sprayed in the vicinity of the fish, added to a container holding the fish, or the fish removed to a separate bath, depending upon the circumstances. Several anesthetics which are unsuitable for sustained anesthesia are satisfactory for rapid immobilization, provided the exposure is of short duration.

Sustained Anesthesia. Under suitable conditions fish can safely be sustained under anesthesia for several days. Choice of the proper anesthetic is critical with regard to toxicity and stability. Prior to anesthesia the fish should be starved 24 to 48 hours to prevent regurgitation of food.

For surgery on captured fish a simple procedure is to anesthetize the fish to the surgical plane; place it in a trough or other restraining device and immerse the head in an anesthetic bath for the duration of the procedure. With longer term surgery, more sophisticated procedures are required. One successful system employs two water baths, one containing untreated water, the other, the anesthetic solution. The level of anesthesia can be carefully controlled by recirculating water from the treated bath over the gills. Steps should be taken to maintain the oxygen level near saturation and the ammonia level minimal. Filtration may be required to maintain water quality (Klontz and Smith 1968).

Recovery. Fish in deep anesthesia may have to be moved gently to and fro in their normal swimming position in order to revive them. It is helpful to direct a gentle stream of water toward the fish's mouth; thus providing a low velocity current over the gills. It is inadvisable to use a strong current or insert a hose directly into the mouth as this may cause rather than alleviate, hypoxia (Klontz and Smith 1968). The water in which the fish is being revived must be of good quality.

Some species recovering from certain anesthetics may undergo violent, uncontrolled swimming movements, and steps must be taken to prevent self-inflicted injuries. For example, this is usually the case with yellowtail *Seriola dorsalis* when recovering from quinaldine anesthesia. A variety of physiological changes have been observed in fishes following anesthesia; some of which may persist for over a week (Houston et al. 1971). During this period additional stress may result in mortality and should be minimized.

8.10.5.4 Field Collection

In most places a special permit is required for chemical collecting. In addition, the use of many anesthetics is governed by Food and Drug Administration regulations; the violation of which carries severe penalties. Those using anesthetics are advised to be thoroughly familiar with all pertinent regulations.

Tidepools and Ponds. Anesthetics are useful in making tidepool collections. The water volume is estimated, the desired dose calculated, then added. As the fish are immobilized, they are removed as quickly as possible to untreated water. When collecting from tidepools it is desirable to collect as the tide is rising. A moderate amount of surge in the pool helps to flush anesthetized fish out of crevices, and dilution of the pool with incoming water will reduce the mortality of specimens not collected. With the proper anesthetic and dose the mortality of uncollected specimens is negligible (Gibson 1967, Moring 1970).

Reef and Shore. Many species of reef and shore fishes can be collected with anesthetics. Quinaldine (10–20 percent) is now widely used for this purpose. One-half to one liter of the solution is normally used for each collection. Species susceptibility is highly variable. For example, angelfishes and butterflyfishes are highly susceptible; squirrelfishes moderately susceptible and moray eels highly resistant. The effectiveness will vary with the physical situation in which the fish are encountered as well as the skill and experience of the collector. Most anesthetics are at least somewhat repellant and generally the fish need to be in a situation where they can be constricted within the anesthetic for several seconds such as in small caves, short crevices, or under rocks. The anesthetic is usually dispensed from a squeeze bottle in sufficient dose to immobilize or partially immobilize the specimens on the first application. The fish can then be collected with a hand net or in the case of small specimens, a manual "slurp" gun (Figure 8–29).

Sometimes sedentary specimens can be collected by trickling a light dose slowly downstream toward them. This only works with sedentary fishes that are not readily repelled by the anesthetic.

Fishes in burrows are often more difficult to collect with anesthetics than would be anticipated. Sometimes the burrows are so deep that the fish cannot be reached with the discharge from a normal squeeze bottle. In this case the attachment of tubing, such as a piece of aquarium air line, to the bottle, may be helpful. Usually the anesthetic should have repellant qualities which will cause the fish to emerge. Otherwise, the fish may be anesthetized, but unrecoverable. With some non-repellant anesthetics a noxious chemical may be added.

Scripps Aquarium has developed a successful

**Figure 8-29
Slurp Gun Used
to Collect Small Fish**

Photo: © National Geographic Society

system for collecting garden eels *Taenioconger Species*, which heretofore have been difficult to obtain. A piece of clear plastic, 2 meters by 2 meters, is placed over the area of the burrows and weighted down along the edges with sand. Approximately 1 liter of 13 percent quinaldine solution in ethanol is applied under the plastic. The area is then left undisturbed for 20 minutes after which time the sedated and immobilized eels are gathered gently by hand. A single collection in a well developed colony may yield over 40 eels. This technique can be applied to other burrowing species although the dosage and time of exposure may have to be varied.

Coral Heads. It is usually advantageous to enclose coral heads with a loose fitting net before applying the anesthetic. Some species of fishes such as wrasses and hawkfishes reside in coral at night and can be actively collected at that time with the aid of anesthetics.

Large Scale Collections. It is sometimes desired to collect fishes over a large portion of a reef. One useful technique is to enclose the desired area with a seine, and administer a large enough quantity of anesthetic to rapidly immobilize the enclosed population. Divers should work as a team to recover the fish due to the danger of becoming entangled in the net. Procedures to free entangled divers should be planned in advance.

Handling Large Fish. Sharks and other large fish captured by hook may be advantageously immobilized by spraying a strong anesthetic solution directly over the gills before bringing them aboard. Gilbert and Wood (1957) used a 1000 ppm tricaine solution.

Transportation. Anesthetics have been used in the transportation of fishes with conflicting results. The effectiveness depends upon a number of factors including type of anesthetic, species of fishes, temperature, time in transit, preconditioning of fish, and water quality. Most fishes can be successfully transported without the use of anesthetics. If it is deemed beneficial to use anesthetics, prior information should be gathered for species and conditions concerned either from the literature or by experimentation.

Summary. There is much controversy in the popular aquarium literature concerning the use of anesthetics as collecting agents for aquarium fishes, primarily because of the considerable concern regarding delayed toxicity. A survey of the literature, including Gibson (1967), Moring (1970) and various reports in "Investigations in Fish Control", indicates that in the majority of species experimentally subjected to repeated anesthetization delayed mortality is negligible. Professional aquarists at Scripps Aquarium, Steinhart Aquarium and others, have demonstrated that many other species not subjected to formal experimentation can be safely collected and handled without significant mortality.

The majority of aquatic biologists concerned with collecting, agrees that with judicious application, anesthetics are useful and successful collecting agents. Misuse of chemicals, especially if widespread, can be very harmful. For example, the practice of using sodium cyanide to collect aquarium fishes, as is sometimes done in underdeveloped countries, is ill-advised and has resulted in human deaths, as well as delayed mortalities of fishes.

Recommendations. Tricaine (MS-222) is a highly soluble powder; virtually odorless, and easy to use. It has proved to be a successful anesthetic in a wide variety of applications and under a wide variety of conditions in both fresh and seawater. There is abundant literature available describing its properties and use. Tricaine is a good choice where sustained sedation or surgical-level anesthesia is required. High cost precludes its use as a collecting agent.

Quinaldine has been widely used to collect or handle fishes. It is of low solubility in water and is generally dissolved in acetone, ethyl alcohol, or isopropyl alcohol prior to use in water. Quinaldine is not useful where sedation-level anesthesia is the goal, nor desirable for major surgery or other painful procedures as it is a poor analgesic. Liquid quinaldine can be readily converted to a water soluble salt which greatly facilitates its use. The salt, mixed with MS-222 in proper proportions, combines desirable properties of both chemicals.

McNeil-JR-7476 (Propoximal, Propoximate) is a new low-cost, low-toxicity, potent, water-soluble anesthetic which shows particular promise as a collecting agent. Table 8-3 summarizes commonly used fish anesthetics including recommended dosages.

8.10.6 Diver Operated Devices

The capture of live fish pose special problems to the diver. The distribution of fish inhabiting coral reefs is neither uniform nor random. Some are territorial and maintain discrete regions while others may live in schools and roam widely. There are also diurnal variations resulting in the fish changing their habitats during a 24 hour period.

Conventional methods of capture such as seining, trawling, and long-lining are not appropriate for capturing fish around coral reefs. For this reason a number of "special" techniques are used. There have been an array of suction devices called "slurp guns" on the market for sometime. These are powered by either rubber tubing, spring, or other means (Figure 8–29).

When using a slurp gun the diver after cornering the fish, usually in a hole, pulls the trigger, and a plunger draws back sucking a large volume of water in through a small opening thus drawing small fish (1 to 3 inches) into the gun. They are then moved into a holding container, and the gun readied for another shot. The disadvantages are: small size of fish, the diver must be very close, and the fish must usually be in a hole where they cannot escape.

Glass or plastic *bottles* may also be used to entrap small fish, however fish may feel a pressure wave in front of the jar and swim away. All bottles must be fully flooded with water prior to submerging. A more successful technique is to use a piece of plastic core liner, or plastic tube with a screen across one end. This may be slipped over fish more easily. Small gill nets may be used on the bottom by divers. Animals such as sea urchins may be broken up near the net to attract fish, or divers may herd fish into the net. Fish once entangled may be withdrawn and placed in "goodie bags" or wire cages.

As discussed earlier, fish *traps* may also be effective if baited appropriately and placed at a proper point either on the bottom or in the water

Table 8-3
**Commonly Used and
Potentially Useful
Fish Anesthetics**

Anesthetic	Qualities	Dosage (varies with species, temperature, etc.)	Common Use	Remarks	References
Chloral hydrate	Solid, soluble, inexpensive.	1-4 g/1.	Sedation	Low potency. Not widely used.	McFarland 1959 McFarland 1960 Bell 1967
Cresols	Liquid, mix 50:50 with acetone to facilitate solution.	20-40 mg/1 for immobilization.	Collection.	Para-cresol is the most effective isomer. Undesirable toxic effects.	Howland 1969
Methylpentynol (Oblivon, Dormison)	Liquid, moderate solubility.	0.5-2ml/1. 1500-8000 mg/l.	Sedation or deep anesthesia.	Fairly widely used but less desirable than others. Low potency.	Bell 1967 Klontz and Smith 1970 Howland and Schoettger 1969
Phenoxyethanol (2 phenoxyethanol)	Oily liquid.	0.1-1 ml/1.	Immobilization.	Used frequently with salmonids.	Klontz and Smith 1968 Bell 1967
Propoxate (McNeil R7464)	Crystalline; soluble.	1-4 mg/1.	Collection. Immobilization general.	New; very promising as a collecting agent.	Thienpoint and Niemegeers 1965 Howland 1969
Quinaldine (Practical grade)	Oily liquid. Low solubility, dissolve in 10-50% acetone, ethanol, or isopropyl alcohol to facilitate solution.	5-70 ml/1.	Widely used for collection, immobilization.	No sedation stage, poor analgesic. Efficacy varies widely with species & water characteristics. Long exposures toxic.	Schoettger and Julin 1969 Locke 1969 Moring 1970 Gibson 1967 Howland 1969
Quinaldine sulfate (QdSO₄)	Crystalline solid.	15-70 mg/1.	Collection. Immobilization.	Prepared from liquid quinaldine. Same properties; easier to handle.	Allen and Sills 1973 Gilderhus, Berger, Sills, Harman 1973a

Anesthetic	Qualities	Dosage (varies with species, temperature, etc.)	Common Use	Remarks	References
Rotenone	Available as powder or emulsion.	0.5 ppm	Ichthyocide; occasionally live collections.	Used to salvage fish from freshwater ponds. Limited use in sea water for live collecting.	Tate, Moen, Severson 1965
Sodium cyanide	Solid.	DO NOT USE	Live collections in Philippines and elsewhere.	Dangerous to humans; high mortality of fishes.	
Styrylpyridine (4 Styrylpyridine)	White powder; soluble.	20-50 mg/1.	Immobilization; deep anesthesia.	Not widely used but a successful anesthetic.	Klontz and Smith 1968
Tricaine (MS-222, tricaine methanesulfonate)	White crystalline powder; readily soluble.	15-40 mg/1 for sedation. 40-100 mg/1 for deep anesthesia. 100-1000 mg/1 for rapid immobilization.	Deep anesthesia; immobilization. Most widely used anesthetic.	Expense bars its use for collections. Used extensively in surgery, fish handling, transport. Wide literature.	Investigations in fish control, various reports. Klontz and Smith 1968 Bell 1967
Urethane	Carcinogenic.	DO NOT USE	Deep anesthesia; immobilization.	Carcinogenic.	Wood 1956
Mixtures of MS-222 and QdSO$_4$	Powders, readily soluble.	Various, e.g., 10:20 ppm QdSO$_4$: MS-222 equals 25 ppm QdSO$_4$ or 80-100 ppm MS-222.	Immobilization; deep anesthesia.	Combines desirable properties of each anesthetic. Too costly for general field collections.	Gilderhus, Berger, Sills, Harman 1973b

Table: Donald Wilkie

column. Divers may remove fish and rebait the trap while it remains on the bottom.

Deepwater fish may be caught on hook and line, reeled to 60 to 100 feet where they are met by divers who insert hypodermic needles into those with swim bladders and *decompress the fish* in this manner. There is an 80 percent recovery rate on many species of rock fish. A dip net fastened to the end of a pole spear is useful in collecting fish near the bottom. The fish may be pinned against a rock or sand bottom, taken out of the net and placed in an appropriate container; again the needle decompression may be helpful.

Many larger fishes such as rays, skates, or harmless sharks may either be caught by hand or by a loop of heavy monofilament line on the end of a pole (such as a snake stick). Electric fishes and rays should not be taken with metal poles or rods (See Paragraph 15.4).

Invertebrates may be collected using gloves. A pry bar, screwdriver, putty knife, or diving knife may be useful in removing some specimens from their substrate. Delicate animals such as nudibranchs may be placed in separate vials or jars and kept in a net bag. Vials and jars should be open at the beginning of the dive, but completely filled with water before returning to the surface.

Traps are effective for crabs, lobsters, and occasionally octopuses. Nylon net bags are more easily used for collecting than bottles or plastic bags. Animals which are neutrally buoyant will float out of the bottle or plastic bag when it is reopened to add another specimen.

Animals which live in the upper few centimeters of sediment or sandy bottom may be sampled by using either a scoop which has a line inscribed showing a given volume or a cylinder of plastic, stainless, aluminum, or other material which can be forced into the soft substrate. A simple cake server or spatula can be inserted from the side to act as a closure as the core of sediment is withdrawn from the bottom. The diameter of the cylinder should be such that it fits snugly over the mouth of the collecting bottle so the material can be forced into a labeled jar.

Nylon or other plastic screens can be obtained in a variety of mesh sizes. These may be tied over ends of plastic tubes as a sieve or sewn into a bag in which sediment samples may be placed. A gentle shaking will cause animals smaller than mesh size to drop through mesh into another container.

**SECTION 9
REGIONAL
AND SPECIAL
DIVING**

REGIONAL AND SPECIAL DIVING 9

9.0 GENERAL

Underwater environmental characteristics such as temperature, visibility, marine life, and other factors vary significantly from region to region and influence the amount and type of work that can be carried out under water.

The following paragraphs give some diving conditions most likely to be encountered in various regions around the United States and in some selected parts of the world. The discussions are general and intended only to give an overview of regional diving characteristics.

WARNING

When Diving in an Unfamiliar Region, Information About Local Conditions Should Be Obtained From Divers Who Are Familiar With the Waters. A Checkout Dive Should Be Made With a Diver From the Area.

9.1 GEOGRAPHIC REGIONS

For purposes of discussion, the geographic regions are divided as follows:

Region	Encompasses
Northeast	Maine through New Jersey
Mid-Atlantic	Delaware through South Carolina
Southeast	Georgia through Florida's East and West Coast
Gulf of Mexico	Florida's Pan Handle through Texas
Northwest	Southeast Alaska through Oregon
Mid-Pacific	Northern and Central California
Southwest	Point Conception to the Northern Baja Peninsula

Also discussed are polar and tropical waters and inland waters of the United States.

9.1.1 Northeast

Diving in Northeastern waters can be described as an exciting and chilling experience. Generally, the best diving conditions in terms of water temperature, sea state, and underwater visibility are from June through October. As one progresses east and north along the New England coast, water temperatures decrease and underwater visibility increases.

Water temperatures near the surface during the spring and summer when a substantial thermocline exists, range from 50° to 70° F. Bottom temperatures at 100 feet range from 48° to 54° F. During the winter months the water column is essentially homogeneous with temperatures going as low as 28.5° F. Subzero air temperatures and strong winds result in chill factors as low as 70° to 80° F below freezing. The diver must exert caution not to extend his time in the water or be exposed in a wet condition out of water to the point where he loses the manual dexterity of his hands and feet. Three-eights inch wet suits and variable volume dry suits are becoming the standard dive suits for winter diving in the Northeast (See Paragraph 9.3.2).

Underwater visibility is primarily a function of sea state and vertical turbulence in the water column. Horizontal visibility of 50–80 feet is occasionally seen throughout the year, usually associated with periods of calm seas. Proximity to the land mass or estuaries/harbors results in decreased visibility due to the mixing of fresh water with salt and the associated load of suspended material. One to several times a summer "red ·tide" conditions will exist with visibility of less than one foot. Coastal waters within the Gulf of Maine have an average visibility range of 25 to 35 feet, while visibility in waters south of Cape Cod averages 10 to 15 feet.

Several species of brown algae comprise the *large kelp* of the New England coast. None of these kelp form surface canopies as do those off California (See Paragraph 9.3.5). New England kelp will occasionally extend 25 feet off the hard ocean bottom and, although they present a formidable looking barrier to divers, they are virtually harmless in terms of the diver becoming entangled. Generally, these algal plants are sparsely distributed and seldom project more than 6–8 feet from the bottom.

Currents along the New England coast are primarily tidal in origin and generally do not exceed 0.5 knots. Faster currents may be encountered in channels and river mouths. Caution should be exerted especially while diving in strong currents and cold water because of the potential for overbreathing the regulator. *Surf* conditions are modest compared to California surf but are especially hazardous along rocky, precipitous coastlines such as the coast of Maine. Short period waves of 5–10 feet in height create very rough and turbulent sea states along such rocky coasts and can sweep divers over barnacle covered rocks.

Hazardous Marine Animals. Relatively few species of fishes and invertebrates are potentially harmful to divers off the New England coast. Several species of sharks are occasionally seen, but are very rarely harmful to divers. They are the mako, dusky, tiger, great white, hammerhead and the most commonly encountered blue shark. Occasionally the filter feeding basking shark will be mistaken for a dangerous shark. The torpedo ray (electric ray) (See Figure 15–18), cow nosed ray, and sting ray are found off southern New England (Cape Cod and South). Documented diver-shark or diver-ray encounters are relatively rare along the New England coast.

The most bothersome fish is the *goosefish* which may weigh as much as 100 pounds and grow to 5 feet in total length. The goosefish lies partially buried on the ocean floor waiting for unsuspecting "meals" to pass by. This fish is approximately one-half head and mouth and one-half tail. It is indeed a formidable adversary that may startle and perhaps grab onto a diver. The *wolffish* is another bottom oriented creature that is highly respected by fishermen and divers for his strength and aggressiveness when bothered. The six large canine tusks are capable of considerable damage as many fishermen have found when boating this species.

The *green sea urchin* with its many stout spines that easily puncture a rubber wet suit can also inflict injury to divers. Unless the tip of the spine is removed surgically from the diver it will result in a painful "lump" under the skin for months or years. The green sea urchin is found in very dense concentrations on hard substrates to depths of 50 to 60 feet.

9.1.2 Mid-Atlantic

Water temperatures off the Mid-Atlantic States will range, during the summer months, from about 60° to 75° F. During winter, water temperatures will drop as low as 38° to 45° F in the northern portions and 45° to 55° F in the southern portions.

Visibility in these waters is highly variable, depending on time of year, weather conditions, prevailing currents and distance from shore. It is not uncommon to have visibilities up to 60 feet offshore (5+ miles). In near-shore waters, 10–25 feet can be expected with occasional drops in visibility to 3–5 feet. In bays and rivers, visibility seldom exceeds 15 feet and zero visibility is not uncommon. Large changes in visibility with tides can be expected in the latter areas and up to 3 miles offshore near bays or rivers.

Strong tidal currents with rapid drops in visibility can be expected in the Chesapeake Bay and around the Outer Banks of North Carolina. Strong subsurface counter-currents in large rivers and bays have been encountered.

Stinging jellyfish are sometimes so abundant in estuaries that complete protection (including hands) is required. Gloves are recommended when working around rocks or structures due to the prevalence of sea urchins, oyster shells, stinging hydroids and barnacles. Sharks have been known to molest divers engaged in spearfishing.

Surf is generally moderate and most beaches are sand rather than rock, thus making entry from shore relatively easy.

9.1.3 Southeast

Waters off the Southeastern United States are, for the most part, tropical. Warm *temperatures* prevail, and can go as high as 75° to 80° F during the summer months. In the more northern portions of this region, off Georgia, a less tropical condition prevails. Water temperature during the summer in this area hovers around 70° F. During winter, water temperature in the southernmost areas stays around 65° to 70° F; in the more northernly waters, however, temperatures drop as low as 50° to 55° F.

Visibility in the southern waters is good to excellent in the offshore areas; closer to shore, however, around shelves, it drops to 25 to 30 feet, and in harbors and bays, it can become poor. Farther north, visibility drops drastically both offshore and near shore and averages 20 to 25 feet.

When diving at the boundary of major oceanic *current systems* such as the Gulf Stream, special care must be exercised because of the episodic turbulent eddies that occasionally spin off the main mass of moving water. Extra care also must be taken because of the meandering nature of the current edge. A diver may encounter relatively quiet water at the beginning of a dive that will suddenly change into one of high current velocities with currents in excess of one knot. Dives in boundary regions must be planned to anticipate the possible encounter of high current speeds and appropriate surface support must be provided. Quite often there are sharp boundaries between water masses of different current velocities in the water column as the diver descends. Usually the current slows a foot or two above the bottom and if the diver hugs the bottom contours he can work unimpaired by the currents. However, the tending boat must be aware of the current differential and establish a reference to the diver's position or the boat may be carried away from the dive site. Dropping a well anchored buoy over the side at the beginning of the dive is a good means of establishing such a reference. Carefully monitoring the bubbles of the diver is extremely important in this type of diving. Some means of diver recall must be established in case the surface boat loses sight of the diver's position (See Paragraph 6.2.3).

9.1.4 Gulf of Mexico

Water temperature in the Gulf of Mexico drops to a low of about 55° during winter months and rises to about 86° F in the summer. Visibility offshore is generally good to excellent, with ranges around some reefs noted in excess of 100 feet. *Visibility* near shore is poor, particularly in the areas proximate to river outfalls, in bays and estuaries, and off some beaches. A mass of clear offshore water may move inshore and increase the visibility near shore up to 75 feet in regions southeast of Mobile.

Currents in the Gulf are considered negligible but are still a direct concern to divers as described in Paragraph 9.1.3. At times, significant currents are encountered around offshore oil platforms, and local knowledge must be relied upon. Weather conditions and resultant running seas are unpredictable. Unforecasted storms with 6- to 12-foot seas have, at times, quickly curtailed diving operations.

9.1.5 Northwest

Diving activities in the northwest range from southeast Alaska through Oregon.

Water temperatures in southeast Alaska range from around 34° to 38° F during winter months to an average of about 45° to 50° F during the summer. Serious consideration must be given to proper diving dress so that duration of a dive is not impaired by the effects of cold. During winter, temperature and wind conditions may combine such that some bays, inlets, and near shore waters will freeze over.

Visibility in Alaskan waters varies drastically from place to place and from time to time. The best visibility is found along the outside coastlines and in the Aleutians where at best it may range from 40 to 80 feet. Visibility in inside waters of bays and straits is usually 15 to 20 feet. At any location visibility can become limited to 5 feet or less during intense phytoplankton blooms or storms. A condition develops late each spring in southeast Alaska where visibility in the upper 30 to 40 feet of the water column may be near zero due to phytoplankton, but below that layer the water may be very clear (visibility of 40 feet, or more). Although this deep, clear water is usually dark because of the shading effect of the overriding low visibility water, there is usually sufficient ambient light to work.

Currents and tides are strong and unpredictable in southeastern Alaskan waters. Tides are extremely heavy, and can cause currents as high as 10 knots in narrows. Currents also vary significantly and have been observed by divers to change direction within minutes.

Much of the Alaskan coastline is steep and rocky with many areas too steep to allow divers to either enter or leave the water. Entry and exit points must be carefully selected before a dive. Most sections of coastline are accessible only from boats. During times of heavy seas or swells many near shore diving locations become completely unworkable.

Alaskan waters harbor relatively few *hazardous marine organisms.* Those that cause divers the most physical damage are the urchins, barnacles, and jellyfishes with their respective potential for punctures, abrasions, and stings. Dense beds of kelp can cause some problems to divers, especially when swimming on the surface. Sharks and whales are common, but rarely, if ever, seen under water and generally would not influence diving activity in any way. Presence of killer whales, which are also common, might be an exception. Although no known diver/killer whale encounters have taken place in Alaska, general caution should keep divers out of the water if these animals are known to be near. Sea lions are very abundant in some areas of Alaska and although they are not known to have ever harmed a diver, they can psychologically upset a diver not accustomed to their presence under water. Sea lions are strongly attracted to divers and because of their large size, speed, and agility, and occasional bellowing rushes at divers, they can be disruptive to an otherwise routine dive.

Farther south, in the waters of Washington and Oregon, *water temperatures* range from about 43° to 60° F over the year in protected areas such as Puget Sound. In open ocean waters, depending on water masses moving through, temperatures ranging from 40° to 60° F may be encountered over the year. Visibility is usually low, ranging from 5 to 25 feet in coastal water near beaches and from zero to 70 feet in protected Puget Sound waters.

Currents, in certain areas, are strong and unpredictable. This is especially true in river diving, where very low visibility can result in orientation problems. Logs, stumps, wrecked automobiles, fishing hooks and lines, and similar bottom trash also pose distinct dangers to a river diver.

9.1.6 Mid-Pacific

The Mid-Pacific region includes the waters of Northern and Central California. Generally from San Francisco north, the best diving conditions occur from June through September, in terms of underwater visibility as well as water temperatures. From San Francisco south to Point Conception, good diving conditions may continue through December.

From San Francisco north to the Oregon border, summer *temperatures* generally range from about 48° to 56° F. Fall and early winter temperatures

from 52° to 60° F, and late winter and spring temperatures from 45° to 54° F. A thermocline generally exists at depths from 20 to 40 feet during late spring and summer. The difference in surface and bottom temperature during this period ranges between 2° and 5° F. A full wet suit, including hood, boots, and gloves is a necessity when diving in this area.

Visibility varies quite drastically throughout the area from summer to winter. From Fort Bragg to the Oregon border, late spring and summer visibility ranges between 10 and 15 feet. In the late summer and fall, underwater visibility increases to about 15 to 25 feet. During the winter and early spring, visibility decreases to 0 to 10 feet. South of Fort Bragg down to San Francisco visibility ranges from 10–20 feet increasing to 30 feet in the fall. From Santa Cruz north to San Francisco, visibility ranges from 5 to 15 feet in the early spring and summer, 10 to 25 feet in late summer and fall, and 0 to 10 feet during winter and early spring. From Point Conception to Santa Cruz visibility ranges from 15 to 25 feet during the late spring and summer to 15 to 50 feet in the fall and occasionally may reach 100 feet near Carmel Bay. During winter and early spring one can expect 5 to 20 foot visibility. The main factor controlling visibility in this area is the huge plankton bloom, which occurs during upwelling in the spring and summer and the dirty water conditions caused by rough seas and river runoffs during the winter and early spring.

Three species of surface canopy forming brown algae, *kelp*, occur on the Pacific coast. From Monterey north, the dominant kelp is the bull kelp. This particular species forms large beds but because of its structure, does not pose the same entanglement hazard to the diver as the giant kelp (See Paragraph 9.3.5).

Surf conditions north of Point Conception are probably the most important consideration in planning a dive. Even on calm days divers can expect two to three foot surf in most areas and on rough days it is not uncommon to see waves ten or more feet high. The diver should always scout the proposed diving area before going into the water to determine the safest area of entry and, if conditions should change, alternate exit sites (See Paragraph 13.1.1).

Long-shore *currents* and tidal currents are common and tend to be severe in northern and central California. Divers should especially watch for strong currents on very windy days around headlands, offshore rocks, and reefs. Rip currents are very common along beaches and in coves.

Hazardous Marine Animals. As in other areas, the diver must watch for sea urchins, jellyfish, and rockfish. The latter because of venomous, anal, dorsal, and head spines. Shark attacks in this area are rare. During the last 15 to 20 years, less than two dozen attacks on divers have been recorded. There are, however, certain areas and conditions that seem to be correlated with potential shark attack. Diving around the Farallon Islands, Bodega Bay, Tomales Bay, and off San Francisco is not recommended except when underwater visibility is ideal. Stingrays and electric rays should be approached with caution; the former because of their puncture producing spine in the tail, and the latter because of the electric shock which they are capable of producing (See Section 15).

There are five *ecological reserves* in this area, where all animals and plants are protected. One at Point Lobos State Reserve, one in the Point Reyes Seashore area, one in Salt Point State Park, one in the Estero de Limantour Reserve in Marin County north of San Francisco and one at Del Mar Landing in Sonoma County. Divers should consult with the park authorities to determine the boundaries and restrictions in marine reserves.

9.1.7 Southwest

Waters of the Southwest include the area from Point Conception to the northern Baja Peninsula.

Water temperatures range from 50° to 60° F in winter and 55° to 70° F in summer, with some locally colder areas due to upwelling. During much of the year, temperatures below 100 foot depths are fairly stable in the 50's and low 60's (°F). In fall and winter there is a great deal of mixing in the upper layers and no discrete temperature zonation is noted. However, a distinct summer thermocline at 40- to 60-foot depths causes a sharp temperature drop and should be accounted for when planning dives.

Horizontal visibility ranges from 5 to 10 feet along much of the mainland coast to as much as 100 feet around the off-shore islands. Best visibility conditions are in the late summer and fall. During spring and early summer, visibility is generally less (30–50 feet around the islands), due in part to the prevailing overcasts and heavy fogs. Winter storm conditions and rain runoff can drop visibility to zero for miles along the mainland coast, as the prevailing longshore

current distributes suspended material from storm drains and river mouths.

Shore conditions along the southern California mainland coast range from sand beaches to high palisade cliffs. Ocean access from these areas is often impossible, and a careful check of charts and maps, supplemented by a preliminary entrance site visit, is highly recommended. The offshore islands are generally diveable only by boat. Moderate to heavy *surf* prevails along the entire mainland coast and on the windward sides of the offshore islands. Under certain weather conditions the normally calm leeward sides may also offer hazardous diving conditions.

Currents and tides are not of prime importance here, although there are local exceptions. Currents around the islands, especially during tidal changes, may attain speeds of 3 to 4 knots. The direction and relative strength of near-shore currents can be observed both topside and under water by watching the degree and direction of kelp layover.

Hazardous marine organisms include: sharks (especially around the offshore islands) such as blue, horned, swell, angel, and leopard; whales, killer whales, moray eels, sea urchins and jellyfishes. Divers should be aware of the appearance and locations of these species (See Section 15).

Sewer outfalls are common along the mainland coast, and direct contact with the effluent should be avoided. The discharge point may vary from a few hundred feet to several miles offshore, in from 60 to several hundred feet of water. The effluent may or may not reach the surface as a *boil*, in which temperatures are sharply elevated, paper and other debris is seen, and a definite odor is detected. If diving must be conducted in these areas, such precautions as extensive immunization, use of full-face diving gear, and scrupulous post-dive hygiene must be observed. Most discharge points are marked on charts and may be evidenced on the surface by the aforementioned *boil* and/or an orange and white striped spar buoy anchored near the pipe terminus.

As in Northern California, *ecological reserves*, with various restrictions, have been established. Inquiries can be made at the local offices of the California Department of Fish and Game for the locations and current restrictions.

Diving in northern Mexican (Upper Baja California) waters is similar to that in lower southern California. However, heavy fines and boat impound-

Figure 9-1
Floating Ice

Photo: John Beagles

ment can result from diving in Mexico without the proper permits which are obtainable through the Mexican Government, or Mexican customs officials in San Diego.

9.1.8 Arctic and Antarctic

The single most important aspect of diving in arctic and antarctic environments is that divers are subjected to extremes in cold temperatures, both in the water and on the surface. Another factor is that dives may be undertaken either through ice or in the immediate vicinity of floating ice (Figure 9–1).

Temperatures in arctic waters can be as low as 28° F and can rise as high as 40° to 45° F. Surface temperatures can get as low as −40° to −50° F. Diving dress is of utmost importance. For short dives, thick wet suits can be worn, but the variable-volume dry suit offers decided advantages (See Paragraph 4.8.4).

Protection against surface temperatures is also a necessity. Predive planning must include a heated shelter as close to the dive site as possible. Divers in diving dress should be protected from exposure before a dive and, more importantly, after a dive.

Marine life of concern in polar waters includes seals and sea lions. Although generally non-aggressive and at times inquisitive and friendly, these mammals should be watched and not antagonized.

Mothers with young, and young males should be treated with extra caution. Extreme caution must be exercised when diving in areas frequented by polar bears and killer whales.

9.1.9 Tropics

Diving in tropical waters presents some of the most interesting diving available. Visibility is excellent in most instances, and marine life abounds for the observer, photographer, and scientist.

Visibility in tropical waters is generally 50 feet and upward. There is little variance throughout the year although waters tend to become a bit murky and silty after a storm, during plankton blooms, or from silting near shore. Water *temperatures* hover around 70° F during winter months and go as high as 82° F in shallower waters during the summer.

Marine life is abundant and some of it dangerous to a diver. Sharks thrive in these waters and precautions should be taken when they are sighted. A wide variety of poisonous marine animals (jellyfish, scorpionfish, sea snakes) also abound (See Section 15).

9.2 LAKE AND RIVER DIVING

9.2.1 Great Lakes

Temperature changes with relation to depth and season are the most common environmental conditions to be considered by Great Lakes divers. In a typical freshwater lake the upper layer temperature generally ranges between 55° and 75° F in late summer. However, the waters below the thermocline will approach the temperature of maximum density for fresh water, 39.2° F. Consequently, when working below the thermocline, which averages 60 feet deep in late summer, the diver must plan accordingly with respect to buoyancy and thermal protection.

During the winter months the water temperature will range between approximately 32° F near the surface and 39.2° F on the bottom. During the winter months and early spring, a significant portion of the Great Lakes is ice covered. Occasionally, divers are required to work under 2 to 16 inches of ice in order to make observations, collect samples, or maintain scientific equipment. Diving under ice is particularly hazardous, requires special techniques and equipment, and should only be undertaken when absolutely necessary (See Paragraph

9.3.3). Divers and surface support personnel may be subjected to atmospheric temperatures of −30° F with wind chill factors approaching −100° F.

Visibility in the Great Lakes will range from about 100 feet in Lake Superior to less than 1 foot in Lake Erie. Visibility is influenced by local precipitation and run-off, nutrient enrichment, biological activity, local bottom conditions, and diver activity. Significant seasonal variations should be anticipated.

Storms and severe wave conditions can be expected from September to December. Divers working offshore must use adequate vessels and monitor weather forecasts.

Swift *currents* may be encountered in rivers and straits connecting the lakes. Divers must use considerable caution and be properly trained in the techniques of diving in currents.

9.2.2 Inland Lakes

Basic techniques involved in diving in the inland waters of the United States, i.e., lakes, rivers, quarries, are little different from those used in ocean waters. The following points, however, should be considered.

Depth gauges used by divers are calibrated for the density found in sea water. Some differences are noted when they are used in fresh water, and a diver must account for these differences (See Table 9-2).

Lakes vary from clear mountain lakes with low sediment input to reservoirs, sediment laden rivers, or glacial lakes, which usually have a milky appearance. Bottom terrain is as important a consideration as *visibility* when planning a dive. Lakes may have vertical rocky sides, rocky outcrops, ledges, and talus slopes, or be sedimentary in nature such as old farm land. Algal blooms occur during the warmer months and may totally attenuate light even at shallow depths. Thermoclines also occur and temperature and visibility may vary greatly.

Some of the hazards found may be old cables or heavy equipment around dams, electric cables, rope, fish-line, fishing lures, and perhaps old cars. Many lakes have never been cleared of trees, barns, houses, water towers, etc. Bottom sediment is easily stirred up, as is sediment which has settled on trees or brush. The diver should stay off the bottom if possible, and move slowly when working on the bottom.

It should also be remembered that altitude tables should be consulted when diving at higher elevations (See Paragraph 9.3.7).

9.2.3 Rivers

Rivers throughout the world vary in size, turbidity, and in the terrain through which they flow; diving conditions will vary with the river.

As an example, the Colorado down stream from Hoover Dam runs through a rocky gorge which varies between 300 feet and 600 feet wide. Water depth varies between 10 and 60 feet. The current is 6 to 8 knots. Visibility is 30 to 60 feet and the temperature 50° to 54° F. The water is clear enough to avoid the obstructions. A diver who grabs hold of the bottom to stop and look at an object should hold the face mask or it will be torn off by the currents. There are sand beaches and rock ledges where the diver may exit and wait for a pickup boat.

Any river should be thoroughly studied and conditions known before the dive is planned. Log jams are a hazard as are submerged objects such as sharp rocks, trees, limbs, old cars, barbed wire, and the ever present monofilament fishing lines, nets, and lures. Rapids or steep profiles are hazardous as a diver may be slammed against a rock or other submerged object and sustain serious injury or be held by the current.

Where there is considerable surface current, diving in large holes may be done by dropping directly to the bottom. At some distance below the surface, the diver may be surprised to find either no current or one going slightly toward the head of the hole.

Another difficulty in a fast flowing stream is the blocking of light by bubbles. In or under white water it may be almost dark. Rivers carrying large amounts of sediment, either normally or as a result of recent rains, will also be extremely dark. In some instances, the sun will appear only as a red glow when the diver has his face mask just submerged and is looking skyward.

Diving with underwater lights in turbid waters does little for the diver, as the light is attenuated by the particles suspended in the water.

9.3 SPECIAL CONDITIONS

Dives are often conducted in areas that present special hazards requiring careful planning. There is no substitute for experience when planning for cave diving, under ice diving, or diving in wrecks.

Some of these special conditions are discussed below.

9.3.1 Cave Diving

Cave diving is performed in both inland fresh waters and ocean blue holes. To the scientist, this unique laboratory offers new areas of research.

In cave diving, emphasis should be given to: dive planning, life support systems, and specialized techniques.

WARNING
Only Experienced and Specially Trained Divers Should Undertake Cave Diving.

Planning for a cave dive includes selection of equipment, determination of the physical and physiological limits of the least experienced diver in the group, and establishing a safe contingency plan for emergency situations.

Normally, no more than three divers should be on a cave dive. Upon the completion of a dive, each diver should arrive at the mouth of the cave with a minimum of $^1/_3$ of his initial air supply.

A life support system, in addition to the standard diving equipment, must include a compass, light, safety reel, and line. A suitable safety reel should feature a line guide, drum, buoyancy chamber, good turns ratio, and be capable of carrying approximately 400 feet of $^1/_{16}$ inch 160 pound test to $^1/_8$ inch 440 pound test braided nylon line. The reel should be neutrally buoyant, compact, and rugged (Figure 9–2). Large reels and lines create too much extra drag and exertion on the diver.

For long duration dives, double tanks are normally used. There are many combinations of regulators and manifolding arrangements. The configuration recommended is one in which two tanks are manifolded together making the air supply common but offering two regulator outlets. If one regulator fails the second one may be used with the total remaining air supply. If any other manifold configuration is selected, octopus regulators should be used (See Paragraph 6.3.1).

Manual buddy breathing may be impractical and occasionally impossible due to distance and cave configuration. Many divers now use the quadropus system which is the octopus system with the addition of an automatic inflator for the buoyancy compensator. It is further recommended that cave divers carry a small auxiliary tank containing

Figure 9-2
Safety Reel

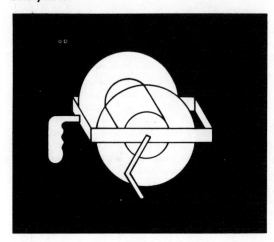

20–40 cubic feet of air mounted between their doubles for emergencies.

Special attention must be given to buoyancy control and lighting. At least two lights should be carried on any cave dive.

Specialized techniques must be utilized to offset the natural hazards of cave diving, which include ceiling overhead, darkness, visibility, current and physical peculiarities of the cave. Perhaps the greatest specific hazard in cave diving is that of silt, and much effort must be made to avoid it.

Swim techniques include buoyancy control, body positioning, and other skills utilized by the diver. There are over 40 known and practiced swim techniques in cave diving.*

There are several kinds of lines used for safety and navigation in cave diving.

Temporary lines are the most commonly used and consist of a safety reel and line. When running a safety line, the reel man should maintain tension against the reel drum so the line remains taut. The line should be tied within surface light and two wraps should be made approximately every 50 feet. The line should be centered in the cave as much as possible. The reel man is first in and last out. The buddy is responsible for unwrapping the safety wraps on exiting the cave and providing light for the man who is tying or untying the line. Physical contact with the line should be *avoided* except when visibility decreases.

Permanent lines are used for complete exploration

---

*Tom Mount, 1973: personal communication.

or mapping of caves.

In general, the diver should not penetrate further into a cave than he is capable of forming visual references and he should not assume that he can swim to the end of any line. The air cutoff point should allow the one-third rule to be incorporated to provide diver safety. The reader is referred to the National Association of Underwater Instructors' (1973) manual on cave diving practices.

9.3.2 Diving in Cold Water

Diving in cold water introduces several equipment problems not found in warmer waters. The major problem is associated with the regulator. The majority of single hose regulators have a tendency to freeze in the free-flow position after approximately 20–30 minutes of exposure. Some models are presently being manufactured which are especially designed to resist freezing. A special cap is provided which can be filled with an antifreeze agent. The standard double hose regulator rarely develops this problem. The diver's mask also shows an increased tendency to fog or freeze in cold water. The application of saliva is ineffective in preventing this fogging. Partially flooding the mask, and flushing the seawater over the faceplate temporarily relieves this condition. Several closed-circuit scuba systems have been evaluated under extreme cold water conditions with satisfactory results (Jenkins 1973).

The standard foamed-neoprene wet suit has been used in cold water and will provide thermal comfort for about 60 minutes in water temperatures below 40° F. A major drawback is that the diver is wet when he completes his dive, and will undoubtedly be very cold.

There are two types of divers' dress presently available which have been used with success under severe thermal conditions. The hot water wet suit which provides a continuous flow of preheated water to the diver (See Paragraphs 4.8.2 and 4.8.3), and the variable volume dry suit which allows the diver to control the amount of air in the suit, and, therefore, its insulating ability (See Paragraph 4.8.4).

Regardless of the type of dress used in cold water, the hands and feet will probably become cold, with a resultant loss in dexterity even when using standard 1/4-inch wet suit gloves and boots. The resultant loss in efficiency, and increased discomfort, will frequently be a key factor in the termination of a dive.

Certain procedures, if followed by the diver and surface-support crew, can greatly reduce the effects of exposure to cold water.

The wet suit should be maintained in the best possible condition to reduce water flushing in and out of the suit and the diver *should exercise as much as possible* during the dive so as to generate body heat. A dive should be terminated upon the onset of involuntary shivering or severe loss of manual dexterity.

Upon exiting cold water, a diver will probably be fatigued and greatly susceptible to additional cold. Immediately flushing the diver's wet suit, gloves, boots, etc., with warm water upon surfacing will have a comforting, heat replacing effect. Facilities must be provided which will allow him to dry off in a comfortable, dry, and relatively warm environment, to regain lost body heat. The diver should remove any wet dress, dry off, and don warm, protective clothing as soon as possible. If required to perform a repetitive dive, conservation of body heat, and consequently selection of diver's dress is extremely important.

To provide the diver with the energy required for cold water diving, adequate rest and nutrition is a necessity. A diver should have a minimum of 6–8 hours sleep prior to the dive. Adequate physical preparation the week prior to diving is also recommended. On the day of the dive, the diver should have a breakfast high in carbohydrates and protein.

9.3.3 Diving Under Ice

In addition to the problems and limitations already discussed concerning diving in cold water, there are additional specific precautions that must be taken when diving under ice. Diving under ice is hazardous, and should be done only by experienced individuals.

Most ice diving is done from large, relatively flat ice platforms, firmly frozen to the shore. Diving from drifting ice or among broken free ice is dangerous and should be done only when required. When the ice is solid and firm, relatively little surface action or current will be encountered. Also, in most instances, good visibility can be expected.

Entry into the water through ice is important. The hole should be large enough for at least two divers, preferably three. If the ice is thick, power-driven augers and/or chain saws may be required. For some diving operations, in particular those utilizing self-contained equipment, two or more holes may be desired.

In all diving operations under ice, there should be a surface tender and at least one standby diver. If a safety line is used, the end should be securely fastened at the surface. Excursions under the ice should be as well planned as possible before the divers enter the water. Time under the ice and the distance the diver travels from the point of entry, should both be minimal. Under normal circumstances, this distance should be limited to 30 yards, and only under the most unusual circumstances should it exceed 50 yards. If mission requirements necessitate traveling long distances under ice, more than one hole should be cut and kept open.

A bright light hanging just below the surface at the entry hole is highly desirable. A sonic pinger or hydrophone may provide some assistance by allowing a diver to more easily locate the exit. Because of the reduced light level under ice during the day and the additional safety equipment required because of the lack of direct access to the surface, night diving under ice requires no additional procedures or precautions other than surface lighting at the dive site.

If the weather is severe, a tent or shed can be constructed over the access hole. This will provide surface-support personnel and the diver with protection from the wind and, together with a small portable heater, will provide adequate warmth (Jenkins 1973; Andersen 1973).

9.3.4 Diving With No Bottom Reference

Special precautions are required when diving in water that allows no reference to the bottom. These conditions may be found when diving in deep ocean water, extremely dirty water, or when diving at night. A lack of reference points can be disturbing to non-experienced divers and create a form of vertigo.

Deep water diving makes depth and distance estimates difficult. When possible, a weighted line suspended from a surface buoy should be used at the dive site. When working from a large vessel a small boat should be used to tend the divers directly. Wind and surface currents often carry the vessel away from the dive site. Deep water dives are often conducted to support submersible operations or check buoys and instruments. Buoys that have been deployed for over a day attract

sharks, therefore no garbage should be dumped at the dive site. A useful aid in marking a dive site is a small open jar of fluorescent dye dropped into the water. The vertical column of dye left behind as the jar drops through the water will be distorted by currents, giving a visual display of the current pattern in the water column.

Dirty water, where visibility may be reduced to zero even at high noon, presents similar problems of orientation. When possible, divers should be tended from the surface or a descent line used.

Night diving presents an orientation problem similar to that encountered in dirty water or deep ocean water diving. A fixed reference may not be visible and the diver must rely upon a line or other method of relocating the surface. A light suspended below the support boat will provide a return beacon in clear water.

9.3.5 Kelp Diving

Kelp is found in dense beds along much of the colder and temperate coasts of the Americas. Attaching to practically any solid substrate (i.e., rock, concrete, steel, etc.), it forms a tree-like structure, the trunk of which is composed of a few to perhaps several hundred intertwining stipes. A pneumatocyst (float) is found at the base of each blade which causes the frond to be buoyed upward resulting in part of it floating on the surface. This may form a dense canopy which will have numbers of thin spots or openings scattered throughout. Entries or exits are easily made through these openings or by swimming in under the edge of the canopy.

When working from a boat, it is best to anchor in an opening so that the wind or current will drift the boat back on the anchor line to a second opening. Divers may also anchor outside the bed and swim in. Disengaging an anchor from kelp is difficult.

The feet first, legs-together water entry is preferable to the head first role or back entry which can result in entanglement. Once through the surface canopy, the diver will find himself in a forest-like area. When the diver approaches the surface he should raise his arms over his head, unless there is a convenient opening. As he enters the canopy he should use his arms to move the kelp fronds aside and surface through the hole. Once on the surface, he should stay in the vertical position so he can either exhale and sink, or submerge by raising his arms from his sides back over his head, thus forcing the body under water. Excessive movement may cause entanglement.

Kelp can easily be broken with a fingernail or pulled off. It is unwise to remove kelp from the regulator with a knife if the kelp is thick and the regulator hose cannot be seen or felt.

The diver who has run out of air and is forced to return to shore or a boat through a kelp bed has several choices. He may simply skin dive from opening to opening and if he needs a breath between openings he can come up through the main canopy. This is done easily with a little practice. He may also do a variation of the "dog paddle" in which the body is parallel to the surface and the swim fins used in a very close flutter kick. The arms reach across the kelp to an extended position then grasp the kelp and press down, with elbows close to the body to keep as streamlined a shape as possible. The regulator second stage should not trail behind the diver or it will become entangled in the kelp. Swim fins with adjustable heel straps may also pose a problem as the kelp fronds can become caught in the strap adjusting buckle and strap end. This may be eliminated by taping the strap end to the main strap. Knives worn on the belt or on the outside of the calf of the leg will also act as kelp catchers. Consequently, knives should be worn inside the calf. Inflating buoyancy compensators while under a kelp canopy may also increase the chance of entanglement

Egergia (ribbon kelp) grows from the intertidal to perhaps 45 feet in depth, and although quite thick it seldom forms the thick canopy associated with *Macrocystis*. "Elk kelp" (*Pelagophycus porra*), is a deeper-growing plant found usually in 45–60 feet to 150 feet of water. It consists of a single stipe, 1/2 inch across growing from a small holdfast. The stipe enlarges 3 to 6 feet from the float and is spherical and hollow in structure. The top of this ball gives rise to antler-like protrusions, each with several blades which may be 3 feet wide and 15 feet long. Elk kelp seldom reaches the surface in a healthy state but forms a bed 15 to 30 feet down. Often when the diver penetrates a large kelp bed in 60–90 feet of water, he will find a second canopy of elk kelp below the first, with a resulting drop in already low light levels.

All kelp beds are influenced by currents and surge and major beds may disappear in a swift current

as a result of being held down on perhaps a 45° angle. This has its advantages as the kelp streams in the direction of the current and may be used for navigation.

9.3.6 Wreck Diving

Diving around wrecks subjects the diver to many of the same hazards found in cave diving or diving under the ice.

Diving in or around wrecks exposes the diver to inherent dangers that must be considered both in planning the dive and in carrying it out. First, there may not be a direct route to the surface should an emergency arise; second, in many instances the diver will be venturing into an unknown area where risk of entanglement and reduced visibility due to stirred up silt are ever-present hazards. If the wreck is full of passageways, small entrances, chambers, etc., a line to the outside of the wreck should be used to insure a safe exit route. If warranted, because of depth and long duration dives, a spare air supply and regulator should be placed outside the wreck as a safety measure. Sharp objects inside a wreck are often hidden by algae, sea polyps or other marine growth. Decayed wood and corroded metal can collapse, and fishing nets, line, and hooks should be watched for. Underwater enclosures are havens for sea life of all types. Hazardous marine life should be considered at all times.

Remember, the only known way out is the way in.

9.3.7 Diving at High Elevations

An important factor to consider when diving at altitudes above sea level is the effect the increased elevation will have on various types of depth gauges. The bourdon tube and bellows type depth gauges will indicate a depth *shallower* than the actual depth, while the capillary tube type gauge will indicate a depth that is *greater*. Another factor that will affect the accuracy of the depth gauge is that the gauges are calibrated for use in seawater. Fresh water, being less dense than seawater, will result in the depth gauge reading slightly *shallower* than the same gauge would in seawater.

The bourdon tube and bellows depth gauges indicate the total ambient pressure (in air or water) minus 1 atmosphere, and are calibrated for sea level. As altitude increases, they will sense the decrease in atmospheric pressure, and, were it not for the mechanical stop, actually would move backward. Consequently, this type of depth gauge will not indicate depth when submerged until the effect of the decreased atmospheric pressure is overcome, and, therefore, will always read shallower.

The capillary tube gauge utilizes the compression effect of water pressure on an entrapped quantity of air to indicate depth. If the air in the tube is of a lesser pressure than sea level when the gauge is submerged, such as when diving in the mountains, the entrapped air, while of the same volume, will be less dense. Consequently, it will take less water pressure to compress the entrapped air, and the depth gauge will indicate a depth greater than the actual depth.

Unless altitude and fresh water corrections are made to depth gauges, as discussed in the previous paragraphs, a descent line should be used to measure the depth of dive and decompression stops.

One of the criteria used for the computation and validation of the U.S. Navy Standard Air Decompression Tables, was that they would be used at sea level where standard atmospheric pressure is 14.7 psi. Because atmospheric pressure varies significantly with altitude, decompression tables, depth of stops, rate of ascent and repetitive dive planning may have to be altered for safe diving at altitudes above 1000 feet. Sea level equivalent depths and rate of ascent may have to be altered based on dive site atmospheric pressure and density of water. Variations in pressure for a given altitude can be as much as 0.5 psi due to latitude and seasonal changes (U.S. Standard Atmospheric Supplements 1966). This is equivalent to 1000 feet of altitude or more based on standard atmospheric pressure. Variations in pressure for a given altitude can be as much as 1.0 psi due to daily weather conditions (Weatherwise Feb. 1971). This is equivalent to 2000 feet of altitude or more based on standard atmospheric pressure.

Upon surfacing, the lowered oxygen partial pressure may cause air hunger and pulmonary difficulties.

AIR DIVING 10

10.0 GENERAL

Compressed air is the most commonly used breathing medium. The medical and decompression aspects of air diving are well known, have been thoroughly tested, and indicate a margin of safety not yet achieved with mixed gas.

Several definitions are important to an understanding of various aspects of air diving. The most important of these are:

No-Decompression Diving. In no-decompression diving, a diver can return directly to the surface at a rate of 60 feet per minute without spending time at shallower depths to allow inert gas to be eliminated from the body (U.S. Navy Diving Manual 1973).

Decompression Diving. In decompression diving, a diver must return to the surface according to a decompression schedule, utilizing timed stops at shallower depths, which allows inert gas to be safely eliminated from the body.

Single Dive. A single dive is the first dive of the day conducted more than 12 hours after the completion of a previous dive.

Repetitive Dives. A repetitive dive is a dive performed within 12 hours of a previous dive. A repetitive dive may be a *no-decompression repetitive dive* or a *decompression repetitive dive*, depending on the depth and time of the repetitive dive and the previous dive.

Bottom Time. Bottom time is the total elapsed time beginning when a diver leaves the surface and ending when he begins ascent back to the surface.

Surface Interval. The surface interval is the elapsed time between surfacing from the previous

dive and the time when the diver leaves the surface on the repetitive dive.

Decompression Stop. The decompression stop is the required time the diver must stop and hold his depth relatively constant, during ascent following a decompression dive. Decompression stops are tabulated in decompression tables.

Diving with air as the breathing medium can be conducted using a variety of life support equipment. The most widely used is the open-circuit scuba, where compressed air is carried by the diver. A diver may also use air supplied through an umbilical utilizing a full face mask, demand regulator, a lightweight diving helmet, or deep-sea diving equipment.

When entering the water on an air dive a diver can descend at any comfortable rate. However, there are several physiological reasons for limiting the rate of descent, among them the possibility of a squeeze; the inability to equalize pressure on both sides of the eardrum; pains in the sinuses; and a tendency toward dizziness, or narcosis which may occur when rapidly descending. Practical reasons for limiting the descent rate are a matter of prudent evaluation of the effects of current and a careful approach to an unknown bottom.

The 1973 edition of the U.S. Navy Diving Manual has incorporated changes in the standard air decompression tables. Due to confusion which resulted from table designation changes associated with frequent revisions, all table numbers have been eliminated. The tables are now designated by their name only.

10.1 NO-DECOMPRESSION DIVING

During any dive the body absorbs a quantity of inert gas. The amount absorbed depends on many

Note: The U.S. Navy Decompression Tables, referred to in this section, are included in Appendix D.

Former Table	New Name	Application
1-10 1-14	U.S. Navy Standard Air Decompression Table Short name: Standard Air Table	No locally available decompression chamber. Conditions dictate in-water decompression. Normal and exceptional exposure dive schedules. Repetitive dive normal decompression schedules only.
1-11	No-Decompression Limits and Repetitive Group Designation Table for No Decompression Air Dive Short name: No-Decompression Table	Decompression not required. Repetitive dives.
1-12 1-13	Residual Nitrogen Time Table for Repetitive Air Dives Short name: Residual Nitrogen Table	Repetitive Group Designations after surface intervals greater than 10 minutes and less than 12 hours. Residual nitrogen times for repetitive air dives.
1-26	Surface Decompression Table Using Oxygen	Recompression chamber available with oxygen breathing system. Conditions do not allow in-water decompression. No repetitive dives.
1-27	Surface Decompression Table Using Air	Recompression chamber available without oxygen breathing system, or diver forced to surface prior to completing decompression. Conditions do not allow in-water decompression. No repetitive dives.

factors, including the physical condition of the diver, the level of exertion, the temperature of the water, the depth of the dive, and the time spent at depth. The longer a diver remains at depth the more time the body has to absorb the inert gas (which, in the case of air diving is nitrogen). As depth increases the partial pressure of the nitrogen in the breathing air is increased, and the greater the absorption of nitrogen into the body tissue. In no-decompression diving, the body has not experienced the increased partial pressure of nitrogen for sufficient time to require decompression.

Dives to 26 feet or less do not require decompression, regardless of the bottom time. Dives deeper than 26 feet may require decompression. The no-decompression time limits for various depths are shown in the No-Decompression Table and range from 310 minutes at 35 feet to 5 minutes at 190 feet.

10.1.1 Nonrepetitive No-Decompression Dives

If a diver remains on the surface for a period of 12 hours or more between dives, the dives are considered nonrepetitive. As long as each nonrepetitive dive conforms with the no-decompression depth and time limits of the *No-Decompression Table*, the diver

is able to ascend directly to the surface upon completion of the dive and not experience the symptoms of decompression sickness or "bends" as described in Section 16.

If a diver exceeds the no-decompression limits of the *No-Decompression Table* on a particular dive, and has not been on a dive for the previous 12 hours, the dive becomes a decompression dive and he must ascend to the surface in accordance with the appropriate decompression schedule contained in the *Standard Air Decompression Table*. This case is discussed in Paragraph 10.2.

10.1.2 Repetitive No-Decompression Dives

A repetitive no-decompression dive is any dive occurring *less* than 12 hours after a previous dive, in which a diver may ascend directly to the surface without the necessity of decompression stops. The depth and time limits of a repetitive no-decompression dive *cannot* be obtained directly from the *No-Decompression Table* as was the case for the nonrepetitive dive. A diver performing a repetitive dive must compute his maximum no-decompression bottom time for the maximum diving depth he anticipates. A worksheet, "Repetitive Dive Worksheet" (Figure 10-1) is provided to assist in performing

Figure 10-1
Repetitive Dive Worksheet

I. PREVIOUS DIVE:
_____ minutes   ☐ Standard Air Table
_____ feet   ☐ No-Decompression Table
_____ repetitive group designation

II. SURFACE INTERVAL:
_____ hours _____ minutes on surface.
Repetitive group from I _____
New repetitive group from surface
Residual Nitrogen Timetable _____

III. RESIDUAL NITROGEN TIME:
_____ feet (depth of repetitive dive)
New repetitive group from II. _____
Residual nitrogen time from
Residual Nitrogen Timetable _____

IV. EQUIVALENT SINGLE DIVE TIME:
_____ minutes, residual nitrogen time from III.
+ _____ minutes, actual bottom time of repetitive dive.
= _____ minutes, equivalent single dive time.

V. DECOMPRESSION FOR REPETITIVE DIVE:
_____ minutes, equivalent single dive time from IV.
_____ feet, depth of repetitive dive
Decompression from (check one):
☐ Standard Air Table ☐ No-Decompression Table
☐ Surface Table Using Oxygen ☐ Surface Table Using Air
☐ No decompression required
Decompression Stops:
_____ feet _____ minutes
_____ feet _____ minutes
_____ feet _____ minutes
_____ feet _____ minutes
_____ feet _____ minutes
Schedule used _____
Repetitive group _____

this calculation. This worksheet may be reproduced for use in the field. The following is the proper procedure for using the worksheet to compute a repetitive no-decompression dive.

Step 1. Previous Dive Residual Nitrogen

This step determines the level of residual nitrogen in tissues upon surfacing from the previous dive. The residual nitrogen level is dependent upon the depth and duration of the previous dive. It is represented in either the Standard Air Table or the No-Decompression Table as a "repetitive group" letter. Enter the Standard Air Table or the No-Decompression Table, as appropriate, to the previous dive, and determine the repetitive group letter for the depth and bottom time of the previous dive. The No-Decompression Table is used if the previous dive was within no-decompression limits; the Standard Air Table is used if the previous dive required de-

compression. Enter the repetitive group letter on the worksheet (Step 1).

Step 2. Surface Interval Residual Nitrogen

This step determines the level of residual tissue-nitrogen at the end of the surface interval. The surface interval is the elapsed time between surfacing from the previous dive and the time when a diver leaves the surface on the repetitive dive. The level of residual nitrogen is dependent upon the post dive level determined in Step 1 above, and the surface interval that will have elapsed when the repetitive dive commences. Using these factors, enter the No-Decompression Table. Instructions for entering the table are located below the tabulation. Select the new or "adjusted" repetitive group letter. This adjusted repetitive group letter represents the residual nitrogen level at the end of the surface interval. Enter this letter on Step 2 of the worksheet.

Step 3. Residual Nitrogen Time

This step transforms the post-surface interval residual nitrogen level to a "residual nitrogen time." The residual nitrogen time depends on the depth of the repetitive dive, and the "adjusted" repetitive group letter obtained from Step 2. Using the adjusted repetitive group letter, enter the _Repetitive Dive Table_ horizontally to the depth of the repetitive dive or next greater depth and record the time shown on Step 3 of the worksheet.

Step 4. Repetitive Dive Bottom Time

This step determines the maximum allowable bottom time for a diver's repetitive no-decompression dive. Upon leaving the surface on his repetitive dive, the diver may assume that he has already expended the bottom time represented by his residual nitrogen time, at the depth of his repetitive dive as determined in Step 3. He therefore subtracts this time from the allowable no-decompression time shown in the No-Decompression Table for the depth of his repetitive dive. The time remaining is the maximum bottom time for a no-decompression repetitive dive.

Instructions for the use of each U.S. Navy table are included in the table.

10.2 DECOMPRESSION AIR DIVING

All air dives of sufficient depth and duration to preclude direct ascent to the surface (those exceeding the time-depth limits of the No-Decompression Table) are considered decompression dives and require adherence to the decompression schedule of the Standard Air Table.

To safely control the rate at which nitrogen is eliminated from the tissues, the diver must stop during ascent at predetermined depths for a specified time. These depths and times are shown in the Standard Air Table. Ascent on the appropriate dive schedule of the Standard Air Table allows a partial equalization of the nitrogen partial pressure between the body and the ambient pressure before the differential can reach a level harmful to the diver. For example, using the Standard Air Table, during an air dive to 60 feet and an 80-minute bottom time, a diver's tissues have absorbed too much nitrogen to allow direct ascent to the surface. The diver can ascend to a depth of 10 feet, however, without causing the differential between the partial pressure of nitrogen in the tissues and the ambient pressure to reach a harmful level. The diver, therefore, ascends to a 10-foot decompression stop and remains at the stop for 7 minutes before continuing his ascent to the surface. During the 7-minute stop at 10 feet, enough nitrogen has diffused out of the tissues to reduce the partial pressure differential to a safe level, allowing the diver to surface.

10.2.1 Nonrepetitive Decompression Dives

A nonrepetitive decompression dive is any dive that does not occur within 12 hours of a previous dive and that exceeds the depth and/or the time limitations of the No Decompression Table for no decompression dives. A diver ascending from a nonrepetitive decompression dive must do so in strict accordance with the appropriate decompression schedule of the Standard Air Table. The following example illustrates the use of the Standard Air Table in arriving at the appropriate decompression schedule.

Assume that a diver is to ascend from a dive of 71 feet with 78 minutes of bottom time. Enter the depth column of the table with "the exact depth of the dive or the next greater tabular value," in this case 80 feet. At the 80-foot level, select the listed bottom time that is "exactly equal to or next greater than the actual time of the dive," in this case 80 minutes. By reading across the table in the 80 feet for 80 minutes schedule, it is determined that the

diver must proceed directly to a 20-foot decompression stop, at a rate of approximately 1 foot per minute, and remain for 2 minutes. The diver then proceeds to a 10-foot stop, and remains for 31 minutes. The diver then may proceed to the surface.

10.2.2 Repetitive Decompression Dives

A repetitive decompression dive is any dive performed within 12 hours of a previous dive that requires adherence to a decompression schedule upon ascent. The proper decompression schedule of the Standard Air Table cannot be selected on the basis of the repetitive dive alone, but must be calculated on the basis of the repetitive dive, the surface interval, and the previous dive. The following tables are used in determining the proper decompression schedule.

No-Decompression Table

Residual Nitrogen Table

Standard Air Table

The tables are formulated to express residual nitrogen level within the body from the previous dive in terms of "residual nitrogen time." The residual nitrogen time is added to the actual bottom time of the repetitive dive in determining the proper decompression schedule of the Standard Air Table to use in ascending from the repetitive dive.

A worksheet, "Repetitive Dive Worksheet" (Figure 10-1) has been prepared to assist in the determination of the appropriate decompression schedule.

Step 1. Previous Dive, Residual Nitrogen

This step determines the level of residual nitrogen in a diver's tissues upon surfacing from the previous dive and is represented in either the Standard Air Table or the No-Decompression Table for each previous dive schedule as a "repetitive group" letter. Enter this repetitive group letter on the worksheet (Step 1).

Step 2. Surface Interval, Residual Nitrogen

This step is required to determine the level of residual tissue nitrogen at the end of the surface interval. The level of residual nitrogen is dependent upon the post-dive level determined in Step 1 above, and the surface interval. Using these factors enter the Residual Nitrogen Table. Select the new or "adjusted" repetitive group letter. This adjusted repetitive group letter represents the residual nitrogen level at the end of the surface interval. Enter this letter on Step 2 of the worksheet.

Step 3. Residual Nitrogen Time

This step is necessary to transform the post-surface interval residual nitrogen level to a "residual nitrogen time." This calculation results in the time required for a diver to accumulate the nitrogen level of a normal dive at the depth of the repetitive dive. The residual nitrogen time is dependent upon the depth of the repetitive dive, and the adjusted repetitive group letter obtained from Step 2. Using the adjusted repetitive group letter, enter the Residual Nitrogen Table horizontally to the depth of the repetitive dive or the next greater depth, and record the time shown in the Residual Nitrogen Table on Step 3 of the worksheet.

Step 4. Equivalent Single Dive Time

This step computes the equivalent single dive time for decompression purposes. This is accomplished by adding the actual bottom time of the repetitive dive to the residual nitrogen time determined in Step 3. This sum represents a theoretical bottom time for a single nonrepetitive dive at the depth attained during the repetitive dive. The theoretical bottom time constitutes the depth and duration of an "equivalent single dive" and is used in selecting the appropriate decompression schedule from the Standard Air Table for the repetitive dive. This is accomplished in Step 5.

Step 5. Decompression for Repetitive Dive

During this step the appropriate decompression schedule for the repetitive dive is selected. This is accomplished by entering the Standard Air Table at the actual depth, or the next greater tabular value, of the repetitive dive and the "equivalent single dive time," or next greater tabular value computed in Step 4. Record the decompression stops on the Repetitive Dive Worksheet for Decompression Dives under Step 5.

10.3 AIR SUPPLY REQUIREMENTS

Air must be provided at a pressure that will overcome both the ambient pressure at depth and the pressure drop resulting from equipment resistance. In special instances, it may be necessary to calculate air supply requirements prior to conducting the operation.

10.3.1 Scuba Air Requirements

The following simplified method of calculating scuba air requirements may be used.

A. To determine the volume of air remaining in a partially charged scuba cylinder, calculate as follows:

1. $\text{(Gauge readout in psig)} \times \dfrac{\text{Rated cylinder volume in cu ft free air}}{\text{Rated pressure and psig including 10 percent overpressure}}$

   $= $ remaining volume in cu ft

2. Since, $\dfrac{\text{rated cylinder volume}}{\text{rated pressure}}$ is constant for a given cylinder, the constant value for steel cylinders can be determined.

   $\dfrac{71.2 \text{ cu ft cylinder volume}}{2475 \text{ psig maximum pressure}} = 0.0288 \text{ rounded to } 0.03$

   For aluminum cylinders rated at 3000 psig is

   $\dfrac{71.2 \text{ cu ft}}{3000 \text{ psig}} = 0.0236 \text{ rounded to } 0.024$

3. Sample problems:
   (a) 71.2 cu ft cylinder pressure readout=1500 psig.

   $1500 \text{ psig} \times 0.03 = 45 \text{ cu ft}$

   (b) *Twin* 71.2 cu ft cylinder pressure readout = 1000 psig.

   $1000 \times 0.03 \times 2 = 60 \text{ cu ft}$

B. To estimate air requirements at a given depth and exertion level.

1. Determine approximate pressure at depth in *at*mospheres *a*bsolute (ata)

$$\begin{aligned}
\text{Surface} &= 1 \text{ ata} \\
33 \text{ ft} &= 2 \text{ ata} \\
66 \text{ ft} &= 3 \text{ ata} \\
99 \text{ ft} &= 4 \text{ ata} \\
132 \text{ ft} &= 5 \text{ ata}
\end{aligned}$$

Examples:
a. Pressure at 60 ft = approx. 3 ata
b. Pressure at 75 ft = approx. 3.5 ata

2. Estimate exertion level and air consumption at surface pressure in cubic feet/minute (cfm)

Physical exertion affects gas-supply duration. Because the work rate can vary greatly from dive to dive, the duration of the given gas supply can also vary greatly, even at the same depth. The following gas consumption rates for various levels of exertion can be used for rough calculations. For more accurate calculations, each diver should record his own gas consumption for dives under various levels of exertion.

Moderate exertion/warm water.................. 1 cfm
Heavy exertion or moderate exertion/cold
water... 2 cfm
Heavy exertion/cold water........................ 3 cfm

3. Estimate air consumption at depth:

Pressure in ata × surface consumption = level in cfm

Estimated air consumption at depth (eac)
Example:
a. Estimate consumption (in cfm) for a dive to 30 ft in cold water with heavy exertion:

$$2 \text{ ata} \times 3 \text{ cfm} = 6 \text{ cfm}$$

4. Estimate total air consumption for a given dive requirement.
(a) Most convenient procedure to use is the total dive time including ascent (tdt) at standard rate of 60 ft/min
(b) Multiply tdt × eac = Total Air Requirement (tar)

Examples:
a. Estimate the air requirements for a 15 minute dive to 100 ft in warm water with moderate exertion.

4 ata × 1 cfm × (15 min

+ 2 min [ascent time]) = 68 cu ft

b. Estimate the air requirements for a 20 minute dive to 50 ft with heavy exertion.

$$2.5 \text{ ata} \times 2 \text{ cfm} \times 20 \text{ min} = 100 \text{ cu ft}$$

c. Estimate duration of an air supply:

$$\frac{\text{Pressure readout (psig)} \times \text{Constant (K)}}{\text{Pressure at depth (ata)} \times \text{Surface Air Consumption}}$$
$$= \text{Estimated duration of air supply}$$

Example:
Estimate how long a diver can work at 65 feet in cold water (heavy exertion) using standard twin 70's (2250) with a pressure readout of 1800 psig.

$$\frac{1800 \times 0.03 \times 2}{3 \times 3} = 12 \text{ min}$$

10.3.2 Surface-Supplied Requirements

When using a free-flow mask or lightweight helmet, a hose pressure of at least 50 psi over ambient is required for divers in less than 120 feet of water and 100 psi over ambient is required for depths exceeding 120 feet. Hose pressure requirements are increased when using exceptionally long tethers. Modern free-flow/demand masks are designed to function at hose pressures of 50–200 psi (depending on make) over ambient. Therefore, the recommended hose pressure (3/8-in. ID hose) for a free-flow/demand mask (and hookah) is 100 psi in excess of ambient pressure at working depth (Somers 1972).

Hose pressure may be calculated using the following formulas:
For depths less than 120 feet:

$$P_s = 0.445D + 65$$

where

P_s = supply air pressure (psig)
D = depth of water in feet
65 = absolute hose pressure (50 psi + 14.7 psi)

For depths over 120 feet:

$$P_s = 0.445\ D + 115$$
115 = absolute hose pressure (100 psi + 14.7 psi)

NOAA Diving Manual

where

P_s = supply air pressure (psig)
D = depth of water in feet

For example, the hose pressure for a helmet diver working at 100 feet is:

$$P_s = 0.445\,(100) + 65$$
$$= 110 \text{ psi}$$

If a small compressor cannot maintain the pressures recommended above, always maintain a pressure of at least one atmosphere in excess of absolute bottom pressure. This is necessary to provide the diver with immediate available pressure in the event of a fall, thereby possibly preventing barotrauma, or increase flow requirements.

Adequate ventilation is required to keep CO_2 concentration at a tolerable level. For free-flow mask and lightweight helmet, the volume of air available should be at least 4.5 cfm at depth. The free-flow/demand mask used in the demand mode will require from 1 to 3 cfm to depth depending upon the diver's activity level.

The volume of free air (as measured at the surface) required by a diver may be calculated using the following formulas.

For free-flow equipment:

$$R = 4.5\ P(d)$$

R = flow rate in cfm
P = ambient pressure at working depth in atmospheres
(d) = number of divers to be supplied

For example, two divers working at a depth of 100' using a lightweight helmet would require

$$R = 4.5 \times 4 \times 2$$
$$= 36 \text{ cfm}$$

For demand equipment:

$$R_d = C_s(P)$$

R_d = demand flow rate in cfm
C_s = surface consumption rate in cfm
P = ambient pressure at working depth in atmospheres

A diver doing heavy work at a depth of 100' using a demand mask will require

$$R_d = 3 \times 4$$
$$= 12 \text{ cfm}$$

10.3.3 Surface-Supplied Requirements Using High-Pressure Air Flasks

When conducting surface-supplied diving operations in depths less than 130 feet, a four-to-twelve 240 or 350 cu ft cylinder high-pressure air cascade system is satisfactory for diving with a free-flow/demand mask. Six 240 or 350 cu ft cylinders are mounted on a cradle fitted with a manifold system. Several 6-cylinder cradles may be used for extended operations. A two- or four-cylinder unit is used for small boat operations (usually limited dive durations and/or shallow water). The high-pressure cylinders are charged using a high-pressure air compressor driven by an electric motor or diesel engine. This system provides a sufficient air supply and enables divers to operate without the excessive noise of a compressor motor during diving operations. This enhances communications considerably and provides more pleasant conditions for surface personnel. On large operations, one cradle unit can be recharged while others are in operation. In addition, the same system may be used to support scuba diving operations.

A pressure reduction regulator system is required to reduce the high cylinder pressure to working pressure. For shallow-water work, a single one- or two-stage gas reduction regulator (4000 cu ft per hour or higher and 250 psi outlet pressure) with a high flow capacity is satisfactory. Two or more cylinders are connected in series and the regulator is attached to the manifold. When using a single regulator system, the diver should be equipped with a self-contained emergency air supply and a low-pressure volume tank on the surface.

For deep water, a more elaborate air regulator system is recommended. Air control systems are not standardized; they are usually designed to the specifications of individual divers or diving firms. The system should include two regulators, two diver outlets, and connections for primary and emergency air supplies. Either regulator may be supplied by air from the primary or emergency air source at a given time. In the event of a regulator malfunction, the Dive Master or tender may immediately activate ball valves to isolate the faulty regulator and switch the diver to the stand-by regulator. Furthermore, in the event of primary air supply failure (e.g., line rupture), the emergency air supply may be activated and the primary system isolated for repair. Even with the redundancy in the air control system, it is recommended that divers be equipped with self-contained emergency air supplies (Somers 1972).

The amount of time a diver may spend on the bottom when using air supplied from a high-pressure air flask can be calculated using the following equation:

$$\text{Number of minutes on bottom} = \frac{CN[A-(15+E+1)]}{4.5D(E+1)}$$

where

C = capacity of one flask in cu ft of free air

N = number of flasks (minus one for reserve if a secondary air supply is not available)

A = gauge pressure of air in the flasks in atmospheres (psi divided by 14.7)

E = gauge pressure at depth to which dive is to be made in atmospheres (feet divided by 33)

D = number of divers

For example two divers are to be supplied by eight compressed air flasks charged to 1470 psi (8 cu ft flask at 14.7 psi) with two additional flasks held in reserve. Depth of the dive will be 99 feet. The allowable time on the bottom will be

$$T = \frac{8(8)\left[\dfrac{1470}{14.7} - \left(15 + \dfrac{99}{33} + 1\right)\right]}{4.5(2)\left(\dfrac{99}{33} + 1\right)}$$

$$T = 144 \text{ min}$$

If the depth and duration of the dive are such that decompression is necessary, the length of time spent on the bottom must be reduced to allow sufficient air for decompression. The amount of air required for decompression is the sum of the cubic feet of air used at each stop:

$$\text{Cubic feet of air used at stop} = \left(\frac{SD}{33} + 1\right) 4.5 T_{SD}$$

where

SD = stop depth in feet

T_{SD} = duration of time at stop depth plus the ascent time from the preceding stop in minutes

10.4 DECOMPRESSION TABLES

In using the decompression tables in Appendix D the following instructions must be adhered to:

All dives which are not separately listed are covered in the tables by the next deeper and next longer schedule. *Do Not Interpolate.*

Enter the tables at the listed depth that is exactly equal to, or is the next greater than, the maximum depth attained during the dive.

Select the bottom time from those listed for the selected depth that is exactly equal to, or is next greater than the bottom time of the dive.

Use the decompression stops listed on the line for the selected bottom time.

Ensure that the diver's chest level is maintained as close as possible to each decompression depth for the number of minutes listed.

Commence timing each stop on arrival and resume ascent when specified time has elapsed.

Observe all special table instructions.

Always fill out a Repetitive Dive Worksheet or similar systematic guideline.

For cold or arduous dives and under conditions that prohibit accurate decompression, the next deeper and longer schedule should be used. For example, for a dive to 110 feet for 30 minutes in cold water, decompress using the 120 feet for 40 minutes schedule. Diving at high elevations requires the use of special tables to determine equivalent sea pressure depths for decompression (See Section 9).

10.5 SURFACE DECOMPRESSION FOR AIR DIVING

For routine dives it is standard practice to carry out decompression by stopping at the prescribed depths in the water. Under normal conditions this procedure is safe if proper surface support facilities and personnel are available. There are occasions however, particularly after deep dives or relatively shallow dives of long exposure time, where sea conditions such as strong currents, cold water, heavy weather, or other emergencies prevent a diver from taking adequate decompression time in the water. Other conditions may also dictate the use of surface decompression. These may be summarized as follows:

- Treatment of decompression sickness.
- Cases requiring medical care in which decompression has not been completed.
- Programs in which numerous divers are in the water making repeated dives requiring decompression—thus taxing surface support.
- Extended deep diving in cold water.
- Diving conducted from shipboard where the ship cannot remain on station.

There are two tables used in surface decompression. These are:

U.S. Navy Surface Decompression Table Using Oxygen

U.S. Navy Surface Decompression Table Using Air (See Appendix D).

10.5.1 Surface Decompression Using Oxygen Following an Air Dive

The Surface Decompression Table Using Oxygen is used for surface decompression from an air dive. It is essential that only pure oxygen be breathed during this procedure. If the oxygen supply is interrupted or oxygen toxicity symptoms appear, the decompression may be completed on air. If this occurs, use the Surface Decompression Table Using Air disregarding the time spent on oxygen. The notes following the Surface Decompression Table Using Oxygen and the Surface Decompression Table Using Air are self-explanatory and should be observed.

10.5.2 Surface Decompression Using Air Following an Air Dive

The Surface Decompression Table Using Air may be used following an air dive. When surface decompressing on air, do *not* use the Standard Air Table, but adhere to the Surface Decompression Table Using Air.

10.6 NO-CALCULATION REPETITIVE DIVE TABLES

A system has been developed that simplifies the process of computing allowable repetitive dive bottom times and residual nitrogen times (Reuter 1971). This system is a rearrangement of standard U.S. Navy Tables (See Tables 10–1 and 10–2). These tables, and the procedures for using them, are included in this simplified method.

10.6.1 Instructions

For a "no decompression" dive:
1. Find the depth to which you have dived along the top of Table 10–2.
2. Drop down to the figure which denotes your Bottom Time.
3. Go across to the right and follow the arrow upward until you find the time spent out of the water since the last dive (Surface Interval).
4. Go across to the right to find the allowable Bottom Time (white numbers) for the next dive. These are listed under the appropriate depths at the top of each column. The Black Numbers are "Residual Nitrogen Times" and are only important for figuring "Decompression Dives."
5. If the "no decompression" limits are exceeded, go to Table 10–1 for Decompression stops and times.
6. If the diver's surface interval is less than 10 minutes, add the Bottom Times of the preceding and following dives, use the maximum depth attained and consider the two dives as one.
7. SHORTENED OR OMITTED DECOMPRESSION: If a diver surfaces after a dive and finds he has not adequately decompressed but has no symptoms of decompression sickness, he has a maximum surface interval of 5 minutes to determine what his decompression for the dive should have been, get back in the water and begin the following decompression procedure:
   a. Make a stop at 40 ft. for 1/4 the 10 ft. stop time.
   b. Make a stop at 30 ft. for 1/3 the 10 ft. stop time.
   c. Make a stop at 20 ft. for 1/2 the 10 ft. stop time.
   d. Make a stop at 10 ft. for 1 1/2 times the 10 ft. stop time, then surface.

Table 10-1
Modified U.S. Navy
Standard Air
Decompression Table

Depth (feet)	Bottom Time (min)	Decompression stops (min) 20(ft)	10(ft)	Repetitive Group
	200		0	(*)
40	210		2	N
	230		7	N
	100		0	(*)
	110		3	L
50	120		5	M
	140		10	M
	160		21	N
	60		0	(*)
	70		2	K
	80		7	L
60	100		14	M
	120		26	N
	140		39	O
	50		0	(*)
	60		8	K
	70		14	L
	80		18	M
70	90		23	N
	100		33	N
	110	2	41	O
	120	4	47	O
	130	6	52	O
	40		0	(*)
	50		10	K
	60		17	L
	70		23	M
80	80	2	31	N
	90	7	39	N
	100	11	46	O
	110	13	53	O
	30		0	(*)
	40		7	J
	50		18	L
90	60		25	M
	70	7	30	N
	80	13	40	N
	90	18	48	O
	25		0	(*)
	30		3	I
100	40		15	K
	50	2	24	L
	60	9	28	N
	70	17	39	O
	20		0	(*)
	25		3	H
110	30		7	J
	40	2	21	L
	50	8	26	M
	60	18	36	N

Depth (feet)	Bottom Time (min)	Decompression stops (min) 20(ft)	10(ft)	Repetitive Group
	15		0	(*)
	20		2	H
120	25		6	I
	30		14	J
	40	5	25	L
	50	15	31	N
	10		0	(*)
	15		1	F
130	20		4	H
	25		10	J
	30	3	18	M
	40	10	25	N
	10		0	(*)
	15		2	G
140	20		6	I
	25	2	14	J
	30	5	21	K
	5		0	C
	10		1	E
150	15		3	G
	20	2	7	H
	25	4	17	K
	30	8	24	L
	5		0	D
	10		1	F
160	15	1	4	H
	20	3	11	J
	25	7	20	K
	5		0	D
170	10		2	F
	15	2	5	H
	20	4	15	J
	5		0	D
180	10		3	F
	15	3	6	I
	5		0	D
190	10	1	3	G
	15	4	7	I

*See U.S. Navy No Decompression Table for Repetitive Groups in "No Decompression Dives."

Table 10-2
Simplified Linear Table
for Repetitive
Air Dives

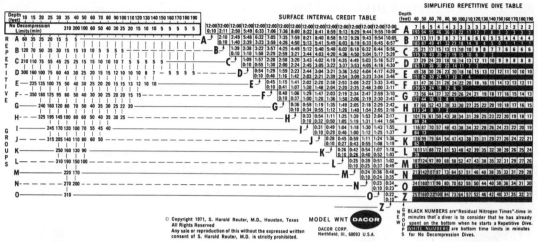

SIMPLIFIED REPETITIVE DIVE TABLE

BLACK NUMBERS are "Residual Nitrogen Times"—time in minutes that a diver is to consider that he has already spent on the bottom when he starts a Repetitive Dive. WHITE NUMBERS are bottom time limits in minutes for No Decompression Dives.

SURFACE INTERVAL CREDIT TABLE

Use of Table 10–1:

a. All decompression stops are timed in minutes.

b. Ascent rate is 60 feet per minute.

c. The chest level of the diver should be maintained as close as possible to each decompression depth for the number of minutes listed.

d. The time at each stop is the exact time that is spent at that decompression depth.

10.6.2 Definitions

1. Bottom time (in minutes) starts when the diver leaves the surface and ends only when the diver starts a direct ascent back to the surface. Always select the exact or next greater bottom time exposure.

2. Depth (in feet). The deepest depth of descent. Always enter the tables on the exact or next greater depth reached.

3. Residual Nitrogen Time—Time in minutes that a diver is to consider he has already spent on the bottom when he starts a repetitive dive.

4. Surface Interval—Time in hours and minutes actually spent on the surface between dives.

5. Repetitive Dive—A dive begun within 12 hours of surfacing from a previous dive.

PLAN YOUR DIVE—DIVE YOUR PLAN

Always carry the Dive Tables on a dive—
they may save your life.

10.6.3 Examples

There are four basic problems for which the U.S. Navy dive tables can provide answers. The "No-Calculation" Linear System can solve these problems very simply and quickly (Reuter 1971).

Let us consider a hypothetical diver who descends to 50 feet remaining at that depth for 60 minutes (bottom time). He then returns to the surface for three hours (surface interval) before starting his next dive.

A. FIRST REPETITIVE DIVE (Second Dive)

What will be his allowable bottom time for a no-decompression dive if he wishes to dive to 70 feet on his first repetitive dive (second dive)?

1. Drop down the 50 foot column in Table 10–2 to the 60 minute line.

2. Go across to the right to "H" Repetitive Group.

3. Follow the arrow upward until reaching the limits within which three hours falls (2:24 to 3:20).

4. Go across to the right ("D" Repetitive Group) to the 70 foot column where the bottom time limit is found to be 30 minutes (white number—black background). This is the maximum time that can be spent without having to make decompression stops. If less time was spent, proceed to example B. If more time was spent, proceed to example C.

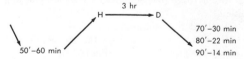

3 hr

H — D

50'–60 min
70'–30 min
80'–22 min
90'–14 min

B. SECOND REPETITIVE DIVE (Third Dive)

If the repetitive dive was made to 70 feet for only 15 minutes bottom time instead of the maximum 30 minutes allowed, how would the tables be used to determine the next repetitive dive (third dive)?

1. Add the 15 minutes bottom time used on the second dive to the 20 minutes bottom time which is the time that a diver is to consider that he has already spent at 70 feet when he *starts* the second dive (residual nitrogen time) — totaling 35 minutes. This residual nitrogen time (20 minutes) is shown in black figures above the bottom time limits in white figures (30 minutes).

2. Returning to Table 10–2, drop down the 70 foot column to 35 minutes.

3. Go across to the right to enter the Surface Interval Credit Table as a "G" diver.

4. Suppose 1 hour was now spent on the surface.

5. Follow the arrow after "G" upward until reaching the limits within which 1 hour falls (0:41 to 1:15).

6. Go across to the right to become an "F" diver.

7. If the next dive were made to 50 feet, the maximum no-decompression bottom time would be 53 minutes (white number — black background). For a 60 foot dive, 24 minutes or 70 foot dive, 19 minutes.

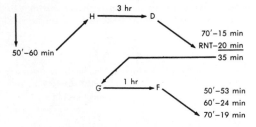

C. DECOMPRESSION REPETITIVE DIVE

How does the diver determine his decompression stops if he finds his bottom time at 70 feet is 55 minutes instead of the maximum 30 minutes allowed?

1. Add the 55 minutes bottom time used on the second dive to the 20 minutes bottom time which is the time that a diver is to consider he has already spent at 70 feet when he *starts* the second dive (residual nitrogen time) — totaling 75 minutes.

2. Go to Table 10–1 Standard Air Decompression Table.

3. In the depth column locate 70 feet.

4. Go across to the right, in the 80 minute line (exact or next greatest bottom time) to find that an 18

minute decompression stop is necessary at 10 feet.

5. The letter next to 18 is "M" which indicates a new repetitive group designation following decompression.

6. Suppose 2 hours were now spent on the surface.

7. Enter Table 10–2 following the arrow after "M" upward until reaching the limits within which 2 hours falls (1:40 to 2:05).

8. Go across to the right to become an "H" diver.

9. If the next dive were made to 50 feet, the maximum no-decompression bottom time would be 34 minutes (white number — black background). For a 60 foot dive, 8 minutes or 70 foot dive, 7 minutes.

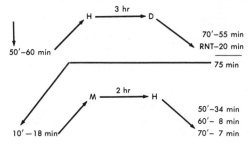

D. SURFACE INTERVAL FOR NO-DECOMPRESSION REPETITIVE DIVE

Suppose the diver wishes to go to 70 feet for this first repetitive dive (second dive) for a bottom time of 40 minutes without the necessity of decompression stops? The proper surface interval must now be determined.

1. Enter Table 10–2 at the 50 foot column dropping down to 60 minutes (as in problem A).

2. Go across to the right to find the repetitive group which is "H".

3. Leave this table remembering the group designation and go to the Simplified Repetitive Dive Table in the 70 foot column.

4. Dropping down to the exact bottom time desired (40 minutes), or the next greater, stop at the 41 minute bottom time limit line which is in the "B" group line.

5. Go to the left until the "H" column is reached. The minimal surface interval for a no-decompression dive is found to be 4 hours and 50 minutes.

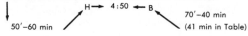

SECTION 11
MIXED GAS
AND OXYGEN
DIVING

MIXED GAS AND OXYGEN DIVING

11.0 GENERAL

Mixed gas diving is differentiated from other techniques in that the breathing medium is a closely controlled mixture of oxygen and an inert gas. Commonly used mixed gases include controlled combinations of nitrogen-oxygen (N_2-O_2) and helium-oxygen (He-O_2). Neon-oxygen (Ne-O_2) and hydrogen-oxygen (H-O_2) have been used experimentally. While mixed gas diving is more complex in terms of equipment and techniques, these complexities are compensated for by the increased capability to dive to greater depths and stay for longer periods of time.

11.1 MIXED GAS COMPOSITION

With one exception, all diving is conducted using a mixture of gases as a breathing medium. This exception is the closed circuit oxygen scuba, discussed in Paragraph 11.5, in which pure oxygen is used exclusively. Air diving uses a mixture of gases, however, the ratio of gases is not controlled, but is that found naturally in the atmosphere. In mixed gas diving, the ratio of the diluent gas is changed to control the partial pressure of the oxygen. This distribution is important in the preparation of the breathing medium, its composition, the diving apparatus itself, and decompression procedures.

The following paragraphs discuss various aspects of N_2-O_2 and He-O_2, oxygen concentration, and carbon dioxide control as they apply to diving.

11.1.1 Nitrogen-Oxygen Mixtures

A controlled mixture of nitrogen and oxygen used as a breathing gas that utilizes a higher concentration of oxygen and less nitrogen than natural air has the advantage of requiring less decompression time than air dives of the same depth and duration. The safe use of controlled mixtures of N_2-O_2 requires the use of a special diving apparatus, principally semiclosed mixed-gas scuba. Common mixtures are:

1. 60 percent oxygen—40 percent nitrogen mixture; maximum depth, 55 feet

2. 40 percent oxygen—60 percent nitrogen mixture; maximum depth, 99 feet

3. $32\frac{1}{2}$ percent oxygen—$67\frac{1}{2}$ percent nitrogen mixture; maximum depth, 129 feet

Of the three, the latter two mixtures (40–60 and $32\frac{1}{2}$–$67\frac{1}{2}$) are the most commonly used, as the 60–40 mixture borders on the oxygen concentration levels where lung irritation may occur.

The reduced percentage of nitrogen in the above mixtures will reduce the effects of nitrogen narcosis. Because the percentage of oxygen must be correspondingly increased, the oxygen depth and duration limits become the restricting factor. This is generally more restrictive than the depth limits imposed by nitrogen narcosis.

The first observable symptoms of nitrogen narcosis may appear if the nitrogen partial pressure exceeds 3.0 atmospheres. Experienced divers can utilize nitrogen partial pressures up to 5.5 atmospheres (U.S. Navy Diving-Gas Manual 1971).

Nitrogen-oxygen mixtures are also used for saturation diving. Under these conditions a surface equivalent oxygen partial pressure is usually maintained. For example, at 45 to 50 feet a mix of about 91 percent N_2 and 9 percent O_2 is used, while at 100 feet mixes of about 95 percent N_2 and 5 percent O_2 are used (Miller et al. 1971). Further discussions of saturation diving are given in Section 12.

NOTE: The U.S. Navy Decompression Tables, referred to in this section, are included in Appendix D.

11.1.2 Helium-Oxygen Mixtures

Helium-oxygen mixtures are used in preference to air or controlled N_2-O_2 mixtures for diving to depths over 200 feet. The problems associated with nitrogen narcosis are totally eliminated in helium-oxygen dives. In present practice, helium-oxygen is used in closed-circuit mixed-gas scuba and umbilical systems (See Section 4). Presently, two helium-oxygen mixtures are commonly used with umbilical systems.

68 percent helium—32 percent oxygen. This is the "standard" mixture for dives to a maximum depth of 200 feet for 30 minutes.

A second He-O_2 mixture is 60 percent helium—40 percent oxygen to depths of 80 feet.

Experimental dives up to 2,000-foot depths have been conducted in research hyperbaric chambers using helium-oxygen mixtures. The U.S. Navy Diving Manual contains procedures and decompression schedules for dives using helium-oxygen mixtures.

11.1.3 Oxygen Concentration

The partial pressure of oxygen in normal air is about 0.21 atmospheres. With increasing depth, the percentage of oxygen in a breathing mixture must be reduced to maintain the oxygen partial pressure between 0.21 and 0.5 atmospheres. An oxygen partial pressure significantly under 0.21 atmospheres produces hypoxia or oxygen deficiency. The first symptoms of hypoxia occur at about 0.16 atmospheres oxygen partial pressure. An oxygen partial pressure of 0.6 atmospheres causes lung irritation after long periods of exposure, and oxygen poisoning can occur at partial pressures above 0.6 atmospheres. For long term exposures such as encountered in saturation diving, an oxygen partial pressure of about 0.3 to 0.5 atmospheres has proved satisfactory.

Breathing a partial pressure of oxygen of between 1.0 and 1.2 atmospheres is tolerable for a period of up to 4 hours with little danger of oxygen toxicity. This range is normally used during decompression. Depth-time limits for breathing pure oxygen are summarized in Table 11-1.

Breathing of properly controlled oxygen-inert gas mixtures is harmless to the body, providing the oxygen concentration is kept within the partial pressure ranges shown in Figure 11-1.

Table 11-1
U.S. Navy Table, Oxygen Depth-Time Limits

(Depth and time limits of exposure for breathing pure oxygen during working dives)

1. Normal Operations—Depth (ft)	Time (min)
10	240
15	150
20	110
25	75

2. Exceptional Operations—Depth (ft)	Time (min)
30	45
35	25
40	10

An inspection of Figure 11-1 shows that for any fixed depth it is feasible to breathe a wide range of oxygen mixtures without ill effects. For example, at 200 feet, the mixture may be as lean as 3 percent oxygen (0.21 atmospheres partial pressure) or as rich as 17 percent oxygen (1.2 atmospheres partial pressure) without encountering any short term physiological effects. Another use of Figure 11-1 is determining the depth range at a fixed oxygen concentration. For example, at 10 percent oxygen, a depth range between 36 and 360 feet is permissible. See Paragraph 2.3 for a further discussion of oxygen poisoning.

11.1.4 Carbon Dioxide Concentration and Control

Carbon dioxide is generated by the metabolic processes of the body. In normal breathing, the body produces about 1 liter of carbon dioxide for each liter of oxygen consumed. Since the production of carbon dioxide is a constant process, and is introduced constantly into the breathing medium as a diver exhales, a means must be provided for its elimination or control. Excessive amounts of carbon dioxide in a breathing gas have a toxic effect on the diver. Figure 2-4 shows the relationship of physiological effects of carbon dioxide for different concentrations and exposure times. Referring to Figure 2-4, in Zone I, no perceptible physiological effects have been observed. In Zone II, small threshold hearing losses have been found, and there is a perceptible increase in depth of respiration. In Zone III, the zone of distracting discomfort, the symptoms are mental depression, headache, dizziness,

**Figure 11-1
Percentage of Oxygen
in Breathing Mixture
as a Function of Depth
and Oxygen Partial Pressure**

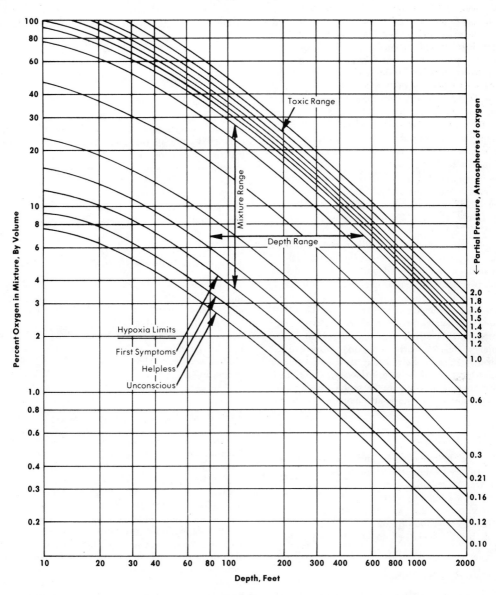

$$\text{Percent O}_2 = \frac{\text{Partial Pressure O}_2\text{, atm} \times 100}{\text{Seawater pressure, atm}}$$

nausea, "air hunger," and a decrease in visual discrimination. Zone IV represents marked physical distress leading to dizziness and stupor, with inability to take steps for self-preservation. The final state is unconsciousness. See Paragraph 2.1.3.2 for a further discussion of carbon dioxide poisoning.

The bar graph shown in Figure 2-4, which is prolonged exposures of 40 days, shows that concentrations of carbon dioxide in air of less than 0.5 percent (Zone A) cause no biochemical or other effects. Concentrations between 0.5 and 3.0 percent (Zone B) cause adaptive biochemical changes, which may be considered a mild physiological strain. Concentrations above 3.0 percent (Zone C) may cause pathological changes.

It is recommended that, for normal diving operations, ventilation rates be provided that result in carbon dioxide partial pressures corresponding to Zones I and II for short-term exposure, and to Zones A and B for long-term exposures.

The principal source of difficulty in carbon dioxide buildup in a diver's breathing gas is the rebreathing of exhaled gas from "dead space" in the diving system. It is essential that dead space be minimized, and that the diving apparatus be ventilated to maintain the carbon dioxide concentration at about 0.01 atmospheres partial pressure (U.S. Navy Diving-Gas Manual 1971). Several means are available to accomplish this. A carbon dioxide absorbent as described in Paragraph 12.3 may be used in closed-circuit systems, or sufficient gas flow from umbilical-supplied sources or open-circuit scuba may be provided to ventilate the mask and exhaust gas to the water.

11.2 GAS MIXING

Mixtures of helium-oxygen and nitrogen-oxygen can be prepared using several methods:
1. Mixing by volume
2. Mixing by weight
3. Continuous mixing by flowmeter
4. Mixing by partial pressure.
Each is briefly described in the following paragraphs.

11.2.1 Mixing by Volume

This technique employs the mixing of a specific volume of each gas into a larger, constant-pressure tank, then compressing the mixture to the desired pressure. This technique is generally limited to installations with large tanks and compressors. The gas mixture is usually analyzed prior to being compressed. Highly accurate mixtures are obtained using this technique (U.S. Navy Diving Manual 1973).

11.2.2 Mixing by Weight

This method employs a highly sensitive and accurate scale. Gas from high-pressure cylinders is added to a single cylinder in proportion to its percentage weight to the total weight of the desired mixture. This type of mixing should not be utilized except by those specially trained in the technique and possessing the calibrated scale necessary to accurately determine small variations in weight changes of the constituent gases (U.S. Navy Diving-Gas Manual 1971).

11.2.3 Continuous Mixing by Flowmeter

This method requires precise calibrated flowmeters that measure the volume flow of pressurized oxygen and diluent gas. The flow of each constituent is controlled by valves to achieve the desired volume ratio of the gas mixture. This method is usually employed when using surface support techniques, with the mixed gas flowing directly to the diver.

11.2.4 Mixing by Partial Pressure

This method employs high-pressure gas sources from which gas is mixed in relation to its desired partial pressure. For example, if a partial pressure of 0.2 atmospheres is desired at a final cylinder pressure of 2,000 psig, oxygen would be added until the cylinder pressure was 400 psig. Then helium (or other diluent) would be added until the 2,000 psig cylinder pressure was achieved. This method is frequently used in filling cylinders aboard ship or in the field. A note of caution: Since exact pressure reading is critical in this technique, it is advisable to use only calibrated pressure gauges. Temperature (Charles' Law) can influence final cylinder pressure; therefore, an analysis of the final gas mixture is desirable (U.S. Navy Diving-Gas Manual 1971).

11.3 SEMICLOSED CIRCUIT MIXED GAS SCUBA DIVING PROCEDURES

A combination of O_2 and any inert gas suitable for breathing can be used with semiclosed circuit scuba, with helium most frequently used for deeper dives and nitrogen for shallower excursions. The percentage of O_2 required is determined by the maximum depth of the dive and will normally be the maximum percentage allowable for a given depth. All gases are mixed, prior to charging the tanks. A diver must not exceed the depth for which the gas was mixed or oxygen toxicity could result.

11.3.1 Advantages and Limitations

There are a number of advantages associated with semiclosed circuit scuba, among which is conservation of gases and the extended bottom time. The ability to use a variety of inert gases and to vary the oxygen content, providing a deep dive capability, is also of importance. By increasing the O_2 content of the breathing mixture the absorption of inert gases can be significantly reduced, thus reducing decompression time and the chances of decompression sickness. By utilizing a higher percentage of oxygen when nitrogen is the diluent gas, the effects of nitrogen narcosis are decreased. These advantages are also applicable to closed-circuit mixed gas diving apparatus.

Semiclosed circuit scuba is more efficient at gas conservation than open-circuit scuba but should the diver exceed the depth for which the gas was mixed, oxygen toxicity could result. Likewise, should the CO_2 absorbent become saturated or a buildup of inert gases develop, hypoxia could result. Finally, the problems associated with training, maintenance, repair, and cost, common to all other rebreathers are also applicable to semiclosed circuit scuba.

11.3.2 Duration

A number of factors directly affect the duration of the gas supply. As with any other diving apparatus, tank capacity and the pressure to which it can safely be charged are important. A flow of gas is discharged from the tanks resulting in gas depletion at a constant rate regardless of depth. An extremely important factor is the duration of the carbon dioxide absorbent. When performing heavy work, the diver will produce carbon dioxide at an increased rate, resulting in a more rapid saturation of the absorbent. If a high work rate is expected it will be necessary to increase the gas flow, further reducing the duration of the gas supply. Most systems have a canister life which will easily exceed the duration of the gas supply. Any restrictions will be specifically outlined in the manufacturer's operation manual.

11.3.3 Equivalent Air Depth (EAD) Calculations

The nitrogen-oxygen EAD for semiclosed circuit scuba is shown in Table 11-2. *Nitrogen-Oxygen Scuba Table.*

Use the following procedure in applying Table 11-2 to establish an equivalent air depth when using semiclosed circuit scuba, This table is not applicable to other scuba systems.

1. Determine the actual diving depth.
2. Select the table corresponding to the N_2–O_2 mixture used for the dive.
3. Enter the column corresponding to the flow setting and diving work condition.
4. Find the next greater value of actual depth tabulated.
5. Read the corresponding equivalent air depth.
6. Decompress according to U.S. Navy Standard Air Decompression Table for the EAD and the actual bottom time.

11.4 CLOSED–CIRCUIT MIXED GAS SCUBA DIVING PROCEDURES

Closed-circuit mixed gas scuba was developed to fill the requirement for a safe and practical breathing apparatus which would conserve breathing gas and yet allow diving to great depths. Closed-circuit mixed gas scuba effectively consumes the entire volume of oxygen, wasting only that which is intentionally purged from the system. These systems extend the duration of the gas supply, and because mixed gas is used, are preferred for deep diving. This equipment is designed to combine oxygen with an inert gas, normally helium, and to maintain the partial pressure of O_2 within safe limits. The partial pressure of oxygen should remain between 0.4 and 0.6 atmospheres, with a variance of up to 1.2 atmospheres for a period of up to 4 hours with little danger

Table 11-2
Nitrogen-Oxygen
Equivalent Air
Depth Table

Oxygen Supply	Non-swimming dive flow setting	Actual depth up to - (feet)	Swimming dive flow setting	Actual depth up to - (feet)	Equivalent air depth (feet)	Maximum Allowable Bottom Time (Minutes)	
						Normal Exposure	Exceptional Exposure
60%		51		55	30	30	60
	4 lpm	64	8 lpm	77	40		30
		77			50		30
40%		36		39	30	No Limit	
		47		51	40	240	No Limit
		58		62	50	100	No Limit
		69		74	60	60	240
	8 lpm	80	12 lpm	85	70	45	160
		91		97	80	30	100
		102		108	90		80
		113		120	100		50
		124		131	110		30
32.5%		33		35	30	No Limit	
		44		46	40	No Limit	
		54		57	50	No Limit	
		65		68	60	240	No Limit
		75		79	70	120	No Limit
		86		89	80	80	No Limit
		96		100	90	60	240
	12 lpm	107	21 lpm	111	100	50	180
		117		122	110	40	110
		128		129	120	30	90
		138		144	130		70
		149		155	140		50
		160		165	150		35
		170		170	160		30

of oxygen toxicity. Some models allow the diver to select a high or low range of O_2 partial pressure for short or long dives, to accelerate decompression.

11.4.1 Advantages and Limitations

The major advantages with closed-circuit mixed gas diving are the conservation of gases and accompanying extended dive duration, quiet operation, the absence of bubbles, and the depths at which the equipment can be operated. The Navy Mk 10 system is designed to be used at depths of over 1000 feet. Nonsaturated shallow dives are practical from surface support platforms, and result in an extended gas supply duration. Closed-circuit mixed gas equipment has been tested in cold water and appears satisfactory; however, the life of the chemicals used to absorb carbon dioxide are significantly decreased and limit the duration of the dive.

The disadvantages associated with closed-circuit mixed gas scuba are both operational and mechanical. The equipment itself is extremely

delicate and complicated. For safe and proper use a diver must be specially trained, and qualified personnel are required for maintenance and repair. The cost of the equipment coupled with the costs of support and maintenance prohibit its use for routine diving tasks. The equipment itself is reliable at shallow depths, but some critical failures, such as fluctuations of oxygen partial pressure, have been recorded on deep cold water dives. The configuration and size of the units vary with some models being significantly more comfortable, and easier to swim with than others.

11.4.2 Duration

Because the oxygen partial pressure can be automatically controlled, closed-circuit mixed gas scuba can be used to greater depths than closed-circuit oxygen scuba. As no oxygen is wasted the duration of a dive is usually limited by the life of the CO_2 absorbent (See Paragraph 11.5.2).

11.4.3 Equivalent Air Depth (EAD) Calculations

In closed-circuit units the duration of the oxygen supply is independent of depth, with oxygen provided to the breathing bags at the rate of consumption. The systems rely on automatic control systems to sense and maintain oxygen partial pressure over a range of preset values. Utilize the following calculation method to determine the EAD when nitrogen is used as the inert gas.

Step 1. Determine nitrogen partial pressure at depth.

$$pN_2 = P - pO_2$$

pN_2 = partial pressure of nitrogen in atmospheres

$P = \dfrac{d}{33} + 1$ = absolute pressure in atmospheres

d = dive depth in feet

pO_2 = partial pressure of oxygen in atmospheres (from unit's preset value)

Step 2. Determine nitrogen absolute pressure at depth.

$$Pe = \frac{pN_2}{0.79}$$

where

pN_2 = partial pressure of nitrogen from Step 1.

$0.79 = \dfrac{\text{Percent } N_2 \text{ in air}}{100}$

Pe = equivalent absolute pressure of nitrogen.

Step 3. Determine the equivalent air depth (EAD)

$$EAD = 33 \ (Pe - 1)$$

where

Pe = equivalent absolute pressure of nitrogen from Step 2.

EAD = equivalent air depth in feet.

Use the next higher depth value from U.S. Navy Standard Air Decompression Table and the bottom time of the diver to determine the proper decompression procedure for use in closed-circuit N_2-O_2 dives.

11.5 CLOSED–CIRCUIT OXYGEN SCUBA DIVING PROCEDURES

Oxygen diving is unique in that it is the only technique in which a diluent gas is not used. Pure oxygen is used as a breathing gas only with the closed-circuit oxygen scuba (except when breathed during decompression). The closed-circuit oxygen scuba is described in detail in Section 4.

When using a closed-circuit oxygen rebreather it is necessary to purge both the apparatus and the lungs with oxygen prior to entering the water. This is necessary to eliminate nitrogen and air from the breathing system. If the excess air is not eliminated from the breathing bags and lungs prior to the initiation of oxygen breathing, sufficient nitrogen may remain in the system to provide a breathable volume after all of the oxygen has been used. During a prolonged dive, the nitrogen eliminated from the body can cause a measurable increase of nitrogen in the breathing medium. The danger of excess nitrogen in a closed-circuit system is that hypoxia (See Paragraph 2.1.3.1) may occur if the volume of nitrogen is enough to markedly dilute or replace the oxygen in the system. Hypoxia gives no warning signals to a diver. Unconsciousness or death may result from hypoxia (See Figure 11–1).

11.5.1 Advantages and Limitations

The advantages of closed-circuit oxygen scuba include freedom from bubbles, almost completely silent operation, and maximum utilization of the breathing medium carried by the diver. A small oxygen supply lasts a long time, and the duration of the supply is not decreased by depth. Divers are not subject to decompression sickness or nitrogen narcosis while using closed-circuit oxygen scuba due to the absence of an inert gas.

The major limitations of O_2 rebreathers are related to the effects of oxygen on the human body. Hypoxia can result if a large amount of inert gas is allowed to build up in the breathing circuit. The system must be thoroughly purged at the beginning of each dive, after one hour of submergence, and again immediately prior to ascent. An excess of carbon dioxide can build up in the system as a result of absorbent exhaustion, wetting of absorbent, improper canister refilling or over-breathing the system.

Because of the chances of oxygen toxicity, the

rebreather is normally used to a working depth of 25 feet for a period of 75 minutes, and any excursions below this depth will result in a greatly decreased allowable bottom time. The maximum permissible dive using this apparatus is 40 feet for a period of 10 minutes. Its use beyond these limits can result in serious or fatal accidents resulting from oxygen toxicity. The degree of training required to use the equipment, coupled with increased maintenance requirements further restrict its use.

11.5.2 Duration

The major factor influencing the duration of a closed-circuit oxygen dive is the time limitation which must be imposed because of oxygen toxicity as shown in Table 11-1.

When using any closed-circuit scuba, utilization of available oxygen is nearly 100 percent because no gas is expelled into the surrounding water except that which is willingly purged from the system or which is automatically vented as the gas expands when surfacing. This permits not only a greater duration of the gas supply, but allows a smaller quantity of breathing gas to be carried. O_2 consumption will vary, dependent primarily upon the diver's exertion level, from 0.5 standard liters per minute (slm) to 3.0 slm. A mean figure of 1.5 slm is a reasonable value for planning purposes (See Figure 2-3).

11.5.3 Medical Aspects

In summary, there are several physiological problems which may arise when using oxygen rebreathers. These include oxygen toxicity, carbon dioxide accumulation resulting from a failure of the absorbent material, and hypoxia. The precautions described in the preceding paragraphs should preclude the onset of these problems. Each of these conditions is discussed in detail in Section 2. Because of the absence of inert gases, there is no requirement for decompression following an oxygen dive.

11.6 SURFACE DECOMPRESSION USING OXYGEN FOLLOWING A NITROGEN-OXYGEN DIVE

Either the U.S. Navy Surface Decompression Table Using Oxygen or the Surface Decompression Table Using Air may be used for surface decompression following a dive in which nitrogen-oxygen was used as the breathing medium. In using these tables, it is essential that an equivalent air depth be determined in selecting the proper decompression depth from the tables. The procedure for determining an equivalent air depth is outlined in Paragraphs 11.3.3 and 11.4.3.

11.7 SURFACE DECOMPRESSION USING AIR FOLLOWING A NITROGEN-OXYGEN DIVE

The procedures outlined in Paragraph 11.6 are applicable to surface decompression using air following a nitrogen-oxygen dive.

SECTION 12
SATURATION
DIVING

SATURATION DIVING 12

12.0 GENERAL

As interest in the oceans and the capability to work there increases, it is becoming more apparent that facilities must be provided to the scientific and working diver to enable him to remain at depth for long periods of time. In 1958, Captain George Bond, U.S.N., conducted laboratory experiments that led the way to the development of saturation diving (Bond 1964). Saturation refers to the state of dissolved gases in the tissues of a diver. Under a saturated condition, the tissues have absorbed all the nitrogen or other inert gases possible at the saturation pressure. Once this has occurred, the decompression time required at the end of the dive of a given depth does not increase with additional time spent at that depth. Under such conditions, the diver works out of a pressure facility in which the atmosphere is maintained at approximately the same pressure as that of the water in which he is working. His "habitat" may be an ocean floor installation, or it may be a pressurized chamber on board a surface vessel from which he travels to his work location in a pressurized personnel transfer capsule (PTC). In either case, he does not undergo decompression between dives; he is decompressed only after the total dive sequence is completed.

This method of diving is essential for the scientist who needs to spend long periods on the bottom and for the working diver who cannot afford the cost-benefit ratio of short dives and frequent long decompressions. Since 1958, saturation diving programs have been conducted in over 15 nations, both in land-based hyperbaric chambers and in the open sea. The depths of such programs have ranged from 35 to 2,000 feet.

While the U.S. Navy and the commercial diving industry are devoting significant efforts to develop deep saturation diving technology in the 500- to 2000-foot range, the scientific community is con-centrating on the use of saturation diving in shallower waters (50 to 300 feet).

This section discusses various aspects of saturation diving and provides tables for excursion diving, decompression, repetitive dives, and aborted dives from saturated conditions in the 50- to 250-foot range.

12.1 GENERAL PRINCIPLES OF SATURATION DIVING

The tissues of a diver's body absorb inert gases as a function of the partial pressure of the breathing medium, the duration of the dive, the type of breathing gas mixture being used, the characteristics of the individual diver's tissue, and his condition at the time of the dive. In dives of long duration, the body tissue becomes saturated with dissolved inert gas at the partial pressure of the breathing medium in approximately 24 hours. The techniques of saturation diving make use of the fact that once the body reaches this equilibrium, it can safely remain saturated for long periods of time (Pauli and Cole 1970).

Two basic approaches are commonly used in saturation diving. They are:

1. Habitat/Ocean Floor Laboratory. A habitat is a pressure or ambient vessel, placed on the floor of the ocean, which provides support, comfort, and a base of operation for the saturated diver and his equipment. Habitats usually are maintained at ambient pressure. Water is prevented from entering the habitat by the gas pressure inside. This permits divers to enter and exit the habitat usually by means of an opening in the habitat floor.

2. Deep Dive Saturation System. A deep dive saturation system consists of a deck decompression chamber (DDC) located on a surface support platform, and a pressurized personnel transfer capsule (PTC) in which the saturation diver commutes to

and from his work site. The DDC, which provides facilities for the comfort of the saturated diver, is maintained at the pressure of the work site depth. The PTC (which can be a diving bell or a lock-out submersible) is also maintained at working depth pressure. The PTC is mated to the DDC to enable the diver to remain at working pressure at all times during transfer operations.

12.2 OPERATIONAL FACTORS

The saturation diver working from a habitat or PTC has direct access to his work. As mentioned earlier, the bottom time or time at the work site is greatly extended because compression and decompression procedures are not required with each excursion into the water. A significant psychological advantage also accrues to divers with the reassurance and convenience of a dry chamber from which to make excursions or to which they may return quickly in case of fatigue or other difficulty.

12.2.1 Breathing Equipment and Mixture

The saturated diver may use a variety of underwater breathing apparatus. Open-circuit scuba, closed-circuit scuba, or umbilical-supplied breathing apparatus (hookah) all are suitable for use from either a habitat or a deep dive saturation system. These systems are described in detail in Section 4. The majority of these systems are designed to support diving operations at depths compatible with a habitat or deep dive system.

The breathing medium used in the habitat or deep dive system is dependent on the depth of the work site. Relatively shallow systems (0 to 100 feet) use compressed air or nitrogen-oxygen breathing media, while deep systems currently are using helium-oxygen mixtures. Experiments are being conducted that should result in other gases being used in the future such as argon, neon, and hydrogen.

12.2.2 General Procedures

A diver experiencing saturation for the first time on the seafloor has much to learn. Although the general procedures and equipment are the same as when diving from the surface, there are some important differences. The diver must:

- Become familiar with the habitat, its operation, and all emergency procedures (See Paragraph

12.4 and Section 14).
- Return to a pressurized or ambient chamber rather than the surface following a dive.
- Orient geographically to avoid getting lost, using lines or transects laid out from the habitat.
- Provide himself with redundant regulators and tanks.
- Wear a compass at all times.
- Always wear a depth gauge and know the vertical excursion limits (See Paragraph 12.5).
- Not wear a flotation device that could accidentally inflate and carry him to the surface.
- Not wear a quick-release weight belt.
- Take particular care with equipment when compressing to depth and making excursions. Items such as cameras, sealed containers, etc., may implode or explode because they often are not designed to withstand both excess internal and external pressures.

Missions must be planned to account for time, distance from the habitat, number of divers, breathing gas (composition and quantity), vertical excursions, life of carbon dioxide absorbent in closed-circuit breathing systems, and any special diver heating or communication equipment that may be required.

12.3 LIFE-SUPPORT FACTORS

Each habitat has its own characteristics that must be learned by a diver (See Section 14). Training programs usually are given, which provide the necessary information. There are a few things, however, that are directly related to the saturated condition of a diver in all habitats.

For most habitats and personnel transfer capsules, the partial pressure of oxygen should be maintained at between 0.19 to 0.5 atmospheres. The carbon dioxide partial pressure should be between 2 to 7 millimeters of mercury. Carbon monoxide, as a trace contaminant, must not exceed a partial pressure of 15×10^{-3} millimeters of mercury.

Buildups of carbon dioxide in habitats and PTC's are prevented by the use of a carbon dioxide scrubbing system or by venting. The heart of a scrubbing system is a chemical, usually barium hydroxide, soda lime, or lithium hydroxide, which absorbs the carbon dioxide. The length of time this absorbent will remain active prior to becoming saturated with CO_2 is directly related to the CO_2 output of the

Table 12-1
Characteristics
of Three Carbon
Dioxide Absorbents

Characteristic	Absorbent		
	Barium Hydroxide	Lithium Hydroxide	Soda Lime
Absorbent density, lb/ft^3	65.4	28.0	55.4
Theoretical CO_2 absorption, lb CO_2/lb	0.39	0.92	0.49
Theoretical water generated, lb/lb CO_2	0.41	0.41	0.41
Theoretical heat of absorption, BTU/lb CO_2	670[1]	875[1]	670[2]
Useful CO_2 absorption, lb CO_2/lb (based on 50 percent efficiency)	0.195	0.46	0.245
Absorbent weight, lb per diver hr (0.71 lb CO_2)	3.65	1.55	2.90
Absorbent volume, ft^3 per diver hr	0.0558	0.0552	0.0533

[1]Based on calcium hydroxide reaction only.
[2]Based on generating gaseous H_2O.

divers and the ambient temperature. The storage and replacement of canisters is a simple process. The number of canisters required depends on the length of the mission. The man-hour rating of a particular absorbent is provided by the manufacturer. It is known, however, that the efficiency of some CO_2 absorbents decreases drastically at lower temperatures.

Table 12—1 summarizes the characteristics of barium hydroxide, lithium hydroxide, and soda lime. Barium hydroxide is used in underwater breathing apparatus, hyperbaric chambers, ocean floor laboratories, and submersibles. Soda lime, a lower cost material, is not used in underwater breathing apparatus because it forms a highly caustic solution with water; however, it appears acceptable for use in scrubbers for other closed systems. Lithium hydroxide is the lightest of the absorbents, but requires the same canister volume as the others and is much more expensive. It also forms a caustic solution with water.

The rate at which carbon dioxide is absorbed is influenced by temperature, and is considerably lower at 40° F than at 70° F. In some scrubbers sized for adequate performance at 70° F, absorbing capacity at 40° F may be as little as 1/3 that at 70° F. This effect is strongly dependent upon the canister design and the rate of carbon dioxide absorption, being most evident in absorbers working at peak flow rates, and least evident in oversized scrubbers and those used intermittently.

It appears highly desirable to provide external insulation and heating of scrubbers for use in cold water as a means of minimizing size and assuring that the design absorbent capacity can be obtained. This is also advisable as a means of avoiding moisture condensation. A possible alternative is to design for about three times the absorbent capacity needed at 70° F.

The efficiency of absorbents is also influenced by relative humidity. The absorbing capacity quoted for barium hydroxide and soda lime absorbents is obtained only when relative humidity is above 70 percent. Lower humidity levels result in less absorbent capacity. Breathing-gas humidity will normally be well above 70 percent unless the scrubber is preceded by a dehumidifier.

Under conditions of high gas humidity and low scrubber surface temperature, it is possible to condense water on the canister walls or in the absorbent. This is undesirable because wet absorbent is inactive and impervious to air flow, reducing absorptive capacity and increasing pressure drop through the canister.

Divers must remain alert for early symptoms of carbon dioxide poisoning (See Figure 11-2). An auxiliary scrubbing system frequently is used as a backup in case of primary system failure. If a backup scrubber system is not available, the chamber (habitat) should be ventilated at a rate of 2 cubic feet per minute (chamber volume) of breathing gas for each diver at rest, and 4 cubic feet per minute for each diver not at rest (Lanphier 1957). Comfortable temperature and humidity ranges have been found to be 78° to 83° F and 50 to 75 percent. respectively, in air or nitrogen/oxygen environments at shallow depths. At deeper depths, or when saturated in a helium/oxygen atmosphere, a temperature as high as 92° F may be required to maintain a comfortable environment.

12.4 EMERGENCY PROCEDURES

A well-conceived operation must include a contingency plan that charts a course of action should a primary life-support system fail or other emergency arise. Any contingency plan should consider diver safety as first priority. Emergency conditions in a habitat or personnel transfer capsule, however minor, pose threats to diver safety that are not found in nonsaturated diving. If a situation arises which makes the habitat uninhabitable, an alternate place must be available where divers can go and undergo decompression safely.

The following emergency procedures are general in nature and are intended to be applicable to all habitats and personnel transfer capsules. Since, however, most habitats and PTC's are "one of a kind" systems, certain differences in hardware and design will dictate specific procedures that should be followed for each.

WARNING

Complete Emergency Procedures Must Be Developed for Each System, and All Surface Support Personnel as Well as Divers Must Become Familiar With Them.

12.4.1 Fire

Fire is probably the most critical emergency that can threaten a saturation system. Shallow water habitats using air as a breathing medium are more susceptible to fire, because air becomes more combustible under pressure than gas mixtures with a lower oxygen content. It has been shown that burning rates under hyperbaric conditions are primarily a function of the percentage of oxygen present (Schmidt et al. 1973).

In shallow habitats using nitrogen-oxygen as a breathing medium, fire is less of a danger because oxygen is partially replaced by nitrogen. At greater depths, where helium is used with low percentages of oxygen, fire is even less of a threat. Care must be taken, however, when oxygen is used during decompression.

WARNING

Overboard Dump Systems for Decompression Are Essential in Order to Eliminate Exhaled Air From the Atmosphere and Prevent the Buildup of Oxygen Levels in the Habitat.

In the event of fire, the general procedures below should be followed:

1. Shut off all power to the chamber.

2. Put on emergency breathing masks and eye protection masks. Some habitats have masks for both oxygen and the chamber's saturation breathing medium; use the mask with the breathing medium.

3. Notify the surface immediately, using the primary communication system, an emergency/backup system, or, when available, a diver underwater communication system.

4. Attempt to extinguish the fire using water.

5. Attempt to remove all flammable materials from the immediate area of the flames. Attempt, also, to discard smouldering material from the chamber.

6. Personnel not directly involved in fighting the fire should don diving gear and leave the chamber.

7. If the fire becomes out of control, abandon the chamber notifying the surface of this action if conditions permit. Proceed to available underwater bottom stations and await surface support.

12.4.2 Loss of Power

Most shallow water habitat systems have a primary power source and an emergency or standby power source. Primary power is usually 110 volts a.c.; emergency is 12 volts d.c. In some systems the emergency power is designed to activate automatically upon failure of the primary source.

Should primary power fail, perform the following procedures:

1. Activate the emergency power source if this system was not activated automatically by primary-source failure.

2. Notify surface support personnel and stand by to assist in isolating and remedying the cause of the failure.

12.4.3 Loss of Communications

Most saturation systems will have a backup system of communication. Sound-powered phones that require no external power often are used. In some cases, communications may be possible over diver communication circuits. When a communications failure occurs, communications should be immediately established on a secondary system, the surface notified of the primary system failure, and attempts made to reactivate the primary system.

12.4.4 Blow-Up

Inadvertent surfacing, commonly called a "blow-up," is a serious hazard facing a saturated diver, especially when he is using self-contained equipment and is not physically "attached" to a habitat or PTC by an umbilical or tether. Extreme caution must be exercised by a saturated diver while away from a habitat to avoid any circumstance that would require making an emergency ascent to the surface or a situation that might result in an accidental surfacing.

If a diver should surface, however, the following action must be taken:

1. Return the diver to the habitat or PTC immediately; or, if a recompression chamber is immediately available at the site, recompress the diver to his saturated depth.

2. If brought back down to a habitat or PTC, notify surface support personnel immediately.

3. Have the diver begin breathing pure oxygen immediately at depths no greater than 60 feet (U.S. Navy Diving Manual 1973).

4. Surface support personnel will determine whether the diver must undergo emergency recompression.

12.4.5 Lost Diver

A saturated diver performing work away from a habitat or PTC should be continually aware that he is dependent on that facility for life support. Any excursion should be carefully planned so that the way back is known and assured. As in all diving, buddy divers are a necessity. In a saturated condition, it is especially necessary for diving buddies to stay close together and to continually be aware of their location, significant landmarks, and the distance and direction back to the habitat or PTC. Many habitats, particularly those permanently fixed and continually used, have transect lines extending to various underwater areas. Divers should become familiar with these transect patterns and use them as reference points during excursions.

Should a diver become lost, the following actions should be taken:

1. Begin signaling by banging on a scuba cylinder with a knife, rock, or other hard object.

2. To conserve breathing gas, ascend to a depth where the bottom can still be seen clearly but which is not above the maximum upward excursion depth (See Table 12-3).

3. Begin making slow circular search patterns looking for familiar landmarks or transect lines.

4. Should a diver become "hopelessly" lost *at saturation depths not exceeding 100 feet* he should, while still having ample air, ascend slowly to the surface. Upon reaching the surface, take a quick (less than 30 seconds) compass sighting on the support system or buoy over the habitat and return to the bottom. He then should proceed directly toward the habitat after rejoining his buddy. It is critical that this action occur while ample air still remains.

12.4.6 Night Diving

Night excursions from a habitat are not uncommon, particularly for the scientific observation of marine life. Particular care must be taken to ensure that divers do not become lost during these excursions. Each diver must be equipped with two diver's lights, well maintained in good working condition, and equipped with fresh batteries. It is recommended, also, that each diver be equipped with an emergency light, preferably a flashing strobe, should a primary light fail or the diver becomes separated from his buddy. In emergencies, the strobe can be used for navigation if the diver shields his eyes from the flash. Also recommended is a flashing strobe on the habitat or PTC to assist divers in return should their lights fail.

12.5 EXCURSION DIVING FROM A SATURATION SYSTEM

Excursion diving from saturation in a habitat or DDC/PTC system requires special preparations and strict adherence to excursion diving tables.

A saturated diver may be compared to a diver at the surface who is saturated at 1 atmosphere, whereas the habitat diver is saturated in multiples of 1 atmosphere. The surface diver can make dives (excursions) to depth and return directly to the surface without decompression as long as he has not absorbed more gas during the excursion than his body can safely release. Similarly, habitat divers can make excursions either to greater depths (downward) or lesser depths (upward) by following the depth/time limitations of the excursion tables.

General rules cannot easily be given. Many factors change the conditions, such as cold, workloads, equipment used, experience, etc., and all such factors must be considered in any excursion or decompression. The following recommendations

Table 12-2
Downward No-Decompression
Excursion Breathing Air
From Nitrogen-Oxygen
Saturation

Saturation Depth fsw	80	85	90	95	100	105	110	115	120	125	130	135	140	145	150	155	160	165	170	175	180	185	190	195	200	205	210	215	220	225	230	235	240	245	250
30	350	267	156	113	91	78	68	60	55	50	45	40	36	32	28	24	22	18	15	13	12	11	10	9	8	8	7	7	6	6	5	5	5	5	—
35	▲	▲	283	229	143	108	89	77	68	61	54	46	41	37	34	31	28	25	22	20	16	14	13	11	10	9	9	8	7	7	6	6	6	5	5
40	▲	▲	▲	301	240	202	147	112	92	80	70	59	50	44	39	35	32	30	28	25	23	21	17	15	13	12	11	10	9	8	8	7	7	6	6
45	▲	▲	▲	▲	323	253	210	181	137	108	91	69	56	48	42	38	34	31	29	27	25	23	22	21	18	16	14	12	11	10	9	9	8	8	7
50	▲	▲	▲	▲	▲	350	267	219	187	164	140	86	64	53	45	40	36	33	30	28	26	24	22	21	20	19	18	16	14	13	12	11	10	9	8
55	▲	▲	▲	▲	▲	▲	314	245	203	174	153	137	86	63	52	45	40	36	32	30	27	25	24	22	21	20	19	18	17	15	13	12	11	10	9
60	▲	▲	▲	▲	▲	▲	▲	284	224	187	161	142	127	85	63	52	45	39	35	32	29	27	25	23	22	21	19	18	17	17	15	13	12	11	10
65	▲	▲	▲	▲	▲	▲	▲	▲	315	236	191	162	145	128	111	85	63	51	44	39	35	32	29	27	25	23	22	20	19	18	17	16	14	12	11
70	▲	▲	▲	▲	▲	▲	▲	▲	▲	279	213	174	148	129	114	103	84	62	51	44	39	35	31	29	26	25	23	21	20	19	18	17	16	15	14
75	▲	▲	▲	▲	▲	▲	▲	▲	▲	▲	▲	288	228	191	165	145	95	66	53	45	40	35	32	29	27	25	23	22	20	19	18	17	16	16	15
80											▲	▲	▲	▲	317	225	215	122	70	55	47	41	36	32	29	27	25	23	22	20	19	18	17	16	15
85												▲	▲	▲	▲	▲	328	265	225	95	66	54	46	40	36	32	29	27	25	23	22	22	19	18	17
90													▲	▲	▲	▲	▲	▲	339	275	168	97	68	55	47	41	37	33	30	28	26	24	23	21	20
95														▲	▲	▲	▲	▲	▲	▲	306	227	143	113	80	62	52	46	40	37	33	31	28	26	25
100															▲	▲	▲	▲	▲	▲	▲	341	281	193	135	109	93	72	59	50	44	40	37	33	31
105																▲	▲	▲	▲	▲	▲	▲	354	308	262	174	129	107	77	62	53	46	41	38	35
110																	▲	▲	▲	▲	▲	▲	▲	▲	334	294	257	176	132	83	65	55	48	43	39
115																		▲	▲	▲	▲	▲	▲	▲	▲	347	303	270	243	163	91	68	57	49	44
120																			▲	▲	▲	▲	▲	▲	▲	▲	▲	329	291	261	237	101	72	59	51

Time in Minutes — Excursion Depth (fsw)

▲ Up to six hours (360 min).
Saturation $PO_2 = 0.21$ ata, (Normoxic) breathing Air on excursions.
Source: Hamilton et al 1973.

are based on *computed* gas loadings, testing in hyperbaric chambers, and limited open sea tests. (Hamilton et al. 1973; Koblick 1974) They may need to be modified in the light of relevant experience.

Some basic criteria for computation and validation are as follows:

Criteria for Computation

Half-times....................... 5–480 minutes
Inert gas......................... Nitrogen only
Habitat gas composition...... $PO_2 = 0.21$ atmospheres; balance nitrogen
Excursion gas................... Air
Excursion times rounded down to next minute.

Validation (Dry Chamber)

Saturation depths tested..... 30, 50, 60, 90 and 120 feet of sea water.
Downward excursions:
Depths tested............. 85–300 feet of sea water.
Upward excursions:
Depths tested............. 5–85 feet of sea water.

Validation (Open Sea)

Saturation depths tested..... 45, 96, 106 feet of sea water.
Downward excursions........ 50–160 feet below saturation depth (maximum depth 265 feet).
Upward excursions............ 40–75 feet (above saturation depth).

Normoxic mixtures were used on all saturation exposures except the 45 foot open-sea test. A normoxic breathing mixture is one in which the partial pressure of oxygen is kept at the surface equivalent (0.20 atmospheres), thus is the same as breathing air at one atmosphere. (Air was used at a depth of 45 feet which converts to a 35.5 foot normoxic mixture.) Air was used on all excursion dives for both dry chamber and open-sea tests.

A dive that loads slow tissue (Paragraph 2.2.3.1) half-time compartments, prejudices subsequent dives that are limited by these compartments. No-stop dives that are short do not appreciably affect subsequent dives, after a suitable time interval. A most important factor is the degree to which a given dive approaches the time limit for that depth; one that runs to the maximum allowable time will likely have more effect than one that does not. In the subsequent paragraphs, a dive is "short" if it is about 20 minutes or less. "Long" dives are defined as more than one hour. Where depth is not mentioned it is not of prime concern. In all cases, a 4-hour habitat interval between excursions should precede either a downward or an upward excursion.

12.5.1 Downward Excursions

- A short downward excursion has little effect on subsequent downward dives, short or long (following a 4-hour interval).
- Short downward excursions have some effect on subsequent upward excursions. An 18-hour interval should be observed if limits are approached.
- A long downward excursion will have little effect on a subsequent short downward excursion.
- A long downward excursion will prejudice a subsequent long downward excursion; the time

Saturation Depth fsw	0	5	10	15	20	25	30	35	40	45	50	55	60	65	70	75	80	85	90
							Time in Minutes Excursion Depth (fsw)												
30	36	48	60	■	■	■	■												
35	30	37	48	60	■	■	■	■											
40	24	31	40	52	60	■	■	■	■										
45	17	24	31	40	52	60	■	■	■	■									
50	12	18	25	32	42	60	■	■	■	■	■								
55	7	13	18	25	32	42	60	■	■	■	■	■							
60	▲	7	13	18	25	32	42	60	■	■	■	■	■						
65	▲	▲	8	14	20	27	34	44	60	■	■	■	■	■					
70	▲	▲	▲	8	14	20	27	34	44	60	■	■	■	■	■				
75	▲	▲	▲	▲	9	15	21	28	36	47	60	■	■	■	■	■			
80	▲	▲	▲	▲	▲	9	15	21	28	36	47	60	■	■	■	■	■		
85	▲	▲	▲	▲	▲	5	10	16	23	30	37	48	60	■	■	■	■	■	
90	▲	▲	▲	▲	▲	▲	5	10	16	23	30	37	48	60	■	■	■	■	■
95	▲	▲	▲	▲	▲	▲	▲	6	12	18	24	31	40	52	60	■	■	■	■
100	▲	▲	▲	▲	▲	▲	▲	▲	6	12	18	24	31	40	52	60	■	■	■
105	▲	▲	▲	▲	▲	▲	▲	▲	▲	7	13	18	25	32	42	60	■	■	■
110	▲	▲	▲	▲	▲	▲	▲	▲	▲	▲	7	13	18	25	32	42	60	■	■
115	▲	▲	▲	▲	▲	▲	▲	▲	▲	▲	▲	7	13	18	25	32	42	60	■
120	▲	▲	▲	▲	▲	▲	▲	▲	▲	▲	▲	▲	7	13	18	25	32	42	60

▲ Beyond Excursion Limits.
■ No time limit.

Saturation PO_2 = 0.21 ata, (Normoxic) breathing Air on Excursions.

Source: Hamilton et al 1973.

limit for the second excursion should be cut in half (following a 4-hour interval).

■ Long downward excursions may seriously prejudice subsequent upward excursions. Following a 6-hour excursion at more than 30 feet below habitat depth, a subsequent upward excursion, if it approaches limits, should not be done prior to a 36-hour interval (if necessary, 50 percent of allowable time between 18 and 36 hours).

■ Bottom time begins upon departure from saturation depth and ends on return to saturation depth.

■ Descent can be made as fast as desired. A slow descent is preferred, but reduces bottom time. Ascend at any desired rate not to exceed 30 feet per minute.

Plan the daily diving schedule in order to make any anticipated shallow excursions prior to deep excursions.

When determining downward excursion times, using Table 12–2, the saturation depth should be rounded to the nearest 5-foot interval above the actual saturation depth.

Examples: Downward Excursion Breathing Air

1. Habitat is at 100 feet (normoxic mixture), and you wish to make a dive to 200 feet to collect specimens. How long can you stay at 200 feet?

a. Find the 100-foot depth of the habitat in Table 12–2, and read across to the 200-foot column.

b. You can stay at 200 feet for <u>135 minutes</u>.

2. Habitat is at 60 feet with air as breathing mixture and you wish to dive to 150 feet.

a. Table 12–4 can also be used directly with air as habitat gas.

b. Enter Table 12-2 using 60 feet and read across to 150 foot column.

c. You can stay at 150 feet for <u>63 minutes</u>.

12.5.2 Upward Excursions

Upward excursions are short decompressions in themselves, and do not prejudice subsequent excursions (unless they have resulted in bubble formation).

Even though upward excursions do not prejudice subsequent upward or downward excursions, a 4-hour interval between dives should be observed. Following a long dive only a few feet below habitat depth, subsequent upward excursions should be

Table 12-4
Air-Normoxic
Equivalent Depths

Normoxic Depth (FSW)	Equivalent Air Depth (FSW)
0	0
3.9	5
7.9	10
11.8	15
15.8	20
19.7	25
23.7	30
27.6	35
31.6	40
35.5	45
39.5	50
43.4	55
47.4	60
51.3	65
55.3	70
59.2	75
63.2	80
67.1	85
71.1	90
75.0	95
79.0	100
82.9	105
87.9	110
90.8	115
94.8	120
98.7	125
102.7	130
106.6	135
110.6	140
114.5	145
118.5	150

safe if based on the depth of the long dive rather than on the habitat depth.

When determining upward excursion times, using Table 12-3, the saturation depth should be rounded to the nearest 5-foot interval below the actual saturation depth.

The following comments relate to upward excursions only:

Begin timing on departure from saturation depth and end upon return to saturation depth.

Ascend at 10 to 30 feet per minute. Descend at a rate not to exceed 75 feet per minute.

If bends symptoms are noted, descend immediately to the habitat. If descent to the habitat is interrupted by ear problems, it is preferable to discontinue descent to clear the ear rather than incur ear damage.

Examples: Upward Excursion Breathing Air

1. Habitat is at 100 feet (normoxic mixture) and you want to make an upward excursion to a depth of 45 feet to work on an instrument package. How much time can be spent at 45 feet without risking decompression sickness?

   a. Enter Table 12-3 at 100 feet and follow across to the 45 foot column.

   b. You can stay at 45 feet for <u>12 minutes</u>.

2. Habitat is at 60 feet with air as breathing mixture and you want to ascend to a depth of 25 feet.

   a. Convert air depth (60 feet) to normoxic depth (47.4 feet) using Table 12-4.

   b. Enter Table 12-3 using 50 feet and read across to 25 foot column.

   c. You can stay at 25 feet for <u>60 minutes</u>.

12.6 DECOMPRESSION FROM SATURATION DIVES

In some shallow systems (50 feet or less) the divers may swim to the surface, immediately enter a recompression chamber, recompress to the saturation depth, and begin decompression. This method is possible if the surface interval is less than 5 minutes and the depth less than 50 feet based on laboratory studies (Edel 1969) and its use by over 25 divers in a saturation program (Weeks 1972; Walden and Rainnie 1971). Other systems are designed to decompress divers in the habitat. This can be done with the habitat on the bottom at shallow depth, locking out the divers for a short swim to the surface upon completion of decompression (Wicklund 1973). In other cases, the habitat can be raised to the surface and towed to a shore base where decompression is completed and standby facilities may be available (Koblick et al 1974).

In deep dive systems, saturation divers in a habitat are usually transferred to a PTC and transported to a surface decompression chamber at depth pressure. Decompression is then accomplished in accordance with the standard procedures for the depth and breathing medium.

This section contains decompression procedures and tables for saturation dives made using air and using a normoxic mixture of nitrogen and oxygen. These tables have been developed over the past 5 years and are based upon computer models, hyperbaric chamber experiments, and open sea saturation programs.

Decompression tables and procedures for saturation dives made using helium and oxygen are not included. The reader is referred to the U.S. Navy Supervisor of Diving for these procedures.

Table 12-5
Standard Decompression Schedules Following Normoxic Nitrogen-Oxygen Saturation Exposures

Decompression Using Air and Oxygen
Saturations From 0 to 100 FSW at 5 FSW Intervals

Saturation Depth Range (FSW)	First Stop			Subsequent Stages		
	Depth (FSW)	Gas	Time At Stop (HR: MIN)	Depth (FSW)	Gas	Time At Stop (HR: MIN)
96 — 100	80	Air	3:00	75	Air	4:00
91 — 95	75	Air	3:00	70	Air	4:00
86 — 90	70	Air	3:00	65	Air	4:30
81 — 85	65	Air	3:00	60	Air	4:30
76 — 80	60	Air	3:00	55	Air	5:00
71 — 75	55	Air	3:30	50	Air	5:00
66 — 70	50	Air	3:30	45	Air	5:00
61 — 65	45	Air	3:30	40	Air	5:00
56 — 60	40	Air	4:00	35	Air	0:30
				35	Oxygen	1:00
51 — 55	35	Oxygen	1:00	35	Air	0:30
				35	Oxygen	1:00
				30	Air	2:00
46 — 50	30	Air	2:00	30	Oxygen	1:00
				25	Air	0:30
				25	Oxygen	1:00
41 — 45	25	Oxygen	0:30	25	Air	0:30
				25	Oxygen	1:00
				20	Air	3:00
36 — 40	20	Air	1:30	20	Oxygen	1:00
				15	Air	0:30
				15	Oxygen	1:00
31 — 35	15	Oxygen	1:00	15	Air	0:30
				15	Oxygen	1:00
				10	Air	4:00
26 — 30	10	Air	2:00	10	Oxygen	1:00
				5	Air	0:30
				5	Oxygen	1:00
				5	Air	0:30
22 — 25	5	Oxygen	0:30	5	Oxygen	1:00
				30	Oxygen	0:30
0 — 21	No Decompression			Surface		

12.6.1 Standard Decompression Procedures for Normoxic Nitrogen-Oxygen Saturation Exposures

12.6.1.1 Basis

These decompression schedules have been designed for decompression from saturation exposures to a normoxic nitrogen-oxygen breathing mixture at depths ranging from 22 to 100 fsw. The 1200-minute nitrogen half-time used in the calculation of these schedules was selected after analysis of the HYDRO-LAB, TEKTITE I, TEKTITE II, and FLARE decompression schedules. The schedules are for use by, and have been based on, the experiences of scientist-divers who vary widely

in age and physical conditioning.

12.6.1.2 Use of Oxygen

Oxygen has been utilized heavily on an intermittent basis in these schedules to reduce the decompression time. The lengths of the oxygen breathing periods have been determined so that no more than a 2 percent decrement in the vital capacity of the diver will occur. This would then allow use of the U.S. Navy Recompression Treatment Tables 5, 5A, 6 and 6A (See Appendix D) immediately following the saturation decompression without a 4 percent decrement in vital capacity being exceeded. (This represents the smallest detectable change in vital capacity resulting from

Table 12-5a
Sample Use
of Table 12-5

Decompression Using Air and Oxygen
Saturations From 0 to 100 FSW at 5 FSW Intervals

Saturation Depth Range (FSW)	First Stop			Subsequent Stages		
	Depth (FSW)	Gas	Time At Stop (HR: MIN)	Depth (FSW)	Gas	Time At Stop (HR: MIN)
96 — 100	80	Air	3:00	75	Air	4:00
91 — 95	75	Air	3:00	70	Air	4:00
86 — 90	70	Air	3:00	65	Air	4:30
81 — 85	65	Air	3:00	60	Air	4:30
76 — 80	60	Air	3:00	55	Air	5:00
71 — 75	55	Air	3:30	50	Air	5:00
66 — 70	50	Air	3:30	45	Air	5:00
61 — 65	45	Air	3:30	40	Air	5:00
56 — 60	40	Air	4:00	35	Air	0:30
				35	Oxygen	1:00
51 — 55	35	Oxygen	1:00	35	Air	0:30
				35	Oxygen	1:00
				30	Air	2:00
46 — 50	30	Air	2:00	30	Oxygen	1:00
				25	Air	0:30
				25	Oxygen	1:00
41 — 45	25	Oxygen	0:30	25	Air	0:30
				25	Oxygen	1:00
				20	Air	3:00
36 — 40	20	Air	1:30	20	Oxygen	1:00
				15	Air	0:30
				15	Oxygen	1:00
31 — 35	15	Oxygen	1:00	15	Air	0:30
				15	Oxygen	1:00
				10	Air	4:00
26 — 30	10	Air	2:00	10	Oxygen	1:00
				5	Air	0:30
				5	Oxygen	1:00
				5	Air	0:30
22 — 25	5	Oxygen	0:30	5	Oxygen	1:00
				30	Oxygen	0:30
0 — 21	No Decompression			Surface		

the toxic effects of oxygen on the pulmonary system.) It has been assumed that, during the air breathing periods, a recovery of 0.1 percent vital capacity per hour occurs if the oxygen partial pressure is less than 0.5 atmospheres. The oxygen breathing periods are programmed into the schedules at the shallow depths since this is where they produce the greatest saving in time. Oxygen is breathed in an alternating fashion to increase the total time during which it can be breathed, and also to provide frequent breaks from mask breathing for rest periods and eating.

The final stop in each decompression schedule is a ½-hour period at 30 fsw breathing oxygen. This is to compress any bubbles that have formed or expanded during the decompression and thus aid in their resolution.

The time units in these schedules are ½-hour blocks to reduce bookkeeping and operator problems.

12.6.1.3 Decompression Parameters

Nitrogen half-time: 1,200 minutes

Maximum allowable surface supersaturation: 48 fswa

Nitrogen supersaturation delta value: 5 fswa of additional supersaturation per 5 fsw of added depth

Decompression stop interval: 5 fsw

Ascent rate: noncritical (20 to 60 fsw/minute acceptable)

Table 12-6
Summary Table
of Standard Decompressions
Following Normoxic
Nitrogen-Oxygen
Saturation Exposures

Saturation Depth Range (FSW)	Normal Oxygen at Greatest Depth (%)	Total Oxygen Time (HR:MIN)	Total Decompression Time (HR:MIN)
96 —100	5.2	11:30	64:30
91 — 95	5.4	11:30	60:30
86 — 90	5.6	11:30	56:30
81 — 85	5.9	11:30	52:00
76 — 80	6.1	11:30	47:30
71 — 75	6.4	11:30	42:30
66 — 70	6.7	11:30	38:00
61 — 65	7.1	11:30	33:00
56 — 60	7.5	11:30	28:30
51 — 55	7.9	11:30	24:00
46 — 50	8.3	9:30	21:30
41 — 45	8.9	8:00	17:30
36 — 40	9.5	6:30	14:00
31 — 35	10.2	5:30	11:00
26 — 30	11.0	3:30	6:00
22 — 25	11.9	2:00	2:00
0 — 21	12.8	0:00	0:00

12.6.1.4 Use of Decompression Tables

Table 12–5 consists of three columns: (1) Saturation Depth Range; (2) First Stop, with Depth, Gas, and Time At Stop; and (3) Subsequent Stages, the remainder of the decompression schedule with Depth, Gas, and Time At Stop.

To determine the decompression schedule for a given saturation depth, choose the appropriate saturation range from the first column; move horizontally to the middle column to determine the first stop; move horizontally to the end column for the second stop; then move down the column vertically for the rest of the schedule. The following example illustrates the use of the table:

To determine the decompression schedule for a saturation exposure at 50 fsw:

1. Locate 50 fsw in left-hand column, i.e., 46 to 50 fsw Saturation Depth Range.

2. Move horizontally to the middle column to determine the depth, gas, and time for the first stop; i.e., 2 hours at 30 feet breathing air.

3. Move horizontally to the right-hand column for the first subsequent stop (the second stop), i.e., 1 hour at 30 feet breathing oxygen.

4. Subsequent stops are determined by reading vertically down the right hand column; i.e., the third stop is 30 minutes at 25 fsw breathing air, the fourth stop is 1 hour at 25 fsw breathing oxygen, etc., to

the bottom of the column and "surface."

A replica of Table 12–5 is provided in Table 12–5a where the above example is marked off by heavy lines and shading.

Table 12–6 provides a summary of decompression times and related data for normoxic nitrogen-oxygen saturation exposures. For example, at a depth of 90 feet, 5.6 percent oxygen would provide a diver with the same amount of oxygen as he gets when breathing air at the surface (1 atmosphere). The other columns are self-explanatory.

12.6.2 Emergency Decompression Tables

For emergency situations, decompression tables having shorter decompression times than those found in Table 12—5 have been developed. These tables are to be used *only* in situations where the divers are young, in excellent physical condition, and have no history of decompression sickness. The tables use a faster nitrogen half-time and a 5-minute time-base to speed decompression.

The 670-minute nitrogen half-time used was found by analysis to be the shortest safe half-time allowed for by the TEKTITE II 100-foot decompression. This schedule has been used successfully in hyperbaric chambers with six young athletes and four professional divers; and by nine scientists in 100-foot open-sea saturation dives in Puerto Rico. (Schmidt et al. 1973; Lambertsen and Wright 1973). Details of oxygen usage, special features, and the decompression parameters, with the exception of half-time and the use of a 5-minute time base, are identical to the standard table. The resulting decompression times are shown in Table 12—7. The decompression schedules are derived from this table in the same manner as when using Table 12—5. Similarly Table 12—8 may be interpreted in the same manner as Table 12—6.

Tables 12—5 and 12—7 can be used to decompress from air saturations by determining air/normoxic equivalent nitrogen pressures) Table 12—4 contains these equivalent values for depths ranging from surface to 118 fsw normoxic. For example, if one were to saturate on air at a depth of 50 feet, it would be equivalent to saturating at a depth of 39.5 feet on a normoxic breathing mixture. When using Tables 12—5 or 12—7, one would enter the table based on a dive of 39.5 fsw. The converse is also true. If a normoxic saturation dive were made at 79 fsw, it is equivalent to an air dive at 100 fsw. The method

Table 12-7
Emergency Decompression Schedules Following Normoxic Nitrogen-Oxygen Saturation Exposures

Decompression Using Air and Oxygen
Saturations From 0 to 100 FSW at 5 FSW Intervals

Saturation Depth Range (FSW)	First Stop Depth (FSW)	First Stop Gas	First Stop Time at Stop (HR: MIN)	Subsequent Stages Depth (FSW)	Subsequent Stages Gas	Subsequent Stages Time at Stop (HR: MIN)
96—100	80	Air	1:30	75	Air	2:15
91—95	75	Air	1:30	70	Air	2:25
86—90	70	Air	1:30	65	Air	2:30
81—85	65	Air	1:35	60	Air	2:35
76—80	60	Air	1:40	55	Air	2:40
71—75	55	Air	1:40	50	Air	2:45
66—70	50	Air	1:45	45	Air	2:45
61—65	45	Air	1:45	40	Air	2:00
56—60	40	Air	0:30	40	Oxygen	0:30
				35	Oxygen	1:00
51—55	35	Oxygen	0:45	30	Air	0:30
				30	Oxygen	1:00
46—50	30	Oxygen	0:45	25	Air	2:00
				25	Oxygen	1:00
41—45	25	Oxygen	1:00	20	Air	0:30
				20	Oxygen	1:00
36—40	20	Oxygen	1:00	15	Air	2:00
31—35	15	Oxygen	0:30	15	Oxygen	1:00
26—30	10	Oxygen	0:30	10	Air	0:30
				10	Oxygen	1:00
				5	Air	0:30
				5	Oxygen	0:30
22—25	5	Oxygen	0:30	30	Oxygen	0:30
0—21	No Decompression			Surface		

of calculating equivalent air depths from normoxic breathing mixtures is described in Paragraph 11.3.3.

WARNING

To Avoid Problems Involving Oxygen Toxicity, Saturation Exposures at Depths Greater Than 60 FSW on Air Should *Not* Be Attempted.

Oxygen toxicity is discussed in detail in Paragraph 2.3.

12.6.3 Diving After Decompression From Saturation Exposure

For dives after decompression from a nitrogen saturation exposure, a diver should wait 150 minutes and then be placed in Group Z of the U.S. Navy Repetitive Diving Tables, (See Appendix D). The U.S. Navy Repetitive Diving Tables are then to be used as directed, moving to lower classes after the time intervals given in the tables. (The end of the initial 150-minute delay should be taken as the 10-minute time in Class Z.)

Example:

0800 Surface from completed saturation decompression. However, more coral specimens are needed from 50 feet. The diver must determine how long he will have to wait before he can go to 50 feet for 30 minutes without decompressing.

1030 End of 150 minutes, diver is in Group Z. From the Repetitive Diving Tables it is calculated that 2 hours and 18 minutes are required for the tissues to release sufficient nitrogen for a 34-minute dive to 50 feet (Group H).

1248 Dive to 50 feet for 30 minutes and surface without decompressing.

Since this procedure becomes more conservative as the surface interval increases, longer delays before making a second dive are recommended.

Table 12-8
Summary Emergency Decompressions
Following Normoxic Nitrogen-Oxygen
Saturation Exposures

Saturation Depth Range (FSW)	Normal Oxygen at Greatest Depth (%)	Total Oxygen Time (HR:MIN)	Total Decompression Time (HR:MIN)
96—100	5.2	7:30	34:55
91— 95	5.4	7:30	32:40
86— 90	5.6	7:30	30:15
81— 85	5.9	7:30	27:50
76— 80	6.1	7:30	25:20
71— 75	6.4	7:30	22:40
66— 70	6.7	7:30	20:00
61— 65	7.1	7:30	17:15
56— 60	7.5	7:30	14:00
51— 55	7.9	6:45	12:45
46— 50	8.3	5:45	11:15
41— 45	8.9	5:00	8:30
36— 40	9.5	4:00	7:00
31— 35	10.2	3:00	5:30
26— 30	11.0	2:30	3:30
22— 25	11.9	1:00	1:00
0— 21	12.8	0:00	0:00

It is also recommended that dives requiring decompression stops not be undertaken for 72 hours following surfacing from a saturation decompression. However, no time interval is necessary to resaturate a diver who has just completed saturation decompression.

12.6.4 Flying After a Saturation Exposure Decompression

Before flying after a saturation exposure decompression, a delay of 36 hours is recommended (See Paragraph 6.4).

SECTION 13 SURFACE SUPPORT PLATFORMS

SURFACE SUPPORT PLATFORMS 13

13.0 GENERAL

Diving from ·surface support platforms can be grouped generally into the following categories:

a. From the shore
b. From a pier or stationary platform
c. From a small boat
d. From a ship.

The following discussions give some characteristics of each and some general guidelines to follow.

13.1 DIVING FROM THE SHORE

A diver can expect to encounter a wide variety of conditions when entering the water from the shore. Shorelines vary greatly, and diving from a particular one will require individual preparation and planning.

Prior to entering the water from the shore, special attention should be given to the predive equipment checkout. As diving equipment quite probably will be placed on the ground near the water, small dirt particles could enter an area where a perfect seal or close tolerance is required. Even the smallest amount of dirt in the regulator or reserve valve could cause a serious air leak or the valve to malfunction. Extra care must be taken to ensure that diving equipment is kept as free from dirt as possible.

If the dive from shore is to be made at a precise underwater location, it is advisable to clearly mark the spot at the water surface. This can be done by using a marker buoy or surface float. A small marker buoy floating on the surface can be difficult for a diver to see. Compass bearings, underwater contours or features, or triangulation methods with known shore positions can help in initially locating a dive spot.

When diving from the shore without a boat, the use of a surface buoy or float with a diving flag to indicate divers below is recommended. If entry conditions permit (surf, etc.) divers should carry and/or tow the marker with them to the dive site. It is also advisable that each diver be equipped with a day/night signal flare for signaling the shore in an emergency. They provide a quick means for accurately locating a diver on the surface.

Entering the water from a smooth, unobstructed shoreline where the water is relatively quiet should pose no problems. Most lakes, rivers (where currents near shore are not swift), bays, lagoons, quarries, and ocean coastline where surf is negligible, fall into this category.

13.1.1 Through Surf

Entering the water through even moderate surf, burdened with diving equipment, is a difficult and potentially hazardous operation. A careful analysis of surf conditions should be made, and, if conditions are considered too severe to allow safe passage to open water, the dive should be terminated.

WARNING

Before Attempting to Dive Through Surf on an Unfamiliar Beach, Consult Local Divers Concerning Surf Conditions.

Time should be taken prior to entering the water to observe the surf. As swell, waves traverse vast expanses of ocean with little modification or loss of energy. However, as the waves enter shallow water, the motion of the water particles beneath the surface is altered. When the wave enters water of depth equal to or less than one-half the wavelength, it is said to "feel bottom." The circular orbital motion of the water particles becomes elliptical, flattening with depth. Along the bottom, the particles oscillate in a straight line parallel to the direction of wave travel.

As the wave "feels bottom," its wave length decreases and steepness increases. Furthermore,

Figure 13-1
Schematic Diagram of Waves
in the Breaker Zone

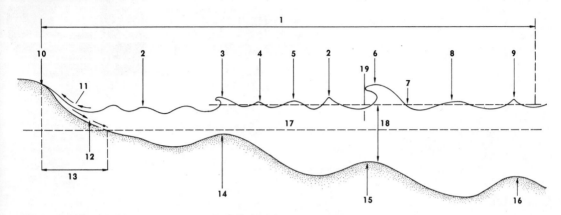

(1) Surf Zone; *(2)* Translatory Waves; *(3)* Inner Line of Breakers; *(4)* Peaked-up Wave; *(5)* Reformed Oscillatory Wave; *(6)* Outer Line of Breakers; *(7)* Still-Water Level; *(8)* Waves Flatten Again; *(9)* Waves Break Up but Do Not Break on This Bar at High Tide; *(10)* Limit of Uprush; *(11)* Uprush; *(12)* Backrush; *(13)* Beach Face; *(14)* Inner Bar; *(15)* Outer Bar (Inner Bar at Low Tide); *(16)* Deep Bar (Outer Bar at Low Tide); *(17)* Mean Lower Low Water (MLLW); *(18)* Breaker Depth, 1.3 Height; *(19)* Plunge Point (Baker et al. 1966).

as the wave crest moves into water where the depth is about twice that of the wave height, the crest changes from rounded to a higher, more pointed mass of water. The orbital velocity of the water particles at the crest increases with increasing wave height. This sequence of changes is the prelude to the breaking of the wave. Finally, at a depth of approximately 1.3 times the wave height, when the steepest surface of the wave inclines more than 60 degrees from the horizontal, the wave becomes unstable and the top portion plunges forward. The wave has broken; this is *surf* (Figure 13–1). This zone of "white water," where the waves finally give up their energy and where systematic water motion gives way to violent turbulence, is the *surf zone.* The "white water" is a mass of water with bubbles of entrapped air.

Having broken into a mass of turbulent foam, the wave continues landward under its own momentum. Finally, at the beach face, this momentum carries it into an uprush or swash. At the uppermost limit, the wave's energy has diminished. The water transported landward in the uprush must now return seaward as a backwash, or current flowing back to the sea. This seaward movement of water is generally not evident beyond the surface zone or a depth of 2–3 feet (Somers 1972).

By watching the surf for a short period of time, water entry can be timed to coincide with a small set of waves.

When ready to enter, approach the water, fully dressed for diving. When reaching the water's edge, spit on the faceplate, rinse and adjust to face, and place snorkel in mouth. Turn around and back into the water. Knees should be slightly bent and the diver should lean back into the wave with one hand on the faceplate. If conditions are good, begin swimming seaward on the surface using a snorkel. If heavy sets are encountered, it may be necessary to switch to scuba.

WARNING

If a Diver Inhales at the Same Time a Trough Passes Overhead, It May Have the Same Effect as Inhaling While Ascending and Could Cause an Embolism.

Swimming over breakers should not be attempted. As they approach, duck the head and dive into and through them.

Once safely through the surf, check all equipment. Even a moderate surf can knock equipment out of adjustment or tear it away.

Sand in the mask, regulator, or fins may be found after passing through surf. Take time to remove it prior to continuing the dive. Sand in the exhaust valve of a regulator can cause it to seal improperly and water, as well as air, may enter the mouthpiece when inhaling. Sand in the fins, while only mildly irritating at first, can cause a painful abrasion by the end of a dive.

Exiting from the water through the surf is basically the opposite procedure from entering. Wait just seaward of the surf for a small set of waves. When a set is selected, begin swimming shoreward immediately after the passage of the last of the larger waves. The smaller waves breaking behind will assist in progress toward the beach. Using this assisting wave action, swim toward the beach until in approximately waist-deep water. At this point, while there is still enough water for support and balance, pivot around, face the waves, and plant the feet firmly. Stand up, and bending enough to maintain balance, back out of the water. As soon as the surf is cleared turn and remove fins.

If knocked over by surf action after standing up, do not try to stand again. Let the waves carry you onto the beach. Dig hands and fins into the bottom to prevent being swept seaward by the backwash. Crawl out of the surf on hands and knees.

13.1.2 Surf on a Rocky Shore

Prior to entering surf from a rocky shore, evaluate the wave conditions. Do not attempt to stand or walk on rocks located in the surf zone. A knock down can be hazardous. Select the backwash of the last large wave of a series, and enter the water. The backwash should carry through the rocks. Maintain a prone swimming position and face the next oncoming wave. Grasp a rock or kick to keep from being carried back toward the shore. Then kick seaward after the wave passes.

When exiting on a rocky shore, stop outside the surf zone and evaluate the wave conditions. Exit toward the beach on the backside of the last large wave of a series. As momentum from the wave is lost, grasp a rock or kick to avoid being carried seaward by the backwash. Maintain position, catch the next wave, and move shoreward. Exercise caution moving over slippery rocks.

13.1.3 From a Coral Reef

Diving operations from a reef should be planned, if possible, at a high tide when water covers the reef. For a diver with equipment on, walking on a reef is hazardous. Footing is uncertain, reefs are generally pocked with holes, and areas that look solid may break under a diver's weight.

NOTE:

Coral Shoes or Hard-sole Neoprene Boots Should Be Worn Around Coral.

In some instances, an area may be encountered on the shore side of the reef where water is deep enough for swimming. In this case, the outer side of the reef will break up the wave action sufficiently to allow passage over the inside, calm area without trouble. If a channel can be located which will allow passage through the reef, follow it, submerged if possible, into deep water. If a satisfactory passage cannot be located, approach the edge of the reef, wait for a wave to pass, and slip over.

13.2 DIVING FROM A PIER OR STATIONARY PLATFORM

Diving from a pier or platform rather than directly from the shore offers many advantages. Entry into deep water can be made without having to traverse a surf line, rocks, or other obstacles. Also, if the dive site is under, or in proximity to the pier, the use of surface-supplied diving equipment can be considered. Usually, all required equipment can be transported directly to the dive site by vehicle.

Ladders should be used to get down as close to the water as possible before entry. Any of the approved entry techniques, such as stepping in or rolling in can be safely used for heights of up to 10 feet. Immediately prior to entering, carefully check for floating debris or submerged obstructions. Floating debris is common around a pier, and pilings normally rot or break off just below the waterline.

Once in the water, swim to the dive site on the surface, if the site is relatively close to the pier or platform. If the dive site is a significant distance, the use of a small boat is advisable.

When it is required to swim under a pier or platform, do so submerged, whenever possible. Under water a diver has more control of his movements and rough contact against pilings, cross-supports, and other potentially hazardous objects is more easily avoided.

When exiting the water onto a pier or platform, stop at the ladder and remove fins. (The ladder, ideally, should extend 3 to 4 feet into the water.) Climbing a ladder with fins is awkward and dangerous, and should be avoided. Tanks and other cumbersome equipment should also be removed and tied securely to a line dropped from the top.

Figure 13-2
Entering the Water
Using the "Roll-In" Method

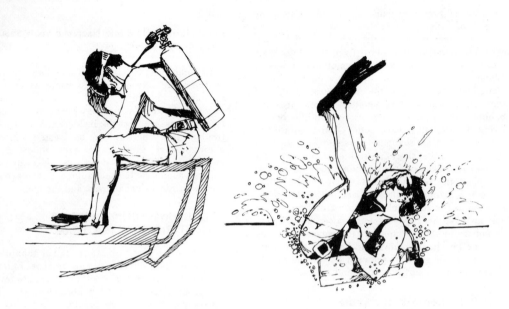

Climb the ladder without fins or heavy equipment, and haul the equipment up onto the pier after reaching the pier top. Even if topside assistance is at hand, remember to climb up on to the pier before hauling up the equipment.

13.3 DIVING FROM A SMALL BOAT

The small boat is probably the most common surface support platform used by divers using self-contained equipment. Configurations and types vary greatly and run from small, inflatable boats to larger solid-hulled vessels (See Figure 6–4).

In planning a dive using a small boat as a platform, the following characteristics should be considered. The boat:

a. Should provide a means for divers to easily and safely enter and leave the water.

b. Must be seaworthy and not loaded beyond the capacity recommended by the manufacturer for the expected water conditions.

c. Must be large enough to adequately accommodate all members of a dive party, the diver's life-support equipment, and any special equipment being used in support of the dive.

d. Should provide some means of shelter in cold and/or inclement weather for the dive party while going to the dive site and, most importantly, for the divers after they leave the water and are returning to shore.

e. Must be properly maintained and in good repair.

f. Must be maneuverable if it is to be used as a pickup boat.

g. Must carry a diver's flag.

13.3.1 Entering the Water

Entering the water can be safely accomplished from a small boat by several methods. Sitting on the gunwale and rolling into the water is considered best (Figure 13-2). Sit on the gunwale facing the center of the boat with both feet inside. Extend as much of the body as possible over the water while leaning forward to counterbalance. When ready to enter simply sit up, lean backward, and let the weight of the diving equipment carry you back over the side. A second method of entry is the "step-in" method and is normally used when entering the water from a larger boat. Step on to the gunwale, bend slightly forward at the waist, and step off into the water.

When entering the water using the methods described, always hold the face mask firmly in place. Also, any equipment required that cannot be conveniently and safely carried should be secured to a piece of line, hung over the side, and retrieved after entry.

As a general rule, always enter the water slowly, using a method that will result in the least physical discomfort and disturbance to equipment. Each diver should determine the method best suited to him and best suited to various water conditions.

13.3.2 Exiting the Water

When exiting the water into a boat there are two general rules to remember and follow. First, exiting begins while still submerged. While ascending continually look up and around to ensure that the boat is not directly overhead and that you will not strike it when surfacing. Holding an arm over the head is a good practice. Air exhaled on ascent will give a clear indication to the surface that you are ascending. Second, after surfacing do not attempt to enter the boat wearing tanks or other heavy equipment. Remove them and gain assistance from someone in the boat, or from another diver in the water before climbing aboard.

Probably the most widely used method of returning to a small boat is via a diver's ladder. Ladders also provide a secure point for a diver to grasp while still in the water. A ladder may be built in many configurations, but should conform to these general designs:

a. It should extend below the surface of the water 3 to 4 feet. This will provide a place to stand and hold on while removing equipment and allow an easy climb on to the ladder.

b. It must be strong, well built, and capable of being securely fastened to the side so it will not shift when subjected to the action of the seas and a diver's weight.

c. It is highly desirable that it be wide enough to accommodate two divers, side by side (about 5 to 6 feet).

d. It should be angled away from the boat at 10 to 15 degrees from the vertical, to give the diver an easier ascent.

e. The rungs should be flat and wide to be comfortable to the feet.

Figure 13-3
Diver's Platform

Another method of assisting a diver into a small boat is the use of a platform rigged to the stern or side of the boat and suspended just below the surface of the water. A diver can swim on to the platform, sit securely while removing equipment, then stand up and step safely into the boat. A hand or arm hold should be provided. A portable, easily stored platform (Figure 13–3) can be constructed from wood or metal.

13.3.3 Towing a Diver With a Small Boat (Live Boating)

Some underwater tasks require great distances to be covered in a minimum amount of time. These tasks could include inspecting a pipeline, surveying a habitat site, searching for a lost instrument, observing fish populations over a wide area, or any number of similar situations.

When carrying out such tasks, the free-swimming diver may be inefficient, and a quicker method of search or survey should be employed. Such devices as swimmer propulsion units, wet subs, towed sleds, or live boating may be used.

As its name implies, live boating is diving from a boat underway. The diver holds onto a line attached to the boat and by varying his depth according to the contour of the bottom is able to conduct a close-up search of the area over which the boat is transitting. When live boating is used, the following safety precautions are recommended.

- If possible the boat should be equipped with a "jet dive" propulsion system having no rudder or propeller.
- If equipped with a propeller, a cage or shroud should be fabricated.
- A communications system must be set up between the diver and the boat with signals agreed upon and practiced prior to diving. A line separate from the tow or descent line may be employed.

WARNING

The Boat Should _Not_ Be Underway Under Power When the Divers Enter or Leave the Water.

- If diving with scuba, two divers should be towed together.
- If diving with surface-supplied equipment (See Paragraph 7.2.7), one diver can be towed while the other remains in the boat suited up and ready to dive.
- A ladder or platform should be available for reboarding.
- The boat should be equipped with charts, radio, first aid kit and resuscitator, emergency air supply, plus all equipment required by the Coast Guard for safe boating operations.
- The boat operator must know the procedure for alerting the Coast Guard in case of an accident.
- All personnel onboard must be thoroughly briefed on the dive plan.
- If the operation must be conducted in heavy currents, divers should enter the water as far up-current as required and drift with the current while holding to the line attached to the drifting boat.

When inspecting a pipeline or instrument cable, the diver, in surface-supplied equipment, may choose to walk on the pipeline or alongside the cable towing the boat behind him.

WARNING

Never Attempt This Form of Diving With Inexperienced Personnel.

13.4 DIVING FROM A SHIP

As in all diving operations, diving from a large ship

requires complete planning prior to the dive or series of dives. As a ship represents a significant economic investment, all logistics factors involving personnel, equipment (diving and scientific), weather, etc., must be thoroughly considered.

13.4.1. Personnel Considerations

When using a ship as a surface support diving platform, the ship's captain has the final decision in any matter pertaining to the vessel. It is imperative that close communication be initiated and maintained with the captain so that the intent of the diving operations is well understood and that the diving operations are carried out with a maximum of safety and reliability.

It is highly desirable that the captain have prior knowledge of diving techniques and procedures. Although this is often a prerequisite not easily attained, a captain with this background can add immeasurably to a diving operation's success.

When diving from a ship, it is recommended that the following personnel requirements be considered prior to beginning a cruise.

Diving Medical Officer. (For a detailed discussion of his duties see Paragraph 6.1.3.2)

Dive Master. The Dive Master is responsible for all diving portions of the operation. In conjunction with the Science Coordinator (when required), he schedules all dives and designates divers and dive teams. He should inform the captain as to the operational necessities for the dives, and, as required, assist him in carrying out these requirements (See Paragraph 6.1.3.1).

Science Coordinator. In conjunction with the Dive Master and the captain he formulates and carries out the scientific goals of the diving missions. On a regular basis throughout the cruise, these goals are reevaluated and, when necessary, redirected (See Paragraph 6.1.3.3).

13.4.2 Use and Storage of Diving and Related Equipment

A suitable "diving locker" should be designated and used for storing diving equipment. The designated area should be well ventilated, large enough and equipped so that diving equipment can be hung up to dry. The diving locker should be kept locked when not in use and the key maintained by the Dive Master.

Fresh water aboard ship is always at a premium

and is usually closely monitored. Consideration must be given to the washing of suits, regulators, etc., after each dive. On air conditioned ships, the run-off from the condenser will provide an adequate supply of fresh water for gear washdown. If fresh water cannot be used, the use of a prebottled cleansing solution should be considered prior to the cruise. All diving equipment should then be thoroughly washed in fresh water the last day of the cruise.

During preplanning stages, the stock of back up diving gear must be considered. Equipment easily lost, such as knives, weight belts, etc., should be stocked in excess so that divers can be quickly reequipped. Spare parts and replacements for critical life-support items such as regulators should be available on board.

Air compressors play an important role in a shipboard diving operation. The compressor should be positioned with intake toward the bow of the ship (the ship will swing into the wind while at anchor), away from the exhausts of main, auxiliary, or any other engines, and free from fume contamination from paint lockers, gasoline and other solvents. Cool running of the compressor requires good ventilation; it should preferably be done at night in hot climates. When filling air cylinders, salt water from the ship's seawater system may be flushed over the tanks as a coolant. Oil-lubricated compressors should have some type of oil/water separator built into the system. It is also highly desirable to have a filtration column which eliminates CO, CO_2, hydrocarbons, oil, water, and other contaminants in accordance with breathing air specifications (See Paragraph 5.1.3.1).

13.4.3 Safety Considerations

In most instances, when a large ship is selected for a diving platform, it is because the diving must be undertaken a considerable distance from shore or in a remote region. When the distance is beyond the range of rapid emergency assistance and/or transport (usually a round trip by helicopter), the Dive Master should have a preplanned procedure for prompt, adequate treatment on board ship and, when necessary, evacuation to a destination where further treatment can be received.

The Dive Master should contact the source of emergency assistance and rapid transport nearest the dive site. He should determine the maximum round-trip range of an emergency transport vehicle, including the distances and times from a shore base to the dive site, and back to the nearest recompression chamber.

The following paragraphs discuss some of the more significant safety aspects that should be considered when diving from a ship.

13.4.3.1 Recompression Chambers

On cruises that are out of the rapid emergency assistance and/or transport range, where decompression diving is planned, or where repetitive diving is scheduled, it is highly desirable to have a recompression chamber on board ship and a trained, qualified operator to run it. The possibility of decompression sickness, gas embolism, or an emergency free ascent requiring immediate surface recompression cannot be discounted. Ideally, a double-lock chamber should be provided (See Section 16). As a minimum, a portable single-lock chamber can be provided, which does not provide the safety and relative comfort of a double-lock but does afford an immediate recompression capability that can be used until more sophisticated facilities can be reached.

The Dive Master should recognize that the availability of a recompression chamber on board is not a mandatory requirement when diving from a ship. However, in precruise planning, the nature of the cruise and the diving that is scheduled should be reviewed with this in mind. The advisability of an on-board chamber should then be weighed against these considerations.

13.4.4 Diving Operations

13.4.4.1 Using Surface-Supplied Equipment

All personnel, divers and surface tenders, must perform a thorough check of equipment. The ship's captain must be notified that divers are about to enter the water, and his clearance obtained before the diving operation can commence.

Entry into the water should be made using a ladder. Jump entries are discouraged above a height of 10 feet.

Check the air supply system, helmet or mask, and communications and ensure they are functioning properly. If not, corrections must be made prior to descent.

A descent line should be used. Descent rate will depend on the diver; generally, however, it should not exceed 75 feet per minute.

Figure 13-4
Umbilical Diving From
a Large Vessel

Photo: A. Y. Bryson

If descending in a tideway or current, keep the back to the current so you will be forced against the descent line (See Paragraph 6.1.5.2).

When the bottom is reached, inform the surface tender, and proceed to the work site. The surface tender must also keep the diver constantly informed of his bottom time. The diver should always be notified a few minutes in advance of termina-

tion time so he can complete his task and prepare for ascent.

Divers and surface tenders should review thoroughly the line pull signals given in Paragraph 6.2.2. Although voice is the primary means of communication between divers and surface tenders when surface-supplied equipment is used, the line is the backup communication should the voice

NOAA Diving Manual

system fail.

When the work is completed, return to the ascent line and signal the surface tender that you are ready for ascent. The surface tender should pull in excess umbilical line slowly and steadily. The diver should never let go of the ascent line, but may assist the tender by climbing the line. The surface tender or Dive Master must inform the diver well in advance of his decompression requirements. A diving stage may be required for long decompressions. When decompression is completed, return on board ship via the ladder or diving stage with assistance as required from the surface tenders (See Paragraph 7.2).

13.4.4.2 Using Self-Contained Equipment

While a ladder or stage can be used, a small boat is recommended for final water entry, transportation to and from a specific dive site, and pickup from the water. An experienced boat handler, familiar with working with divers, should man the boat and stay in the boat while divers are in the water.

Prior to entering the boat, a complete predive check of equipment should be made. The captain should be informed that divers are about to enter the water, and his concurrence obtained.

Diving equipment and scientific and working equipment necessary for the dive should be lowered over the side into the boat using lines or, if available, a stage. Divers should follow into the boat using a ladder or the stage.

Operations from the boat should follow the general guidelines given in Paragraph 13.3.

Returning to the ship from the boat is basically a reverse procedure from entering. A ladder or diving stage should be used to board the ship. Diving equipment and scientific and working equipment should be raised to the deck using lines or the diving stage. The boat handler should remain in the boat to secure all gear at the surface, staying well clear of the equipment being raised.

13.4.5 Diving From a Ship Underway

Although not normally practiced, divers may be required to dive from a ship while underway, to perform work or make underwater observations not possible in a static condition. This type of operation is inherently more dangerous than other diving operations and strict compliance to certain rules is mandatory (See Paragraph 8.10.4).

Only self-contained diving equipment should be used when entering the water from a moving ship. Although special requirements may dictate higher speeds, the ship should proceed preferably at speeds under 3 knots. The use of a small boat, manned at all times divers are in the water by an experienced boat handler familiar with diving procedures should be considered.

Entry into the water from a moving ship is critical. A spot should be selected on the side of the ship well aft and, if possible, aft of the ship's propeller(s). Never enter the water directly off the stern. Propellers and the ship's movement through the water cause turbulence that could buffet a diver severely, or damage or tear off equipment.

The step-in method (See Paragraph 13.3.1) is recommended for entry from a moving ship. This allows maximum distance between the side of the ship and the point of entry. Caution should be exercised in using the step-in method when the deck of the ship is high off the water surface, as too long a jump can cause diver injury or damage to equipment. Although each diver will establish personal limits for entry height, a general rule is don't jump over 10 feet to the surface of the water. If the deck of the ship is more than 10 feet from the water, the use of a side-mounted platform attached to the ship should be considered, which would allow the diver to get closer to the water.

Most dives from a ship underway will involve the ship towing equipment behind (trawls, sleds, etc.), which the diver will observe or use during his dive. This equipment may be on the surface, partially submerged, or submerged. The small boat should maintain a position behind and just to the side of the towed equipment. The divers should enter the water in succession, with enough time interval between entries to avoid one diver landing on another, yet not too much time so that the divers are widely separated in the water.

Each diver should drift back and grasp the cable being used by the ship to tow the equipment. He should work his way back along the cable until the equipment is reached, descending into the water as required.

When surfacing, each diver should wait for pickup by the small boat. The carrying of signal flares by the diver is advised under conditions where it may be difficult for the boat to locate the diver after he has surfaced.

SECTION 14
UNDERWATER SUPPORT PLATFORMS

UNDERWATER SUPPORT PLATFORMS 14

14.0 GENERAL

The development and use of underwater support platforms has evolved from recently acquired knowledge of basic diving physiology (Section 2), saturation diving (Section 12), and breathing media (Section 5). The reader is directed to these sections for appropriate detailed discussions. The principal purpose in using underwater platforms is to extend the diver's usefulness while submerged. One way is to provide a means to increase the diver's time on the bottom, either by permitting him to live in a submerged habitat or by reducing the time required for descending and ascending. Another way is to increase the diver's mobility and lessen his physical activity, thereby expanding his productive time under water.

This section discusses two types of underwater support platforms and two types of underwater propulsion systems.

14.1 UNDERWATER HABITATS

During the past two decades diving technology and medicine have added a new dimension to underwater research: the underwater habitat with extended duration diving. Early underwater habitat operations were directed primarily toward hardware, technique, and physiology projects rather than experimental studies in marine science. These habitats and diving apparatus were neither technically nor logistically perfected nor designed to accommodate the average diving scientist. Rather, they were designed to determine engineering feasibility or to demonstrate the capability of humans to survive the rigors of the undersea environment.

Since these pioneering experiments, numerous other underwater structures have been developed and used to support diving activities. Underwater habitats provide the diving scientist with the necessary refuge for rest and resupply while permitting unlimited access to the environment. Living and working under water, the scientist is capable of making observations over long periods of time and of designing sophisticated experiments which cannot be performed in the laboratory. It should be realized, however, that the advantages of using a habitat depend upon the nature and objectives of the particular diving operation. It is therefore necessary to evaluate a particular habitat design in relation to the specific diving project in which the habitat is to be used (High et al. 1973).

A recent report (University of New Hampshire 1972) describes those features of an underwater habitat which are considered desirable based on a nationwide survey. Recognizing that such characteristics must be tailored to mission objectives those desirable features of a general nature are summarized in Table 14–1. While detailed specifications are not appropriate in this manual the general guidelines provided in Table 14–1 will acquaint the reader with certain features to be expected in habitats of the future.

In designing and selecting habitats for use in marine science programs, both technical and logistical criteria must be applied if systems are to match missions. The report cites six major criteria in evaluating a habitat system. These are mission adequacy, operational adequacy, flexibility, technical confidence, safety, and cost. These criteria are summarized in Table 14–2 (University of New Hampshire 1972). Further details of habitats, their design, and their use may be found in Table 14–3 (Parrish 1972).

No attempt will be made to provide detailed outlines of specific scientific projects accomplished to date using underwater habitats. For these details the reader may consult Pauli and Cole (1970) and Miller et al. (1971).

Projects best undertaken from underwater habitats are those requiring long term *in situ* monitoring of environmental parameters or organisms. Although

**Table 14-1
Desirable Features
for Future Underwater
Habitats**

Overall Size About 8′ × 38′

Separate Wet Room:	Living Room:
Large entry trunk	Bunks
Wet suit rack	Quick-cook oven
Hot shower	Food freezer and refrigerator
Hookah and bibb	Water heater
Scuba charging	Toilet
Wet lab bench	Individual desk and storage
Specimen freezer	Dry lab bench
Clothes dryer	Compactor
Diving equipment storage	Library
Rebreathers	Tapes, TV, radio
	Emergency breathing system
	Computer terminal

Hemispherical windows

Temperature and humidity control

Separate double chambers

On-bottom and surface decompression capability

Suitable entry height off bottom

Submersible decompression chamber for
emergency escape

External survival shelter

External lights at trunk and viewports

External bottle storage and charging

Habitat to diver communication

Diver to diver communication

Adjustable legs

Mobility

External or protected internal chemical hood

in shallow water these activities may be undertaken from the surface, it often becomes more economical and feasible for the scientist to work or observe from an underwater chamber. As scientists learn more about the advantages and techniques of habitat-based operations, they should be able to increase their in-water time and efficiency two- to three-fold. Beginning at about 80 feet the burdens of decompression in conventional diving become prohibitive. Ecological community assessments for example may require many hours on the bottom. For this type of activity, saturation diving becomes an efficient tool.

There is also a need in the marine sciences for nonsaturation underwater work chambers and simple bottom platforms. Such facilities, although restricted in size and capability, are excellent for some shallow water projects as well as serving as a facility for preparing scientists for saturation diving. The scientist-diver can simulate saturation and thus acquire the necessary "self-discipline" and training required for total saturation. Also, various research techniques and experiments can be field tested without the complexity, expense, and total commitments of a saturation dive.

SUBLIMNOS (Figure 14–1), a Canadian habitat, is an inexpensive shallow-water habitat built for the purpose of creating greater accessibility for a longer duration to the budget-limited scientist. The habitat provides a "day-long" work capability for up to four divers. The upper chamber is nine feet tall and eight feet in diameter. Access is afforded through a 35 inch hatch in the floor of the living chamber.

SUBIGLOO (Figure 14–2) also Canadian, has been used in Arctic exploration programs with great success in 1972 and 1974. It is constructed of two 8-foot acrylic hemispheres on aluminum legs. It affords an unrestricted view thus serving as an excellent observational platform (Stang 1974).

LAKE LAB (Figure 14–3) was designed for 48 hours of continuous operation for two persons to depths of 30 feet.

LAKE LAB operations are controlled from a shore-based mobile van. The van is equipped with low and high pressure air compressors, high pressure air storage units, a habitat control console, communicators, first aid and emergency supplies, diving equipment lockers, work bench, and other equipment necessary for support of the habitat operation.

Table 14-2
Habitat System
Evaluation Criteria

1. Mission Adequacy:
   A. Habitability:
      Functional arrangement
      Ease of operating and housekeeping
      Motion stability
      Bottom stay and visibility
      Ease of access to water
      Psychological environment for research
   B. Degree of Meeting Mission Requirements:
      Site selection survey capability
      Availability of required outside scientific support
      Availability of required outside functional support
      Training time
      Depth, bottom type, slope, currents
      Adequacy of adverse weather capability
      Effect of premature storm termination
      Minimum disturbance to environment

2. Operational Adequacy:
   A. Weatherability
   B. Operating Complexity:
      Preparation and checkout
      Transit
      Site preparation, mooring, emplacement, startup, recovery
      Operations, logistics support, communication, safety support
   C. Upkeep—Surface and Subsurface Equipment:
      Simplicity
      Reliability
      Redundancy
      Maintainability
      Repairability
   D. Other:
      Adequacy of surface accommodations
      Availability of special tow boats and personnel when required
      Need for special logistics services
      Shore logistics base requirements
      Training program complexity

3. Flexibility:
   A. Changing Requirements Within Region:
      Greater depth—bounce dive
      Longer missions
      Fixed site
      Smaller crew
      Larger crew—modularity
      Outfitting for different experiments
   B. Meeting Requirements from Other Regions:
      Transportability
      Other environmental conditions
   C. Future Growth to All-Weather Capability
   D. Utilization of Elements for Other Than Habitat Programs

4. Technical Confidence:
   A. Effect of Technical Uncertainty:
      Mission adequacy
      Operational adequacy
      Safety
      Cost—schedule

5. Safety:
   A. Consider Following Hazards for Probability of Happening, Detection Capability, Availability of Standard Safety Devices, Backup Actions Available:
      Lack of endurance of primary utilities
      Failure of primary utilities
      Failure of umbilical
      Failure of surface communications
      Contaminated atmosphere
      Fire
      Flooding
      Diver incapacitated in habitat
      Diver incapacitated in water
      Hazard requiring evacuation
      Inoperative primary decompression facility
      One diver bent
      Adverse weather
      Loss of air while diving
      Accidental diver surfacing
      Exceeding excursion limits
      Diver lost
      Predator hazard
      Failure of swimmer vehicle while remote
      Entanglement of diver or equipment with lines, moorings
      Surface support diver accidents
      Object dropped on habitat or diver
      Vessel moor shifting
      Surface crewman incapacitated
      Failure in emplacement/recovery system
      Failure in PTC–DDC mating system

6. Cost:
   A. Cost Per Day:
      Development cost amortization
      Manufacturing cost amortization
      Operating costs—personnel, consumables, lease costs
      Maintenance costs—preventive maintenance, spares, repair
      Insurance, port and dock charges
   B. Development Time Required
   C. Funding Increments Required
   D. Utilization of Existing Hardware
   E. Savings if Several Identical Systems Used

Figure 14-1
SUBLIMNOS

Decompression is accomplished by swimming to the surface and immediately entering a deck recompression chamber.

HYDRO-LAB (Figure 14–4), although not the smallest facility, is of a simple design and inexpensive to operate, using a self-contained unattended surface life-support buoy. The main structure is an 8-foot by 16-foot cylinder supported on four short legs 3 feet above a concrete base. The habitat is submerged by venting ballast tanks in the concrete base and saddle buoyancy tanks located along the habitat cylinder. Pipe fittings which project from the base permit the ballast tanks to be filled with air when the habitat is to be raised.

Entry into the habitat is through a well at one end which also functions as a lock when the chamber pressure is less than ambient. Personnel can dry transfer from a lockout submersible to the habitat through a tunnel fitted with a mating pedestal. The single room is furnished with two bunks, two folding chairs, a collapsible table, a dehumidifier and air conditioner.

A 23-foot long life-support barge floats at the surface above the habitat. Umbilicals carry electrical power (7.5 kw, 110 vac, 60 Hz) and high and low pressure air to HYDRO-LAB from a diesel-powered generator and compressor. A 250-gallon water storage tank gravity feeds fresh water at ambient temperature to a hand-held shower nozzle next to the entry trunk. Decompression is conducted in the habitat.

EDALHAB (Figure 14–5) was designed and built as an engineering project by students from the University of New Hampshire. The habitat was constructed mainly of salvaged and donated materials.

The living quarters are enclosed in an 8-foot by 12-foot cylinder with a small viewing port at each end. The interior is insulated using 1½-inch thick unicellular foam. Entry is made through a hatch centrally located in the floor. The interior has two permanent bunks (which fold to form a large seat), and a collapsible canvas cot.

The habitat rests on an I-beam frame which, in turn, is supported 8 feet off the bottom by four adjustable cylindrical legs. Large (4,600 lb.) weights suspended from either end of the frame are raised and lowered by diver-operated hand winches. Four large emergency buoyancy tanks are located along the side of the cylinder and can be filled

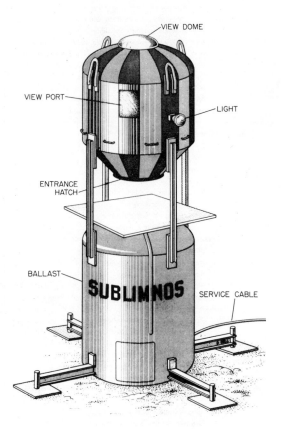

VIEW DOME

VIEW PORT

LIGHT

ENTRANCE HATCH

BALLAST

SUBLIMNOS

SERVICE CABLE

Figure 14-2
SUBIGLOO

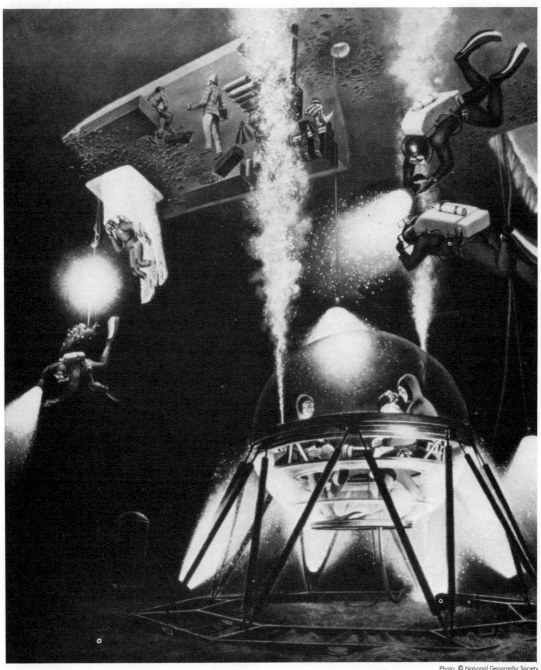

14-5

Figure 14-3
LAKE LAB

Photo: Lee Somers

Figure 14-4
HYDRO-LAB

Photo: Laurence Bussey

with air through a valve on the habitat exterior. Communications, air, and power are provided from the support ship to the habitat through umbilicals. Decompression is accomplished by swimming to the surface and immediately entering a deck recompression chamber.

The Puerto Rico International Undersea Laboratory (PRINUL) "LA CHALUPA" (Figure 14–6) was designed as an underwater marine laboratory. It is operated by the Marine Resources Development Foundation for the Commonwealth of Puerto Rico.

The habitat has been used at depths of 50–100 feet. It can easily be moved from one location to another and emplaced in about one hour. It readily supports a crew of five.

Surface support is provided by a self-contained utility buoy which supplies power, water, high and low pressure gas, and communications equipment. A control van on shore houses watch directors who continuously monitor the system's status, weather, and diver activities.

Upon completion of the mission, the habitat is brought to the surface with the aquanauts in the pressurized living compartment. The habitat is then towed to shore for completion of decompression.

Two 2-man submersible decompression chambers are attached to the habitat for emergency use. These can be entered, pressurized to gain buoyancy, and released from the main habitat. Once on the surface they can be transported (in their pressurized state) by helicopter and locked on to a shore-based decompression chamber.

TEKTITE (Figures 14–7 and 14–7a) was constructed as a four-man habitat. The habitat consists of two pressure hulls attached to a rigid base, connected by a pressurized cross-over tunnel. The two cylinders are divided into two compartments each: bridge, crew quarters, equipment room, and wet room. The bridge serves as control center for the habitat system and as a dry laboratory for scientists. The crew quarters contain four bunks, a small galley, storage and entertainment facilities. The equipment room contains the environmental control system, transformers, frozen food, and toilet facilities.

Air, water, electrical power, and communications are provided from shore facilities through umbilicals. The environmental control system maintains temperature at about 80° F with a 65 percent relative humidity. Noise levels are low. One or more hemispherical windows in each compartment and a cupola on top of one cylinder permit the scientists excellent viewing in all midwater and bottom areas adjacent to the habitat.

Decompression may be accomplished by swimming to the surface and immediately entering a chamber or by entering a personnel transfer capsule on the bottom and being locked in to a deck decompression chamber.

As scientists extend their ocean floor goals even deeper into the sea, the need for a habitat capable of remaining at depths up to 600 feet for extended periods of time becomes apparent.

The AEGIR habitat (Figure 14–8) is capable of supporting six scientists at 580 feet for up to 14 days.

The personnel chamber consists of three compartments: living, control, and laboratory. The living and laboratory compartments are identical in size and shape. Each is cylindrical with dished heads; the inside diameter is 9 feet and the length 15 feet. The control compartment, located between the two cylinders, is spherical with an inside diameter of 10 feet. The three compartments are connected by two necks with an inside diameter of 36 inches. The support platform, in the shape of twin 70-foot long pontoons each 9 feet in diameter, is capable of controlling the ascent and descent of AEGIR independent of surface control. However, a support ship tends the habitat when it is submerged, and continuous communications with a pier support station are maintained.

Upon completion of the mission the habitat is brought to the surface with the aquanauts in the pressurized compartment. The habitat is then towed to shore for completion of decompression.

14.2 BELL DIVING SYSTEMS

While most underwater habitats are fixed on the sea bed and not transportable with divers inside, semimobile underwater support platforms known as diving bells have proven their worth in numerous types of undersea tasks.

The diving bell (Figure 14–9) usually accommodates from 2 to 4 divers, and is normally only one component of an integrated system designed to provide divers with a safe, dry, and sometimes heated elevator to their work site. On board the support ship or barge are the deck decompression

**Figure 14-6
PRINUL
Cut-a-way View**

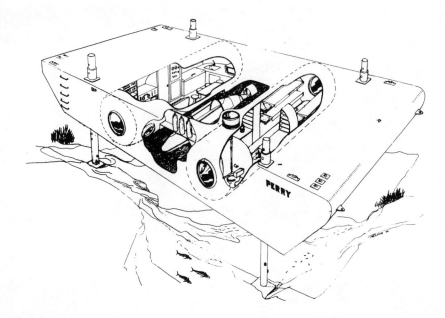

chamber(s), control van, and electric and hydraulic generators and motors to provide power for the various components as well as the handling system (Figure 14–10).

Bell diving systems are expensive to operate and maintain, but do offer advantages over a fixed habitat if a large area of bottom is to be covered, or if heavy tools and substantial surface support are required.

Under saturated conditions, one or more teams of divers can live in relative comfort in the deck chamber(s). Hot meals can be passed in 3 times a day, and surface personnel have direct contact with the divers.

Upon commencing a job, the divers climb into the top or side-mating bell and are lowered to the work site. Upon reaching the required depth, the divers open the lower hatch and exit to start work (Figure 14–11). If necessary, the bell can be moved closer to the job site by maneuvering the ship. Upon completion of the task, the divers reenter the dry environment of the bell and are raised to the surface. This cycle can continue, with two teams, for days or weeks if necessary. Decompression is carried out after completion of the mission.

Commercial bell diving systems are designed to be operated between 450–1500 feet. Up to 1973, 95 percent of the work done by commercial bell systems was done at depths of 150 to 300 feet. Projected are commercial dives in the North Sea to 1000 feet, with several jobs already contracted in the 450- to 750-foot range.

The deepest U.S. Navy bell dive to date has been the 1010 foot dive in 1972 with the MARK II Deep Dive System (Figure 14–12). In 1970, the MARK I Deep Dive System completed a series of 850 foot dives off the coast of California. The divers, using hot water suits, operated from a bell whose temperature was maintained at 92° F. They worked for periods up to 3.5 hours in 42° F water temperature (Figure 14–13) (Bussey 1970).

Today, most work done from diving bells is in support of the offshore oil industry. Additionally, the various navies of the world use bell diving systems for salvage, search and recovery, and instrument implantation. However, scientific diving from bells may soon be a requirement in order to conduct bottom surveys or conduct experimentation at continental shelf depths.

Figure 14-7
TEKTITE

14-11

Figure 14-7a
TEKTITE
Cut-a-way View

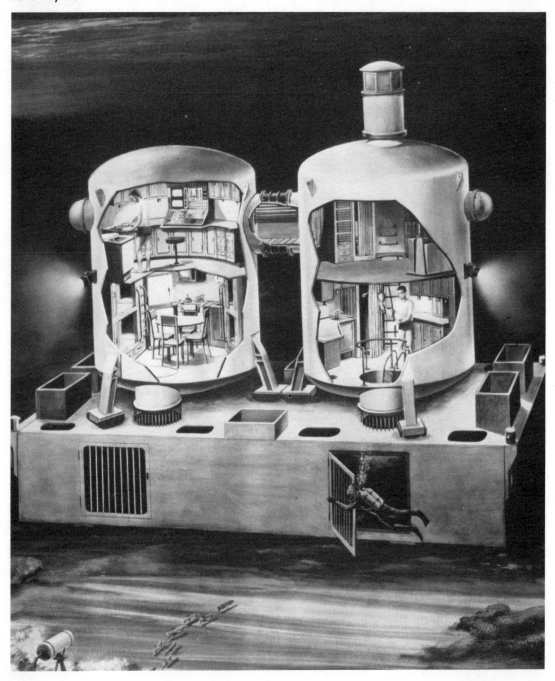

Figure 14-8
Diagram of AEGIR

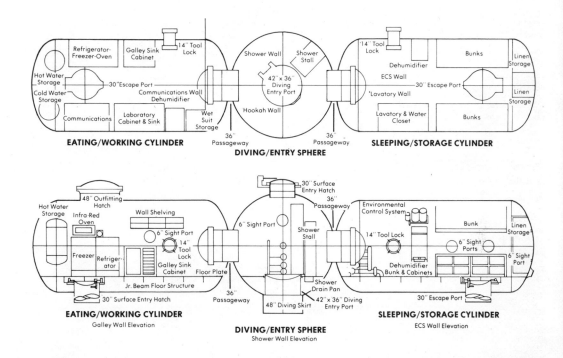

14.3 DIVER LOCK-OUT SUBMERSIBLES

The third type of underwater platform used by divers is the lock-out submersible (Figures 14–14 through 14–15). Whereas most research submersibles have one or two compartments designed to maintain the crew at a pressure of 1 atmosphere, some submersibles, as well as possessing direct observation and manipulator facilities, possess lock-out capabilities which permit divers to leave the submersible. These vehicles allow divers to be transported to the working site at surface pressure. Numerous viewing ports allow an initial survey to assess working conditions. Lock-out submersibles have a separate chamber capable of being pressurized to ambient pressures so the pilot and other personnel may remain at atmospheric pressure within the submersible while the divers are in the water. Depth and working conditions determine whether the divers use self-contained breathing systems or an umbilical supplied from the submersible. The benefit of a diver lock-out capability

is that it reduces diver exposure time, allowing decompression to begin immediately upon return to the vehicle. Some lock-out submersibles have the capability of mating to deck decompression chambers. This allows the diving team to saturate in the chamber on deck, and be transported to the work site via the submersible.

The value of the lock-out submersible to the scientist is readily apparent. If required to move, change depths, or remain for extended periods of observation, all are within the immediate resources of the vehicle. If required to go to a depth not readily accessible to a diver in the water, the lock-out submersible is an ideal vehicle.

Although the diver/scientist normally does not pilot the submersible, he must be familiar with the vehicle's capabilities and operating procedures.

A detailed plan must be developed prior to any operation including at least one shallow water excursion so the divers can learn the operating characteristics, the use of all high- and low-pressure systems, as well as decompression and emergency

Table 14-3
Classification of Underwater Habitats

Program or Habitat Name	Operator and Country	Weight	Dimensions	Ballast	Fixed	Readily Movable	Mobile	Operations	Crew	Depth	Duration	Atmosphere	Power	Gas	Comments
ADELAIDE	Australia							1967-68					Pontoon Barge		
AEGIR (Habitat II)	Makai Range Inc. USA	200t	L=2x4.6m D=2.8m Ball D=3m Total L=15.2m				*	Hawaii, '69	4-6	147m	14 days	Variable	Ship	Autonomous	Can ascend and descend by completely internal control
AQUATAT I AQUATAT II	Technautics Corp. USA					*			3-5						6 viewports 1.8m² viewing area (shallow water)
BACCHUS BAH I	Germany		L=6m D=2m			*		Baltic Sea Sept. '68 / Ost Sea June '70	2	10m / 10m	11 days / 14 days 2.5 mo.	Air	Ship	Ship	
CARIBE I	Cuba		L=3m D=15m					1966	2	15m	3 days		Ship	Partly autonomous	
CHERNOMOR I	USSR		L=8m D=3m					Gelendehuk, Black Sea	4	5m 14m	30 days				
CHERNOMOR II	USSR	70t						Design 1967-73	4	25m 35m	4 weeks				
EDALHAB	Univ. of New Hampshire USA		L=3.7m D=2.4m	5.5t	*			Alton Bay, New Hamps. 1970-71	4	7.6m	36 hours	Air	Land	Land	
GLAUCUS	UK							1965		9m	1 week				
HEAVY DUTY SEA BED VEHICLE	Cammell-Laird Ltd., UK	65t	L=12m W=7m H=4.2m				*	Design	4+	180m	5 days		Surface		
HEBROS I (KHEBROS I)	Bulgaria		L=5.5m D=2m					Bay of Varna July '67	2	10m					
HELGOLAND	Germany	75t	L=9.0m D=2.5m H=6m			*		North Sea 1969-74	4	23m	10 days	Air	-buoy		(About 64 tons) Capable of depths to 100m)
HUNUC	Union S. Africa					*		1971							Discontinued
HYDRO-LAB	Perry Foundation, Inc., USA		L=4.9m D=2.4m	40t	*			1966 continuous to '74 Bahama Islands		20m	14 days	Air	Surface buoy		Numerous occupations since '66. Transfer from submersible at either ambient or atmospheric pressure possible
ICHTHYANDR 66 (Idhtiandr) (Ikhtiandr)	USSR	600kg	L=22m W=1.6m H=2m			*		Crimean Coast Black Sea August 1966	1-2	11m	7 days	Air	Land		Single chambered lab, 6.8m³ 4 viewports
67	USSR	4.5t	W=8.6m H=7.0m	27t		*		Crimean Coast Black Sea August 1967	2-5	12m	2 weeks each	Air	Surface		3 Chambers
68	USSR					*		Crimean Coast Black Sea Sept. 1968	Several crew	20m	8 days total		Land		15m³ displ.
69	USSR					*		Design		20m					
KARNOLA	Czechoslovakia							1968	5	8-15m					
KITJESCH	USSR		L=5.6m D=2.6m			*		Crimean Coast Summer, '68	4	15m			Shore		Volume = 30m³ 3 chambers (converted railway tank car)
KOCKELBOCKEL	Netherlands		D=1.9m H=4.6m	9.5t		*		Sloterplas 1967	2-4	15m	Short period	Air	Autonomous		
KRAKEN	UK		L=2.6m W=1m H=2.3m					Firth of Lorne, Oban Argyle, Scotland	2	30m	Several weeks	7%O₂ 93%N₂			(Proposed) 2 compartments
LA CHALUPA	Puerto Rico, USA	133t	L=5.8m W=2.4m H=2.4m	22t				Caribbean 1972-74	5	33m	2 weeks	N₂-O₂	Surface buoy		Autonomous operation up to 48 hr. On board computer
LAKE LAB	Univ. of Michigan, USA		W=3.0m H=2.1m	24t	*			Grand Traverse Bay, Lake Michigan	2	10m	48 hrs.	Air	Shore		
LORA	Canada					*		Newfoundland 1974	3	8m	24 hrs.	Air	Surface		
MALTHER I	East Germany	14t	L=4.2m D=1.8m H=3.5m	(1.4m³ of iron) 11 mp	*			Malther Dam Nov.-Dec. '68	2	8m	2 days	Air	Land	Autonomous	Volume = 10m³
MAN-IN-SEA I	Edwin A. Link USA	19t	L=3.2m D=0.9m			*		Villefranche Mediterranean, Sept. 1962	1	61m	1 day	3%O₂ 97%He	Ship		Aluminum cylinder
MAN-IN-SEA II (SPID)	Edwin A. Link USA		L=2.4m D=1.2m			*		Great Stirrup Cay, Bahamas June 1964	2	142m	2 days	4%O₂ 96%He	Ship		Flexible rubber tent (submersible, portable, inflatable dwelling)

Program or Habitat Name	Operator and Country	Weight	Dimensions	Ballast	Fixed / Readily Movable / Mobile	Operations	Crew	Depth	Duration	Atmosphere	Mode of Supply Power	Mode of Supply Gas	Comments
MEDUSA I	Poland	3t	L=2.2m		*	Lake Klodno July 1967	2	24m	3 days	37%O2 63%N2	Land		
MEDUSA II	Poland		L=3.6m W=2.2m H=1.8m Total H=2.5m		*	Baltic Sea July 1968	3	30m	14 days	Air	Ship		Autonomous operation up to 50 hrs.
MINITAT	Department of the Interior, USA	4.5t	H=3.5m D=2.4m		* *	Design	3 2	26m 50m	7 days 14 days	N2-O2	Surface		4 view ports not used
OKTOPUS	USSR				*	Crimean Coast Black Sea July 1967	3	10m	Several weeks	Air			
PERMON II	Czechoslovakia		L=2m W=2m		*	Split, Yugoslavia Adriatic Sea July '66	2	3m	Discont.		Autonomous		Displacement = 5m³ Discontinued Decompression within habitat possible
PERMON III	Czechoslovakia	1.5t		5t	*	Czech. Lake March '67	2	10m	4 days		Land	Autonomous	
PRECONTINENT I (CONSHELF I) (DIOGENE)	Jacques Cousteau France		L=5.2m D=2.5m		*	Marseille, Mediterranean Sept. '62	2	10m	1 week	Air			
PRECONTINENT II (CONSHELF II) "STAR HOUSE" "DEEP HOUSE"	Jacques Cousteau France				*	Shaab Rumi Reef, Red Sea July '63	5 2	11m 27m	30 days 1 week	Air 5%O2 20%N2 75%He	Ship		
PRECONTINENT III (CONSHELF III)	Jacques Cousteau France	130t	L=14m Sphere D=7.5m H=8m	70t	*	France, Mediterranean Sept. '65	6	100m	22 days	1.9-2.3% O2 1%N2 Balance He	Surface	Autonomous	
ROBIN II	Italy				*	Genoa, Mediterranean March '69	1	17m	7 days				Light, permeable plastic hull
ROBINSUB I	Italy		L=2.5m W=1.5m H=2m		*	Ustica Is. Mediterranean July '68	1	10m		Air	Land		Wire cage, plastic tent, Vol. = 5m³
ROMANIA LSI	Romania					Bicaz Lake 1968	2				Ship		
SADKO I	USSR		Sphere D=3m	8.5t	*	Caucasian Coast, Black Sea Oct. '66	2	45m 40m 25m	6 days 6 hours 1 month	(Capable of Volume = 14m³ ship or land)			
SADKO II	USSR		Twin spheres D=3m	21t	*	Caucasian Coast, Black Sea, Summer 1967	2	25m (50-60m)	6 days		Land/ ship	Autonomous	Buoyancy = 12t
SADKO III	USSR					Zukhumy Bay, Black Sea	6	25m	6 days				
SD—M/1	UK		L=2.7m W=1.5m H=2.1m		*	Malta Mediterranean		9.1m		Air	Autonomous	Resupply tanks from surface	Discontinued
SD—M/2	UK				*	Malta Mediterranean	1-2	6.1m	10 man-days	Air	Autonomous	Resupply tanks from surface	
SEALAB I	US Navy USA		L=12.2m D=2.7m H=4.5m		*	Argus Is., Bermudas July '64	4	59m	11 days	4%O2 17%N2 79%He	Ship		Double chamber
SEALAB II	US Navy USA	200t	L=17.4m D=3.7m H=4.5m		*	La Jolla, California Pacific Ocean Sept. '65	10	60m	15-30 days	4%O2 25%N2 71%He	Ship	Autonomous	3 teams, 15 days ea. plus 1 man 29 days
SEALAB III	US Navy USA		L=2.4m D=3.7m H=4.5m		*	Planned for San Clemente Island, California	5-12	200m		2%O2 6%N2 92%He			Suspended
SHELF I	Bulgaria		L=6m D=2.5m			Cape Maslenos 1970		20m	6 days	Air	Surface Ship		
SUBIGLOO	Canada		2.5m sphere		*	Dec. '72 May '74	2	13m	up to 24 hours	Air	Surface		Designed as acrylic work station
SUBLIMNOS	Canada		H=2.7m D=2.4m	9t	*	Little Dunks Bay, Tobermory, Lake Ontario installed June '69 to date	2-4	10m	up to 24 hours	Air	Land		Designed for "day long" occupation—overnight accommodations feasible for short periods.
TEKTITE I	US Navy USA		Twin cylinders H=5.5m D=3.8m	79t	*	Lameshur Bay, US Virgin Is. 1969	4	12.7m	59 days	N2-O2	Ship		
TEKTITE II	Department of the Interior, USA		Twin cylinders H=5.5m D=3.8m	79t	*	Lameshur Bay, April-Nov. '70	5	12.7m	11-30 days	N2-O2	Land		11 crews 5 each

Figure 14-9
CACHALOT
Diving Bell

Photo: James Miller

procedures. Lock-out submersibles always have space in the diving chamber for at least two divers. A good practice is to pair up a member of the submerisble's crew with a scientist so that the crew member can act as a tender when the scientist is in the water. It is preferable to locate the submersible close enough to the dive site so that excursions can all be made using a tethered hookah. This is essential under conditions of high currents (greater than 0.5 knot). Extreme care must be taken when selecting a dive site. Velocity and direction of currents, bottom topography, obstacles on the bottom and maneuverability of the submersible all must be assessed and taken into account prior to any diving. If proper precautions are taken the lock-out submersible can be an excellent tool for the diving scientist.

14.4 FREE FLOODED SUBMERSIBLES

While conventional 1 atmosphere and diver lock-out submersibles require a pressure resistant hull, a free flooded submersible (wet sub) can be thought of as an underwater convertible. When in use, these vehicles (Figure 14-16) are full of water and the divers breathe using scuba equipment. This equipment can be open-circuit, semi-closed, or closed-circuit systems and may be worn on the back or mounted in the vehicle depending upon the nature of the mission and the design of the submersible.

Several configurations of wet subs exist. In some, as many as four divers sit one behind the other while others are designed to have divers side-by-side either sitting or in the prone position. These

**Figure 14-10
CACHALOT**

Photo: James Miller

14-17

**Figure 14-11
Diver Works Down
From a Submersible
Decompression Chamber**

**Figure 14-12
United States Navy
MARK II Deep Dive System**

vehicles are used primarily for transporting divers over long distances at speeds up to 4 knots in order to conserve time and air and to assist diver/scientists in conducting ocean floor surveys. They can also be used as small underwater pickup trucks. Wet subs are excellent tools for all kinds of survey work as they can cover large areas carrying photographic and television cameras as well as divers.

In planning operations involving wet subs certain factors must be considered:

1. Training is essential in general operating procedures and especially in obstacle avoidance.

2. When making long excursions with a wet sub under normal diving conditions a buoy should be used to permit easy tracking by a surface support boat.

3. Because a diver can be easily lulled into a false sense of security, bottom time and depth must be carefully monitored.

4. A good compass mounted on the sub is essential for navigation.

5. Divers will get cold faster because they are essentially motionless in the water, thus generating little body heat.

6. Use under saturated conditions requires careful planning in terms of ascertaining current velocity, direction, and reserve air supply so that a diver could swim back to the habitat should the sub's propulsion system fail.

7. Most wet subs have extensive maintenance requirements.

WARNING

When Using Either a Wet Sub or Swimmer Propulsion Unit (See Paragraph 14.5) Under Saturated Conditions, Precautions Must Be Taken to Avoid Accidental Ascent. If This Should Occur Rapid Egress Must Be Made.

14.5 SWIMMER PROPULSION UNITS

Swimmer propulsion units (SPU's) (Figure 14–17) are usually powered torpedo-shaped devices designed to pull a diver through the water at speeds ranging from 1 to 3 knots. They are especially useful against currents or to cover long distances. Most commercially available units are battery powered, are easily maintained, and have been found to be quite reliable. Many come equipped with lights and can readily accept a compass mounted on the top of the unit. One note of caution is that divers may get cold faster than normal because of the continuous passage of water over them and the fact that they are not generating body heat as if they were swimming. Swimmer propulsion units are valuable additions to the diver's equipment and add greatly to his flexibility in carrying out underwater programs.

Figure 14-13
United States Navy
MARK I Deep Dive System

Photo: Brooks Institute of Photography

Figure 14-14
Diver Locked Out
of Submersible SHELF DIVER

Figure 14-14a (bottom)
Lock-Out Submersible
SHELF DIVER

Figure 14-15
BEAVER MARK IV
Lock-Out Submersible

Photo: Perry Submarine Builders

Photo: International Underwater Contractors

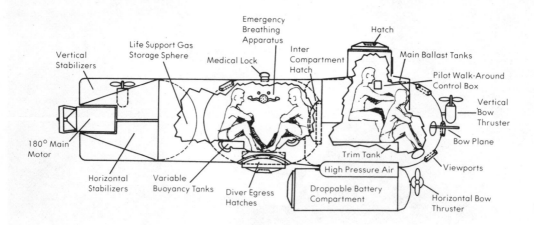

Figure 14-16
Free Flooded Submersible

Photo James Miller

Figure 14-17
MARK I Swimmer
Propulsion Unit

Photo: Farallon Industries

MARINE ANIMALS HAZARDOUS TO DIVERS

15

15.0 GENERAL

Many marine animals are potentially hazardous to divers. Although only a few are serious physical threats, many lesser hazards can seriously impair a diving program by reducing the diver's effectiveness. The material that follows introduces some of these hazards. For convenience, hazardous marine animals have been artificially classified here as: a) those that passively lacerate or abrade; b) those that sting; c) those that bite; and d) those that shock. This classification has limitations: the categories obviously overlap, and although most hazardous species fall naturally into one or another of these categories, some can be placed only arbitrarily.

15.1 MARINE ANIMALS THAT PASSIVELY LACERATE OR ABRADE

The animals described here are non-venomous forms that do not strike out at divers, as do some of those discussed in subsequent paragraphs. Nevertheless, herein lie the major hazards to the working diver, even though divers must bring themselves into contact with these creatures in order to sustain injury. Because his skin has been softened by the water, the diver is especially vulnerable to the many sharp edges and abrasive surfaces that are present in the sea, especially on certain hard-bodies, bottom-dwelling animals like barnacles, mussels and corals (Figure 15–1). A careless diver will almost certainly injure himself when working among such creatures, especially if unprotected by a diving suit, as often is the case in warmer water.

On any one occasion, injuries of this sort rarely are serious; however, wounds resist healing when continually exposed to water, and in time a careless individual may accumulate an array of ulcerated

First aid treatment for injuries caused by marine organisms is contained in Section 17.

sores that incapacitates him as a diver. To compound the problem, there seems to be a relatively high incidence of secondary infection in such wounds. Thus, long-term diving programs can be crippled by failure to take special care to avoid these minor injuries.

15.2 MARINE ANIMALS THAT STING

Many marine animals can inflict venomous wounds. These diverse forms are considered together in this section no matter whether the venom is introduced into the victim by spines on the body, by stinging cells, or by fangs in the mouth. The toxicity of the venom, as well as the amount of venom introduced, varies from one species to another, and sometimes between individuals of a single species. Furthermore, humans can differ from one another in their sensitivity to a given venom. The reactions of humans to the stings of marine animals can range from no noticeable reaction at all, to mild irritations, to rapid death. It is wise to avoid all marine organisms of types known to be venomous; however, occasional contact is inevitable for even the most cautious of experienced divers.

15.2.1 Sea Urchins

Generally the most troublesome animals for divers on tropical reefs are venomous sea urchins (Figure 15–2). This is especially true after dark, when visibility is reduced and many of the noxious sea urchins are more exposed than in daylight. Sea urchins may also be a problem in temperate waters, where they lack the venomous spines of the tropical species.

Most difficulties with venomous sea urchins result from accidental contact with certain long-spined species. The smaller secondary spines that lie among the larger primary spines do the most

Figure 15-1
Coral

Photo: Laurence Bussey

damage: apart from their venom, these spines invariably break off in the wound, and, being brittle, frequently cannot be completely removed. Gloves and protective clothing are some protection during minor brushes with these animals, but do not help much when a diver strikes forcibly against them. To avoid painful injury when working close among venomous sea urchins, one can only remain alert to avoid contact.

Reportedly some of the short-spined tropical urchins are hazardous, owing to tiny pincer-like organs, called pedicellariae, that occur among the spines. Although some pedicellariae contain a potent venom, they are very small structures that probably do not threaten divers who incidentally come into contact with the urchins that carry them. One can handle these urchins without concern for pedicellariae by wearing gloves.

15.2.2 Jellyfishes

Grouped here are a variety of organisms that mostly drift or swim slowly at the water's surface or at middepths. They have gelatinous, semi-transparent bodies, often bell-shaped, from which trail tentacles armed with stinging cells, called nematocysts.

Figure 15-2
Sea Urchins

Photo: Edmund Hobson

Figure 15-3
Portuguese Man O'War

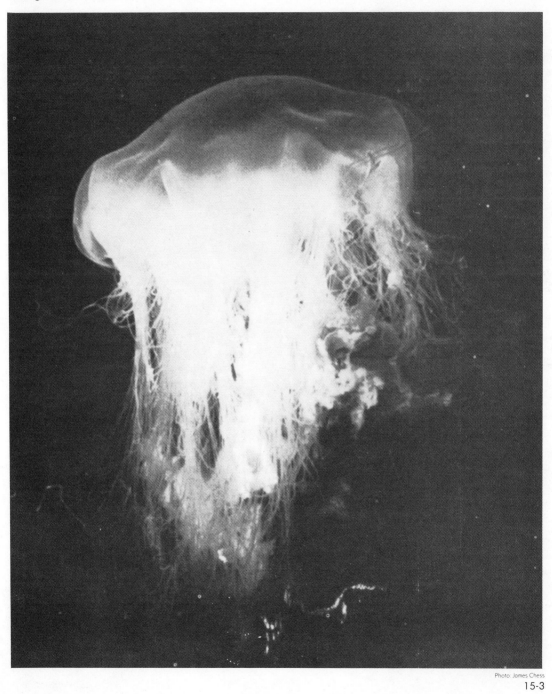

**Figure 15-4
Sea Blubber**

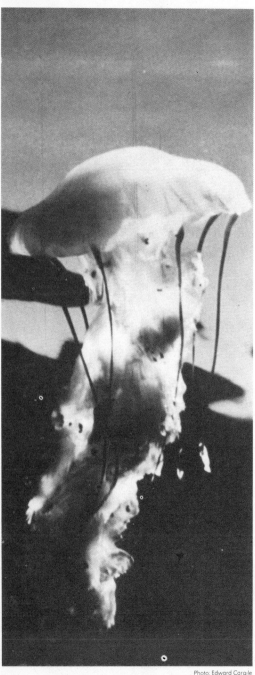

Photo: Edward Cargile

**Figure 15-5
Stinging Hydroids**

Photo: James Chess

Nematocysts are characteristic of a large group of related, though superficially very diverse, marine animals known as coelenterates. In addition to the jellyfishes, this group also includes the hydroids and stinging corals, considered below. Among the different coelenterates there are many types of nematocysts, but all function similarly. When the animal is disturbed, the nematocyst forcibly discharges a venomous thread that, in some species, can penetrate human skin. Of those that affect humans, the reactions range from mild irritations to death.

The portuguese man o'wars, which are grouped together in the genus *Physalia*, are part of a larger assemblage of coelenterates known as siphonophores (Figure 15–3). Siphonophores differ from the other forms considered here as jellyfishes in that each organism is a colony of diverse individuals, each performing for the entire colony a specialized function, like swimming or capturing prey. Their gelatinous, gas-filled float, which may be 6 inches or more in diameter, buoys the man o'wars at the surface, and from this trail tentacles as much as 30 feet long that bristle with nematocysts. Man o'war stings can be dangerous to humans, so divers should stay well clear of them. Unfortunately, even the

Figure 15-6
Stinging Coral

Photo: James Chess

most careful diver can entangle himself in a man o'war tentacle because these nearly transparent structures trail so far below the more visible float. It is especially difficult to detect fragments of tentacles that have been torn from the colony and are drifting free. The nematocysts on these essentially invisible fragments can be as potent as those from an intact organism, and chances are that divers who repeatedly enter tropical water sooner or later will be stung by one.

More properly regarded as jellyfishes are a group of coelenterates known as scyphozoans, each individual of which is an independent animal. These include the common jellyfishes encountered by divers in all oceans. Although many can sting humans, only a relatively few are dangerous. One, the sea blubber, is a large jellyfish of the genus *Cyanea* that is routinely encountered by divers in temperate-zone coastal waters of both the Atlantic and Pacific Oceans (Figure 15–4). Divers should be aware that there is a chance of a secondary sting even after the diver has left the water. Divers in Alaska frequently handle *Cyanea* or brush aside the trailing tentacles of these animals. This practice is safe enough in itself, but segments of tentacles usually adhere to the neoprene gloves and later touching the glove to bare skin, especially on the

face, will produce a sting as painful as any received directly from the animals.

The most dangerous of the jellyfishes belong to a tropical subgroup of scyphozoans known as cubomedusae, or, commonly, as sea wasps. Sea wasps have an extremely virulent sting. One species in the southwest Pacific has caused death among humans. Fortunately, the more dangerous sea wasps are only rarely encountered by divers.

15.2.3 Stinging Hydroids

Stinging hydroids occur on many reefs in tropical and temperate-zone seas. Typically they are feather-like colonies of coelenterates (Figure 15–5) that, like jellyfishes, are armed with nematocysts. Because colonies of these animals may be inconspicuous, often only a few inches high, they can easily go unnoticed. Except to the occasional human that is hypersensitive to their stings, hydroids generally are more of a nuisance than a hazard. Usually divers are affected when they brush against these animals with the more sensitive parts of their body, such as the inner surfaces of their arms. Although any sort of clothing largely protects divers from stinging hydroids, the danger of stings on the hands and face still exists.

Figure 15-7
Bristle Worm

Photo: Richard Rosenthall

**Figure 15-8
Cone Shells**

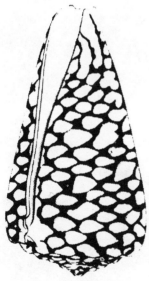

**Figure 15-8a
Anatomy of a Cone Shell**

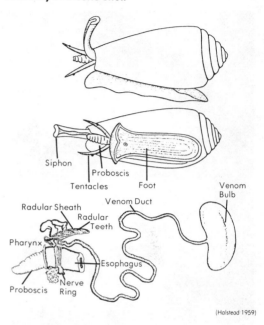

(Halstead 1959)

15.2.4 Stinging Corals

Stinging corals (Figure 15−6), often called "fire coral," belong to a group of colonial coelenterates known as millepores. They are widespread on tropical reefs among the more familiar stony corals, which they superficially resemble. The nematocysts of millepores affect humans in about the same way as those of the stinging hydroids.

15.2.5 Marine Worms

Marine worms that can be troublesome to divers are included in a group known as polychaetes. Two types reportedly inflict venomous wounds: they are the bristle worms and the blood worms.

Bristle worms (Figure 15−7), which divers often encounter when overturning rocks, have tufts of sharp bristles along their segmented bodies that, in many species, can be extended when the animal is irritated. It has not been established that these bristles are venomous, but there is evidence that this is so for at least some species.

Blood worms burrow in mud or sand and some species can be a problem to divers that handle them. Their jaws contain venomous fangs, whose bite is comparable to a bee sting.

15-7

Figure 15-9
Sculpin

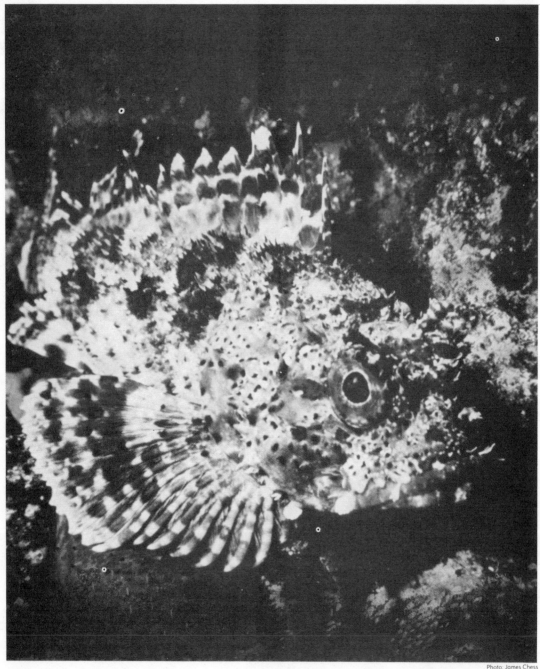

Photo: James Chess

NOAA Diving Manual

**Figure 15-10
Lionfish**

Photo: Edmund Hobson

**Figure 15-11
Dasyatid Stingray
Buried in the Sand**

15.2.6 Cone Shells

Of the many diverse kinds of shelled mollusks in the sea, only some of the tropical cone shells are hazardous to divers (Figures 15–8 and 15–8a). Cone shells, characterized by their conical shape, are an especially attractive hazard because collectors are drawn to the colorful shells of the most dangerous species. There are more than 400 kinds of cone shells, each with a highly developed venom apparatus used to stun the small animals that are its prey. Thus the weapon is offensive not defensive—a fortunate circumstance that reduces the possibility of humans who handle these animals being stung. Although only a relatively few are dangerous to divers, reportedly some of these can be deadly. Because cone shells inject their venom with a harpoon-like structure at the narrow end of their shells, one handling these animals should grasp them at the wide end.

15.2.7 Octopuses

When an octopus bites into prey with its beak, a venom enters the wound and subdues the prey. This venom is not normally toxic to humans. While

Photo: Edmund Hobson

Figure 15-12
Eagle Ray

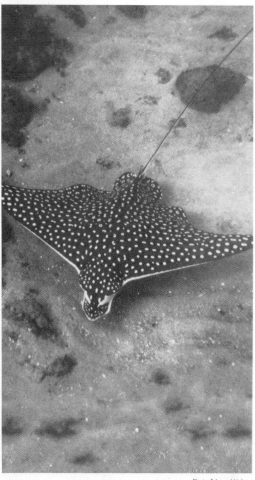

Photo: Edmund Hobson

Figure 15-13
Surgeonfish

Photo: Edmund Hobson

there have been relatively few cases of octopus bites on humans, one diver in Australia who allowed a rare blue ring octopus to crawl over his bare skin was bitten on the neck, and died within 2 hours.

15.2.8 Venomous Fishes

Many fishes inflict venomous wounds. Most do so with their fin spines, but some with spines on their heads or elsewhere on their bodies. Generally these fishes injure only those divers that deliberately handle or provoke them; however, some wound divers that unintentionally touch them, or come too close.

Scorpionfishes. The most widespread and numerous family of venomous fishes are the scorpionfishes. This family, which numbers several hundred near-shore species, has representatives in all of the world's seas, but the most dangerous forms occur in the tropics. Generally scorpionfishes inject the venom with their dorsal fin spines, less often with the spines of their anal and pelvic fins.

Many scorpionfishes are sedentary creatures that, looking much like the sea floor, lie immobile and unseen. An example is the sculpin (Figure 15–9), a common near-shore species of southern California. Another example, the stonefish, is common in shallow, tropical waters of the western Pacific and Indian Oceans; this species has the most potent sting of all scorpionfishes, and has caused deaths among humans. Although scorpionfishes of this type are not aggressive toward divers, being so well camouflaged they can readily be stepped on or brushed against unless special care is taken.

In contrast to the cryptic sculpin and stonefish, another group of scorpionfishes, the brilliantly hued lionfishes (Figure 15–10), stand out strikingly against their surroundings. Because lionfishes are beautiful animals that make little effort to evade humans, inexperienced divers might be tempted to grasp hold of one. This could prove a painful mistake, because lionfish venom is especially potent.

Scorpionfishes represent a wide variety of fishes that inflict venomous puncture wounds with their fin spines, or with spines elsewhere on their bodies. Other fishes similarly armed include: the weever fishes, family *Trachinidae*; toadfishes, family *Batrachoididae*; stargazers, family *Uranoscopidae*; marine catfishes, family *Ariidae*; rabbitfishes, family *Siganidae*; and surgeonfishes, family *Acanthuridae*. Generally these fishes do not generate the force that drives their venom apparatus into the victims; this force is supplied by the victims themselves, who are handling, or have otherwise come into contact with these fishes. A number of fishes, however, do actively thrust their venom apparatus into their victims, an action that often produces a deep laceration. Some of these fishes are discussed next.

Stingrays. Stingrays carry one or more spike-like spines near the base of a flexible tail that they actively whip at those threatening them. Although these spines can inflict venomous puncture wounds, similar to those of fishes discussed above, more often they inflict a slashing laceration. Humans are most threatened when wading on sandy bottom in shallow water, or when swimming close to the sand. Walking with a shuffling motion will tend to frighten stingrays away. Species of the family *Dasyatidae* present the greatest danger, combining as they do large size, the habit of lying immobile on the sea-floor, often under a covering of sand, and carrying a large spine relatively far back (compared to other stingrays) on a whip-like tail (Figure 15–11). Large rays of this type can drive their spine through the planks of a small boat, or through a human arm or leg. Swimmers coming into contact with the bottom have been mortally wounded when struck in the abdomen by a stingray lying unseen in the sand.

Less dangerous are stingrays of the family *Myliobatidae*, which include the bat rays and eagle rays (Figure 15–12), even though these too can be large animals with long venomous spines on their tails. The spines of these species are at the bases of their tails rather than farther back, and so are less effective weapons than the spines of the dasyatid rays. Too, the myliobatid rays are less cryptic than the dasyatids: rather than lying immobile on the bottom most of the time, they more often swim through the midwaters, their greatly expanded pectoral fins flapping gracefully like the wings of a large bird. When on the sea floor, myliobatid rays usually root actively in the sand for

Figure 15-14
Sea Snake

Photo: Ron Taylor

their shelled prey, and thus are readily seen.

Surgeonfishes. As noted above, some surgeonfishes (Figure 15–13) can inflict venomous puncture wounds with their fin spines; these wounds are much like those produced by scorpionfishes, and other similarly armed. Many surgeonfishes can also inflict deep lacerations with knife-like spines they carry on either side of their bodies, just forward of their tails. It has not been established that these weapons are venomous, but there is evidence that this is so in at least some species. The more dangerous surgeonfishes, which belong to the genus *Acanthurus*, usually carry these spines flat against their bodies in integumentary sheaths; however, when the fishes are threatened they erect these spines at right angles to their bodies, and with quick, lashing movements of their tails, they can seriously damage adversaries. Divers injured by surgeonfishes usually have speared, or otherwise molested them.

15.2.9 Sea Snakes

Sea snakes have a highly virulent venom, so it is fortunate for divers that these animals generally do not bite humans unless roughly handled. Some-

15-11

Figure 15-15
Grey Reef Shark

Photo: Edmund Hobson

times a sea snake that is manhandled amid a netload of fishes will bite a fisherman, but generally they are nonaggressive toward divers that incidentally meet them under water. Sea snakes inhabit the tropical Pacific and Indian Oceans, being especially numerous in the East Indies and nearby waters. Divers most often see them amid rocks and coral, where they prey on small fishes (Figure 15–14). They are agile underwater swimmers, and divers should not lose respect for their deadly bite simply because they are reportedly docile.

15.3 MARINE ANIMALS THAT BITE

Serious injuries from marine animals that bite are rare, and in themselves have no impact on most diving programs. Despite this fact, however, the possibility of such injury usually has substantial psychological impact. It is the most widely publicized diving hazard, and a continual mental distraction for many inexperienced divers. The working diver should have a realistic perspective of this potential hazard.

15.3.1 Sharks

Sharks have generated more sensational publicity as a threat to divers than have any other animals, even though their bites are among the most infrequent of all injuries that divers sustain in the sea. The notoriety is understandable: injuries from shark bites generally are massive, and frequently fatal. Nevertheless, one must recognize that only a very few of the many species of sharks in the sea threaten humans.

The vast majority of sharks are inoffensive animals that threaten only small creatures like crabs and shellfish. However, some sharks normally inoffensive will bite divers that molest them. Included here are such common forms as nurse sharks (family *Orectolobidae*) and swell sharks (family *Scyliorhinidae*). These animals appear docile largely because they are so sluggish, but large individuals can seriously injure a diver. With the understanding that any large animal with sharp teeth is a potential hazard to be left alone, we can turn to those sharks that may initiate unprovoked attacks on divers.

Figure 15-16
Moray Eel

Photo: Edmund Hobson

Most sharks known to attack humans without apparent provocation represent four families: the *Carcharhinidae*, which include the grey sharks, white-tip shark, blue shark and tiger shark; the *Carchariidae*, which include the sand sharks (including the species called grey nurse shark in Australia, not to be confused with those called nurse sharks in American waters, above); the *Lamnidae*, which include the mako shark, and white shark; and the *Sphyraenidae*, which include the hammerheads. These are relatively large, active animals whose feeding apparatus and behavior give them the potential to grievously injure divers. Except for the hammerheads, whose name well characterizes their appearance, these sharks all look much alike to the untrained eye. Certainly the characteristics distinguishing them will not impress most divers that encounter them under water.

The grey reef shark (Figure 15–15), which is numerous on tropical Pacific reefs, is typical of the potentially dangerous species. Any animal over about 3 feet long that looks generally like this should be regarded cautiously, and if over about

8 feet long it should be avoided—even if this requires the diver to leave the water. Sharks of these species between about 3 and 7 feet long are numerous in shallow tropical waters, and diving operations there often cannot be performed unless their presence is tolerated. When such sharks are present, divers should avoid making sudden or erratic movements, and common sense dictates that there should be no injured or distressed animals in the water. These are cues well known to precipitate shark attacks. When operations continue in the presence of sharks, each group of divers should include one man that keeps the sharks in view, alert for changes in their behavior. The chances of trouble are minimal so long as the sharks swim slowly, with movements that appear natural. However, the situation immediately becomes dangerous if the sharks accelerate their movements—appearing tense—and especially if they also assume what seem to be unnatural postures, like pointing the pectoral fins noticeably downward, arching the back and elevating the head. The moment sharks show such behavior divers should leave the water.

Figure 15-17
Barracuda

Photo: James Chess

NOAA Diving Manual

Figure 15-18
Torpedo Ray

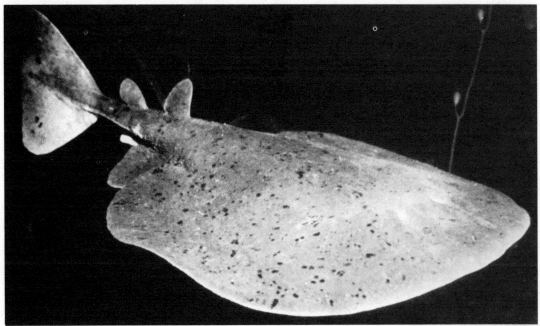

Photo: James Chess

15.3.2 Moray Eels

Moray eels (Figure 15–16) are a potential hazard on tropical reefs, and a few species occur in the warmer temperate regions of California and Europe. They are secretive animals, with a body-form that is highly specialized for life within reef crevices, and only occasionally are they exposed on the reef top. Although relatively few grow large enough to seriously threaten divers, these may be over 6 feet long, and their powerful jaws, with long needlelike teeth, can grievously wound humans.

Divers that have been injured by morays usually have reached into a reef crevice for some object and been struck by an unseen moray that probably felt threatened, or possibly mistook the hand for prey. Generally in this situation the moray will release its hold upon recognizing that it has taken hold of something unfamiliar, and if the diver can resist his natural impulse to pull free he may escape with no more than a series of puncture wounds. But such presence of mind in this situation is rare, and the diver often receives severe lacerations when he wrenches his hand from between the backward-projecting teeth of the eel.

15.3.3 Barracudas

Barracuda (Figure 15–17) that grow to more than about 4 feet long are potential hazards. These animals can severely injure divers. Fortunately, there have been relatively few attacks by barracuda on humans.

Large barracuda often follow divers about, as if expressing interest, but probably there is no danger in this interest. In these situations the barracuda has had a good look at the divers, and even the smallest diver is much larger than anything the barracuda is apt to eat. Barracuda have large canine teeth adapted for seizing the fishes that are their prey. These teeth however are ill-suited to tear pieces from a large animal like man. Attacks on divers are most likely to occur where the barracuda has not had a good look at its victim. Where visibility is limited, for example, the barracuda may see only a moving hand or foot, which may appear as prey in the murk. An attack may also occur when a diver jumps into the water, as when entering from a boat. To a nearby barracuda the diver's splash may simulate the splash of an animal in difficulty—hence vulnerable—and the barracuda may strike without

Figure 15-19
Elephant Seal

Photo: Morgan Wells

realizing what is there. Thus one should be especially alert in murky water, and avoid unnecessary splashing when large barracudas may be present.

15.3.4 Other Fishes That Bite

Any large fish with sharp teeth or powerful jaws can inflict a damaging bite. Generally however such fish are hazardous to divers only when handled. The pufferfishes and triggerfishes can be especially troublesome in this respect. These fishes have teeth and jaws adapted to feeding on heavily armored prey, and large individuals are quite capable of biting off a human finger.

In the tropics, some of the larger sea basses can grow to over 7 feet long. These giant beasts are potential hazards. Their mouths can engulf a diver, and there are reports of them having done so.

15.3.5 Seals and Sea Lions

Juvenile and female seals and sea lions frequently frolic in the water around divers. Underwater encounters with sea lions can be expected if the animals are anywhere around during a dive. Their activity can be distracting or even frightening, but rarely holds any danger. Large bull seals and sea lions, although aggressive on the above-water rocks of their breeding rookery, apparently do not constitute a serious threat under water.

15.3.6 Whales

Common sense should tell divers to avoid large whales under water. Usually whales stay clear of divers, so that most incidents occur when a diver puts himself in jeopardy by provoking the whale. Whales may be startled when a diver approaches too close, and strike the diver senseless in their sudden surge of evasive action. Such a blow can be damaging out of water; under water it can be tragic.

Killer whales have a bad reputation, mostly because they feed aggressively on other marine mammals, including seals, sea lions and porpoises, with which human observers often are emotionally attached. The evidence indicates, however, that their reputation as a major threat to divers is overstated. Nevertheless, they have the potential for grievous assault on divers owing to their large size and predatory habits, and this potential dictates caution.

15.4 MARINE ANIMALS THAT SHOCK

Among marine animals that produce an electric shock, the only one significantly hazardous to divers are the electric rays which have representatives in all the oceans of the world. The torpedo ray of California (Figure 15–18) is an example. Electric rays are slow-moving animals and alert divers should have little trouble steering clear of them. As is true of so many undersea hazards, divers threatened by these animals are mostly those that have molested them. The shock, which can be as much as 200 volts in large rays, is generated by modified muscles in the forward part of the animals disc-shaped body. It is enough to severely jolt a diver.

SECTION 16
RECOMPRESSION CHAMBERS AND TREATMENT PROCEDURES

RECOMPRESSION CHAMBERS AND TREATMENT PROCEDURES 16

16.0 GENERAL

A diver returning to the surface from a deep dive must undergo decompression during which inert gas is eliminated from his body. This requires the diver to stop at specified depth increment for specified periods of time before continuing his ascent. The U.S. Navy Standard Air Decompression Table defines the required increments of depth and time to properly decompress from an air dive. Circumstances can occur, however, in which decompression procedures cannot be followed in the water. In these cases, the decompression must be carried out in a recompression chamber.

Surface Decompression. There are occasions, particularly after deep dives or relatively shallow dives of long exposure time, where sea conditions such as strong currents, cold water, heavy weather, or other emergencies prevent a diver from taking adequate decompression time in the water while ascending to the surface. Surface decompression in a recompression chamber is then required (See Sections 10, 11, and Appendix D).

Decompression Accidents. Decompression accidents, such as decompression sickness or gas (air) embolism, require treatment in a recompression chamber.

It is important to note that the use of a recompression chamber is the only technique presently known that can adequately deal with the two circumstances outlined above. Recompression in the water is not generally possible nor practical in either case.

16.1 RECOMPRESSION CHAMBERS

A recompression chamber is a pressure vessel capable of simulating depth. Two configurations of recompression chambers are most common: the single lock chamber and the double lock chamber. Single lock chambers, as the name implies, contain only one pressure compartment. Double lock chambers contain two chambers capable of being pressurized independently. The double lock chamber possesses significant advantage over the single lock in that medical personnel and tenders may enter and exit the chamber to render aid during treatment of a stricken diver. Both the single and double lock chambers should be equipped with the following systems:

1. A two-way communications system.
2. Demand oxygen breathing apparatus.
3. Pressurization and exhaust systems.
4. Fire extinguishing system.
5. External lighting.
6. View ports.
7. Depth control gauges, control manifolds.
8. A medical lock to allow entry of food or medicine.
9. Heating and air conditioning systems (highly desirable).
10. Stop watches (elapsed time with hour, minute, and second hands).

Recompression chambers are usually cylindrical steel pressure vessels designed to withstand an internal working pressure of at least 5 to 6 atmospheres (75 to 90 psig).

The U.S. Navy has two basic chamber configurations: a double lock chamber capable of withstanding an internal pressure of 200 psi (Figure 16-1); and a single lock chamber capable of withstanding 100 psi (Figure 16-2). Most recompression chambers are 54-60 inches in inside diameter, but may vary from as little as 30 inches to as large as 10 feet inside diameter. Large chambers used to decompress divers after long periods of saturation are comfortably outfitted with toilet facilities, cots, and showers, but these are generally found only at sites where large scale diving operations are being conducted.

Small, portable chambers that allow the immediate recompression of a diver are valuable, especially

Figure 16-1
Double Lock
Recompression Chamber

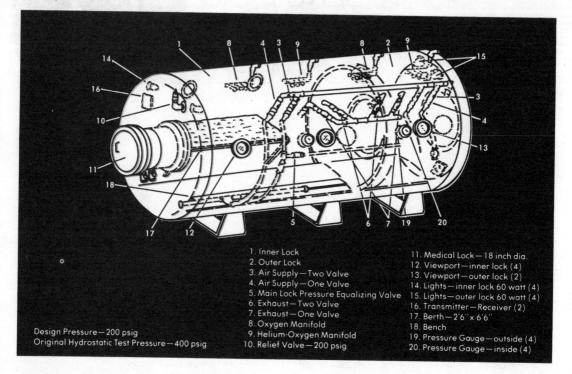

1. Inner Lock
2. Outer Lock
3. Air Supply—Two Valve
4. Air Supply—One Valve
5. Main Lock Pressure Equalizing Valve
6. Exhaust—Two Valve
7. Exhaust—One Valve
8. Oxygen Manifold
9. Helium-Oxygen Manifold
10. Relief Valve—200 psig

11. Medical Lock—18 inch dia.
12. Viewport—inner lock (4)
13. Viewport—outer lock (2)
14. Lights—inner lock 60 watt (4)
15. Lights—outer lock 60 watt (4)
16. Transmitter—Receiver (2)
17. Berth—2'6" x 6'6"
18. Bench
19. Pressure Gauge—outside (4)
20. Pressure Gauge—inside (4)

Design Pressure—200 psig
Original Hydrostatic Test Pressure—400 psig

if they can be used as a transport device to move the stricken diver to a large, well-equipped chamber. Since time is of the essence in treating gas embolism, a short delay in recompressing a stricken diver, even if only a few minutes in duration, can be fatal. Therefore, immediate recompression in a small chamber is of infinitely more value than any advantages gained in chamber sophistication if the move to the larger chamber involves a time delay in recompression (Figure 16–3).

16.1.1 Recompression Chamber Design and Certification

Recompression chambers are generally designed to the requirements of the American Society of Mechanical Engineers, ASME Code, Section VIII, *Unfired Pressure Vessels*. This code is comprehensive in terms of the structural integrity of the vessel and includes all aspects of material selection, welding, penetrations into the pressure vessel walls, flanges for entry or exit, and testing. Only high quality pressure gauges and ancillary equip-

ment should be used in outfitting a recompression chamber, and these should be calibrated and tested frequently, especially prior to a diving operation. Chambers which meet the requirements of the ASME Code are marked with the following mark and information:

U or UM

1. The official U or UM code stamp depicted above.

2. Manufacturer's name.

3. Maximum allowable working pressure psi at ____° F.

4. Manufacturer's serial number.

5. Year built.

Additional markings describe other features of the pressure vessel. Refer to Paragraph UG–115 of Section VIII of the ASME Unfired Pressure Vessel Code for additional information on vessel marking.

Figure 16-2
Single Lock
Recompression Chamber

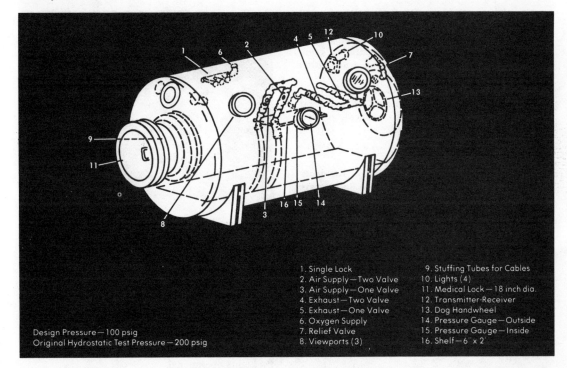

1. Single Lock
2. Air Supply—Two Valve
3. Air Supply—One Valve
4. Exhaust—Two Valve
5. Exhaust—One Valve
6. Oxygen Supply
7. Relief Valve
8. Viewports (3)
9. Stuffing Tubes for Cables
10. Lights (4)
11. Medical Lock—18 inch dia.
12. Transmitter-Receiver
13. Dog Handwheel
14. Pressure Gauge—Outside
15. Pressure Gauge—Inside
16. Shelf—6" x 2'

Design Pressure—100 psig
Original Hydrostatic Test Pressure—200 psig

16.1.2 Recompression Chamber Operator Qualifications and Training (U.S. Navy Recompression Chamber Operator's Handbook 1973)

The operator of a recompression chamber must be thoroughly trained in the mechanical operation of the chamber, and able to recognize the symptoms of decompression sickness and gas embolism.

A chamber operator must:

- Calculate the amount of gas required to take the chamber to depth; ventilate it and determine amount of backup gas required.
- Operate all mechanical systems including air compressors, and maintain and control the air supply to the chamber.
- Recognize and eliminate all sources of combustible materials in the chamber.
- Ensure the existence of adequate fire-fighting materials in the chamber.
- Check all fittings and arrange for oxygen supply.
- Determine ventilation requirements for oxygen

breathing if no O_2 dump system is installed.
- Ensure the accuracy of all gauges and timing devices.
- Thoroughly understand U.S. Navy treatment tables and know how to use them.
- Understand first aid.

16.1.2.1 Manning Requirements

In conducting a recompression treatment, all attending personnel must work as a team for the benefit of the patient. Tenders often initially control recompression from inside the chamber and tend the patient with the advice of a physician familiar with divers' diseases. Outside tenders normally operate the chamber, monitor the time and depth, and communicate with inside personnel.

The minimum team recommended for any recompression treatment consists of:

- Dive Master—In complete charge of the operation.
- Outside tender #1—Responsible for operation of the gas supplies, ventilation, and pressuriza-

tion and exhaust of the chamber when performed from outside the chamber.

- Outside tender #2—Responsible for keeping individual and overall times on the operation, keeping the log and communicating with inside personnel.
- Inside tender—Must be familiar with the diagnosis of diver-related sickness, monitors and cares for the patient during treatment, and administers first aid as required.

NOTE:

A Local Physician Familiar With Diving Accidents Should Be Available on Scene During a Recompression Treatment.

16.1.3 Chamber Operation

Prior to every operation of the chamber, a predive check of the facility must be conducted. This procedure should only take a few seconds, provided that the personnel are experienced and the chamber is properly maintained and always 100 percent ready. The patient and tender then enter the chamber and treatment is initiated.

16.1.3.1 Pre-Dive Checklist

Chamber
- Clean.
- Free of unnecessary equipment.
- Free of noxious odors.
- Doors and seals undamaged. Seals lubricated.
- Pressure gauges calibrated.

Air Supply System
- Primary air supply adequate for two pressurizations to 165 feet plus ventilation.
- One-valve supply—valve shut.
- Two-valve supply—outside valve open; inside valve shut.
- Equalization valve shut.
- Supply regulator set at required pressure.
- Fittings tight, filters clean, compressors fueled.

Exhaust System
- Terminates clear of chamber.
- One-valve exhaust—valve shut and calibrated for ventilation (See Paragraph 16.1.3.5).
- Two-valve exhaust—outside valve open; inside valve shut.

Figure 16-3
Portable
Recompression Chamber

Oxygen Supply System
- Cylinders full; marked as *BREATHING OXYGEN*; cylinder valves open.
- Replacement cylinders on hand.
- O_2 masks installed and functioning.
- Regulator set at required pressure.
- Fittings tight, gauges calibrated.
- Oxygen manifold valves shut.

Electrical System
- Lights operational.
- Wiring checked, properly grounded.

Communications System
- Primary system operational.
- Secondary system operational.

Fire Prevention System
- Water and sand extinguishers in chamber.
- Combustible material in metal container.
- Fire resistant mattresses and blankets in chamber.

Miscellaneous—Inside Chamber
- Slate and chalk.
- Bucket and plastic bag for body wastes.
- Primary medical kit (See Section 17).

Miscellaneous—Outside Chamber
- Stopwatches.
- Recompression treatment time.
- Decompression time for personnel leaving chamber.
- Cumulative time.
- Spare stopwatch.

Table 16-1
Ventilation Air Requirements for Recompression Treatment Tables

Two patients and one tender in chamber

Depth of Stop (fsw)	Vent Rate (scfm) Air Stop	O₂ Stop	1A	2A	3(O₂)	4(O₂)	5	6	5A	6A
						Ventilation Air Required at Stop (scf) Treatment Table				
165	47.9			1437	1437	5749			719	1437
140	41.9			503	503	1256				
120	37			444	444	1111			138	139
100	32.2		966	386	386	965				
80	27.3		328	328	328	821				
60	22.5	140.7	675	676	4221	8104	5741	8780	5741	8780
50	20.1	125.6	603	603	3768	7234				
40	17.7	110.5	530	530	3314	6363	3540	3541	3540	3540
30	15.3	95.4	916	1831	10984	15790	2060	11900	2060	11900
20	12.8	80.2	770	1540	1541	5585				
10	10.4	65	1250	2501	1250	4532	2180	2180	2180	2180
Pressurization	570		756	1247	1247	1247	453	453	1247	1247
Total for Treatment			6794	12026	29423	58757	13974	26854	15625	29223

- Recompression treatment tables.
- Decompression tables.
- Log.
- Secondary medical kit (See Section 17).

16.1.3.2 Regulator Settings

The air supply regulator should be set to maintain a minimum supply pressure of 50 psig over maximum chamber pressure. Regulator settings for oxygen are dependent on the O₂ masks installed in the chamber, and most should be supplied with gas at between 75 and 100 psig over the chamber pressure.

16.1.3.3 Chamber Ventilation

Ventilation of the recompression chamber with fresh air is necessary to maintain safe levels of carbon dioxide and oxygen inside the chamber. The rates at which air must be circulated through the chamber depend upon the number of personnel inside the chamber, their level of activity, and the gas which they are breathing. The following rules apply:

1. When breathing air in chamber:
   a. 2 scfm (standard cubic feet per minute) for each man at rest.
   b. 4 scfm for each man not at rest.
2. When breathing oxygen by mask in chamber without oxygen dump system:
   a. 12.5 scfm for each man at rest.
   b. 25.0 scfm for each man not at rest.
   c. No additional ventilation for each man not breathing oxygen.
3. Interrupted ventilation:
   a. Not to exceed 5 minutes during any 30 minute period.
   b. When resumed; twice the required scfm for twice the period of interruption then resume normal rate.
4. Oxygen monitoring equipment available:
   a. Ventilate as required to maintain oxygen concentration in chamber below 25 percent.
5. Oxygen dump system installed:
   a. Use ventilation rates for air breathing given in (1) above.

The quantity of air ventilated through the chamber is controlled by regulating the precalibrated exhaust valve outside the chamber (See Paragraph 16.1.3.5). Once the air supply rate is established, the air supply valve is regulated to maintain a constant chamber pressure (See Table 16-1).

16.1.3.4 Air Supply Requirements

A recompression treatment facility must have a primary and secondary air supply system which satisfies the following requirements.

Primary—sufficient air to pressurize the chamber twice to 165 feet and ventilate throughout the treatment.

Secondary—sufficient air to pressurize the chamber once to 165 feet and ventilate for one hour.

Either system may consist of air banks or a suitable compressor or both. The required total capacity is calculated as follows:

1. Primary System Capacity

$$Cp = 12v + 58,757$$

where

Cp = total capacity of primary system; standard cubic feet.

v = chamber volume; cubic feet.

12 = atmosphere equivalent of 165 feet times 2 pressurizations (absolute).

58,757 = total air required to ventilate during a Navy Table 4. treatment; standard cubic feet. (See Table 16–1).

2. Secondary System Capacity

$$Cs = 6v + 8,442$$

where

Cs = total capacity of secondary system; standard cubic feet.

v = chamber volume; cubic feet.

6 = atmosphere equivalent of 165 feet (absolute).

8,442 = maximum ventilation rate of 140.7 scfm for one hour.

16.1.3.5 Valve Calibration

Knowledge of the amount of air that must be used does not solve the ventilation problem unless there is some way to determine the volume of air actually being used for ventilation. The standard procedure is to open the exhaust valve a given number of turns (or fraction of a turn), which provides a certain number of cubic feet of ventilation per minute at a specific chamber pressure, and to use the control valve to maintain a constant chamber pressure during the ventilation period.

1. Mark the valve handle so that it is possible to determine fairly accurately the number of turns and fractions of turns.

2. Check the rules in Paragraph 16.1.3.3 against probable situations to determine the rates of ventilation at various depths (chamber pressures) that are likely to be needed. If the air supply is ample, determination of ventilation rates for a few depths (30, 60, 100, 165 feet) may be sufficient, because the valve opening specified for a given rate of flow at one depth will provide at least that much at a deeper depth. It will be convenient to know the valve settings for rates like 30, 60, or 120 cubic feet per minute because these give a simple relationship between volume and time (60 cubic feet per minute = 1 cubic foot per second, etc.).

3. Determine the necessary valve settings for the selected flows and depths by using the chamber itself as a measuring vessel with the help of a stopwatch.

a. Calculate how long it would take to change the chamber pressure by 10 feet if the exhaust valve were letting air escape at the desired rate close to the depth in question. Use this formula:

$$T = \frac{V \times 20}{R \times \frac{(P+33)}{33}}$$

where

T = time in seconds for chamber pressure to change 10 feet.

V = internal volume of chamber in cubic feet.

R = rate of ventilation desired in cubic feet per minute as measured at chamber pressure.

P = chamber pressure (gauge) in feet of sea water.

b. Take chamber pressure down (with no one inside) to 5 feet beyond the depth in question. Then open the exhaust valve a certain amount and determine how long it takes to come up 10 feet. (For example, if checking for a depth of 165 feet, take chamber pressure to 170 feet and clock the time it takes to reach 160 feet.) Try opening the valve different amounts until you know what setting will give close to the desired time. Write down what the setting is. Calculate times for other rates and depths and determine settings for these in the same way. Make a chart or table of the valve settings found and prepare a ventilation chart using this information and the ventilation rules.

16.1.3.6 Post-Dive Maintenance Checklist

Chamber

- Wipe inside clean with vegetable-base soap and warm fresh water.
- Remove all but necessary support items from chamber.

- Clean and replace blankets.
- All flammable material in chamber must be encased in fire resistant containers.
- Restock primary medical kit as required.
- Empty, wash, and sanitize human waste bucket.
- Restock plastic bags as required.
- Check presence of sand and water buckets in chamber.
- Air out chamber.
- Close (do not seal) outer door. Hang a light on an extension cord inside chamber to keep moisture out.

Air Supply System

- Shut all valves.
- Recharge gauge and record pressure of air banks.
- Fuel compressors.
- Clean compressors as per manufacturer's technical manual.
- Open TWO-VALVE SUPPLY outside valves.

Exhaust System

- Shut ONE–VALVE EXHAUST valves.
- Shut TWO-VALVE EXHAUST inside valves.
- Open TWO–VALVE EXHAUST outside valves.

Oxygen Supply System

- Check O₂ masks, replace as necessary.
- Shut all valves.
- Bleed system.
- Replace cylinders, as required; with "BREATHING OXYGEN".
- Ensure spare cylinders available.
- Clean system if contamination suspected (oxygen cleaning procedures are given in the U.S. Navy Diving Manual).

Electrical System

- Check all circuits.
- Replace light bulbs as necessary.
- If lights encased in pressure-proof housing, check housing for damage.
- Turn off all power.
- Check wiring for fraying.
- If environmental monitoring equipment is used, maintain in accordance with applicable technical manual.

Communications System

- Test primary and secondary systems; make repairs as necessary.

Viewports and Doors

- Check viewports for damage; replace as necessary.
- Check door seals; replace as necessary.
- Lubricate door seals with approved lubricant.

Support Items

- Check and reset stopwatches.
- Ensure presence of Diving Manual, ventilation chart, and log book.
- Restock secondary medical kit as required.
- Check that all log entries have been made.

16.1.3.7 Corrosion Protection

Only steel chambers are painted. Aluminum chambers are normally a dull, uneven gray color and corrosion can be easily recognized. Painting an aluminum chamber will hide and further encourage corrosion.

Corrosion products are best removed by hand or by using a slender pointed tool, being careful not to gouge or otherwise damage the base metal. The corroded area and a small area around it should then be cleaned to remove any remaining paint and/or corrosion products.

Steel chambers should then be painted as follows:

Inside: One prime coat FSN 8010–165–8557; one exterior coat white FSN 8010–577–4739 or equivalent.

Outside: One prime coat FSN 8010–165–8557; two exterior coats gray FSN 8010–577–4737 or equivalent.

If the above paint is not available, steel chambers can be painted inside and outside with zinc-rich Dimetcote No. 5 and top coated with nontoxic, non-lead base white water repellent Amercote No. 241.

Painting should be kept to an absolute minimum.

If it is not known whether the chamber had previously been painted as above, remove *all* old paint and repaint.

16.1.3.8 Safety Rules for Chamber Operation

ALWAYS

1. Take all precautions against fire.
2. Provide water and sand buckets.
3. Use fire retardant materials in the chamber.
4. Ventilate the chamber according to specified rates and gas mixtures.
5. Remain alert for the symptoms of oxygen

toxicity. Remember these symptoms by the acronym V-E-N-T-I-D:

- **Vision.** Any abnormality, such as "tunnel vision" (a contraction of the normal field of vision as if looking through a tube).
- **Ears.** Any abnormality of hearing.
- **Nausea.** This may be intermittent.
- **Twitching.** Usually appears first in the lips or other facial muscles, but may affect any muscle. This is the most frequent and clearest warning of oxygen poisoning.
- **Irritability.** Any change in behavior including anxiety, confusion, unusual fatigue.
- **Dizziness.** Additional symptoms may include difficulty in taking a full breath, an apparent increase in breathing resistance, noticeable clumsiness or incoordination.

NOTE:

See Figure 11-1 For Additional Symptoms of Oxygen Toxicity.

6. Assure proper decompression of all personnel leaving the chamber before treatment is complete.

7. Ensure that the chamber and its auxiliary equipment are in operational condition at all times.

8. Ensure that all personnel are trained in the operation of the equipment and are able to do any job required in treatment.

9. Prepare the chamber for immediate re-use following a treatment.

NEVER

1. Use oil on any oxygen fitting or piece of equipment.

2. Allow gas supply tanks to be depleted or reach low capacity.

3. Allow damage to door seals and dogs. Use minimum force in "dogging down."

4. Leave doors dogged after pressurization.

5. Allow open flames, matches, cigarette lighters, or pipes to be carried into the chamber.

6. Permit electrical appliances to be used in the chamber.

16.2 DIVING ACCIDENTS

Diving accidents requiring recompression of a diver in a recompression chamber include decompression sickness or gas embolism. Frequently it is impossible to accurately diagnose the exact nature or seriousness of a diving accident. If symptoms of decompression sickness or gas embolism are observed, it is of much greater importance to initiate treatment immediately rather than delay treatment for a more accurate diagnosis.

In most diving accidents the stricken diver may need artificial respiration, recompression, and first aid at the same time. Apply all necessary treatment as rapidly as possible observing the following priorities as closely as practical.

1. If a victim requires artificial respiration alone, continue the process until normal breathing resumes.

2. If a victim requires both artificial respiration and recompression, start artificial respiration and maintain it continuously while transporting him to a recompression chamber. Concentrate on artificial respiration, but do not delay moving the victim to the chamber.

3. If gas embolism appears to be the most probable cause of cessation of breathing, and a chamber is available, recompress at once and begin artificial respiration, if possible, as soon as the victim is in the chamber.

4. Treat bleeding or other injuries while conducting artificial respiration and during movement to the recompression chamber.

5. When possible, put the patient on oxygen while transporting him to a treatment facility.

6. Always transport a patient on his left side with the head and chest inclined downward (See Section 17).

16.2.1 Tending the Patient

When conducting a recompression treatment for pain-only decompression sickness, an experienced diver must tend the patient inside the chamber. The inside tender must be familiar with all treatment procedures and the signs, symptoms, and treatment of all diving-related sicknesses.

If it is known before the treatment begins that involved medical aid must be administered to the patient, or if the patient is suspected of suffering from a gas embolism, a physician should accompany the patient inside the chamber. If the chamber is sufficiently large, a second tender may also enter the chamber to assist during treatment.

Inside the chamber, the tender ensures that the patient is lying down and positioned to permit free blood circulation to all his appendages. He closes and dogs the inside door and begins pressurization at the normal rate (when not controlled externally):

Decompression Sickness-pain only
    or serious symptoms............. 25 fpm.
Gas Embolism...................... As fast as possible.

This rate may be decreased as necessary to allow the patient to equalize.

During the early phases of treatment, the inside tender must constantly watch for signs of relief of the patient's symptoms. He should record in a log all vital signs to relay to a doctor outside. Avoid giving the patient drugs which will mask the signs of his sickness. Observation of these signs is the principal method of diagnosing the patient's sickness and the depth and time of their relief designates the treatment table to be used. The final recommendation as to which treatment table should be used, however, must be made by the Dive Master or attending physician OUTSIDE THE CHAMBER.

During decompression of the patient, the tender *may* breathe oxygen beginning at the 40-foot stop. If Table 5, 5A, 6 or 6A is used, the tender normally breathes air throughout the treatment. If the treatment involves a repetitive dive for a tender or, if Table 6 or 6A are lengthened during treatment, the tender *must* breathe oxygen during the last 30 minutes of treatment. If Treatment Table 4 is used, have tender on O₂ as required.

Other responsibilities of the inside tender are:

1. Depressurization of the chamber (when not controlled externally).

2. Releasing the door latches (dogs) after a seal is made.

3. Communications with outside personnel.

4. Providing first aid as required by the patient.

5. Administering oxygen to the patient.

6. Providing normal assistance to the patient as required.

16.2.2 Patient Examination

Normally, the patient is examined inside the chamber pressurized to 60 feet, breathing O₂. When signs of gas embolism are present, the patient must immediately be pressurized to 165 feet.

The minimum examination must include:

1. A discussion with the patient to determine the cause of the accident, how he feels, and his general intelligibility.

2. Testing of the patient's:

- Eyesight
- Hearing
- Reflexes
- Muscular coordination
- Strength
- Balance
- Pulse rate.

16.3 TREATMENT TABLES

The U.S. Navy Treatment Tables with Notes (U.S. Navy Diving Manual, 1973), are to be used in the treatment of gas embolism and decompression sickness.

To explain the procedures of recompression treatment, a set of Recompression Treatment Charts amplifying U.S. Navy Treatment Tables has been adapted from the U.S. Navy Diving Operations Handbook. These are included in Appendix D.

U.S. Navy Treatment Tables, with the accompanying notes, are for the most part, self-explanatory. However, the following specific points should be noted. In using the tables, the patient must be taken to the full depth indicated, but not beyond 165 feet, except as determined by medical personnel. Keep a continuous record and check on the patient for incomplete relief and how he feels during each stop. Make a log entry and record the clock time of each examination. Do not let the patient sleep through changes in depth or for more than 1 hour at a time at any decompression stop. Never continue to decompress a patient if his symptoms get worse during decompression, but treat such a situation as a recurrence of the sickness, and recompress until relief from pain is achieved.

A knowledgeable diver (tender) must attend the patient inside the chamber. The tender must be decompressed according to the standard decompression tables before he leaves the chamber. Personnel outside the chamber must specify and control the compression or decompression of anyone entering or leaving the chamber and must review all decisions concerning treatment or decompression made by a tender inside the chamber.

16.3.1 Decompression Sickness Treatment

Decompression sickness probably results from the formation of gas bubbles in the blood or tissues. It can occur following decompression, such as when a diver comes up from depth or when an aviator goes up to high altitude. Decompression sickness will not occur unless there is an excessive amount of inert gas dissolved in the blood or tissue or unless a diver has had inadequate decompression from a dive.

The primary treatment for decompression sickness is recompression. In treating decompression sickness Treatment Tables 1A, 2A, 3, 4, 5, 5A, 6, or 6A may be used. Treatment Tables 5, 5A, 6 and 6A have proven superior to Tables 1A, 2A, 3 and 4 because of their extensive use of oxygen. Tables 1A, 2A, 3 and 4 can be used when oxygen is not available.

The first step of any treatment involves diagnosing the sickness. Signs and symptoms related to each of the above sicknesses are listed, followed by the action which must be immediately taken once the sickness is confirmed. A flow chart is given to provide the systematic method for treating each sickness. Once the treatment table has been established, treatment is normally concluded by carrying out the decompression procedures specified in that table.

If complications develop during or after treatment, the procedures given in Figures 16–6 or 16–7 will apply.

16.3.2 Decompression Sickness—Pain Only

(Probable occurrence within 6 hours following dive)

DIAGNOSIS

Symptoms:	Signs:
Local pain, usually in joints of arms or legs	Diver complaining of joint pain. Pain not promoted by touch or vigorous rubbing.
Itching	Blotchy skin rash.

IMMEDIATE ACTION

1. Stop massive bleeding if present.
2. Put patient on oxygen if possible.
3. Enter chamber, put patient on oxygen, begin pressurization at 25 feet per minute to 60 feet.
4. Examine patient.

TREATMENT

See flow chart (Figure 16–4).

16.3.3 Decompression Sickness—Serious Symptoms

(Probable occurrence within 6 hours following dive)

DIAGNOSIS

Symptoms:	Signs:
Dizziness, defective vision	Diver staggering.
Paralysis	Paralyzed extremities.
Shortness of breath	Rapid breathing.
Extreme fatigue	Choking.
Extreme pain	Diver complaining of
Abdominal pain	extreme pain;
Ringing in ears	doubled over with pain. Collapse or unconsciousness.

IMMEDIATE ACTION

1. Restore breathing using mouth-to-mouth resuscitation, bag or mechanical resuscitator.
2. Put patient on oxygen if possible.
3. Stop massive bleeding if present.
4. Enter chamber, begin pressurization at 25 feet per minute to 60 feet.
5. Place the patient on his left side with the head and chest inclined downward.
6. Examine patient.

TREATMENT

See flow chart (Figure 16–4).

16.3.4 Gas (Air) Embolism Treatment

A gas embolism occurs when a bubble of gas causes a blockage of the blood supply to the heart, brain, or other vital tissue. The bubble tends to get larger as pressure decreases (Boyle's Law), and the blockage becomes worse. A more complete technical discussion of gas embolism is given in Paragraph 2.2.2.4. Prompt recompression is the only treatment for gas embolism. Treat in accordance with U.S. Navy Treatment Tables 3, 4, 5A and 6A.

16.3.4.1 Gas Embolism

(Probable occurrence within minutes following dive)

DIAGNOSIS

Symptoms:
- Fatigue
- Dizziness
- Blurred vision
- Paralysis or weakness of extremities
- Chest discomfort or pain; progressively worsening

Signs:
- Diver confused, staggering, having difficulty seeing.
- Paralyzed or weakened extremities.
- Blueness, chest pain, rapid shallow breathing (pneumothorax).

- Blueness of skin, lips or fingernails; difficulty breathing; shock (mediastinal emphysema).

- Swelling of neck; crackling sensation when skin moved, change in voice, difficulty breathing (subcutaneous emphysema).

- Collapse or unconsciousness.

IMMEDIATE ACTION

1. Restore breathing using mouth-to-mouth, bag or mechanical resuscitator.
2. Put patient on oxygen if possible.
3. Stop massive bleeding if present.
4. Pressurize patient to 165 feet as fast as possible.
5. Place the patient on his left side with the head and chest inclined downward.
6. Examine patient.

TREATMENT

See flow chart (Figure 16–5).

16.3.5 Complications

There are four major complications which may affect the recompression treatment of a patient. These are:

1. Worsening of the patient's condition during treatment (Figure 16–4).

2. Recurrence of the patient's original symptoms or development of new symptoms during treatment (Figure 16–6).

3. Recurrence of the patient's original symptoms or development of new symptoms following treatment (Figure 16–7).

4. Symptoms remain after completion of treatment. If this occurs, treat once a day on Table 5 until no further improvement can be expected.

16.4 CHAMBER FIRE SAFETY

The presence of oxygen-enriched environments in hyperbaric chambers requires a knowledge of the fire hazards associated with these environments and strict adherence to safety procedures. Although fires in hyperbaric chambers are rare, they occur with astonishing suddenness and often fatal results (Schmidt et al. 1973).

16.4.1 Ignition

Possible sources of ignition in a hyperbaric environment are:

- Sparks—electrostatic sparks; frictional or impact sparks; sparks or arcs caused by interrupting the flow of electric currents.
- Hot Surfaces—heating by shear rates; heating of wires by electricity; incandescent carbon wear particles from electric motor brushes; friction.
- Hot Gases—gas flames and shock waves; adiabatic compression.

The most probable source of ignition in a hyperbaric chamber is from its electrical system. Electrical systems may be complex as often found in research chambers, or fairly simple as used in the field. Some chambers may have no internal electrical systems at all and thereby possess a very low probability of accidental fire but more often than not one sees internal electrical lighting, blowers, scrubbers, and communication systems. Malfunctions in such systems are often able to supply the heat necessary to ignite flammable materials.

Electric motors, such as the type that may be used in scrubbers or fans pose a potentially more hazardous threat than that of a short-lived spark. Particular concern should be given to a locked or jammed rotor causing a sufficient overheat to start a chamber fire.

**Figure 16-4
Decompression Sickness
Treatment Chart**

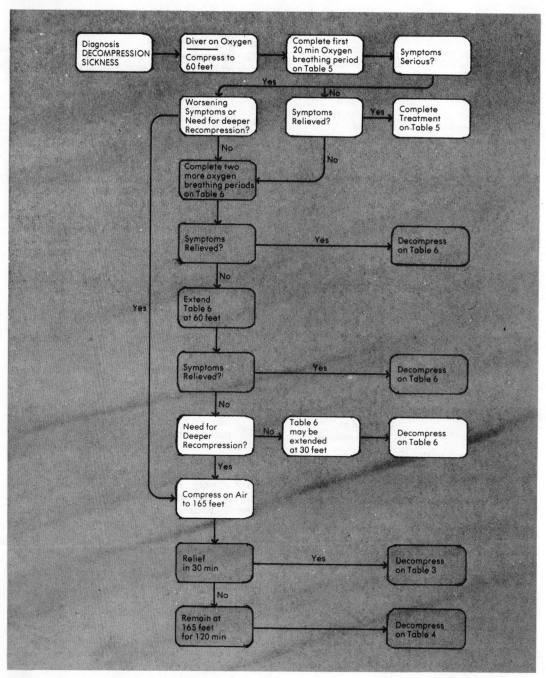

Figure 16-5
Gas Embolism
Treatment Chart

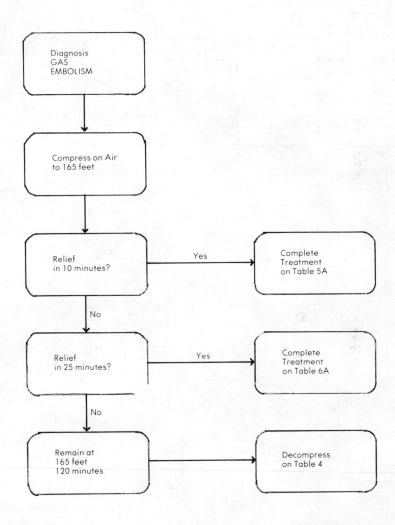

16-13

**Figure 16-6
Recurrence During
Treatment Chart**

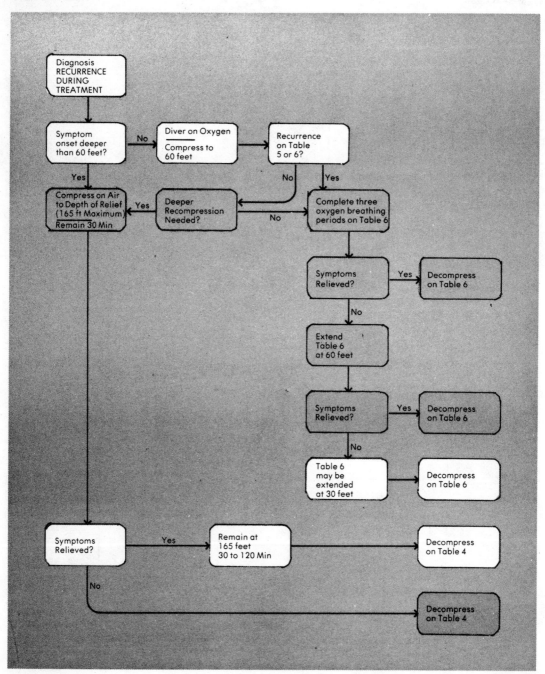

Figure 16-7
Recurrence Following
Treatment Chart

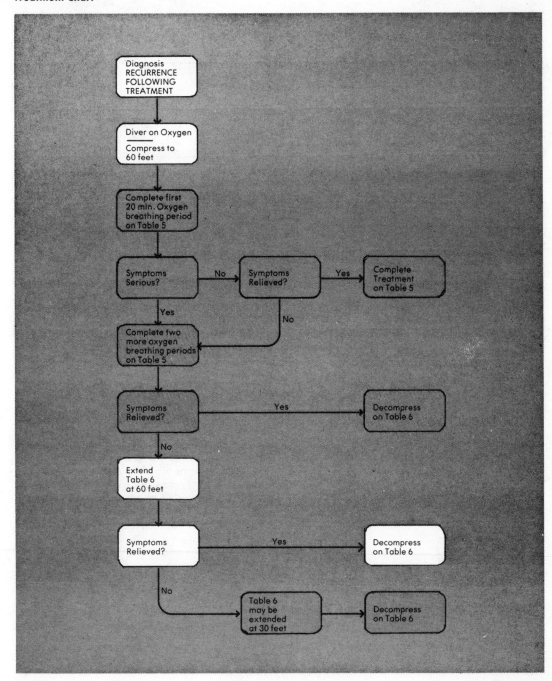

Figure 16-8
Variation With Pressure
of the Ignition Temperature
of Filter Paper Strips
at an Angle of 45 Degrees
in Compressed Air

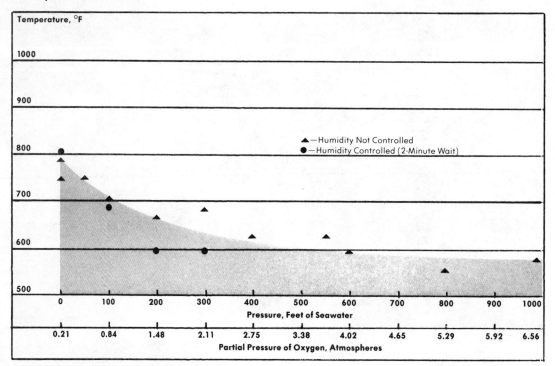

In general, static sparks likely to be generated by personnel can possess sufficient energy to ignite combustible gases and powders in both air and oxygen. These sparks, however, provide a very low probability for ignition of solid materials such as cotton or nylon. Appropriate procedures should be followed, nevertheless, to minimize the likelihood of static spark generation from personnel and equipment. To a large extent generation of electrostatic sparks may be avoided by having as many as possible of the materials electrically conducting and keeping the humidity high.

16.4.2 Combustion

The hazard presented by the possibility of fire in a chamber filled with compressed air increases as the air pressure increases (to about 300 fsw) for two reasons:

a. The higher the pressure, the greater is the ease of ignition of combustible material, and

b. The higher the pressure, the greater (except in the horizontal position) is the rate of combustion.

Figure 16–8 shows that the temperature required to ignite paper in compressed air falls off rapidly as pressure increases, when the paper is at an angle of 45°.

The hazard is greatest when flammable material is so located within the chamber that combustion is propagated vertically. A recent study has revealed a new method of comparing the combustible properties of solid materials by determining their quenching distance (Schmidt et al. 1973).

Although it is more difficult to heat materials to the ignition temperature in a helium environment as opposed to a nitrogen environment (due to the fact that the thermal conductivity of helium is almost six times that of nitrogen), once ignited, flame spread rate is greater in the helium atmosphere as compared to a nitrogen atmosphere.

The risk of fire is not always increased in hyperbaric environments. At high pressures the oxygen percentage in a mixture of oxygen and inert gas is normally reduced in order to reduce the danger of oxygen toxicity.

This decrease in the oxygen percentage may also render the atmosphere incapable of supporting combustion. However, these conditions must be carefully calculated.

16.4.3 Flammability Limits of Hydrogen-Oxygen Mixtures

As experimental diving goes deeper each year, present deep-diving mixtures of helium-oxygen may become too dense for breathing at depths over 2,000 feet. It has, therefore, been suggested that hydrogen be partially or entirely substituted for helium at these pressures, as the density of hydrogen is only about one-half that of helium.

The problem with using hydrogen as a diluent for oxygen is twofold.

1. How to produce the mixture without risk of explosion.

2. How to prevent the possibility of fire or explosion while the diver is in the hydrogen-oxygen environment.

In each case it is essential that the oxygen concentration be kept below a certain critical minimum (the upper flammability limit) necessary for a significant hydrogen-oxygen reaction to occur) It has been determined that the upper flammability limit is 5.3 percent oxygen.

No significant variation has been observed with pressure in the range of 0 to 1,350 feet of sea water. Incorporating a safety factor of 1.5, it appears that a 3.5 percent oxygen- 96.5 percent hydrogen mixture could be used in complete safety providing the proper precautions are taken in preparation of the mixtures and safeguards against leakage to the atmosphere (and ignition sources) are observed. A 3.5 percent oxygen mixture would become respirable at 175 feet of sea water (oxygen partial pressure of 0.21 atmospheres). At the greater depths where hydrogen would most likely be used as a diving gas, the oxygen concentration could be considerably reduced and the safety factor significantly increased.

16.4.4 Materials

When it is impractical to maintain the hyperbaric environment within the region of noncombustion and if all possible sources of ignition within the chamber cannot be precluded with absolute certainty, great care should be exercised in the selection of materials to be placed in the chamber. The results of standard

Table 16-2
Scale of Fire Resistance

Class 0. Burns readily in air at atmospheric pressure.

Class 1. Has an appreciably higher ignition temperature and/or burns at an appreciably lower rate in air at 1 ata pressure than cotton cloth or paper. An example of a Class 1 material is wool.

Class 2. Non-flammable or self-extinguishing in air at 1 ata pressure.

Class 3. Self-extinguishing or burns slowly in air at a pressure of 100 feet of sea water (4.03 ata).

Class 4. Self-extinguishing or burns slowly in air at a pressure of 200 fsw (7.06 ata).

Class 5. Self-extinguishing or burns slowly in a mixture of 25 percent oxygen and 75 percent nitrogen at a pressure of 1 ata.

Class 6. Self-extinguishing or burns slowly in a mixture of 30 percent oxygen and 70 percent nitrogen at a pressure of 1 ata.

Class 7. Self-extinguishing or burns slowly in a mixture of 40 percent oxygen and 60 percent nitrogen at a pressure of 1 ata.

Class 8. Self-extinguishing or burns slowly in a mixture of 50 percent oxygen and 50 percent nitrogen at a pressure of 1 ata.

Class 9. Non-flammable in 100 percent oxygen at a pressure of 1 ata.

flammability tests in the ambient atmosphere are not valid indicators of the burning behavior the same material would exhibit under hyperbaric conditions. Materials have been tested for combustion in air at atmospheric pressure, compressed air and in oxygen-nitrogen mixtures containing increasing amounts of oxygen at a total pressure of 1 atm. abs. The materials were then rated in one of ten classifications shown in Table 16–2 (Schmidt et al. 1973).

Recommendations for material applications in oxygen enriched hyperbaric chambers are given in Table 16–3 where the class numbers correspond to those in Table 16–2.

16.4.5 Fire Detection

Because of the rapidity of fire development in oxygen enriched atmospheres and the consequent extreme hazard to personnel, it is desirable that reliable detection techniques capable of initiating meaningful fire extinguishment or other emergency action be adopted as a mandatory protection requirement. Detectors for this application should provide volume surveillance and permit early and rapid detection of incipient combustion as well as

Table 16-3
Fire Resistant
Materials

Category	Material	Class	Comments
Fabric	Teflon-Coated Beta Fiberglas (4484)	9	Teflon coating increases comfort and durability.
Fabric	Beta Fiberglas (4190B)	9	Completely non-flammable under all conditions; chief disadvantages are possible skin irritation and low abrasion resistance (resulting in poor durability).
Fabric	Teflon	8	Heavy, low moisture regain, lack of wearer comfort.
Fabric	PBI	7	Suitably flame resistant in compressed air; comfortable as clothing and bedding, how,ever, is not commercially available at present.
Fabric	Durette	6	Available (at relatively high cost) and suitable for use in compressed air in terms of flame resistance and comfort. Appears to be the best compromise choice of fabrics at this time.
Elastomer	Fluorel 1071	8	Significantly increases fire safety of breathing masks and hoses.
Paper	Non-Flammable Paper (Dynatech)	9	Writing quality inferior to Scheufelen paper.
Paper	Scheufelen Paper	9	Good choice for all paper articles that are used in chamber.
Electrical Insulation	Kapton	9	Generally unavailable as pre-insulated wire.
Electrical Insulation	Teflon	8	Teflon insulated wire commercially available; wires should always be enclosed in additional mechanical protection and should be protected from overheating.

flame. Table 16–4 indicates the various types of detectors currently available for fire detection (Schmidt et al. 1973). In general, these detectors rely upon either the temperature rise, radiation emission or combustion products with the flame process for activation. Certain of these detectors such as the overheat or rate-of-temperature-rise detectors are not acceptable for oxygen enriched environments because of their inherent slow response time and limited volume coverage. Flame radiation, ultraviolet (UV) and infrared (IR), sensors and smoke detectors in combination appear to be ideally suited for this application.

16.4.6 Fire Extinguishment

Fire extinguishment is accomplished by physical or a combination of physical and chemical actions. These actions involve four basic types of mechanisms.

a. First the combustible material can be cooled to a temperature below that required for ignition or the evolution of flammable vapors.

b. The second mechanism involves smothering the fire by reducing the oxygen or fuel concentration to a level that will not support combustion.

c. A third mechanism involves the separating of fuel from oxidizer by removing one or by mechanically separating the two. This is the major mechanism of mechanical protein foam on jet fuel fires and is often referred to as "blanketing" action.

d. A fourth mechanism involves chemical interference or inhibition of the reactions occurring in the flame front or just before the flame front.

The mode of action and effectiveness of several extinguishing agents is shown in Table 16–5.

Agents such as nitrogen and carbon dioxide depend primarily on the dilution of the oxygen content to a level which will no longer support combustion. Carbon dioxide fire extinguishers can be used in hyperbaric chambers, but independent breathing equipment must be readily available and CO_2

**Table 16-4
Available Test
Chamber Fire
Detection Systems**

Type of System	Specifically Detects Fire or Ignition	Approximate Response Time (Seconds)	Applicability	Volume Coverage
Smoke Detectors Large Particles[1]	No	2-5	No	Yes
Smoke Detectors Small Particles[1]	No	2-5	No	Yes
Infrared Solid State Detectors	Yes[2]	0.1[2]	Yes	Yes
Thermocouples	No	.05	No	No
Continuous Element Overheat Detectors	No	5	No	No
Eutectic Alloy Type	No	5	No	No
Ultraviolet Detectors	Yes	0.010	Yes	Yes

[1]Excellent for incipient fire detection. May detect visible fog also, as during decompression.
[2]Specificity, fast response, and sensitivity are not available in one system.

scrubbers must not be allowed to overheat. In an attempt to replace carbon dioxide as a gaseous fire quenching agent, both nitrogen and helium have been considered and tested. It appears that neither of these inert gases is of value (except by the rapid dilution method in which the entire chamber atmosphere is rapidly diluted), as it is not possible to maintain a significant concentration of the gas in a given location. Due to their narcotic properties, more research is needed before the gases of heavier molecular weight can be considered for such use under pressure.

Although dry chemical agents should provide rapid suppression of flame and excellent radiation shielding when initially discharged, the permanency of the fire extinguishment is doubtful.

Although monobromotrifluromethane (CBrF$_3$, "Freon" 1301) and chlorobromomethane ("Freon" 1011) have been shown to be effective extinguishing agents, a delayed application of the extinguishing agent could produce toxic pyrolysis products if the fire had a head start.

High expansion foam has been shown to be an effective means of extinguishing fires that have been allowed to build up to their full intensity, but there is presently little knowledge as to the physiological safety of such agents due to pyrolysis products or otherwise.

At the present "state of the art", due to safety considerations, *the best extinguishing agent for use in hyperbaric chambers is water.* Water extinguishment operates primarily by cooling. It works best if it strikes the flame or wets the fire, but wetting most substances will retard to prevent their burning, even in oxygen. In spray form, although the fire may not be immediately put out, spread is halted and from this point on extinguishment is almost certain. The spray can be continued indefinitely, assuring safety of chamber occupants. Water at a spray density of 5 milliliters per sq cm per minute (1¼ gallons per sq ft per minute), applied for two minutes is required to extinguish cloth burning in 100 percent oxygen at atmospheric pressure. Water spray systems require special design for hyperbaric chamber applications. The pressure at the spray nozzles must be about 50 psi above chamber pressure to produce the desired degree of atomization and droplet velocities. Spray pattern of nozzles might be affected by chamber pressures. To compensate for the reduced coverage at elevated pressures, the design of the system must provide an adequate number of nozzles, and they must be strategically located, to wet all possible exposed areas within the chamber no matter what the chamber pressure may be. Pressurization is best obtained from a compressed gas source, since pumps have a startup time. Simultaneously with discharge of the water, all electrical power to the chamber should be discontinued to pre-

Table 16-5
Fire Extinguishing
Agents for Oxygen
Enriched Atmospheres

Agent	Mode of Action	Compatibility Personnel	O_2—Fires
Water	1, 2, 5	Excellent	Good
Foam	1, 3, 5	Good	Unknown
Dry Chemical ($NaHCO_3$)	3, 4, 5	Good	Unknown
CO_2	1, 2	Fair	Poor
N_2	2	Poor (Anoxia)	Poor
Freon	1, 2, 4	Good[1]	Very Good

Mode of Action
1—Quenching (Cooling).
2—Inerting (O_2—Dilution).
3—Blanketing.
4—Chemical Inhibition.
5—Radiation Shielding.

[1]May decompose in heat to yield toxic products.

vent shorting and electrical shocks to personnel within the chamber.

A manually-directable fire hose might permit occupants of a chamber to control localized small or incipient fires, and because its use would be less catastrophic than activation of a deluge system it might be used more quickly and with less damage to chamber apparatus.

It is imperative that water deluge systems be thoroughly tested at all applicable operating pressures and conditions. Numerous installations have been disappointing when given realistic tests, and redesign has been necessary.

16.4.7 General Safety Procedures

1. Maintain oxygen concentration and/or partial pressure as low as possible, preferably within the region of non-combustion. Use an overboard dump system where pure oxygen is breathed by mask in a chamber.

2. Eliminate ignition sources.

3. Minimize combustibles, with the complete exclusion of flammable liquids and gases.

4. If combustible materials must be employed, the type, quantity and arrangement in the chamber must be carefully controlled.

5. Fire walls and other containment techniques should be utilized to isolate potential high risk fire zones.

6. A fixed fire extinguishing system should be utilized which incorporates automatic initiation by flame and smoke detectors as well as manual initiation and provides rapid and sufficient agent discharge.

FIRST AID 17

17.0 GENERAL

First aid is the immediate, temporary assistance provided a victim of injury or illness before the services of a qualified physician can be obtained. Its purpose is to save a victim's life and to prevent further injury or a worsening of his condition. When an accident occurs, a knowledge of the proper response can mean the difference between life and death, temporary or permanent disability, or short- or long-term hospitalization. All individuals associated with diving should have a thorough understanding of the basics of first aid. When an injury occurs an immediate, correct response is required. It is *not* the time to be looking for a book that tells you what to do. A matter of seconds can mean the difference between life and death.

This section is not intended to serve as a definitive treatise on first aid, but rather as a general guide to the handling of diver related accidents. The reader is referred to the Standard First Aid and Personal Safety Manual of the American Red Cross 1973.

17.1 INTRODUCTION TO FIRST AID PROCEDURES

In administering first aid, it is essential to maintain critical vital functions these are: stopping bleeding, determining cardiac status or femoral pulse, and assuring an adequate airway. All three may have to be dealt with simultaneously. *Copious bleeding* is the first and most important problem to contend with. Bleeding must be terminated quickly as a human can bleed to death in as little as 3 to 5 minutes. An accident victim will be able to survive longer without breathing or heart beat than if his blood is allowed to be pumped from his body. If the victim is *not breathing*, mouth-to-mouth resuscitation must begin (See Paragraph 17.1.3 and Figure 17–1). Closed chest cardiac massage should

be administered also for cardiac arrest (See Paragraph 17.1.2). Also, all serious injuries will be accompanied by *shock*. This complication can be as serious as the actual injury and must be dealt with quickly. These three factors always require prompt action and are most important in saving a victim's life.

An unconscious diver should always be presumed to have an embolism unless another cause of the unconsciousness can be established quickly (within a few minutes). If an embolism is suspected, the first action is to get the victim into a recompression chamber and under a pressure equivalent to 165 feet as quickly as possible. First aid for other injuries can be administered while proceeding to, or while in the chamber.

Another important factor in administering first aid and one often overlooked is the attitude of the person administering the aid. He should work to inspire the victim's confidence by presenting a panic-free appearance. In serious injuries, telling a victim the extent of his injuries should be avoided. Instead, try to assure him that he will be all right. Knowledge of the actual extent of injuries could cause unnecessary excitement and panic causing complications of the injury and deepening of shock.

17.1.1 Bleeding

In diving, the causes of bleeding are numerous, and in some cases may be an indication of other, more serious injuries.

Bleeding from the mouth, nose and ears is a good indication of some form of pressure related accident. If the diver is unconscious with non-frothy blood coming from his mouth, he probably bit his tongue during the convulsions which accompany oxygen toxicity. Should the diver be unconscious and passing frothy blood from the mouth, it is probably an air (gas) embolism, and should be treated as such. A conscious diver in good condition passing nonfrothy blood from the nose and possibly the mouth is probably suffering from a middle ear squeeze or a bloody nose. Nose bleeds are frequently caused by a sinus squeeze, or too vigorous an attempt to clear the ears during ascent. Bleeding from the ear is usually the result of a ruptured eardrum.

Treatment

Medical aid should be obtained if serious injuries are suspected, or if the bleeding cannot be stopped.

Divers, working around coral, rocks, and wrecks, are especially susceptible to injuries which could result in bleeding. Many marine animals are capable of inflicting severe wounds on the unwary diver (See Section 15). Bleeding from these wounds can be broken down into two general types.

17.1.1.1 Arterial Bleeding

Arterial bleeding is a rupture of the blood vessels which carry blood from the heart to the tissues. These wounds are characterized by bright red blood shooting from the wound in spurts caused by the pumping of the heart.

17.1.1.2 Venous Bleeding

Venous bleeding is the result of a rupture of the blood vessels which return the blood to the heart. These wounds are characterized by dark red blood which exits the wound in a steady flow.

Injuries which occur under water will present a somewhat different appearance. The injury itself may not be felt when it occurs. There will be no spurting in arterial bleeding as the blood will diffuse into the water in a cloud, similar to smoke. The color itself will be significantly different, usually green rather than red (See Paragraph 1.8.1).

Treatment

Minor wounds will not require any immediate treatment and in many cases the diver will be able to continue the dive. Frequently the diver will not even know he has injured himself until after the dive. If it is difficult to stop bleeding and the injury hinders the diver, the dive should be terminated, especially if there are sharks in the area and blood has entered the water. Bleeding can normally be stopped by the application of direct pressure. To prevent infection, the wound should be thoroughly washed with soap and warm water, and then covered with a sterile dressing. If it is

deep, open, or has a large flap of loose skin, a doctor should be consulted.

It is possible, that a diver could suffer a serious injury under water. The first action is to remove the diver from the water before the loss of blood is too severe and or shock sets in. While removing the victim from the water, an attempt should be made to stop the bleeding. The human body contains approximately 6 quarts of blood, and the loss of only 1.5 quarts can have serious and possibly fatal consequences.

The first step in stopping severe hemorrhaging is to apply direct pressure on the wound. This can be done using the hand, finger, a sterile dressing, etc. The most sterile material available should be used, although time should not be wasted looking for something completely sterile. The victim should be lying down, with the injured area elevated higher than the heart unless a broken bone is involved. The victim can be given liquids (coffee, tea, water) if he is conscious and can swallow; however, no alcoholic beverages are allowed. If the victim is unconscious or suffering from an abdominal wound no liquids are permitted.

The tourniquet is a constricting band used to stop the flow of serious bleeding. A traumatic amputation, crushed limb, or uncontrollable bleeding are the only cases in which it should be used or cases where direct pressure fails to stop bleeding. In this case a wide belt or strong piece of cloth should be tied around the limb above the wound, using an overhand knot. A short stick is tied to the band at the overhand knot, and the tourniquet is tightened by rotating the stick. The tourniquet should be only as tight as necessary to stop the bleeding. Once in place, the tourniquet should be loosened only on the advice of a qualified physician.

17.1.2 Heart Failure (Cardiac Arrest)

Respiratory accidents, shock or electrocution can sometimes cause the heart to stop beating. When this occurs, the circulation of blood ceases, and oxygen is no longer provided to the body. In the brain, permanent damage can result in less than 3 minutes.

Signs

Unconsciousness
Cessation of breathing
No pulse
Blueness (cyanosis).

Treatment

Often the heart can be restarted by the use of closed-chest cardiac massage. This treatment substitutes for the action of the heart muscles, actually pumping blood through the body until the heart takes over. Normally artificial respiration will be required simultaneously with cardiac massage.

This treatment should be continued until the victim is pronounced dead by a qualified physician.

When administering closed-chest cardiac massage the following procedures should be used:

1. Lay the victim on his back in an outstretched position, on a hard surface with his head back to maintain a clear airway.

2. Kneel at a right angle to the victim, on either side of the chest, and locate the upper and lower end of the breastbone.

3. With the heel of the hand or the fist, strike the area over the heart from a distance not exceeding 6 inches above the sternum.

NOTE: Artificial respiration will be required simultaneously with the heart massage. When possible, this should be administered by a second individual. If another individual is not available, proceed as in Paragraph 4, following. When another individual is available, proceed as in Paragraph 5.

4. *Treatment by one person.* After striking the heart as described in Paragraph 3 above, give the victim four rapid mouth-to-mouth ventilations. Then, with the heel of one hand on the lower third of the breastbone and the other hand directly on top of that hand, press vertically downward, using some body weight, until the breastbone depresses about 1½ inches. Then release the pressure by lifting the hands. Apply this downward pressure 15 times at the rate of one pressure per second. Then ventilate the victim twice. Repeat this 15 pressures, two ventilations, rate until heart action returns, or the victim is pronounced dead by a physician.

5. *Treatment by two people.* Strike the heart as described in Paragraph 3 above. Then, with the heel of one hand on the lower third of the breastbone and the other hand directly on top, press vertically downward, using some body weight, until the breastbone depresses about 1½ inches. Then release the pressure by lifting the hands. Pressure should be applied with the heel of one hand only. Apply this pressure at the rate of one pressure per second. Simultaneously, a second individual should apply mouth-to-mouth artificial respiration at the rate of one ventilation for each five pressure applications to the heart, without pause in the pressures.

6. Check for a return action every 3 minutes. Evidence will include return of pulse, constriction of pupils, and respiration.

7. Once the victim has recovered he must see a physician, regardless of how complete the recovery may appear. Complications may have set in, resulting in permanent damage.

17.1.3 Respiration and Drowning

Drowning is one of the major causes of diving fatalities. It is usually the result of axphyxia caused by removal of the air supply. Many drownings occur as a result of panic when a diver loses his regulator or mask, becomes tangled, fouled, or fatigued from swimming on the surface. The term drowning indicates that a victim is recovered from the water unconscious, and not breathing. In many cases it can be immediately determined by the circumstances that the individual is not suffering from an air embolism, but if there is any doubt, he should be treated as if suffering from an embolism (See Paragraph 17.4.1).

It should be mentioned that the possibility of a drowning accident can be greatly reduced by proper dive planning, by using only adequate, well-maintained equipment, and by following only authorized, proven diving procedures. By keeping himself physically and mentally fit, and by maintaining his diving proficiency, the diver can also significantly reduce the probability of drowning should an accident or incident occur.

Signs

Unconsciousness
Cyanosis
Cessation of breathing.

Treatment

The only treatment for victims of drowning is immediate artificial respiration. Time is of the essence, as in most cases the victim will already have been without air for a period of minutes, and any exposure to a lack of air for over 3 minutes may result in permanent brain damage. Mouth-to-mouth artificial respiration is the most efficient means of manually circulating air into the victim's lungs. This method may also be used in the water, while transporting the victim to the beach or boat. In this case it will be necessary to turn the victim's

Figure 17-1
Mouth-to-Mouth
Resuscitation

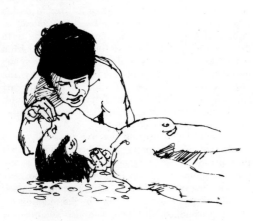

head to the side for access to his mouth. The proper steps for administering mouth-to-mouth respiration are outlined below (See Figure 17–1).

(1) Lay the victim on his back, and loosen any clothing that may have a restricting effect on his chest (wet suit, etc.).

(2) Lift the neck so that the victim's head is tilted back, thus opening the air passage. Check the throat for any obstruction (tongue, false teeth, etc.) and remove same. It may be necessary to hold the victim's tongue out of his throat with the thumb of the hand holding his mouth open.

(3) Open the victim's mouth, pulling the jaw upward toward the chest. Pinch off the nose with the other hand to prevent air leakage.

(4) Place your mouth over the mouth of the victim (mouth and nose of a small child or infant), creating a seal. Blow into the victim until his chest rises. If air cannot be forced into the victim, his throat is still blocked and must be cleared prior to continuing. After exhaling into the victim, remove your mouth and let the air pass out of the victim's lungs. Continue this cycle at a rate of 10–12 times per minute for adults and approximately 20 times per minute for children. If the jaw is damaged or hopelessly blocked, resuscitation can be performed by sealing the victim's mouth and exhaling into the victim through his nose.

A victim of drowning should also be examined for a heartbeat. If the victim's heart has stopped, closed-chest cardiac massages should be administered simultaneously with artificial respiration.

17.1.3.1 Emergency Tracheotomy

In cases when a victim is dying of asphyxia and artificial respiration cannot be administered because of damage to the jaw or face or blockage of the windpipe, it may be necessary to perform a tracheotomy.

WARNING

This Operation Must Be Performed Only Ordinarily in an Emergency and Only by a Qualified Physician.

The proper steps in performing an emergency tracheotomy are outlined below:

1. Place the victim's shoulders on a rolled towel or blanket, so the head is tilted sharply back. The skin will then be pulled tightly over the trachea.

2. Make a vertical incision along the centerline of the neck from the bottom of the Adam's apple to

just above the suprasternal notch (can be felt approximately 1 inch below the Adam's apple), only as deep as the cartilage.

3. The windpipe or trachea will be directly below a layer of muscle. It is of a corrugated appearance, and lies directly in the midline. If it is not visible it may be felt.

4. Make an incision through the trachea (splitting its midline) large enough to pass a hollow tube when the walls are retracted.

NOTE: This is a very dangerous procedure for an untrained person.

17.2 INJURIES AND INFECTIONS

17.2.1 Burns

Burns are classified into three general categories according to severity. The least serious is the first degree burn, which is a reddening of the skin. With second degree burns, the skin will be blistered. The most serious is the third degree burn, in which the tissue is charred beyond repair. Burns can result from either heat or chemical action.

Treatment

The treatment that can be administered to a burn victim by other than a trained doctor is extremely limited. The burned area itself should be covered with a sterile dressing to exclude air. The victim may be given aspirin in minor burn cases to reduce the pain. To assist in replacing body fluids lost, the victim may be given liquids (except alcohol). All burns of more than a minor nature may be accompanied by shock, and the victim must be observed carefully. For all burns except minor reddening, the victim should be examined by a doctor. Burn ointment, grease, baking soda, or other substances must never be applied to serious burns.

17.2.1.1 Sunburn

Sunburn is common to anyone who spends a great deal of time near the water. Avoiding prolonged, direct exposure to sunlight and wearing protective clothing is the best prevention. One of the most affected areas, and painful when burnt is the bridge of the nose. A covering of protective ointment helps prevent burning. Some of the most severe sunburns can be received on cloudy days when the sun is not visible and the individual may

inadvertently permit excessive exposure. Sunburns can be painful, and can result in skin damage to a degree where the individual can no longer perform useful work.

Symptoms

Prickly sensation on back or neck
Pain and tenderness to the touch
Fever.

Signs

Extreme redness
Fever blisters
A tendency to avoid contact with affected area.

Treatment

A variety of sunburn ointments are commercially available which provide partial relief. If no special ointment is available, bandages soaked in tannic acid, boric acid, or vinegar will suffice. The victim should avoid further exposure until the condition has passed. Do not pop blisters or peel the flaky skin which accompanies sunburn or raw sore areas may result.

17.2.2 Fractures

It is unusual for a diver to suffer a fracture while diving. The high density of water (compared to air) generally serves to slow motion and cushion blows so that a broken bone does not result. Diving-related fractures usually occur on the surface. If a diver suffers a fracture while submerged he should immediately terminate the dive.

Fractures can be classed into two general types. A closed fracture consists of a broken bone which has not penetrated the skin. In an open fracture, the broken bone is accompanied by an open wound, frequently with the bone sticking out. This type of wound is complicated by the chance of infection setting into the open wound.

Signs

Limb bent at unusual angle
Swelling in area of fracture
Area of fracture painful and tender
Inability to move the affected limb
In case of compound fracture, bone sticking out through wound.

Treatment

The only first aid required for closed fractures is to splint the affected limb. The limb should be immobilized with a splint. Flat pieces of wood, plastic, metal or any firm substance can be used. Inflatable splints are excellent. The splint serves to prevent movement and consequent complication of the injury. To prevent movement, the splint should be bound to the limb at a minimum of three places, at the wound, and above and below the fracture near the ends of the splint.

When treating an open fracture do not try to move the limb to its natural position. Splint it to prevent movement, and cover the open wound with a sterile dressing. In open fractures, shock will probably be present and its symptoms must be anticipated.

Regardless of the type of fracture, do not try to set the bone yourself. Let this be done by qualified medical personnel.

17.2.3 Wounds

The diver is subject to a wide variety of wounds. The majority, such as coral wounds, wounds from sharp edges, or wrecks, etc., will be of a minor nature and require a minimum of first aid. However, there is always the chance of massive injuries such as might be incurred from a shark attack, barracuda or moray eel bite, or by being struck by a boat propeller. In the latter case, prompt, proper response is necessary to stop bleeding and prevent shock.

17.2.3.1 Minor Wounds

Treatment for minor wounds consists of stopping the bleeding and cleaning the wound.

Bleeding can be quickly stemmed by direct pressure, using either the hand, a pressure bandage or a combination of both (See Paragraph 17.1.1).

If the wound is minor enough not to require medical attention, it should be thoroughly cleaned using fresh water and soap. If medical attention is required, such as minor stitches, the wound should be cleaned and covered with a sterile dressing, but no antiseptic applied.

17.2.3.2 Serious Wounds

The major immediate concern with a major wound is to stop the bleeding and prevent the onset of shock.

In case of serious wounds without amputation, control bleeding with a pressure dressing. In case of serious wounds with amputation, apply a tourni-

quet. Note the time the tourniquet was applied. Should a large chunk of flesh be missing, such as in a shark bite, it will be necessary to put a bandage or dressing directly in the wound. This will absorb blood and speed up coagulation. This bandage should be held tightly in place with another bandage placed directly over it. These steps should be effective in stopping the flow of blood. Once the bleeding is terminated, the victim must be treated for shock. Keep him calm, and lying down. If conscious and able to swallow, liquids can be administered (coffee, tea, water—never alcoholic beverages). Never attempt to give an unconscious victim liquids. Application of antiseptics, ointments, etc., are useless in major wounds and will slow the doctor's treatment as he may have to remove them before treatment. Qualified medical aid must be obtained in the quickest possible manner.

17.2.4 Dermatitis

Divers who are continually exposed to salt water, especially in tropical climates and with no fresh water showers available, are subject to dermatitis (or skin disorders). If not properly cared for, it can spread over the entire body, incapacitating the individual. Small sore spots are bothersome and painful, and can be extremely hard to clear up, even with medication, if exposure to the conditions which caused them continues.

Symptoms

Red rashes
Welts
Severe itching without visible cause
Burning sensation while sweating.

Signs

Inflammation of affected area, blotchy complexion, welts
Skin splitting or peeling
Rashes
Secretion of fluids.

Treatment

The best treatment is removal of the source of irritation. After each exposure the area should be washed with fresh water to remove salt, and thoroughly dried. Avoid wearing wet clothing, wet suits, etc., immediately after use, and if possible rinse diving gear off with fresh water. All affected areas should be cleaned, dried, and sprinkled with an antiseptic powder. Avoid scratching, rubbing or wearing clothing which irritates the affected area. Serious cases may require the temporary termination of the individual's diving or transportation to a more healthy, sanitary environment.

17.2.5 Ear Infection

When operating in some tropical waters, divers are susceptible to various forms of ear infection or fungus. While this does not present any immediate danger it can be extremely painful and may cause hearing loss if ignored.

Otitis externa is probably the leading cause of diver morbidity in saturation diving (Thalmann 1974). Because of high humidity or repeated immersion, the severity of the disease increases rapidly once symptoms develop. The ears can become so painful that the use of masks and even regulators is all but precluded.

Symptoms

Itching or pain in ear
Crusting or scabbing of ear canal
Excretion of fluid from ear canal.

Signs

Accumulation of fungus growth
Fungus flakes at ear opening
Redness or swelling around ear.

Treatment

The best treatment for ear infection is prevention. The ears should be kept clean and dry, if possible. A common hair dryer is helpful. In addition, a good prophylactic program is highly desirable. A recent study (Thalmann 1974) recommends the following procedure:

Irrigate each ear canal separately for 5 minutes with a 2 percent acetic acid in aluminum acetate solution (Domeboro Solution, Dome Laboratories) following each dive.

Dry the outer ear canal with a towel after the solution has run out of the ear.

To ensure the best results, this procedure should be carried out in a regimented manner after all dives, especially when under saturated conditions or in other situations where humidity is chronically high.

The use of cotton swabs is not recommended, as they tend to irritate the ear canal and may perforate the drum. If an infection is contracted,

consult a doctor for treatment.

17.2.6 Ruptured Eardrum

Occasionally a diver will suffer from a ruptured eardrum. The cause of the rupture will be a pressure differential between the middle and outer ear. This can result from "chasing an object to the bottom," trying to descend (or rise) while not being able to clear the ears, or any situation where there is a rapid pressure change.

Symptoms

Severe pain on descent (or ascent) as rupture occurs
Dizziness or nausea as water enters the middle ear
Temporary disorientation
Loss of hearing in affected ear
Ringing in the ear (tinnitus).

Signs

Bleeding from ear
Redness and swelling of eardrum.

Treatment

No immediate treatment is necessary except a discontinuation of diving. See a doctor as soon as possible to prevent possible infection. The eardrum will heal in two to three weeks, and until it is healed, no diving should be attempted.

17.2.7 Electrocution

Electrocution is generally the result of the careless handling of power equipment such as welding and cutting equipment, electric underwater lights, etc. All electrical equipment used under water should be well insulated. In addition the diver should take steps to insulate himself from any possible source of electrical current.

When leaving the water to enter a boat or habitat, do not carry a connected light or electric tool.

Signs

Unconsciousness
Cessation of breathing
Heart failure
Victim may not have been able to separate himself from the source of the shock.

Treatment

The first step in treatment is to secure the source of the shock. This is as much to protect the rescuer as to aid the victim. The victim must then be treated for heart failure (See Paragraph 17.1.2) and administered artificial respiration (See Paragraph 17.1.3). Regardless of how complete a recovery may seem, the victim should be examined by a physician as soon as possible.

17.2.8 Squeeze

When the diver is unable to equalize the pressure differential experienced during ascent or descent, the result can be a squeeze. While the most commonly affected area is the ears, squeezes can occur in the sinuses, face, lung, and suit.

17.2.8.1 Ear Squeeze (Aerotitis Media)

The most frequent cause of an ear squeeze is diving with a cold. The resultant congestion blocks the eustachian tube leading to the throat, and prevents equalization of the pressure in the middle ear. The resulting increase (or decrease, as this can occur on ascent as well as descent) exerts pressure on the eardrum and membrane lining the middle ear, and unless equalized, can result in tissue damage and distortion or, in severe cases, a ruptured eardrum. This injury can also be the result of a failure to clear the ears during a continuous pressure change.

Symptoms

Pain in ear during descent (ascent)
Sudden relief of pain if eardrum ruptures or middle ear equalizes.

Signs

Redness and swelling of the eardrum
Bleeding into external ear.

Treatment

Avoid further exposure to pressure until ear has healed. The ear should be examined by a doctor to assess damage and prevent infection.

17.2.8.2 Sinus Squeeze (Aerosinusitis)

The sinus cavities are air pockets located within the skull bones, with openings into the nasal passage (Figure 2–7). These cavities are lined with a mucous membrane. As with the ear squeeze, sinus squeeze is normally the result of diving with a cold or head congestion. The inability to equalize pressure exerts excessive negative pressure on the mucous membrane, resulting in tissue damage.

Symptoms

Severe sharp pain in sinus area (above, below, between or behind eyes)
Sudden relief from pain as sinus clears
Gradual relief of pain if pressure remains constant.

Signs

Bloody mucous discharge from nose or mouth, or blood in face mask
Tenderness in area of sinus.

Treatment

In minor cases no treatment is required. In severe cases, discontinue diving until injuries heal and sinuses have cleared. In some cases, infection may complicate the injury and a qualified doctor should be consulted.

17.2.8.3 Lung Squeeze (Thoracic Squeeze)

Thoracic squeeze is a hazard primarily to the breath-holding diver. It results when the ambient pressure rises with no corresponding induction of air into the lungs. Tissue damage can result when the size of the lungs has been reduced below that of the tidal volume.

Signs and Symptoms

Feeling of chest compression during descent
Pain in the chest
Possible difficulty in breathing upon return to the surface.

Treatment

In severe cases the diver will require assistance to the surface. Place the diver face down and clear the blood from his mouth. If breathing has ceased, administer artificial respiration, or oxygen if available. Be alert for the symptoms of shock and treat for such if necessary. The services of a doctor should be obtained as quickly as possible.

17.2.8.4 Face Mask Squeeze

This is generally the result of a failure to admit air into the face mask during descent. It can also result, when using a surface-supplied mask without a nonreturn valve, and surface air pressure is lost. The resultant pressure differential between the air pocket in the rigid mask and the flexible tissues of the face can result in serious tissue damage. The tenderest tissues are those covering and around the eyeball and the lining of the eyelids. In serious cases, damage to the optic nerve and blindness may result. This type of squeeze is unnecessary and can be avoided by exhaling into the mask during descent.

Symptoms

Sensation of suctions applied to face, or mask being forced into face

Pain or a squeezing sensation.

Signs

Face swollen and bruised

Whites of eyes bright red

Protrusion of eyeballs, with bleeding in eyeball, behind it and behind eyelid.

Treatment

Apply cold ice packs to the damaged tissues, and administer pain relievers if required. In serious cases obtain the services of a doctor.

17.2.9 Unconscious Diver

When a diver is retrieved from the water while unconscious, or collapses soon after, he should be treated for gas embolism unless the cause of unconsciousness is clearly indicated (See Paragraph 17.4). If he is not breathing, artificial respiration should be started at once. When available, a mechanical resuscitator should be substituted for manual artificial respiration. Continue artificial respiration until the victim recovers or is pronounced dead by a physician.

Prompt recompression is necessary under all but the following cases:

1. Victim regains consciousness and is free of symptoms before recompression starts

2. The possibility of gas embolism or decompression sickness can be completely ruled out

3. Another lifesaving measure is absolutely necessary which makes recompression impossible.

17.2.10 Seasickness (Motion Sickness)

Seasickness can be a distinct hazard to a diver when using small craft as surface support platforms. Diving should not be attempted when suffering seriously from this condition. The effects of vomiting while submerged can be strangulation and death.

Symptoms

Dizziness

Wooziness

Thick dry tongue

Nausea.

Signs

Pallid or sickly green complexion

Slurred speech

Vomiting.

Treatment

A number of motion sickness remedies are commercially available which may help in alleviating the symptoms. However many of these contain antihistamines which tend to make the diver too drowsy or careless to dive. A combination of phenergan, dexedrine, and scopolamine has been found to be effective and can be obtained by prescription. Fresh air and a strong mental attitude against getting sick are frequently the best medicine.

17.3 POISONING

17.3.1 Contact Poisoning

17.3.1.1 Punctures

The diver is subjected to a variety of marine life which can inflict poisonous wounds if handled carelessly. Some of the most frequently encountered are the stingray, cone shell, and a variety of rock and sand fish including the sculpin. For more detailed information on identification of poisonous marine animals see Paragraph 15.2. Wounds from these animals can be equally as toxic as a poisonous snake bite.

Symptoms

Local pain developing within 4 to 10 minutes

Fainting and weakness

An increase in the level of pain, to a maximum in 90 minutes.

Signs

Puncture wound

Local swelling and inflammation

In stingray wounds, the sheath may be left in the wound, and in cone shell stings the tiny barb may remain.

Treatment

Because fainting is common, the victim should

be removed from the water as soon as possible. The wound should be washed with a sterile saline solution if available. If not available, use cold fresh water. The sting or puncture of the ray deposits the only known alkaline poison which is contained in the sheath around the barb. It alone should be treated with a weak acidic solution such as vinegar. If the wound is a small puncture, make a small incision at the site of the wound, encourage bleeding and apply suction if the latter can be done with a suction device and not the mouth. Any foreign matter should be flushed from the wound. The wound should then be soaked in water as hot as the victim can stand for a period of at least 30 minutes, as this may neutralize the venom. Once the pain has subsided, cover and elevate the wound. Be alert for symptoms of shock. Qualified medical assistance should be obtained as soon as possible.

17.3.1.2 Stings

In addition to those animals which can poison by punctures, a variety of marine creatures are capable of stinging. These include jellyfish, stinging coral, and sea anemones. Some of these injuries are minor, will provide only temporary inconvenience and possibly a reddening of the affected area. Others, such as the Portuguese man-of-war and sea wasp are considerably more dangerous and will require immediate first aid.

Signs and Symptoms

(Will vary dependent on species and extent of sting)

(1) Range from a mild prickly sensation to an intense throbbing, shooting pain which can result in unconsciousness

(2) Reddening of the area (welts, blisters, swelling)

(3) Cramps

(4) Nausea

(5) Vomiting

(6) Numbness

(7) Backache

(8) Loss of speech

(9) Frothing at the mouth

(10) Constriction of the throat

(11) Respiratory difficulty

(12) Paralysis

(13) Delirium

(14) Convulsions

(15) Shock

(16) Pieces of tentacle may remain on affected area.

Treatment

The diver should be removed from the water as quickly as possible. The tentacles and stinging fluid should be removed, taking care not to come into contact with them yourself. Apply a weak ammonia or saturated baking soda solution if available, for a period of 2 to 3 minutes.

The best detoxification is meat tenderizer which denatures the poisonous protein. Thoroughly clean the wound using an antibacterial soap, dry or apply cortisone, antihistamine cream or special anesthetic ointment. If not available olive oil, sugar or ethyl alcohol can be substituted. Keep the victim lying down with feet elevated. Administer artificial respiration if required. The victim of serious cases should be examined by a doctor. A special sea sting kit is available commercially.

17.3.1.3 Bites

The most serious poisonous bite is that of the sea snake. These reptiles are closely allied to the cobra, and have a highly toxic venom. The octopus also has a venom, one species of which (blue ring of Australia) can be fatal; however the octopus' shy nature makes a bite unlikely unless the diver is extremely careless. A sea snake bite is usually small and may not even be noticed, and delay of over one hour is common before the reaction sets in.

Symptoms

General ill feeling, anxiety and possibly a feeling of well-being

Sensation of thickening of the tongue

General muscular stiffness

Aching or pain on movement

Weakness, progressing to an inability to move in 1 to 2 hours, beginning in the legs

Droopy eyelids

Tightening of jaw muscles, similar to tetanus

Thirst, burning dryness of throat

Shock.

Signs

Fang marks (two small punctures approximately $\frac{1}{2}$ inch apart) and possibly a fang left in the wound.

Treatment

The victim must remain quiet. If bitten on the arm or leg, a constricting bandage should be placed above the wound, but not tight enough to interrupt arterial flow. The victim should be transported immediately to the nearest medical facility for the antivenom treatments necessary to combat the poison. If possible capture or kill the snake for identification purposes.

17.3.1.4 Coral Wounds

Coral is common to most tropical waters. These tiny animals leave behind a hard, calcium-like skeleton, which is frequently razor sharp and capable of inflicting deep, painful wounds. These wounds tend to be slow in healing, easily infected, and itchy. Some coral have stinging cells similar to those in a jellyfish and produce a sting which rapidly disappears, but may leave itchy welts and reddening.

Signs

Lingering, infected wound
Itchy, red, swollen area or wound.

Treatment

Stinging coral wounds are best treated with meat tenderizer to denature the protein. Soap and water is very useful since live coral is covered with copious bacterial growth. Wash the area with a baking soda or weak ammonia solution, followed by a soap and fresh water wash. When available, use a cortisone ointment or antihistamine cream and take antihistamine orally to reduce the pain and reaction. Once the pain begins to subside, wash the wound with soap and water to remove all foreign matter. An antiseptic should then be used, and the wound covered with a sterile dressing to prevent infection.

17.3.1.5 Sea Urchins

Any diver who has worked in tropical areas is familiar with the sea urchin. The spines, being very brittle, break off at the slightest touch.

Symptoms

Immediate sharp, burning pain
Redness and swelling.

Signs

Spines sticking out of skin or black dots where they have broken off
Purpling of skin around where spines entered
Redness and swelling in affected area.

Treatment

Remove those spines which can be grasped with tweezers. Spines which have broken off flush with the skin are nearly impossible to remove, and probing around with a needle will only succeed in breaking the spines into little pieces. Most of the spines will be dissolved by the body within a week. Others may fester and can then be popped out to the point where they can be removed with tweezers. Some forms have small venomous pinchers which should be removed, and the wound should then be treated as a poisonous sting (See Paragraph 17.3.1.2).

17.3.2 Gaseous Poisoning

17.3.2.1 Carbon Dioxide Poisoning (CO$_2$)

This condition is the result of an excess of CO$_2$ in the breathing gas. It may be caused by a faulty rebreather or a buildup of carbon dioxide in the mask or helmet. Controlled breathing (skip-breathing) while using scuba equipment, is a frequent cause of a number of fatalities. CO$_2$ poisoning usually comes on so fast that the period of rapid breathing goes to unconsciousness in seconds.

Symptoms

Sometimes none
Usually accompanied by an urge to breathe, and noticeable air starvation
Possibly headache, dizziness, weakness, unusual perspiration, nausea.

Signs

Slowing of responses, confusion, clumsiness
Unconsciousness, possibly including muscle twitching and convulsions in extreme cases.

Treatment

A diver should stop, rest, and ventilate his apparatus. Fresh breathing gas will usually relieve all symptoms quickly. If a victim is unconscious, refer to Paragraph 17.2.9.

17.3.2.2 Carbon Monoxide Poisoning (CO)

The most frequent cause of carbon monoxide poisoning is toxic fumes from a compressor exhaust entering the air intake. The addition of CO to the breathing gas prevents the blood from transporting oxygen or carbon dioxide resulting in asphyxia. Only slight traces of CO in the breathing gas can have toxic effects.

Symptoms

Frequently none prior to unconsciousness
Possibly headache, nausea, dizziness, weakness, tightness in the head
Confusion, clumsiness, similar to hypoxia.

Signs

Slow in response, clumsiness, bad judgment
Unconsciousness
Rapid deep breathing progressing to cessation of breathing
Abnormal redness of lips, fingernails, and skin
Extremely red blood.

Treatment

Provide a source of fresh air for the victim, and oxygen if available. Some aftereffects such as a headache and nausea may persist for a while after exposure. If the victim is unconscious treat according to Paragraph 17.2.9.

17.3.2.3 Oxygen Toxicity

Oxygen poisoning is the direct result of breathing pure oxygen or excessive amounts of oxygen under pressure. It most frequently occurs in closed circuit scuba when the depth for which the gas is mixed is exceeded. If not promptly treated death can result.

Symptoms

Twitching in the face
Nausea
Dizziness
Abnormalities of vision and hearing
Difficulty breathing
Anxiety and confusion
Unusual fatigue
Clumsiness
Convulsions.

Signs

Prior to the onset of convulsions, the only sign likely to be noticed is the twitching in the face.
Consciousness is lost at the onset of a convulsion. Breathing normally stops shortly thereafter.
Violent convulsions continue for a minute or two.
Biting the tongue and various physical injuries occur during convulsions.
Breathing generally resumes spontaneously after convulsions.
Victim may remain unconscious for several minutes after convulsion.

Treatment

Convulsions generally stop before any treatment can begin. Concentrate on preventing injury or drowning. Bring the diver to the surface, or if in a chamber, take him off oxygen. If normal breathing fails to resume, administer artificial respiration. If the diver was brought up during convulsion, and there is any reason to suspect an air embolism, recompress and treat immediately (See Paragraph 16.3).

17.3.2.4 Nitrogen Narcosis

Nitrogen narcosis is the result of the narcotic effect of nitrogen when breathed under pressure. These effects may first be noticeable at depths exceeding 100 feet, but become more pronounced at depths greater than 150 feet. The effects produce a sensation of apprehension, with confusion and impaired judgment and a false sense of well-being. Concentration or performance of even simple tasks are difficult. The diver may do things he would normally not attempt (removing his regulator, swimming to unsafe depths without regard to decompression sickness or air supply). With hard concentration on the task at hand most experienced divers can keep these effects under control.

Symptoms

Loss of judgment or skill
A false feeling of well-being.

Signs

Lack of concern for job or safety
Apparent stupidity
Profuse laughter at normally not humorous subjects.

Treatment

There is no treatment as such. The diver must be brought to a shallower depth where the effects are not felt. The onset of these effects can be quickly detected by the surface crew of a surface-supplied dive.

17.3.2.5 Hypoxia

Hypoxia is the lack of sufficient oxygen in the tissues to maintain their normal functions. It can be caused by the absence of air or insufficient oxygen in the breathing gas.

Hyperventilation blows off CO_2, thus reducing the

drive to breathe. A hyperventilating free diver may use up all of the O_2 before he gets the urge to breathe again.

A victim of hypoxia will normally not understand or comprehend what is occurring, and may, in fact, have a feeling of well-being. Hypoxia is similar to and may be accompanied by an excess of carbon dioxide.

Symptoms

Frequently none—The diver may lapse into sudden unconsciousness

Mental changes similar to alcohol intoxication.

Signs

Confusion, clumsiness, slowing of responses
Foolish behavior
Cyanosis (bluish discoloration of the skin)
In severe cases, cessation of breathing.

Treatment

Get the victim to the surface and into fresh air. If under water using a rebreather, manually add oxygen to the breathing circuit. If the victim is still breathing, fresh air will generally cause rapid revival. If the victim is unconscious, he should be treated as if suffering from gas embolism (See Paragraph 17.4.1). Artificial respiration can be administered while the victim is in the recompression chamber.

17.3.2.6 Asphyxia

Asphyxia is the result of both hypoxia and carbon dioxide poisoning. The most frequent causes are complete loss of air supply, or blockage of the windpipe.

Symptoms

Labored or impaired breathing
Headache, dizziness, weakness.

Signs

Unconsciousness accompanied by lack of breathing
Victim acting excited, possibly violent while struggling for air
Violent increase in breathing, followed by the cessation of breathing.

Treatment

The diver should stop and rest until the symptoms disappear.

If a diver is found unconscious, refer to Paragraph 17.2.9.

If blockage of the windpipe is causing strangulation, the obstruction must be cleared. Have the victim cough, pound him on the back, or hold him inverted. If the victim passes into unconsciousness, and the object is within reach, use forceps or fingers to remove it, taking care not to drive the obstruction further down the throat. A face-down position assists in draining fluid from the mouth and permitting the tongue to fall forward. However, the tongue and airway can be checked if the head is turned to the side while the victim is on his back. Should all these measures fail, an emergency tracheotomy should be considered (See Paragraph 17.1.3.1).

17.3.3 Ingestion Poisoning

17.3.3.1 Fish Poisoning

Internal.—Internal poisoning results from the consumption of contaminated marine life. It can be broken down into two general categories, that contracted from eating contaminated fish and that contracted from eating shell fish during certain months of the year.

Ciguatera.—This poisoning results from eating certain unrelated fish which contain a poison (ciguatoxin). The reason for this poison being present is unknown, although it is thought that it comes from certain species of algae eaten by fish. There is no way to distinguish fish with ciguatera from harmless fish except by laboratory analysis or by feeding the suspected fish to animals and watching for a reaction. Ciguatera can occur in a species of fish that was harmless the day before. Fish known to carry ciguatera include barracuda, grouper, snappers and jacks (Ricciuti 1973). About 800 species have been known to produce ciguatera (Fraser-Brunner 1973). Diseased fish seem more prevalent in tropical areas and because the concentration builds up over time, large fish of a given species are more likely to be toxic. The internal organs of diseased fish are particularly toxic.

Symptoms

Reversal of thermal touch sensation (hot feels cold and cold feels hot)
Abdominal pains
Nausea, vomiting
Diarrhea
Numbness of lips, tongue, throat
Fever.

Treatment

A doctor should be consulted as soon as possible, and informed that fish has been consumed within the last 30 hours. In some cases death may result in only 10 minutes, but a period of days is more common. If untreated, death may follow as a result of paralysis of the respiratory system. Assisted ventilation may be effective in those patients with respiratory paralysis. Once contracted, the symptoms may persist for months, particularly the reversal of temperature sensation. It is recommended that fish not be eaten while any symptoms remain, as this may cause a serious recurrence.

Scrombroid Poisoning

Some fish which have been left exposed to sunlight or left standing at room temperature may develop a toxin. Within a few minutes of consumption, symptoms will develop.

Symptoms

Nausea, vomiting
Severe headache
Massive red welts
Severe itching.

Treatment

Seek medical aid as soon as possible.

Shellfish Poisoning

During the summer months, many shellfish which inhabit the Pacific coast and Gulf of Mexico become poisonous. This poison results from the ingestion of poisonous plankton and algae, which does not affect the shellfish, but can be poisonous if the shellfish is consumed by humans. Mussels and clams carry this poison. Abalone and crabs do not feed on plankton and are therefore not affected. In most cases cooking will not neutralize the toxin. The poison works directly on the nervous system and the usual signs such as nausea and vomiting are not generally present. The poison impairs respiration and affects the circulation of the blood. Death, which results in severe cases, is normally the result of respiratory paralysis.

Signs and Symptoms

Onset is variable but may occur within 20 minutes of ingestion
Difficulty breathing, getting progressively worse
Cessation of breathing

Infrequently, nausea, vomiting and other gastro-intestinal ailments.

Treatment

If shellfish poisoning is suspected, seek immediate medical attention.

17.4 GAS EMBOLISM, DECOMPRESSION SICKNESS AND RELATED ACCIDENTS

Air embolism and its related complications are the result of the expansion of gas trapped in the lungs. Most frequently, embolisms are the result of a diver holding his breath during ascent, but they can result from any failure to equalize the pressure in the lungs as air expands under decreasing ambient pressure. Embolism is one of the primary causes of diving fatalities. *If a diver who has had any source of air (or other breathing medium) at depth is unconscious upon surfacing or loses consciousness shortly after surfacing. It must be assumed that he has air embolism and act accordingly at once.*

17.4.1 Gas Embolism

As a diver surfaces, the gas trapped in the lungs expands, rupturing the alveoli. Bubbles of gas are forced into the circulatory system, to the heart, and distributed to the body tissues. As the ascending diver is normally in a vertical position these bubbles tend to travel upward toward the brain. As the bubbles enlarge and pass into smaller arteries they reach a point where they can move no further, and cut off circulation. The effects of halting circulation, especially to the brain, are serious and require immediate treatment. Symptoms of embolism occur within 3–5 minutes of surfacing. One, a few, or all of the symptoms may be present.

Symptoms

Fatigue
Weakness
Dizziness
Paralysis of extremities
Visual disturbances such as blurring
Feeling of blow on chest, progressively worsening
Cough or shortness of breath.

Signs

Sudden unconsciousness (usually immediately after surfacing, possibly before surfacing)

Bloody, frothy sputum

Staggering

Confusion or difficulty in seeing (i.e., moving in a wrong direction, bumping into objects)

Paralysis or weakness in extremities

Collapse or unconsciousness

Convulsions

Cessation of breathing.

Treatment

Immediate first aid is to place the victim with head and chest inclined downward and lying on his left side. This position lessens the chances of bubbles being carried to the brain. Also, breathing 100 percent pure oxygen, if available, is indicated. Begin oxygen treatment in route to a recompression chamber. Treatment for air embolism is immediate recompression in a recompression chamber. This may reduce the size of the bubbles to the point where the circulation of blood may resume. The victim should be recompressed to 165 feet as soon as possible, and treated on the appropriate treatment table. Under no circumstances should the victim be taken back into the water to depth for treatment (See Section 16).

17.4.2 Decompression Sickness

Decompression sickness (bends, caisson disease, compressed air illness) is the result of inadequate decompression following exposure to increased pressures. While immediate recompression is not a matter of life and death as with air embolism, the quicker the victim is recompressed the less will be the chances of permanent damage and the quicker the rate of recovery. While under pressure, the inert portion of the breathing gas (nitrogen, helium, etc.) is passed, into solution in the blood and absorbed by the body tissues. As long as the diver remains under pressure, this gas presents no problems. Should the pressure be quickly removed (as in rapid surfacing) the inert gas can come out of solution and form bubbles in the tissues and blood stream. The controlled ascent permits the body to rid itself of excess inert gas at a rate which will enable it to remain in solution.

Symptoms

Symptoms of decompression sickness are extremely varied, and are in many cases similar to air embolism. The effects of air embolism will be noticeable prior to or immediately after the diver surfaces. Any occurrence of symptoms more than $1/4$ hour after the diver reaches the surface can generally be assumed not to be air embolism. The most frequent symptoms of decompression sickness and the frequency with which they occur are listed below.

Symptoms	Frequency of occurrence (percent)
LOCAL pain:	
(described as deep-boring)........................	89
Leg...	30
Arm..	70
Dizziness (staggering)....................................	5.3
Paralysis..	2.3
Shortness of breath.....................................	1.6
Extreme fatigue and pain.............................	1.3
Collapse and unconsciousness.........................	.5

Signs

Evidence of local pain (rubbing arm, limp, favoring one side)

Staggering, clumsiness, lack of response as if drunk

Paralysis or partial paralysis

Blotchy or noted rash on skin

Shortness of breath

Collapse and unconsciousness.

Treatment

The treatment for decompression sickness is recompression as quickly as possible according to the symptoms (See Section 16). Any symptom except a rash and local pain is considered a serious symptom and should be treated as such. Administer 100 percent pure oxygen in route to a recompression chamber.

While decompression sickness may, in some rare cases, occur up to 24 hours after the exposure to pressure, the vast majority of cases (95 percent) will be evident within 3 hours. Fifty percent will occur within 30 minutes and 85 percent within an hour. Only 1 percent will be delayed over 6 hours.

17.4.3 Mediastinal Emphysema

Mediastinal emphysema may result from a ruptured pleural bubble or injury to the lung, esophagus, trachea, or main stem bronchus. While not serious in itself, it may be an indication of an embolism.

Symptoms

Pain under the breastbone (sternum) which may radiate to the neck, neck bone or shoulder
Shortness of breath
Faintness.

Signs

Blueness (cyanosis) of the skin, lips, or fingernails
Difficulty breathing
Shock.

Treatment

Unless air embolism is also present recompression is not necessary. Medical assistance should be obtained, and oxygen administered if necessary.

17.4.4 Subcutaneous Emphysema

Subcutaneous emphysema has the same initiating mechanism as gas embolism but is not as serious as gas embolism. This condition results when air escapes into the tissues just under the skin (subcutaneous), and normally occurs in the area of the neck and/or collarbone.

Symptoms

Feeling of fullness in neck area
Change in sound of voice.

Signs

Swelling or inflation around the neck
Crackling sensation when skin is moved
Change in sound of voice
Difficulty in breathing or swallowing.

Treatment

Unless complicated by air embolism, recompression is not necessary. Seek the services of a physician and administer oxygen if breathing is impaired.

17.4.5 Pneumothorax

Pneumothorax is the result of the presence of air between the lung and the inner wall of the chest cavity. As the air continues to expand, partial or total collapse of the lung may result. In serious cases, displacement of the heart could result.

Symptoms

Sudden onset of cough
Shortness of breath
Sharp pain in the chest, usually made worse by breathing.

Signs

Blueness (cyanosis) of skin, lips, and fingernails
Pain in chest, evidenced by grimacing or clutching chest
A tendency to bend the chest toward the side involved
Rapid, shallow breathing

Treatment

First aid: administer oxygen. If air embolism is not present, recompression may not be necessary. If breathing is difficult, recompress the victim to a point of relief. Extreme caution must be exercised during subsequent decompression as dissipation of the trapped air may not have taken place. Seek the services of a doctor as in serious cases direct removal of trapped air may be necessary.

17.5 HEAT EXHAUSTION

Heat exhaustion results when cardiac output and vasomotor control are inadequate to meet the needs of increased circulation to the skin in addition to cerebral and muscular demands. The cause is exposure to heat while performing arduous labors. Excessive labor in extreme heat should be avoided. When required, the body (especially the head) should be protected from the sun.

Symptoms

Rapid pulse
Nausea, vomiting
Fainting
Restlessness
Headache
Dizziness
Difficulty breathing
Cold, clammy skin, continued sweating.

Treatment

Lay the victim down in a shaded, cool place, with the head lower than the rest of the body. Protect the victim from chilling. A solution of weak salt water (1 tsp salt to 1 qt water) should be administered. The victim should recover fairly rapidly, but some symptoms such as headache, and exhaustion may linger on.

17.6 HEATSTROKE

Heatstroke results when prolonged exposure to heat raises the body's temperature. It can be avoided by limiting exertion and wearing protective clothing. Heatstroke is a serious emergency, and the body temperature must be quickly lowered or permanent brain damage and possibly death may result.

Signs and Symptoms

Rise in body temperature
Sudden collapse
Skin extremely dry and hot
Extremely rapid pulse.

Treatment

The major factor in treating heatstroke is to lower the body temperature to a safe level as quickly as possible. Bathe the body in cool water or if possible completely immerse the body. Sponge the head and neck with the same cooled water. Have the victim drink a weak solution of salt water (1 tsp salt to 1 qt water). Upon recovery the victim should be examined by qualified medical personnel.

17.7 SHOCK

Shock may be present in any injury, and will certainly be present to some extent in any serious injury. Shock is the result of a loss of circulatory blood, resulting in a drop of blood pressure, and decreased circulation. The resultant drop in the quantity of blood to the tissues can have serious, permanent effects, including death.

Symptoms and Signs

Eyes glassy, lackluster, dilated pupils, tired
Cyanosis (blue lips, fingernails)
Pale or ashen grey skin
Pulse may be normal, or weak and rapid
Wet, clammy skin
Drop in blood pressure
Possibly retching, vomiting, nausea, hiccups.

Treatment

Shock will require prompt medical aid. Only when the circulating volume has been restored can recovery be expected. The victim should be kept lying down with his feet raised above his head approximately 12 inches. Steps should be taken to conserve body heat. If the victim is conscious and can swallow he can be given a solution orally consisting of a level teaspoon of salt and if available $\frac{1}{2}$ teaspoon of soda to a quart of water (never alcoholic beverages). All wounds should be splinted and treated prior to moving the victim. Keep the victim calm and if possible, confident of recovery.

17.8 EMERGENCY MEDICAL KIT FOR HYPERBARIC CHAMBERS

Every diving activity must maintain an emergency kit immediately available for use at the scene of a diving accident or at the recompression chamber. The kit should be small enough to carry into the chamber. Because many sterile items must be considered contaminated after exposure to increased atmospheric pressure, it is desirable to have a primary and a secondary emergency kit. Also, since the contents of the medical kit will be used while under increased pressure, packaging requirements must be considered.

Kit No. 1. Primary Emergency Kit—Diagnostic equipment needed routinely, and equipment most likely to be needed immediately.

Kit No. 2. Secondary Emergency Kit—Equipment and medicines that might be needed, but that can be sent into the chamber if specifically required.

Kit No. 1—

Diagnostic equipment routinely useful:
- Flashlight
- Stethoscope
- Otoscope-Ophthalmoscope
- Sphygmomanometer (aneroid type, never mercury)
- Reflex hammer
- Tuning fork
- Pin and brush for sensory testing
- Tongue depressors

Emergency treatment equipment and medications:
- Tongue depressors taped and padded as a bite pad for use in case of convulsions
- Oropharyngeal airway
- Rubber tubes equivalent to sizes 4 and 6 for temporary use in a tracheotomy, with a safety pin through the end to be kept outside the trachea.
- AMBU resuscitator

- Sterile scalpel and blade assortment
- Sterile hemostats (two each)
- Syringe, 5-cc (two each) with needles
- Bandage scissors
- Epinephrine 1:1,000 aqueous for injection
- Sterile gauze pads
- Cotton balls
- Benzalkonium chloride
- Dextran

Miscellaneous:
- Adhesive tape
- Tourniquet

Kit No. 2 —

Emergency equipment:
- Suture material, sterile
- Suture needles, assorted, sterile
- Sterile syringes
    - 5-cc, 2 each
    - 10-cc, 2 each
    - 30-cc, 2 each
- Sterile needles, 16, 18, 20, and 22 gauge, preferably disposable
- Three-way stopcocks, sterile, 2 each
- Sterile thoracentesis needle, 16 gauge, 4″ long
- Sterile rubber tube for endotracheal suction (a soft-tip tube causes less damage to the trachea)
- Tracheotomy kit

Emergency medications:
- Intravenous fluids:
    - 5 percent dextrose in saline
    - 5 percent dextrose in water
    - Ringer's injection, lactated
- Lidocaine
- Corticosteroid for intravenous or intramuscular injection
- Amobarbital sodium, injectable
- Dextran
- Phenobarbital, injectable
- Diazepam, injectable
- Diphenylhydantoin sodium, injectable
- Chlorpromazine, injectable
- Codeine-tablets
- Aspirin
- An injectable antihistamine
- Sterile water for injection
- Surgical soap

Miscellaneous:
- Nasogastric tube
- Asepto syringe
- Sterile bladder catheterization tray (preferably disposable)
- Intravenous infusion kits, sterile, disposable (two each)
- Gauze roller bandage, 1″ and 2″, sterile
- Band-Aids
- Sterile gloves, surgical
- Sterile towels
- Splints
- Eye patch

APPENDICES

Allen, J. and Sills, J. 1973. Preparation and Properties of Quinaldine Sulfate, an Improved Fish Anesthetic. *Investigations in Fish Control.* No. 47. LaCrosse, Wis.: Bureau of Sport Fisheries and Wildlife.

American Institute of Biological Sciences. 1972. The Metabolism of Some Coral Reef Communities: A Team Study of Nutrient and Energy Flux at Eniwetok. *BioScience,* Vol. 22, No. 9, pp. 541-543.

American National Red Cross, The. 1973. *Standard First Aid and Personal Safety.* 1st ed. Garden City, N.Y.: Doubleday & Company, Inc.

American Public Health Association, The. 1965. *Standard Methods for the Examination of Water and Wastewater.* 12th ed. New York: The American Public Health Association.

Andersen, B. 1973. *Arctic III Expedition Diving Equipment and Human Performance During Diving Operations in the High Arctic.* Landover, Md.: Oceanautics, Inc.

Baker, B. Jr.; Deebel, W.; and Geisenderfer, R. eds. 1966. *Glossary of Oceanographic Terms,* SP-35, 2nd ed. Washington: Oceanographic Analysis Division, Marine Sciences Department, U.S. Naval Oceanographic Office.

Bass, G. 1964. Methods of Wreck Excavation in Clear Water. In *Diving Into the Past,* edited by J. Holmquist and A. Wheeler. St. Paul: Minnesota Historical Society.

Bass, G. 1966. *Archaeology Underwater.* New York: Frederick A. Praeger Publishers.

Bass, G. 1968. The Turkish Aegean: Proving Ground for Underwater Archaeology. *Expedition,* Vol. 10, No. 3, pp. 3-10.

Beckman, E. 1963. Thermal Protection During Immersion in Cold Water. In *Proceedings Second Symposium on Underwater Physiology.* Washington: National Academy of Sciences.

Bell, G. 1967. A Guide to Properties, Characteristics and Uses of Some General Anesthetics for Fish. *Bulletin, Fisheries Research Board, Canada,* 2nd ed., No. 148, pp. 1-4.

Boden, B.; Kampa, E.; and Snodgrass, J. 1960. Underwater Daylight Measurements in the Bay of Biscay. *Journal of Marine Biology Association, United Kingdom,* Vol. 39, No. 2, pp. 227-238.

Bond, G. 1964. New Development in High Pressure Living. *U.S. Naval Submarine Medical Center Report No. 442.* Groton, Conn.: U.S. Naval Submarine Medical Center.

Bouma, A. 1969. *Methods for the Study of Sedimentary Structures.* New York: Wiley-Interscience.

Burr, A. and Duncan, M. 1972. Portable Spectroradiometer for Underwater Environments. *Limnology and Oceanography,* Vol. 17, No. 3, pp. 466-475.

Bussey, L. 1970. Operations With the Mark I Deep Dive System. In *Equipment for the Working Diver 1970 Symposium.* Washington: Marine Technology Society.

Clark, P. and Evans, F. 1954. Distance to Nearest Neighbor as a Measure of Spatial Relationships in Populations. *Ecology,* Vol. 35, pp. 445-453.

Clarke, T. 1970. Territorial Behavior and Population Dynamics of a Pomacentrid Fish, the Garibaldi, *Hypsypops rubicunda. Ecology Monographs,* Vol. 40, pp. 189-212.

Clifton, H.; Hunter, R.; and Phillips, R. 1971. Depositional Structures and Processes in the Non-Barred High-Energy Nearshore. *Journal of Sedimentary Petrology,* Vol. 41, No. 3, pp. 651-670.

Coleman, R. and Krasik, W. 1971. *Oral Muzzle Pressure Effects in Underwater Communication.* CSL/ONR Technical Report #19. Arlington, Va.: Office of Naval Research.

Compressed Gas Association, Inc. 1966. *Handbook of Compressed Gases.* New York: Reinhold Publishing Corporation.

Compressed Gas Association, Inc. 1973. *Commodity Specification for Air.* 2nd ed. Pamphlet G-7.1. New York: Compressed Gas Association, Inc.

Cooper, R. 1970. Retention of Marks and Their Effects on Growth, Behavior and Migrations of the American Lobster, *Homarus americanus. Transactions of the American Fisheries Society,* Vol. 99, No. 2, pp. 409-417.

Cooper, R. 1974. Seasonal Abundance of the American Lobster, *Homarus americanus,* in the Boothbay Region of Maine. *Transactions of the American Fisheries Society,* in press.

Cratin, P.; Warriner, J.; Wert, M.; DeGrow, T.; and Bryson, A. 1973. Preliminary *In Situ* Physicochemical Studies of Oxygen in Seawater. *Hydro-Lab Journal,* Vol. 2. No. 1, pp. 5-8.

Dahl, A. 1973. Surface Area in Ecological Analysis: Quantification of Benthic Coral-Reef Algae. *Marine Biology,* Vol. 23, No. 4, pp. 239-249.

Dawson, E. 1956. *How to Know the Seaweeds.* Dubuque, Iowa: Wm. C. Brown Co.

Dill, R. 1964. *Contemporary Submarine Erosion in Scripps Submarine Canyon.* Thesis, University of California, San Diego, Calif.

Dill, R. 1969. Earthquake Effects on Fill of Scripps Submarine Canyon. *Geological Society of America Bulletin,* Vol. 80, pp. 321-328.

Dill, R. and Moore, D. 1965. A Diver-Held Vane-Shear Apparatus. *Marine Geology,* Vol. 3, pp. 323-327.

Dill, R. and Shumway, G. 1954. Geological Use of Self-Contained Diving Apparatus. *Bulletin of American Association of Petroleum Geologists,* Vol. 38, No. 1, pp. 148-157.

Drew, E. 1971. Botany. In *Underwater Science*, edited by J. Woods and J. Lythgoe. London: Oxford University Press.

Dumas, F. 1962. *Deepwater Archaeology*. London: Routledge & Kegan Paul.

Duncan, M. 1973. *In Situ* Studies of Growth and Pigmentation of the Phaeophycean Nereocystis luetkeana. *Helgoländer wiss. Meeresunters*, 24, pp. 510-525.

Dybern, B.; Jacobsen, L.; and Hallback, H. 1967. On the Habitat Behavior of the Lobster, *Homarus vulgaris*, in Swedish Waters. *Medd. Havsfiskelab., Lysekil*, No. 36, p. 13.

Earle, S. 1972. The Influence of Herbivores on the Marine Plants of Great Lameshur Bay, With an Annotated List of Plants. In *Results of the Tektite Program: Ecology of the Coral Reef Fishes*, edited by B. Collette and S. Earle. Los Angeles: Natural History Museum of Los Angeles County.

Edel, P. 1969. *Delineation of Emergency Surface Decompression and Treatment Procedures for Project Tektite Aquanauts*. Pasadena, Tex.: J. and J. Marine Diving Co., Inc., April 1969.

Edel, P.; Carroll, J.; Honaker, R.; and Beckman, E. 1969. Interval at Sea-Level Pressure Required to Prevent Decompression Sickness in Humans Who Fly in Commercial Aircraft After Diving. *Aerospace Medicine*, Vol. 40, No. 10, pp. 1105-1110.

Emery, A. 1968. Underwater Telescope. *Copeia*, No. 3, pp. 627-628.

Ennis, G. 1972. A Diver-Operated Plankton Collector. *Journal Fisheries Research Board of Canada*, Vol. 29, No. 3, pp. 341-343.

Evans, I. and Sherratt, G. 1948. A Simple and Convenient Instrument for Measuring the Shear Resistance of Clay Soils. *Journal of Scientific Instruction*, Vol. 25, pp. 411-414.

Fager, E.; Flechsig, A.; Ford, R.; Clutter, R.; and Ghelardi, R. 1966. Equipment for Use in Ecological Studies Using SCUBA. *Limnology and Oceanography*, Vol. 11, No. 4, pp. 503-509.

Feinstein, S. 1973. Acuity of the Human Sound Localization Response Underwater. *The Journal of the Acoustical Society of America*, Vol. 53, No. 2, pp. 393-399.

Fisher, R. and Mills, R. 1952. Sediment Trap Studies of Sand Movement in LaJolla Bay. Abstract, *Bulletin of Geological Society of America*, Vol. 63, p. 1328.

Fraser-Brunner, A. 1973. *Danger in the Sea*. London: The Hamlyn Publishing Group Limited.

Gibson, R. 1967. The Use of the Anesthetic Quinaldine in Fish Ecology. *Journal Animal Ecology*, Vol. 36, No. 2, pp. 295-301.

Gilardi, R. 1974. *Safe Handling of Diving Gases*. Presented at the Fourth Annual Diving Safety Symposium, 16 January 1974, at Morgan City, La.

Gilbert, P. and Wood, F. 1957. Method of Anesthetizing Large Sharks and Rays Safely and Rapidly. *Science*, Vol. 126, No. 1266, pp. 212-213.

Gilderhus, P.; Berger, B.; Sills, J.; and Harman, P. 1973a. The Efficacy of Quinaldine Sulfate as an Anesthetic for Freshwater Fish. *Investigation in Fish Control*. No. 49. LaCrosse, Wis.: Bureau of Sport Fisheries and Wildlife.

Gilderhus, P.; Berger, B.; Sills, J.; and Harman, P. 1973b. The Efficacy of Quinaldine Sulfate: MS-222 Mixtures for the Anesthetization of Freshwater Fish. *Investigations in Fish Control*. No. 54. LaCrosse, Wis.: Bureau of Sport Fisheries and Wildlife.

Greenbaum, L. and Hoff, E. 1966. *A Bibliographical Sourcebook of Compressed Air, Diving and Submarine Medicine*. Vol. I, pp. 230-236; Vol. II, pp. 258-260; Vol. III, pp. 245-246. Washington: Office of Naval Research and Bureau of Medicine.

Halstead, B. 1959. *Dangerous Marine Animals*. Cambridge, Md.: Cornell Maritime Press.

Hamilton, E. and Menard, H. 1956. Density and Porosity of Sea-Floor Surface Sediments Off San Diego, California. *Bulletin of American Association of Petroleum Geologists*, Vol. 40, No. 4, pp. 754-761.

Hamilton, R. Jr.; Kenyon, D.; Freitag, M.; and Schreiner, H. 1973. *Formulation of Excursion Procedures for Shallow Undersea Habitats*. UCRI-731. Tarrytown, N.Y.: Union Carbide Corporation, July 1973.

Hesser, C. 1963. Measurement of Inert Gas Narcosis in Man. In *Proceedings Second Symposium on Underwater Physiology*. Washington: National Academy of Sciences.

High, W. 1967. Scuba Diving, a Valuable Tool for Investigating the Behavior of Fish Within the Influence of Fishing Gear. *FAO Conference on Fish Behavior in Relation to Fishing Techniques and Tactics*. Bergen, Norway, 19-27 October 1967. Food and Agriculture Organization of the United Nations.

High, W. 1971. Underwater Fishery Studies Are Valuable. *Commercial Fisheries Review*, Vol. 33, No. 10, pp. 1-6.

High, W.; Ellis, I.; Schroeder, W.; and Loverich, G. 1973. Evaluation of the Undersea Habitats—Tektite II, Hydro-Lab, and Edalhab—for Scientific Saturation Diving Programs. *Helgoländer wiss. Meeresunters*, Vol. 24, pp. 16-44.

Hollien, H.; Coleman, R.; Thompson, C.; and Hunter, K. 1970. Evaluation of Diver Communication Systems Under Controlled Conditions. *Undersea Technology Handbook*. Arlington, Va.: Compass Publications.

Hollien H. and Rothman, H. 1971. Studies of Diver Communication and Retrieval. The University of Florida COM-EX 2 Program, *Tektite II, Scientists-in-the-Sea Report*. Washington: U.S. Government Printing Office.

Hollien, H. and Rothman, H. 1974. Diver Communication. *Research Underwater*, London: Academic Press. In press.

Houston, A.; Madden, R.; Woods, R.; and Miles, H. 1971. Some Physiological Effects of Handling and Tricaine Methanesulphonate Anesthetization Upon the Brook Trout, *Salvelinus fontinalis. Journal Fisheries Research Board of Canada*, Vol. 28, No. 5, pp. 625-633.

Howland, R. 1969. Laboratory Studies of Possible Fish Collecting Aids With Some Toxicities for the Isomers of Cresol. *Investigations in Fish Control*. No. 34. LaCrosse, Wis.: Bureau of Sport Fisheries and Wildlife.

Howland, R. and Schoettger, R. 1969. Efficacy of Methylpentynol as an Anesthetic on Four Salmonids. *Investigations in Fish Control*. No. 29. LaCrosse, Wis.: Bureau of Sport Fisheries and Wildlife.

Jenkins, W. 1973. *A Summary of Diving Techniques Used in Polar Regions*. Panama City, Fla.: Naval Coastal Systems Laboratory.

Jewell, D. 1964. Limnoarcheology in California. In *Diving Into the Past*, edited by J. Holmquist and A. Wheeler. St. Paul: Minnesota Historical Society.

Kindwall, E. 1972. *Aseptic Bone Necrosis*. Paper presented at Professional Diving Symposium, 17 November 1972, at New Orleans, La.

Kinney, J.; Luria, S.; and Weitzman, D. 1968a. Responses to the Underwater Distortions of Visual Stimuli. *U.S. Naval Submarine Medical Center Report No. 541*. Groton, Conn.: U.S. Naval Submarine Medical Center.

Kinney, J.; Luria, S.; and Weitzman, D. 1968b. The Underwater Visibility of Colors With Artificial Illumination. *U.S. Naval Submarine Medical Center Report No. 551*. Groton, Conn.: U.S. Naval Submarine Medical Center.

Kitching, J. 1941. Studies in Sublittoral Ecology. III. Laminaria Forest on the West Coast of Scotland. A Study of Zonation in Relation to Wave Action and Illumination. *Biology Bulletin*, Vol. 80, p. 324.

Klontz, G. and Smith, L. 1968. Methods of Using Fish as Biological Research Subjects. In *Methods of Animal Experimentation* edited by W.I. Gay. New York: Academic Press.

Knudsen, J. 1972. *Collecting and Preserving Plants and Animals*. New York: Harper and Row.

Koblick, I.; Biaggi, J.; Olsen, D.; and Geiger, E. 1974. Undersea Labs for Marine Resource Inventory. *Marine Technology Society Journal*, Vol. 8, No. 1, pp. 12-18.

Kooyman, G. 1968. An Analysis of Some Behavioral and Physiological Characteristics Related to Diving in the Weddell Seal. *Antarctic Research Series*, Vol. 11, pp. 227-261.

Kooyman, G.; Drabek, C.; Elsner, R.; and Campbell, W. 1971. Diving Behavior of the Emperor Penguin *Aptenodytes Forsteri. The Auk*, Vol. 88, No. 4, pp. 775-795.

Kumpf, H. and Randall, H. 1961. Charting the Marine Environments of St. John, U.S. Virgin Islands. *Bulletin of Marine Science Gulf and Caribbean*, Vol. 11, No. 4, pp. 543-551.

LaFond, E. and Dill, R. 1957. *Do Bubbles Exist in the Sea?* USNEL Technical Memorandum 259. San Diego: United States Navy Electronics Laboratory.

Lambertsen, C. and Wright, W. 1973. Multiday Exposure of Men to High Nitrogen Pressure and Increased Airway Resistance at Natural Inspired Oxygen Tension. *Aerospace Medicine, Vol. 44, No. 7, pp. 821-869.*

Lanphier, E. 1957. Diving Medicine. *New England Journal of Medicine*. Vol. 256, No. 3, pp. 120-131.

Larkum, A.; Drew, E.; and Crossett, R. 1967. The Vertical Distribution of Attached Marine Algae in Malta. *Journal of Ecology*, Vol. 55, pp. 361-371.

Locke, D. 1969. Quinaldine as an Anesthetic for Brook Trout, Lake Trout and Atlantic Salmon. *Investigations in Fish Control*. No. 24. LaCrosse, Wis.: Bureau of Sport Fisheries and Wildlife.

McFarland, W. 1959. A Study of the Effects of Anesthetics on the Behavior and Physiology of Fishes. *Institute of Marine Science*, Vol. 6, pp. 23-55.

McFarland, W. 1960. The Use of Anesthetics for the Handling and Transport of Fishes. *California Fish and Game*, Vol. 46, No. 4, pp. 407-431.

McFarland, W. and Klontz, G. 1969. Anesthetics in Fishes. In *Comparative Anesthesia in Laboratory Animals*, edited by E.V. Miller. *Federation Proceedings*, Vol. 28, No. 4, pp. 1535-1540.

McNeil, G. 1972. *Optical Fundamentals of Underwater Photography*. 2nd ed. Rockville, Md.: Mitchell Photogrammetry, Inc.

Macintyre, I. 1974. A Diver-Operated Hydraulic Drill for Coring Submerged Substrates. *Atoll Research Bulletin*, Vol. 185.

Marking, L. 1967. Toxicity of MS-222 to Selected Fishes. *Investigations in Fish Control*. No. 12. LaCrosse, Wis.: Bureau of Sport Fisheries and Wildlife.

Menard, H.; Dill, R.; Hamilton, E.; Moore, D.; Shumway, G.; Silverman, M.; and Stewart, H. 1954. Underwater Mapping by Diving Geologists. *Bulletin of American Association of Petroleum Geologists*, Vol. 38, No. 1, pp. 129-147.

Merifield, P. and Rosencrantz, D. 1966. A Simple Method for Surveying a Small Area Underwater. *Limnology and Oceanography*, Vol. 11, No. 3, pp. 408-409.

Mertens, L. 1970. *In-Water Photography: Theory and Practice.* New York: Wiley-Interscience.

Miles, S. 1966. *Underwater Medicine,* 2nd ed. Philadelphia: J.B. Lippincott Company.

Miller, J,; VanDerwalker, J.; and Waller, R. eds. 1971. *Tektite II, Scientists-in-the-Sea.* U.S. Department of the Interior, Washington: U.S. Government Printing Office.

Milne, P. 1972, *In-Situ* Underwater Surveying by Plane Table and Alidade. *Underwater Journal and Information Bulletin,* Vol. 4, No. 2, pp. 59-63.

Moring, J. 1970. Use of the Anesthetic Quinaldine for Handling Pacific Coast Intertidal Fishes. *Transactions, American Fisheries Society,* Vol. 99, No. 4, pp. 803-806.

Myrberg, A.; Brahy, B.; and Emery, A. 1967. Field Observations on Reproduction of the Damselfish, *Chromis multilineata* (Pomacentridae), with Additional Notes on General Behavior. *Copeia,* No. 4, pp. 819-827.

National Aeronautics and Space Administration. 1973. *Bioastronautics Data Book.* 2nd ed. Edited by J. Parker and V. West. Washington: U.S. Government Printing Office.

National Association of Underwater Instructors. 1973. *NAUI: The Complete Guide to Cave Diving.* NAUI Technical Publication Number Three.

National Safety Council. 1973. How to Purify Compressed Air for Breathing to Meet OSHAct Regulations. *National Safety News,* Vol. 108, No. 4, pp. 54-56.

North, W. 1966-1967. Measurements of Bottom Light Intensities. In *Annual Report, Kelp Habitat Improvement Project,* Pasadena, Calif.: California Institute of Technology.

Parrish, B. ed.; Akyuz, E.; Anderson, J.; Brown, D.; High, W.; Peres, J.; and Piccard, J. 1972. Submersibles and Underwater Habitats: A Review. *Underwater Journal and Information Bulletin,* August 1972, pp. 149-167.

Pauli, D. and Cole, H. eds. 1970. *Project Tektite I.* U.S. Department of the Navy. ONR Report DR 153. Washington: U.S. Government Printing Office.

Peyser, R. 1970. *Corrosion of Steel Scuba Tanks.* Kingston, R.I.: University of Rhode Island.

Prasser, D. 1969. Drowning and Hyperventilation Syndrome. *California Medicine,* Vol. 3, No. 4, pp. 322-324.

Randall, J.; Schroeder, R.; and Starck, W. II. 1964. Notes on the Biology of the Echinoid, *Diadema Antillarum. Caribbean Journal of Science,* Vol. 4, No. 2-3, pp. 421-433.

Ray, C. and Lavallee, D. 1964. Self-Contained Diving Operations in McMurdo Sound, Antarctica: Observations of the Sub-Ice Environment of the Weddell Seal, Leptonchotes weddelli (Lesson). *Zoologica, Scientific Contributions of the New York Zoological Society,* Vol. 48, No. 8, pp. 121-136.

Reuter, S. 1971. *No-Calculation Dive Tables,* Northfield, Ill.: DACOR Corporation.

Ricciuti, E. 1973. *Killers of the Seas.* New York: Walker and Company.

Ryan, E. and Bass, G. 1962. Underwater Surveying and Draughting, A Technique. *Antiquity,* Vol. 36, pp. 252-261.

Salsman, G. and Tolbert, W. 1965. Observations on the Sand Dollar, *Mellita Quinquiesperforata. Limnology and Oceanography,* Vol. 10, No. 1, pp. 152-155.

Sanders, J. 1968. Diver-Operated Simple Hand Tools for Coring Nearshore Sands. *Journal of Sedimentary Petrology,* Vol. 38, No. 2, pp. 1381-1386.

Scarratt, D. 1968. An Artificial Reef for Lobsters, *Homarus americanus. Journal of Fisheries Research Board of Canada,* Vol. 25, No. 12, pp. 2683-2690.

Schaefer, K.; Allison, R.; Dougherty, J.; Carey, C.; Walker, R.; Jost, F.; and Parker, D. 1968. Pulmonary and Circulatory Adjustment Determining the Limits of Depths in Breathhold Diving. *Science,* Vol. 162, No. 3857, pp. 1020-1023.

Schmidt, T.; Door, V.; and Hamilton, R. Jr. 1973. *Chamber Fire Safety.* Technical Memorandum UCRI-721. Tarrytown, N.Y.: Ocean Systems, Inc.

Schoettger, R. and Julin, A. 1967. Efficacy of MS-222 as an Anesthetic on Four Salmonids. *Investigations in Fish Control.* No. 13. LaCrosse, Wis.: Bureau of Sport Fisheries and Wildlife.

Schoettger, R. and Julin, A. 1969. Efficacy of Quinaldine as an Anesthetic for Seven Species of Fish. *Investigations in Fish Control.* No. 22. LaCrosse, Wis.: Bureau of Sport Fisheries and Wildlife.

Schroeder, W. 1974. Collecting and Handling Zooplankton and Epibenthic Organisms Underwater. *Marine Technology Society Journal,* Vol. 8, No. 5, pp. 40-43.

Shepard, F. 1973. *Submarine Geology,* 3rd ed. New York: Harper and Row.

Shumway, G. 1955. Compass-Inclinometer for Underwater Outcrop Mapping. *Bulletin of American Association of Petroleum Geologists,* Vol. 39, No. 7, pp. 1403-1404.

Somers, L. 1972. *Research Diver's Manual.* rev. ed. Technical Report 16. Ann Arbor: Sea Grant Program, The University of Michigan.

Stang, P. 1974. Arctic III Expedition. *Marine Technology Society Journal,* Vol. 8, No. 1, pp. 44-48.

Starck, W. and Davis, W. 1966. Night Habits of Fishes of Alligator Reef, Florida. *Ichthyologica, The Aquarium Journal,* Vol. 38, No. 4, pp. 313-356.

Steimle, F. Jr. and Stone, R. 1973. Bibliography on Artificial Reefs. Publication #73-2. *Coastal Plains Center for Marine Development Services.* Wilmington, N.C.: Coastal Plains Center for Marine Development Services.

Stone, R. and Buchanan, C. 1970. Old Tires Make New Fishing Reefs. *Underwater Naturalist,* Vol. 6, No. 4, pp. 23-28.

Tate, B.; Moen, T.; and Severson, B. 1965. The Use of Rotenone for the Recovery of Live Fish. *Progressive Fish Culturist,* Vol. 27, No. 3, pp. 156-160.

Thalmann, E. 1974. *A Prophylactic Program for the Prevention of Otitis Externa in Saturation Divers.* Washington: U.S. Navy Experimental Diving Unit.

Thienpoint, D. and Niemegeers, C. 1965. R7464—A New Potent Anesthetic in Fish. *International Zoo Yearbook,* Vol. 5, pp. 202-205.

Turner, C.; Ebert, E.; and Given, R. 1968. The Marine Environment Offshore From Point Loma, San Diego County. *Fish Bulletin 140.* Sacramento: State of California Resources Agency.

U.S. Coast Guard. 1972. *Rules of the Road: International — Inland.* August 1, 1972. Washington: U.S. Coast Guard.

U.S. Department of Commerce. NOAA. *Tidal Current Tables* and *Tidal Current Charts.* Rockville. Md.: National Ocean Survey.

U.S. Department of the Interior. 1964, 1966, 1967, 1969, and 1973. *Investigations in Fish Control.* LaCrosse, Wis.: Bureau of Sport Fisheries and Wildlife.

U.S. Department of the Navy. 1944, 1947, and 1953. Indian Ocean HOP-566 (1944); Southwestern Pacific Ocean HOP-568 (1944); Northeastern Pacific Ocean HOP-569 (1947); Northwestern Pacific Ocean HOP-570 (1953). *Atlas of Surface Currents.* Washington: Defense Mapping Agency, Hydrographic Center.

U.S. Department of the Navy. 1969. *International Code of Signals.* United States Ed. Naval Oceanographic Office H.O. 102. Washington: U.S. Government Printing Office.

U.S. Department of the Navy. 1971. *U.S. Navy Diving-Gas Manual.* 2nd ed. NAVSHIPS 0994-003-7010. Washington: U.S. Department of the Navy.

U.S. Department of the Navy. 1971. *U.S. Navy Diving Operations Handbook.* NAVSHIPS 0994-009-6010. Washington: U.S. Government Printing Office.

U.S. Department of the Navy. 1972. *Deep Water Search Procedures,* Report No. 72-2, Naval Ship Systems Command, Washington: U.S. Department of the Navy.

U.S. Department of the Navy. 1973. *U.S. Navy Recompression Chamber Operator's Handbook.* NAVSHIPS 0994-014-5010. Washington: U.S. Department of the Navy.

U.S. Department of the Navy. 1973. *U.S. Navy Diving Manual.* NAVSHIPS 0994-001-9010. Washington: U.S. Government Printing Office.

University of New Hampshire. 1972. *Manned Underwater Platforms.* U.S. Department of Commerce Technical Report No. 111. Durham, N.H.: University of New Hampshire.

VanDerwalker, J. and Littlehales, B. 1971. Tektite II: Part One. Science's Window on the Sea. *National Geographic,* Vol. 140, No. 2, pp. 256-289.

Walden, B. and Rainnie, W. 1971. *Project FLARE, Florida Aquanaut Research Expedition Program Plan.* Woods Hole, Mass.: Woods Hole Oceanographic Institution.

Weeks, A. 1972. FLARE. Exploring the Coral Reefs. *NOAA,* U.S. Department of Commerce, Vol. 2, No. 3. Washington: U.S. Department of Commerce, July 1972.

Wells, J. 1974. The Metabolism of Tropical Benthic Communities: *In Situ* Determinations and Their Implications. *Marine Technology Society Journal,* Vol. 8, No. 1, pp. 9-11.

Wells, J.; Wells, A.; and VanDerwalker, J. 1973. *In Situ* Studies of Metabolism in Benthic Reef Communities. *Helgoländer wiss. Meeresunters,* Vol. 24, pp. 78-81.

Wicklund, R. ed. 1973. *Hydro-Lab Journal,* Vol. 2, No. 1. Riviera Beach, Fla.: Perry Foundation, Inc.

Wood, E. 1956. Urethane as a Carcinogen. *Progressive Fish Culturist,* Vol. 18, No. 3, pp. 135-136.

Woods, J. and Lythgoe, J. eds. 1971. *Underwater Science.* London: Oxford University Press.

APPENDIX B
ADDITIONAL REFERENCES

Adolfson, J. and Berghage, T. 1974. *Perception and Performance Under Water.* New York: John Wiley & Sons, Inc.

Albano, Gaspare. 1970. *Principles and Observations on the Physiology of the Scuba Diver.* Arlington, Va.: Office of Naval Research.

Altman, P. and Dittmer, D. eds. 1971. *Respiration and Circulation.* Bethesda, Md.: Federation of American Societies for Experimental Biology.

American National Red Cross, The. 1973. *Advanced First Aid and Emergency Care.* Garden City, N.Y.: Doubleday & Company, Inc.

Athletic Institute, The. 1970. *Human Performance and Scuba Diving.* Proceedings of the Symposium on Underwater Physiology, 10-11 April 1970, at La Jolla, Calif. Chicago: The Athletic Institute.

Battelle Memorial Institute. 1970. *Proceedings: Purity Standards for Divers Breathing Gas Symposium,* 8-9 July 1970 at Columbus, Ohio: Battelle Memorial Institute.

Bright, C. 1972. Diving in the Arctic. *Naval Research Reviews,* Vol. 25, No. 8, pp. 1-12. Washington: U.S. Government Printing Office.

British Sub Aqua Club, The. 1973. *The Diving Officer's Handbook.* 4th ed. London: The Riverside Press Ltd.

Carrier, R. and Carrier, B. 1973. *Dive: The Complete Book of Skin Diving.* New York: Funk & Wagnalls, Inc.

Chess, J. 1969. An Airlift Sampling Device for Benthic Organisms. *Westinghouse Ocean Research Laboratories Research Memo 69-1S1-OCEAN-M1.* Annapolis, Md.: Westinghouse, Corp.

Clarke, C. and Strenge, W. eds. 1973. *American Cinematographer Manual.* 4th ed. Hollywood: American Society of Cinematographers Holding Corp.

Clifton, H. and Hunter, R. 1973. Bioturbational Rates and Effects in Carbonate Sand, St. John, U.S. Virgin Islands. *The Journal of Geology,* Vol. 81, No. 3, pp. 253-268.

Clifton, H,; Phillips, R.; and Hunter, R. 1973. Dispositional Structures and Processes in the Mouths of Small Coastal Streams, Southwestern Oregon. In *Publications in Geomorphology, State University of New York,* pp. 115-140.

Council for National Co-operation in Aquatics. 1970. *The New Science of Skin and Scuba Diving,* 3rd rev. ed. New York: Association Press.

Cross, E. 1970. Technifacts, High-Altitude Decompression. *Skin Diver,* Vol. 19, No. 11, p. 17.

Crossett, R. and Larkum, A. 1966. The Ecology of Benthic Marine Algae on Submarine Cliff Faces in Malta. *Underwater Association,* Report 1, pp. 57-61.

Davis, F.; Osborn, J.; Baddeley, A.; and Graham, I. 1972. Diver Performance: Nitrogen Narcosis and Anxiety. *Aerospace Medicine,* Vol. 43, No. 10, pp. 1079-1082.

Dobbs, H. 1972. *Camera Underwater.* 2nd ed. London: Focal Press Limited.

Dowling, G. 1963. *Diver's Instrumented Observation Board.* U.S. Navy Mine Defense Laboratory Report 210. Arlington, Va.: U.S. Government Clearinghouse.

Dueker, C. 1970. *Medical Aspects of Sport Diving.* Cranbury, N.J.: A.S. Barnes and Co., Inc.

Dugan, J. 1959. *Man Under the Sea,* rev. ed. New York: P.F. Collier, Inc.

du Pont de Nemours and Co., E.I. 1969. *The Blaster's Handbook.* 15th ed. Wilmington, Del.: E.I. du Pont de Nemours and Co.

Duran, J. 1972. Hot Water System at NURDC. *Faceplate,* Vol. 3, No. 1, p. 19.

Egstrom, G. and Weltman, G. 1974. *Underwater Work Performance and Tolerance: Final Report.* Los Angeles: University of California.

Egstrom, G.; Weltman, G.; Baddeley, A.; Cuccaro, W.; and Willis, M. 1972. *Underwater Work Performance and Work Tolerance.* Biotechnology Laboratory Technical Report No. 51. Los Angeles: University of California.

Egstrom, G.; Weltman, G.; Cuccaro, W.; and Willis, M. 1973. *Underwater Work Performance and Work Tolerance.* Biotechnology Laboratory Technical Report No. 52. Los Angeles: University of California.

Erickson, R. 1972. *Discover the Underwater World.* Santa Ana, Calif.: U.S. Divers Co.

Evans, A.; Barnard, E.; and Walder, D. 1972. Detection of Gas Bubbles in Man at Decompression. *Aerospace Medicine,* Vol. 43, No. 10, pp. 1095-1096.

Feinstein, S. 1973. Minimum Audible Angle Underwater: A Replication Under Different Acoustic and Environmental Conditions. *Journal of the Acoustical Society of America,* Vol. 54, No. 4, pp. 879-881.

Flemming, N. ed. 1973. Science Diving International. In *Proceedings of the Third Scientific Symposium of Confederation Mondiale Activities Subaquatiques.* Hants, England: Standard Press (Andover), Ltd.

Frey, H. and Frey, S. 1969. *Diver Below!* London: Cillier-Macmillan, Ltd.

Fulton, J. and Gordon, S. 1972. *Diving West.* San Diego: Sports Synergy.

Hansen, R. 1972 and 1973. Air Compressors. *Faceplate,* Vol. 3, No. 2, pp. 26-27; Vol. 3, No. 3, pp. 28-29; Vol. 4, No. 1, pp. 12-15.

Hawkins, T. 1972. Underwater Breathing Apparatus Compared. *Faceplate,* Vol. 3, No. 3, p. 26.

Heezen, B. and Hollister, C. 1971. *The Face of the Deep.* New York: Oxford University Press.

Hogan, W. 1971. *Safe Scuba.* Long Beach, Calif.: William F. Hogan and National Association of Skin Diving Schools, Inc.

Hollien, H. 1973. Underwater Sound Localization in Humans. *The Journal of the Acoustical Society of America,* Vol. 53, No. 5, pp. 1288-1295.

Hurst, C. 1973. Tropical Touch-Me-Nots. *Skin Diver,* Vol. 22, No. 6, pp. 58-60.

Hussain, F. 1970. *Living Underwater,* New York: Praeger Publishers, Inc.

Kenny, J. 1972. *Business of Diving.* Houston: Gulf Publishing Company.

Kinney, J.; Luria, S.; and Weissman, S. 1965. Estimation of Size and Distance Underwater. *U.S. Naval Submarine Medical Center Report No. 462.* Groton, Conn.: U.S. Naval Submarine Medical Center.

Kinney, J.; Luria, S.; and Weitzman, D. 1967. The Visibility of Colors Underwater. *U.S. Naval Submarine Medical Center Report No. 503.* Groton, Conn.: U.S. Naval Submarine Medical Center.

Koehler, W. 1971. *Lure of the Labyrinth.* Costa Mesa, Calif.: Professional Association of Diving Instructors.

Komamiya, K. 1973. Quenching Distance for a Combustible Solid in the Oxygen-Enriched Atmosphere. *The Journal of Fire & Flammability,* Vol. 4, April.

LaFond, E. 1962. Internal Waves. In *The Sea,* edited by M. Hill. New York: Interscience.

Lambertsen, C. ed. 1971. *Underwater Physiology.* New York: Academic Press, Inc.

Lamirande, A. 1972. Fatal Dive in Polluted Waters. *Skin Diver,* Vol. 21, No. 1, p. 72.

Lee, O. 1967. *The Complete Illustrated Guide to Snorkel and Deep Diving.* rev. ed. New York: Doubleday & Company, Inc.

Leggiere, T.; McAniff, J.; Schenck, H.; and van Ryzin, J. 1970. Sound Localization and Homing of Scuba Divers. *Marine Technology Society Journal,* Vol. 4, No. 2.

McKenney, J. 1973. Up to Our Snorkels in Masks. *Skin Diver,* Vol. 22, No. 6.

Majendie, J. 1970. Keeping the Diver Warm, *Faceplate,* Vol. 1, No. 2, p. 10.

Majendie, J. 1970. Arctic Dive. *Faceplate,* Vol. 1, No. 3, pp. 17-18.

Marine Technology Society, 1969. *Underwater Welding Cutting and Hand Tools.* Symposium proceedings, 10-11 October 1967. Washington: Marine Technology Society.

Marine Technology Society. 1970. *Equipment for the Working Diver.* Symposium proceedings, 24-25 February 1970 at Columbus, Ohio. Washington: Marine Technology Society.

Meade, J. 1973. Killer From Beyond Time. *Skin Diver,* Vol. 22, No. 1.

Miller, R. ed. 1964. *Papers in Marine Geology,* New York: The Macmillan Company.

Mount, T. 1972. *The Cave Diving Manual.* Miami, Fla.: National Association for Cave Diving.

Mount, T. 1973. *Safe Cave Diving.* Miami, Fla.: National Association for Cave Diving.

Muellenhoff, W. 1974. Preliminary Summary of Sludge Degradation Studies in a Marine Benthic Environment. *Proceedings of a Research Symposium on Pretreatment and Ultimate Disposal of Waste Water Solids,* 22 May 1974, at Cooke College, Rutgers University, New Brunswick, N.J., in press.

Murry, T. 1969. *A Method for Analyzing Phonemic Errors in Underwater Speech Intelligibility Testing.* CSL/ONR Technical Report #24. Washington: Office of Naval Research.

Myers, J.; Holm, C.; and McAllister, R. 1969. *Handbook of Ocean and Underwater Engineering.* New York: McGraw-Hill Book Company.

National Academy of Sciences and National Academy of Engineering. 1973. *Civil Manned Undersea Activity: An Assessment.* Washington: National Academy of Sciences and National Academy of Engineering.

National Association of Skin Diving Schools. 1973. *The Instructional Aids of the National Association of Skin Diving Schools.* Long Beach, Calif.: National Association of Skin Diving Schools, Inc.

National Association of Underwater Instructors. 1972. *Legal Aspects of Underwater Instruction.* Grand Terrace (Colton), Calif.: National Association of Underwater Instructors.

National Geographic Society, The. 1973. *World Beneath the Sea.* 2nd ed. Washington: The National Geographic Society.

Naval Civil Engineering Laboratory. 1970. *Survey of the Navy's Potential Utilization of Manned Underwater Laboratories.* Port Hueneme, Calif.: Naval Civil Engineering Laboratory.

Naval Civil Engineering Laboratory. 1974. Hydraulic Rock Drill Operates Underwater. *Product Engineering,* Vol. 45, No. 3, p. 13.

Nystrom, D. and Stortz, J. 1973. Hotline—A Communications System for Diving Research. *Sea Technology,* Vol. 14, No. 9, pp. 18-20.

Olney, R. 1969. *The Inquiring Mind: Oceanography.* Camden, N.J.: Thomas Nelson, Inc.

Page, G. 1974. Modification of a Pneumatic Track Drill for Underwater Use by Divers. *Civil Engineering Laboratory.* Report NR NCEL-TN-1339, Port Hueneme, Calif.: Naval Civil Engineering Laboratory.

Parker, E. 1971. *Gene Parker's Complete Handbook of Skin Diving.* 2nd ed. New York: Avon Books.

Penzias, W. and Goodman, M. 1973. *Man Beneath the Sea.* New York: John Wiley & Sons, Inc.

Peterson, M. 1969. *History Under the Sea.* Washington: Smithsonian Institution Press.

Peyser, R. 1970. *Corrosion of Steel Scuba Tanks.* Scuba Safety Report Series, Report No. 1. Kingston, R.I.: University of Rhode Island.

Poole, L. 1955. *Diving for Science.* New York: Whittlesey House.

Rahn, H. ed. 1965. *Symposium on the Physiology of Breath-Hold Diving & the Ama of Japan.* Washington: National Academy of Sciences—National Research Council.

Rasmussen, J. ed. 1973. *Man in Isolation and Confinement.* Chicago: Aldine Publishing Company.

Ross, H.; King, S.; and Snowden, H. 1970. Size and Distance Judgements in the Vertical Plane Underwater. *Psychologische Forschung,* Vol. 33, pp. 115-164.

Schenck, H. Jr. and McAniff, J. 1972. *A Study Analysis of Scuba Accidents Involving U.S. Citizens.* Kingston, R.I.: University of Rhode Island.

Schenck, H. Jr. and McAniff, J. 1972. *Skin and Scuba Diving Fatalities Involving U.S. Citizens, 1971.* Scuba Safety Report Series, Report No. 6. Kingston, R.I.: University of Rhode Island.

Schenck, H. Jr. and McAniff, J. 1972. *Mortality Rates for Skin and Scuba Divers.* Scuba Safety Report Series, Report No. 7. Kingston, R.I.: University of Rhode Island.

Schenck, H. Jr. and McAniff, J. 1973. *United States Underwater Fatality Statistics—1972.* Report No. URI-73-8. Washington: U.S. Government Printing Office.

Schenck, H. Jr.; McAniff, J.; and Carapezza, E. 1970. *Skin and Scuba Diving Fatalities Involving U.S. Citizens, 1970.* Scuba Safety Report Series No. 2. Kingston, R.I.: University of Rhode Island.

Schenck, H. Jr.; McAniff, J.; Schenck, M.; and Schenck, H. 1972. *Diving Accident Survey, 1946-1970, Including 503 Known Fatalities.* Scuba Safety Report Series, Report No. 5. Kingston, R.I.: University of Rhode Island.

Shapiro, S. ed. 1971. *Our Changing Fisheries.* Washington: U.S. Government Printing Office.

Shenton, E. 1972. *Diving for Science.* New York: W.W. Norton & Company, Inc.

Shilling, C. and Werts, M. 1973. *Underwater Medicine and Related Sciences.* New York: IFI/PLENUM.

Smith, C. 1972. Depth Gauge Corrections for Altitude and Fresh Water Diving, *NAUI News,* Sept.—Oct. p. 13.

Society for Underwater Technology, The. 1971. *Diving Regulations.* Seminar proceedings at the Institution of Mechanical Engineers, 4 February 1971 in London, England. London: The Society for Underwater Technology.

Somers, L. 1967. Diving Techniques as Applied to Geological Investigations of the Great Lakes. *Proceedings, Tenth Conference on Great Lakes Research.* Ann Arbor: University of Michigan.

Stewart, J. 1971. *Marine Technicians Handbook.* LaJolla, Calif.: Institute of Marine Resources.

Tenney, J. 1971. *2400 Hours of Saturation Diving.* Scuba Safety Report Series, Report No. 4. Kingston, R.I.: University of Rhode Island.

Terry, R. 1966. *The Deep Submersible.* North Hollywood, Calif.: Western Periodicals Co.

Throckmorton, P. 1970. *Shipwrecks and Archaeology.* London: Victor Gollancz Ltd.

Titcombe, R. 1973. *Handbook for Professional Divers.* Philadelphia: J.B. Lippincott Company.

Tuttle, W. and Schottelius, B. 1965. *Textbook for Physiology.* 15th ed. St. Louis: The C.V. Mosby Company.

Tzimoulis, P. 1974. Push-Button Diving. *Skin Diver,* Vol. 23, No. 7, pp. 4-7.

Undersea Medical Society, Inc. 1973. *Respiratory Limitations of Underwater Breathing Equipment.* Report No. WS:4-15-74. Bethesda, Md.: Undersea Medical Society, Inc.

Undersea Medical Society, Inc. 1974. *Labyrinthine Dysfunction During Diving.* Report No. WS:6-15-74. Bethesda, Md.: Undersea Medical Society, Inc.

U.S. Coast Guard. 1973. *National Search and Rescue Manual.* CG-038. Washington: U.S. Government Printing Office.

U.S. Department of Defense. 1970. *Color Code for Pipelines and for Compressed Gas Cylinders.* MIL-STD-101B. Washington: U.S. Department of Defense.

U.S. Department of the Navy. 1973. *System Certification Procedures and Criteria Manual for Deep Submergence Systems.* NAVMAT P-9290. Washington: U.S. Government Printing Office.

Weltman, G.; Egstrom, G.; Willis, M.; and Cuccaro, W. 1971. *Underwater Work Measurement Techniques: Final Report.* Biotechnology Laboratory Technical Report No. 50. Los Angeles: University of California.

Wicklund, R. ed. 1972-1973. *Hyrdo-Lab Journal.* Riviera Beach, Fla.: Perry Foundation, Inc.

Woodley, J. and Ross, H. 1969. *Distance Estimates of Familiar Objects Underwater.* London: Underwater Association Report.

Woods, J. 1968. Wave-Induced Shear Instability in the Summer Thermocline. *Journal of Fluid Mechanics,* Vol. 32, pp. 791-800.

Woods, J. 1969. On Designing a Probe to Measure Ocean Microstructure. *Underwater Science and Technology Journal,* Vol. 1, No. 1, p. 6.

Woods, J. 1971. Micro-oceanography. In *Underwater Science,* edited by J. Woods and J. Lythgoe. London: Oxford University Press.

Yokayama, T. 1966. *Physiology of Breath-Hold Diving and the AMA of Japan.* Washington: National Academy of Sciences, National Research Council.

Zanelli, L. 1969. *Underwater Swimming, An Advanced Handbook.* South Brunswick, Great Britain: A.S. Barne and Co.

Zanelli, L. ed. 1972. *The British Sub Aqua Club Diving Manual.* 7th ed. London: The British Sub Aqua Club.

Zhukov, L.; Mayer, A,; and Rehtzamer, G. 1964. Use of Underwater Photo and Movie Survey for Investigation of Turbulence in the Sea. *Mat. 11 Knof. Probl.* 'Vzaimodeystviye Atmos Gidros Severn Chasti Atlantisch Okeana'. pp. 151-155.

Zinkowski, N. 1971. *Commercial Oil-Field Diving.* Cambridge, Md.: Cornell Maritime Press, Inc.

APPENDIX C
NOAA DIVING
REGULATIONS

NOAA Circular 74–62

August 12, 1974

1. PURPOSE: This section prescribes the administration and safety rules for NOAA diving. NOAA Circular 72–19, dated 10 February 1972, filed as NDM 64–23, is hereby superseded.

2. GENERAL: NOAA programs frequently involve the need for competent underwater operations. The use of NOAA employees to meet these needs is vital to efficient and economic operations.

    a. Purpose: The purpose of a diving safety program is:

    (1) *Safety:* To ensure that all diving under the auspices of the National Oceanic and Atmospheric Administration is conducted in a manner most likely to minimize accidental injury or occupational illness.

    (2) *Operational Standards:* To set forth rules, regulations, and standards for selection, training, certification, supervision, and equipping of NOAA divers.

    (3) *Reciprocity:* To establish a working reciprocity between Major Line Components (MLC) within NOAA, other government agencies, and private concerns involved in diving.

    b. Policy: The policy of NOAA is to administer its underwater activities in a manner that safely and efficiently achieves its objectives and to maintain adequate protection for its employees, property, and those for whom it has a responsibility.

    c. Scope: These regulations shall apply to all NOAA employees and NOAA sponsored personnel engaged in underwater activities, and shall be administered with NOAA's basic policies uppermost in mind.

    d. Responsibility: Basic responsibility, while diving, rests with the individual. Line and staff management shall be responsible for conducting a safe and efficient diving program. Specific responsibilities will be defined in these regulations.

3. ADMINISTRATION: The Associate Administrator for Marine Resources shall broadly administer NOAA's underwater diving activities through the Director of the Manned Undersea Science and Technology Program.

    a. NOAA Diving Coordinator:

    (1) *Designation*: The Associate Administrator for Marine Resources shall, upon the advice of the NOAA Diving Safety Board, appoint a NOAA Diving Coordinator for the diving program who will be the principal contact within NOAA for diving operational policy and safety procedures.

    (2) *Qualifications:* The NOAA Diving Coordinator shall be a trained diver with a wide range of experience, currently certified NOAA diver with at least five (5) years of diving experience, having logged at least four hundred dives, and having satisfactorily completed a nationally recognized instructor certification course or its equivalent.

    (3) *Responsibilities:* The NOAA Diving Coordinator shall be a member of and chair the NOAA Diving Safety Board, and be responsible for:

    (a) Diver training and safety programs, with the assistance of the Diving Safety Board.

    (b) Annual review, with the Diving Safety Board, of all NOAA diving operations during the preceding calendar year, submitting an annual report at the end of the fiscal year to the Associate Administrator for Marine Resources.

    (c) Arranging and scheduling of inspections at each diving unit.

    (d) Certification of NOAA divers in accordance with this order and issuing letters of authorization (See Exhibit 4).

    (e) Delegating various training responsibilities, with Diving Safety Board recommendations, to other fully certified divers and instructors.

    (f) Reviewing of all budgeted diving projects.

    (g) Reviewing and taking appropriate action on recommendations of changes in operating policy formulated by the Diving Safety Board.

    (h) Reviewing all NOAA diving accidents or potentially dangerous experiences and issuing reports on preventive measures to ensure safe diving.

    (i) Approving the use of specialized types of diving apparatus or gas mixtures, other than open-circuit scuba.

    (j) Remain abreast of new diving techniques and innovations.

    b. Assistants to the Coordinator:

    (1) *Designation:* The NOAA Diving Coordinator shall appoint assistants to enable the Coordinator to effectively administer the NOAA Diving Safety Program.

    (2) *Qualifications:* Assistants to the Coordinator shall be trained divers with a wide range of experience, currently certified NOAA divers with

at least five (5) years of diving experience, having logged at least four hundred (400) dives and satisfactorily completed a nationally recognized instructor certification course or its equivalent.

(3) *Responsibilities:* Assistants to the Coordinator shall be responsible for duties assigned to them by the NOAA Diving Coordinator.

c. Major Line Component Diving Officer:

(1) *Designation:* The Director of each MLC which conducts diving operations shall, upon the recommendation of the NOAA Diving Coordinator, appoint an MLC Diving Officer.

(2) *Qualifications:* The MLC Diving Officer shall be a trained diver with a wide range of experience, currently certified NOAA diver with at least five (5) years of diving experience, having logged at least four hundred (400) dives, and having satisfactorily completed a nationally recognized instructor certification course or its equivalent.

(3) *Responsibilities:* The MLC Diving Officer shall be a member of and represent his MLC at the NOAA Diving Safety Board. He shall be responsible, within his MLC, for:

(a) Planning, programming, directing, and reviewing the diving activities within his MLC to ensure compliance with NOAA policies, procedures and standards relating to underwater operations.

(b) Maintaining familiarity with all diving activities within his MLC and inspecting diving units during regular diving assignments.

(c) Recommending to the NOAA Diving Coordinator divers who have successfully completed the required training and are qualified for NOAA certification.

(d) Planning and coordinating diver training programs, leading to certification of divers, to meet the requirements of regional research and technical operations.

(e) Recommending examiners and/or courses of instruction for certification and training.

(f) Maintaining a file of letters of authorization for divers in his MLC.

(g) Investigating each diving accident which occurs within the MLC, coordinating the reporting thereof, and submitting a report to the NOAA Diving Coordinator within one (1) month of an accident, including recommendations for avoiding a similar accident.

(h) Submitting an annual report of all diving activities and accidents within 20 days after the end of the fiscal year to the Diving Coordinator.

d. NOAA Diving Safety Board:

(1) *Composition:* The NOAA Diving Safety Board shall be composed of the following voting members:

(a) The NOAA Diving Coordinator.

(b) MLC Diving Officers.

(c) Designated MLC representatives who shall meet the qualifications specified for a Major Line Component Diving Officer.

In addition, nonvoting members may participate in the annual Safety Board Meeting. The number of voting MLC representatives and nonvoting members shall be recommended to the Associate Administrator for Marine Resources annually by the Diving Safety Board.

(2) *Revisions:* All recommendations for revisions of these regulations must be agreed upon by two-thirds of the voting members of the Board.

(3) *Responsibilities:* The NOAA Diving Safety Board shall be responsible for:

(a) Recommending policy and changes in operational procedures within NOAA that will ensure a safe and efficient diving program.

(b) Reviewing existing policies, procedures and training needs to ensure a continually high level of technical skills and knowledge throughout the NOAA diving program.

(c) Planning, programming, and directing, in cooperation with the NOAA Diving Coordinator, matters of policy pertaining to the initial certification of new divers and refresher training of experienced divers.

(d) Recommending changes in operating policy, to the Associate Administrator for Marine Resources through the NOAA Diving Coordinator.

(e) Serving as an appeal board in cases where a diver's certification has been suspended.

(f) Planning, programming, and directing diver workshops, seminars, and other activities considered essential to maintaining a high level of competency among divers.

(g) Reviewing NOAA diving accidents or potentially dangerous experiences and reporting on preventive measures to ensure safe diving.

(h) Recommending to the Associate Administrator for Marine Resources the eligible persons to fill the vacancy of NOAA Diving Coordinator.

e. Unit Diving Officer:

(1) *Designation:* Unit Diving Officers shall be appointed for various NOAA installations and ships which conduct diving operations. These diving officers shall, upon the recommendation of the MLC Diving Officer, be appointed by the installation directors or ship commanders.

(2) *Qualifications:* The Unit Diving Officer shall be a trained, currently certified, diver experienced in the types of diving conducted by his organizational unit.

(3) *Responsibilities:* The Unit Diving Officer shall be responsible, within his unit, for:

(a) Ensuring that all diving gear and accessory equipment be maintained in a safe operating condition.

(b) Maintaining an equipment file to include type, brand name, serial number, and repairs completed on compressors, tanks, regulators, depth gauges, pressure gauges, and decompression meters.

(c) Ensuring that a competent Dive Master is in charge of each diving operation.

(d) Submitting an annual report within 10 days after the end of the fiscal year to the MLC Diving Officer.

(e) Immediately reporting all diving related accidents which occur within his unit, and submitting a written report within 10 days to the MLC Diving Officer.

(f) Maintaining a file on each diver in his unit which shall include but not be limited to: diving physical examinations, training records, letters of authorization, monthly diving logs, etc.

f. Dive Master:

(1) *Designation:* Depending upon the project organization, a Dive Master will be assigned by the Unit Diving Officer for all dives. In his absence, the MLC Diving Officer or the Diving Coordinator will assign the Dive Master.

(2) *Qualifications:* The Dive Master shall be a currently certified diver experienced in the type of diving he is responsible for.

(3) *Responsibilities:* The Dive Master shall be in complete charge of the diving operation and shall be responsible for and ensure that:

(a) All diving operations are conducted *safely* in accordance with prescribed NOAA diving safety rules and regulations.

(b) All divers are certified, properly trained, and physically fit to perform the required diving.

(c) All equipment is in a safe operating condition.

(d) Emergency procedures are understood by all personnel prior to diving.

(e) All divers are monitored after each dive for symptoms of decompression sickness.

g. Individual Diver:

(1) *Designation:* Individual divers shall be certified by the NOAA Diving Coordinator in accordance with these regulations.

(2) *Qualifications:* Divers shall be sufficiently trained to undertake the assigned diving tasks.

(3) *Responsibilities:* The individual diver shall be responsible for and ensure that:

(a) He is in good physical condition, and at a high level of diving proficiency.

(b) His equipment is in a safe operating condition.

(c) Diving conditions are safe.

(d) He does not violate the dictates of his training or these regulations.

4. OPERATIONS:

a. Project Review: No proposed diving project (budgeted program) shall be approved, funded, or undertaken before the NOAA Diving Coordinator or his designee has made an adequate review of:

(1) Diver qualifications, certification, and physical condition.

(2) Availability of equipment and personnel needed to complete the project.

(3) Specific standard operating procedures regarding safety, methodology, and emergency procedures.

(4) Support staffing.

Procedures for individual diving tasks undertaken by NOAA divers in support of primarily nondiving projects or operations shall be reviewed by the MLC Diving Officer.

b. Policies:

(1) *Individual Diver Responsibility:* Each diver has the responsibility and privilege to refuse to dive if, in his judgment, conditions are unsafe or unfavorable; if at any specific time he feels he is not in proper physical or mental condition for diving; or if by diving, he would violate the dictates of his training or these regulations. The conditions and reasons for refusing to dive may be required

to be documented. If requested, the incident will be reviewed by the Unit Director with the Unit Diving Officer and diver, and appropriate action may be taken. Any action resulting from this review may be appealed to the NOAA Diving Safety Board.

(2) *Scuba Diving Teams:* Except under emergency conditions, the buddy system of at least two (2) divers will always be required. In the event that diving is shallow within a restricted area, with water conditions of low velocity and turbidity, the buddy diver may remain at the surface fully equipped, maintaining contact with the working diver at all times. A surface attendant shall be present in the immediate area any time diving conditions require it.

(3) *Diver Proficiency:* NOAA certified divers should log an average of at least two (2) diving days per month. Any time six (6) weeks or more elapse without a dive, the diver should, in his own interest, complete a requalifying program. Any time three (3) months or more elapse without a dive, the diver must complete a requalifying program before resuming work dives. The MLC Diving Officer or his designee shall specify the requalifying program. This requirement may be waived by the official in charge of the project, program, or command during emergency conditions. A report of such waiver must be submitted to the NOAA Diving Coordinator through the MLC Diving Officer for review by the NOAA Diving Safety Board. Supervisors will authorize the necessary time and payment for qualifying dives if diving is required for official program activities. Diving equipment will be available during nonduty hours for purposes of maintaining diver proficiency.

(4) *Diving by Non-NOAA Certified Personnel:* Such persons must submit evidence of diving training to the MLC Diving Officer or his designee who will evaluate this training with the standards required for NOAA certification to determine equivalence with a level of NOAA certification. In all cases, a checkout dive shall be observed by the MLC Diving Officer or his designee.

(5) *Non-NOAA Diving:* NOAA personnel may participate in non-NOAA diving programs with which reciprocity has been established by the NOAA Diving Coordinator or his designee.

(6) *Diving Logs:* Divers shall be required to log all dives. All certified divers shall, by the 5th of each month, submit a Diving Log (See Exhibit 5) to the Unit Diving Officer, who shall

forward a copy to the NOAA Diving Coordinator.

(7) *Reporting Diving Accidents:* All diving incidents resulting in injury or with a potential for injury, and all incidents of serious equipment failure, shall be reported in accordance with NOAA Directives Manual 64–11, on "Supervisor's Report of Accident" (NOAA Form 64–1). In addition, a full written report shall be prepared and submitted to the NOAA Diving Coordinator through the MLC Diving Officer within ten (10) days by the Unit Diving Officer to cover facts such as nature of operation, existing conditions, personnel involved, type of equipment used, nature of injury or equipment failure, causal analysis, recommendations for prevention in the future, etc.

5. TRAINING AND CERTIFICATION:

a. Application: NOAA personnel may apply through channels to the appropriate director to be considered for diver training, as the need exists. Personnel applying for training must use NOAA Form 53–1, "Request for Training" when the total training time will include 8 hours or more of formal/ classroom instruction. When requested, the MLC Diving Officer or Unit Diving Officer shall aid the various base or installation directors in analyzing diving needs. A list of certified NOAA divers in the appropriate operating area shall be made available to the director, or other official in charge of a NOAA base or installation.

b. Justification: An employee who applies for certification must volunteer the application of his skills for NOAA programs. The need for the employee's skill in NOAA programs shall be considered before taking action on the application.

c. Physical Examination: Prior to acceptance for initial training or certification, and annually thereafter, each diver shall be required to undergo a diving physical examination. A "Certificate of Medical Examination" (SF–78), and a "Report of Medical History" (SF–93), shall be used. A "Report of Medical Examination" (SF–88), may be used for commissioned personnel. The examining physician shall be provided with the "Medical Evaluation Criteria" (See Exhibit 2) to help ensure an examination appropriate to diving activities. After each major illness, operation, or injury, certified divers shall undergo a medical review and/or examination before resuming diving activities. A copy of all physical examinations will be submitted to the Unit Diving Officer who shall forward a copy to the NOAA Diving Coordinator. Candidates not meeting the physical standards may request a waiver, based on a review by the Diving Medical Review Board (See NDM 06–21), from the NOAA Diving Coordinator. The NOAA Diving Coordinator reviewing requests for waiver may:

(1) Refuse waiver.

(2) Approve waiver and certify fitness for full diving duty.

(3) Approve the applicant for limited duty. This designation should be made only for conditions that are not significantly disabling and do not constitute a significant threat to the candidate or his fellow divers.

d. Basic Diving Training: Initial diving training may be obtained from any program approved by the NOAA Diving Coordinator or designee.

e. Written Examination: All applicants for NOAA certification shall pass a standard written examination on scuba equipment, physics and physiology, general techniques, and first aid as they apply to scuba diving, approved by the NOAA Diving Safety Board. Applicants failing the examination may retake it after two (2) weeks; however, the re-examination grade must then be ten (10) points above the minimum passing grade.

f. Diving Evaluation: The prospective diver must demonstrate his proficiency and skill in diving to the MLC Diving Officer or his designee.

g. Certification: Upon completion of preliminary training, satisfactory written and medical examinations, and diver evaluation, NOAA employees shall be considered for certification in the following categories:

(1) *Trainee:* Any employee who has completed an approved scuba course consisting of less than fifteen (15) open-water dives. Trainees do not perform working dives.

(2) *Limited:* Divers who have completed basic certification requirements, but because of limited experience or operational needs must be restricted in diving activities, may be eligible for a limited certification once they have completed at least fifteen (15) open-water dives.

(3) *Unlimited:* Divers who have demonstrated a high level of competence, a wide range of experience and good judgment, and who have logged at least one-hundred (100) dives, of which at least three (3) will be with the MLC

Diving Officer or his designee at varying degrees of difficulty, shall be eligible for unlimited NOAA certification.

(4) *Instructor:* Divers who have a wide range of experience currently certified with at least five (5) years of diving experience, having logged at least four hundred (400) dives, and having satisfactorily completed a nationally recognized instructor certification course, or equal, shall be eligible for NOAA Instructor Certification. Each applicant's qualifications shall be reviewed by the NOAA Diving Safety Board.

h. Issuance: NOAA diver certification may be issued by the NOAA Diving Coordinator upon recommendations of the MLC Diving Officer and the Unit Diving Officer. Recommendations shall include a summary of diving experience, a diving critique by the Unit Diving Officer, and evidence of satisfactory passing of a diving physical. The NOAA Diving Coordinator shall issue a Diving Identification Card (See Exhibit 6), and a Letter of Authorization (See Exhibit 4) to the diver, with a copy of the letter to the diver's official personnel folder, the MLC Diving Officer, and the Unit Diving Officer.

i. Terms of Certification: All diving certifications shall lapse after three (3) months or more without a dive, or thirteen (13) months from the date of the last physical examination.

j. Recertification: The MLC Diving Officer or his designee may recertify a diver whose certification has lapsed after the diver has again demonstrated ability to perform satisfactorily.

k. Suspension of Certification: NOAA diver certification may be suspended for cause by the Unit Diving Officer, MLC Diving Officer or NOAA Diving Coordinator. Violation of any regulation in this circular, or lack of good judgment may be considered cause. The diver shall be informed in writing of the reasons for suspension, and will be given the opportunity to appeal his suspension to the NOAA Diving Safety Board.

l. Refresher Training: NOAA certified divers may be given periodic refresher training.

6. NOAA DIVING SAFETY RULES: The NOAA Diving Safety Rules (See Exhibit 1) shall be adhered to on all diving operations.

7. EXCEPTIONS: Deviations from these regulations may be approved by the MLC Diving Officer or his designee when he is assured that such procedures are safe and essential to program operation. Emergency conditions may warrant actions contrary to the dictates of this circular. A written report of deviations shall be submitted to the NOAA Diving Coordinator for review by the NOAA Diving Safety Board.

8. EXHIBITS: For convenience of reference, the following exhibits are attached to this circular:

Exhibit No.	Title
1	Diving Safety Rules
2	Medical Evaluation Criteria
3	Ship Operations Checklist
4	Sample Format for Letter of Authorization to Dive
5	Monthly Diving Log
6	NOAA Diver's Identification Card

Dr. John W. Townsend, Jr.
Associate Administrator

Exhibit 1
NOAA Diving
Safety Rules

1. Certification: Each diver must have a valid NOAA Certification or NOAA-approved equivalent.

2. Solo Diving: No one may dive unattended.

3. Depth Limits: Dives shall not exceed 130 feet. Proposals for planned dives to depths greater than 130 feet will require written approval by the NOAA Diving Coordinator or his designee.

4. Decompression Tables: Decompression tables should be copied for use by some photographic method which reproduces an exact copy. If this method is not available, then the hand copied schedule should be checked for accuracy by several persons.

5. Decompression Dives: Diving activities which exceed the limits of no decompression will be permitted only under the following conditions:

a. *Proposal:* A detailed dive plan has been reviewed by the NOAA Diving Coordinator or his designee.

b. *Competence:* The project leader must demonstrate to the MLC Diving Officer or his designee that the Dive Master and all members of the diving team have a thorough knowledge of decompression and repetitive dive principles.

c. *Dive Team:* The team must be composed of no less than three (3) divers, (the third diver must be suited and must stand by on the surface).

d. *Equipment:* Each participating diver must wear a watch, depth gauge, and have on his person a decompression schedule for the maximum proposed depth of dive.

6. Diving at High Altitudes: Decompression tables, depth of stops, rate of ascent and repetitive dive planning must be altered for safe diving at altitudes above 1,000 feet. Sea level equivalent depths and rate of ascent should be computed based on dive site atmospheric pressure and density of water. Upon surfacing, the lowered oxygen partial pressure may cause air hunger and pulmonary difficulties. Depth values for bourdon tube and bellows depth gauges must be corrected for altitude and density of water. Decompression meters should not be used.

7. Flying After Diving: Before flying, a diver who has completed any number of dives on air and decompressed following the U.S. Navy Standard Air Decompression Tables should wait at sea level breathing air for the computed surface interval that allows him to be classified as a Group D diver in the U.S. Navy Repetitive Diving Table. The aircraft cabin atmosphere must not exceed 8,000 feet altitude.

8. Over-Bottom Dives: Dives in waters where a diver could sense a loss of orientation or descend below safe diving depths are to be considered over-bottom dives. No over-bottom dives shall be made unless some direct contact with the surface is maintained, such as net web, a marked line suspended from a surface float, or depth gauges for all participants, which permits the diver to determine whether he is descending or ascending. All such divers must be equipped with a buoyancy compensating device.

9. Boat Tending: During dives beyond swimming distance from shore, or those in areas of strong currents, a small boat with a qualified operator will tend the diver.

10. Ship Activities: When appropriate, during ship-related diving activities, the "Dive Safe Ship Operations Checklist," NOAA Form 64-3, will be utilized and completed (See Exhibit 3).

11. Recompression Chamber: The location, accessibility and telephone number of all accessible and operable recompression chambers shall be available to all participating divers before each diving operation.

12. Emergency Procedures: The MLC Diving Officer, with the approval of the NOAA Diving Safety Board, will prescribe emergency procedures to be used in handling diving-related accidents in his operational area, and all divers shall be familiar with these procedures.

13. First Aid Training: All divers should have appropriate First Aid training.

14. Equipment:

a. *Life Support:* Open circuit scuba using compressed air shall be standard. Other types of equipment (i.e., surface-supplied diving equipment, closed-circuit rebreathers, semi-closed units or other types of diving apparatus utilizing gas mixtures) may be approved for use by the NOAA Diving Coordinator. Individuals requesting use of closed-circuit rebreathers, semi-closed units, or other types of equipment must have been trained and qualified in the use of such equipment.

b. *Harness and Weight Belt:* All harness and weight belts must have a quick release, operable by a single motion by either hand.

c. *Flotation Device:* Each diver shall wear

an adequate inflatable vest or other flotation device.

d. *Compass:* An underwater compass shall be carried by each diver when, in the opinion of the Dive Master, lack of underwater orientation is likely to occur and may create a hazard.

e. *Depth Gauge:* One underwater depth gauge shall be carried by each diver when diving in an area of unknown depth, or an area of uneven bottom contours when a diver might reasonably exceed his *planned dive depth.*

f. *Decompression Meter:* Use of decompression meters will be authorized only by the NOAA Diving Coordinator or his designee. Decompression meters will not be used for dives which require decompression stops. Decompression meters can be used as an alternative method of determining the allowable time at depths before a decompression stop is required. In all cases at least two meters must be used simultaneously with the more conservative meter used to determine the allowable dive time. Decompression meters must be recalibrated every eighteen (18) months by a qualified technician.

g. *Diving Watch:* A diving watch shall be worn by each member of a diving team who may reasonably expect to exceed the "no decompression" limit.

h. *Diving Flag:* An appropriate diving flag shall be shown while actively diving in areas subject to boating or other hazardous traffic.

i. *Air Compressor:* No person shall operate a scuba air compressor without having first read the instructions and assisted an operator experienced in its operation. An operational log shall be maintained for all NOAA scuba compressors.

15. Equipment Maintenance: All diving gear and accessory equipment shall be maintained in a safe operating condition. Manufacturers' recommended servicing policy shall be followed. Equipment in questionable condition shall be repaired, overhauled, or discarded. All regulatory valves, depth gauges, and decompression meters must be critically examined, calibrated or checked for accuracy by a competent mechanic, or appropriate specialist every eighteen (18) months. A record of the inspection and repair will be filed with the Unit Diving Officer.

16. Air Tank Inspection and Testing: The interior of all air cylinders must be visually inspected annually by a trained person; cylinders shall be hydrostatically tested at least every three (3) years. The date of the last test must be recorded on the tank.

17. Air: Tanks shall be charged only with air certified as meeting established air standards.

Exhibit 2
Medical Evaluation
Criteria and Report

PART I
MEDICAL EVALUATION CRITERIA

These criteria are to be used by the examining physician in evaluating an applicant's physical fitness for diving.

Clinical Evaluation: The applicant should be free of chronic disabling disease or disability. His history should be free of disease or disability of the type which could recur under diving conditions, or strenuous physical activity. Any disease which might prevent active exercise should disqualify the applicant. There should be no bleeding tendency.

Ears: Individuals with acute or chronic ear infection should not dive. Scarring from otitis is not a contraindication to diving. Individuals with perforation of the drum should be disqualified. Healed perforations of the drum of at least two months duration will not be disqualifying. Special care should be taken to keep the ears well cleared during the dive. Acute or chronic otitis externa with discharge, or moderate amounts of cerumen in the external canal, should be considered harmful in diving until the canals are clear. Check tympanic movement with Valsalva. There should be no disease of the mastoids or disturbances in equilibrium.

Audiogram Tracing: This should be done on each applicant to rule out preexisting hearing losses in frequency ranges which could be further impaired by diving. Damage to the drum from diving could further compromise a hearing loss. Chronic otitis externa, a common infection in divers, may thicken the ear drum and thereby increase the hearing loss. This examination should be done as a baseline and repeated every five years if diving routinely. It should be done often if injury occurs to the ears or symptoms referable to any ear structures develop.

Nose and Sinuses: Persons having acute or chronic sinus trouble should not dive unless free drainage of the sinuses is assured. Congestion, secondary to upper respiratory infection or hay fever, is a contraindication to diving until free passage of air is possible. Persons with acute upper respiratory infections may be passed, but should be strictly cautioned against diving until the upper respiratory infection has completely cleared.

Mouth and Throat: Bridgework or dentures should fit solidly. The applicant should be capable of retaining a diving mouthpiece. Acute infectious diseases of the soft tissue of the oral cavity are disqualifying until remedial treatment is completed.

Vascular: Peripheral vascular disease which might interfere with gas exchange in an extremity should disqualify the applicant. Varicose veins or hemorrhoids should be minimal or absent.

Heart: Thrust, size, rhythm, and sounds should be normal.

EKG: Divers should have on record an initial normal exercise electrocardiogram. Beyond age 40, an exercise electrocardiogram should be performed annually.

Blood Pressure: Blood pressure should not exceed 145 millimeters systolic, or 90 millimeters diastolic on repeated examinations for unrestricted diving.

Pulse: Pulse should be normal.

Lungs and Chest: Persons with evidence of chronic lung disease, interference with free air passage, or with poor gas exchange, should be disqualified. A history of asthma, with no attacks in the preceding three years, should not disqualify the applicant from diving, as long as there is no residual evidence of the disease. A vital capacity test is necessary only when the examiner is clinically suspicious of a disease. A history of pneumothorax or thoracotomy shall disqualify the applicant.

Chest X-ray: A report of a 14 x 17 chest x-ray, taken within 12 months prior to this physical, shall be normal and the results reported with this examination.

Gastrointestinal: Persons having symptomatic acute or chronic gastrointestinal disease, including ulcers, shall be disqualified.

Serology: Should be performed because of equipment sharing.

Hemoglobin and Red and White Blood Cells: Should be within normal limits.

Blood Type and RH Factor: Required on first examination only.

Neuromuscular: The applicant should be able to demonstrate fine and gross muscular coordination. Reflexes should be normal. Joints should be free from disabling arthritic conditions.

Endocrine: Endocrine disturbances shall disqualify the applicant.

Neuropsychiatric: Neuropsychiatric disturbances may disqualify the applicant. This area is obviously most difficult to evaluate. If the response of the patient to stress is questionable, seriously consider disqualifying him. Emergencies below the surface require cool judgment. The alternative is death, perhaps for others. Emotional immaturity or instability and recklessness are serious liabilities, not only for the person contemplating diving, but also for his companions. Anyone exhibiting poor temperament should be disqualified. Claustrophobia, as well as other phobias, inability to tolerate face masks, accident proneness, etc., should be included as poor temperament. Screen for history of headache, dizziness, fainting spells, soaking sweats, dyspnea, palpitations, stuttering, attempted suicide, sleepwalking, disciplinary problems. Elicit feelings about: living in a restricted environment, possibility of bodily harm, lack of privacy, separation from home and family. Observe appropriateness of emotional reactions during examination.

Alcoholism, unusual use of drugs, medicines, intoxicants, or drug addiction shall disqualify the applicant.

Central Nervous System: History of syncope, epilepsy, convulsions, organic disease of the central nervous system or history of head injury with sequelae shall disqualify the applicant.

All abnormalities of the cranial nerves, deep tendon reflexes, balance, position discrimination, sensation or coordination (including gait) should be recorded in detail.

Skin: The skin should be free of active, acute, or chronic disease which may prove undesirable from the standpoint of equipment sharing.

Visual Acuity: A normal ophthalmoscopic and extra-ocular musculature examination shall be given. Although vision for distant objects under water is often decreased by particulate matter in the water, and the low levels of illumination that may be encountered, the refractive changes introduced by the water environment enlarge objects by about one-fourth. The examining physician and the MLC Diving Officer should, in each instance, determine whether the applicant's visual status is compatible with safety during diving. The following criteria may be helpful as a guide in rendering this decision:

a. Individuals with uncorrected vision of 20/50 or better for near and distant in one or both eyes, and with no evidence of organic ocular disease are unrestricted.

b. Individuals with uncorrected visual acuity of 20/50 to 20/100 for distance and the equivalent of 20/50 or better for near in one or both eyes, and with no evidence of organic ocular disease, may dive if the applicant is advised of the risks associated with the restricted vision.

c. Applicants with uncorrected vision of less than 20/100 for distance and less than 20/50 for near, in one or both eyes, and with no evidence of organic ocular disease should be restricted from diving unless optical correction worn underwater improves vision to 20/100 or better for distance, and 20/50 or better for near, in one or both eyes. These individuals should be advised of the risks associated with decreased vision.

d. Applicants with significant organic ocular disease affecting both eyes should be restricted from diving.

Height/Weight: The applicant should not be obese. His height and weight should be within the limits of the following chart:

Height (inches)	Max. Weight	Height (inches)	Max. Weight	Height (inches)	Max. Weight	Height (inches)	Max. Weight
64	164	68	184	72	205	76	230
65	169	69	189	73	211	77	236
66	174	70	194	74	218	78	242
67	179	71	199	75	224		

Exhibit 2—Continued

PART II

U.S. DEPARTMENT OF COMMERCE
NATIONAL OCEANIC AND ATMOSPHERIC ADMINISTRATION

DIVING FITNESS MEDICAL EVALUATION REPORT

APPLICANT (Name)	DATE

☐ Approved: I find no defects which I consider incompatible with diving.

☐ Disapproved: Applicant has defects which, in my opinion, would clearly constitute unacceptable hazards to his health and safety in diving.

REMARKS   (Regarding Medical Evaluation Criteria, etc.)

NOTE: The evaluation report as shown above should be given to the applicant for transmittal to the Unit Diving Officer.

I have discussed the applicant's defects, if any, which would not seriously interfere with his diving, but which may seriously compromise his subsequent health. He understands the nature of the hazards and the risks involved in diving with these defects.

SIGNATURE (Examining physician)

ADDRESS (Street)

CITY	STATE	ZIP CODE

TELEPHONE NUMBER

NOAA Diving Manual

Exhibit 3
Dive Safe Ship
Operations and Checklist

NOAA FORM 64-3
(6-74)

U.S. DEPARTMENT OF COMMERCE
NATIONAL OCEANIC AND ATMOSPHERIC ADMINISTRATION

DIVE SAFE SHIP OPERATIONS—CHECKLIST

Please Note: Signing of this checklist will indicate that the individual has been advised of the diving operation and that he has completed the required actions to insure that "SAFETY" of the divers will not be jeopardized.

Personnel indicated below shall sign form prior to commencement and upon completion of diving operations.

Diving operations will **not** commence until **all** required signatures are received and this form is returned to the Dive Master.

PERSONNEL	PRIOR TO DIVE	TIME	AFTER COMPLETION	TIME
REPAIR ACTIVITY:				
Repair Authority				
CO				
XO				
ODD				
SHIPS ALONGSIDE:				
OOD				
OOD				
OOD				
OOD				
SHIP BEING WORKED ON:				
Engineering Officer				
Boatswain				
SECURE: (appropriate authority initials)				
Rudder				
Trash Disposal Unit				
Tank Blows				
Tank Vents				
Shaft Locked				
Sea Suctions				
Sea Discharges				
U/W Electrical Equipment				
Other U/W Equipment not Listed				
Appropriate Diving Signal Displayed				
Appropriate Diving Signal Removed				
REMARKS				

DIVE MASTER	OOD

NOAA FORM 64-3
(6-74)

Exhibit 3—Continued

U.S. DEPARTMENT OF COMMERCE
NATIONAL OCEANIC AND ATMOSPHERIC ADMINISTRATION

DIVE SAFE SHIP OPERATIONS
(See reverse for checklist)

THE FOLLOWING MESSAGES ARE TO BE TRANSMITTED OVER THE ADDRESS SYSTEM:

PRIOR TO COMMENCEMENT AND EVERY 30 MINUTES THEREAFTER THROUGH COMPLETION:

"There are divers working over the side. **DO NOT** operate any equipment over the side, rotate screws, cycle rudder, take suction from or discharge to sea, blow or vent any tanks, activate sonar or underwater electrical equipment, open or close any valves or cycle trash disposal unit before checking with the Dive Master _____

(Name)

AFTER COMPLETION:

"Diving operations are now complete. Normal and routine work may be carried on in accordance with previous instructions."

NOTE:

No particular sequence is required in signing diving form. Upon completion of all notifications and actions, the Dive Master will indicate his belief that safe operations can commence by signing at the bottom of the checklist on the reverse. In the event that there is a delay in the commencement of diving operations, each person whose signature appears on the checklist will be informed.

DIVING OPERATIONS

DATE OF OPERATION	COMMENCEMENT TIME	COMPLETION TIME

NAME OF SHIP

NATURE OF DIVING OPERATIONS:

**Exhibit 4
Letter of
Authorization**

**U.S. DEPARTMENT OF COMMERCE
National Oceanic and Atmospheric Administration**
Rockville, Md. 20852

(Sample Format for Letter of Authorization to Dive)

LETTER OF AUTHORIZATION

TO DIVE FOR THE NATIONAL OCEANIC AND ATMOSPHERIC ADMINISTRATION

SOCIAL SECURITY NUMBER_____
LEVEL OF CERTIFICATION_____

TO: John Doe
        (Name of Diver)

        Fishery Biologist
        (Title)

        Seattle, Washington
        (Official Station)

FROM: The NOAA Diving Coordinator
        National Oceanic and Atmospheric Administration

AUTHORIZATION

    You are authorized to use self-contained underwater
breathing apparatus incident to the performance of your
official duties subject to prescribed NOAA policy and
regulations governing use of such equipment.

RESTRICTIONS

REMARKS

    Examined and found technically qualified and psycho-
logically adapted for diving.

_____   _____
NOAA DIVING COORDINATOR   Date

C-13

Exhibit 5
Monthly Diving Log

NOAA FORM 64-4
(6-74)

U. S. DEPARTMENT OF COMMERCE
NATIONAL OCEANIC AND ATMOSPHERIC ADMINISTRATION

MONTHLY DIVING LOG

NAME – (Last, First, Middle Initial)

SOC. SECURITY NO.

MAJOR LINE COMPONENT	ORG. CODE	DIVER STATUS (Note 1)	DATE (mo/yr)

INSTRUCTIONS

1. Use a separate line for each dive.
2. Print all information.
3. Submit this report to the Unit Diving Officer by the 5th of the month for the preceding month.
   The Unit Diving Officer shall forward a copy of this report to the NOAA Diving Coordinator.
   A negative report is required.
4. For saturation missions, log all excursions as dives using all columns if applicable.
5. Use notes provided to code information on the form. Leave column blank when information
   is not applicable and explain in remarks.

NOTES

1. 1 Trainee; 2 Limited; 3 Unlimited; 4 Instructor; 5 Non-NOAA (identify)
2. 1 Nonsaturation; 2 Saturation; 3 Saturation Support (includes all dives necessary to support
   a saturation mission–prior to, during, and after)
3. 1 Biological Survey; 2 Geological Survey; 3 Oceanographic Survey; 4 Physiological;
   5 Maintenance/Repair; 6 Search/Recovery; 7 Test/Evaluation; 8 Training; 9 Recreation
4. 1 Shore; 2 Small boat; 3 Ship; 4 Diving bell; 5 Submersible; 6 Habitat; 7 Chamber; 8 Pool
5. 1 Open circuit SCUBA; 2 Closed circuit SCUBA; 3 Umbilical supplied
6. 1 Air; 2 Helium–Oxygen; 3 Nitrogen–Oxygen; 4 Oxygen

7. LOCATION CODES

NAC: North Atlantic Coastal – Maine through Rhode Island
MAC: Mid-Atlantic Coastal – Connecticut through Virginia
SAC: South Atlantic Coastal – North Carolina through southeast Florida
GMC: Gulf of Mexico Coastal – southwest Florida through Texas
PVC: Puerto Rico, U. S. Virgin Islands, and Canal Zone

AKC: Alaska Coastal
NPC: North Pacific Coastal – Washington through Oregon
MPC: Mid Pacific Coastal – northern through central California
SPC: South Pacific Coastal – southern California
HIC: Hawaii Coastal
PTT: Pacific Territories and Trustees

GLW: Great Lake Waters
OIW: Other Inland Waters
FCW: Foreign Coastal Waters
DOW: Deep Ocean Waters – beyond
        the Continental Shelf
OTH: Other

DAY	TYPE OF DIVE (note 2)	PURPOSE OF DIVE (note 3)	DIVE PLATFORM (note 4)	EQUIPMENT (note 5)	BREATHING MEDIA (note 6)	MAXIMUM DEPTH (feet)	BOTTOM OR EXCUR. TIME (minutes)	DECOMPRES-SION TIME (minutes)	LOCATION OF DIVE (note 7)	REMARKS AND CONDITIONS ENCOUNTERED

SATURATION MISSION DATES (Mo/Day–Mo/Day)	FACILITY USED	BREATHING MEDIA (note 6)	SATURA-TION DEPTH (feet)	SATURATION TIME (Days/Hrs)	DECOMPRESSION TIME (Days/Hrs/Min)	LOCATION OF FACILITY (note 7)	REMARKS AND CONDITIONS ENCOUNTERED

NOAA FORM 64-4 (6-74)

Exhibit 6
NOAA Diver's
Identification Card

The NOAA Diver's Identification Card shall serve to indicate the diver's level of certification and attest to the fact that the bearer is a NOAA employee authorized to partake in NOAA diving assignments as the level of certification indicates.

The NOAA Diving Coordinator shall have the authority to issue the Diver's Identification Card upon the recommendation of the MLC Diving Officer, who shall have adequate knowledge of the requesting diver's ability to perform diving tasks.

The form used for the Identification Card is shown below, and it shall be invalid until it is signed and properly completed with respect to all details indicated.

NOAA DIVER'S IDENTIFICATION CARD

NAME OF DIVER

LEVEL OF CERTIFICATION		SOCIAL SECURITY NO.
DATE OF BIRTH	HEIGHT	WEIGHT
HAIR	EYES	SEX

SIGNATURE

EMERGENCY INFORMATION ON REVERSE

EMERGENCY INFORMATION—In case of unconsciousness or illness from undetermined causes, notify:

NAME

ADDRESS

PHONE

DURATION—This certificate is of such duration as is provided in the currently effective NOAA Diving Regulations, unless sooner suspended or revoked.

NOAA DIVING COORDINATOR	DATE OF ISSUE

NOAA FORM 64-2   **U.S. DEPARTMENT OF COMMERCE**
NATIONAL OCEANIC AND ATMOSPHERIC ADMIN.

EMERGENCY ASSISTANCE

RECOMPRESSION CHAMBER	HOSPITAL	COMMUNICATIONS
Location	Location	Location
Contact	Contact	Contact
Response Time	Response Time	Response Time
AIR TRANSPORTATION	**GAS SUPPLIES**	**DEEP DIVING SYSTEM**
Location	Location	Location
Contact	Contact	Contact
Response Time	Response Time	Response Time
DIVING MEDICAL OFFICER	**SEA TRANSPORTATION**	**DIVING UNITS**
Location	Location	Location
Contact	Contact	Contact
Response Time	Response Time	Response Time

U.S. Navy Experimental Diving Unit • Panama City, Florida • Duty Phone Number (904) 234-4355

Former Table	New Name	Application
1—10 1—14	U.S. Navy Standard Air Decompression Table Short name: Standard Air Table	No locally available decompression chamber. Conditions dictate in-water decompression. Normal and exceptional exposure dive schedules. Repetitive dive normal decompression schedules only.
1—11	No-Decompression Limits and Repetitive Group Designation Table for No-Decompression Air Dive Short name: No-Decompression Table	Decompression not required. Repetitive dives.
1—12 1—13	Residual Nitrogen Time Table for Repetitive Air Dives Short name: Residual Nitrogen Table	Repetitive Group Designations after surface intervals greater than 10 minutes and less than 12 hours. Residual nitrogen times for repetitive air dives.
1—26	Surface Decompression Table Using Oxygen	Recompression chamber available with oxygen breathing system. Conditions do not allow in-water decompression. No repetitive dives.
1—27	Surface Decompression Table Using Air	Recompression chamber available without oxygen breathing system, or diver forced to surface prior to completing decompression. Conditions do not allow in-water decompression. No repetitive dives.

The 1973 edition of the U.S. Navy Diving Manual has incorporated changes in the standard air decompression tables. Due to confusion which resulted from table designation changes associated with frequent revisions, all table numbers have been eliminated. The tables are now designated by their name only.

The Decompression and Treatment Tables contained in this Appendix are taken directly from the U.S. Navy Diving Manual, Volume I, 1973.

The following publications list the locations of recompression chambers:

1. Directory of World-Wide, Shore-Based, Hyperbaric Chambers, Volume I—United States and Canada, NAVSHIPS 0994-010-4011, January 1971.

2. Directory of World-Wide, Shore-Based, Hyperbaric Chambers, Volume II—Other Than U.S. and Canada, NAVSHIPS 0994-010-4011, January 1971.

3. International Listing of Chambers, National Association of Underwater Instructors, February 1972.

Photo. Robert Merriman

AIR DECOMPRESSION TABLES

U.S. Navy Standard Air Decompression Table
The U.S. Navy Standard Air Decompression Table has combined the Standard Air Table and the Exceptional Exposure Air Table into one table as titled above. To clearly delineate between the standard and exceptional exposure decompression schedules, the exceptional exposure schedules have been printed in color.

The USN decompression tables are the result of years of scientific study, calculation, animal and human experimentation, and extensive field experience. They represent the best overall information available, but as depth and time increases, they tend to be less accurate and require careful application. Lacking the presence of a trained Diving Medical Officer or someone otherwise qualified, the tables must be rigidly followed to ensure maximum diving safety. Variations in decompression procedures are permissible only with the guidance of a qualified diving medical officer in emergency situations.

These limits are not to be exceeded without the approval of the Diving Officer in charge of the operation, and then, only after careful consideration of the potential consequences involved.

If the bottom time of a dive is less than the first bottom time listed for its depth, decompression is not required. The diver may ascend directly to the surface at a rate of 60 feet per minute. The repetitive group designation for no-decompression dives is given in the No-Decompression Table.

As will be noted in the Standard Air Table, there are no repetitive group designations for exceptional exposure dives. Repetitive dives following an exceptional exposure dive are not permitted.

Example—

Problem—Diver Bowman has just completed a salvage dive to a depth of 143 feet for 37 minutes. He was not exceptionally cold or fatigued during the dive. What is his decompression schedule and his repetitive group designation at the end of the decompression?

Solution—Select the equal or next deeper and the equal or next longer decompression schedule. This would be the 150/40 schedule.

ACTION	TIME	TOTAL ELAPSED ASCENT TIME
	(min:sec)	(min:sec)
Ascend to 30 feet at 60 fpm	1:53	1:53
Remain at 30 feet	5:00	6:53
Ascend to 20 feet	0:10	7:03
Remain at 20 feet	19:00	26:03
Ascend to 10 feet	0:10	26:13
Remain at 10 feet	33:00	59:13
Ascend to surface	0:10	59:23
Repetitive Group Designation	"N"	

U.S NAVY STANDARD AIR DECOMPRESSION TABLE

Depth (feet)	Bottom time (min)	Time first stop (min:sec)	Decompression stops (feet) 50	40	30	20	10	Total ascent (min:sec)	Repetitive group
40	200						0	0:40	*
	210	0:30					2	2:40	N
	230	0:30					7	7:40	N
	250	0:30					11	11:40	O
	270	0:30					15	15:40	O
	300	0:30					19	19:40	Z
	360	0:30					23	23:40	**
	480	0:30					41	41:40	**
	720	0:30					69	69:40	**
50	100						0	0:50	*
	110	0:40					3	3:50	L
	120	0:40					5	5:50	M
	140	0:40					10	10:50	M
	160	0:40					21	21:50	N
	180	0:40					29	29:50	O
	200	0:40					35	35:50	O
	220	0:40					40	40:50	Z
	240	0:40					47	47:50	Z
60	60						0	1:00	*
	70	0:50					2	3:00	K
	80	0:50					7	8:00	L
	100	0:50					14	15:00	M
	120	0:50					26	27:00	N
	140	0:50					39	40:00	O
	160	0:50					48	49:00	Z
	180	0:50					56	57:00	Z
	200	0:40				1	69	71:00	Z
	240	0:40				2	79	82:00	**
	360	0:40				20	119	140:00	**
	480	0:40				44	148	193:00	**
	720	0:40				78	187	266:00	**
70	50						0	1:10	*
	60	1:00					8	9:10	K
	70	1:00					14	15:10	L
	80	1:00					18	19:10	M
	90	1:00					23	24:10	N
	100	1:00					33	34:10	N
	110	0:50				2	41	44:10	O
	120	0:50				4	47	52:10	O
	130	0:50				6	52	59:10	O
	140	0:50				8	56	65:10	Z
	150	0:50				9	61	71:10	Z
	160	0:50				13	72	86:10	Z
	170	0:50				19	79	99:10	Z

* See No Decompression Table for repetitive groups
**Repetitive dives may not follow exceptional exposure dives

U. S NAVY STANDARD AIR DECOMPRESSION TABLE

Depth (feet)	Bottom time (min)	Time first stop (min:sec)	Decompression stops (feet)					Total ascent (min:sec)	Repetitive group
			50	40	30	20	10		
80	40						0	1:20	*
	50	1:10					10	11:20	K
	60	1:10					17	18:20	L
	70	1:10					23	24:20	M
	80	1:00				2	31	34:20	N
	90	1:00				7	39	47:20	N
	100	1:00				11	46	58:20	O
	110	1:00				13	53	67:20	O
	120	1:00				17	56	74:20	Z
	130	1:00				19	63	83:20	Z
	140	1:00				26	69	96:20	Z
	150	1:00				32	77	110:20	Z
	180	1:00				35	85	121:20	**
	240	0:50			6	52	120	179:20	**
	360	0:50			29	90	160	280:20	**
	480	0:50			59	107	187	354:20	**
	720	0:40		17	108	142	187	455:20	**
90	30						0	1:30	*
	40	1:20					7	8:30	J
	50	1:20					18	19:30	L
	60	1:20					25	26:30	M
	70	1:10				7	30	38:30	N
	80	1:10				13	40	54:30	N
	90	1:10				18	48	67:30	O
	100	1:10				21	54	76:30	Z
	110	1:10				24	61	86:30	Z
	120	1:10				32	68	101:30	Z
	130	1:00			5	36	74	116:30	Z
100	25						0	1:40	*
	30	1:30					3	4:40	I
	40	1:30					15	16:40	K
	50	1:20				2	24	27:40	L
	60	1:20				9	28	38:40	N
	70	1:20				17	39	57:40	O
	80	1:20				23	48	72:40	O
	90	1:10			3	23	57	84:40	Z
	100	1:10			7	23	66	97:40	Z
	110	1:10			10	34	72	117:40	Z
	120	1:10			12	41	78	132:40	Z
	180	1:00		1	29	53	118	202:40	**
	240	1:00		14	42	84	142	283:40	**
	360	0:50	2	42	73	111	187	416:40	**
	480	0:50	21	61	91	142	187	503:40	**
	720	0:50	55	106	122	142	187	613:40	**
110	20						0	1:50	*
	25	1:40					3	4:50	H
	30	1:40					7	8:50	J
	40	1:30				2	21	24:50	L
	50	1:30				8	26	35:50	M
	60	1:30				18	36	55:50	N
	70	1:20			1	23	48	73:50	O
	80	1:20			7	23	57	88:50	Z
	90	1:20			12	30	64	107:50	Z
	100	1:20			15	37	72	125:50	Z

* See No Decompression Table for repetitive groups

**Repetitive dives may not follow exceptional exposure dives

U.S NAVY STANDARD AIR DECOMPRESSION TABLE

Depth (feet): 120

Bottom time (min)	Time to first stop (min:sec)	70	60	50	40	30	20	10	Total ascent (min:sec)	Repetitive group
				Decompression stops (feet)						
15								0	2:00	*
20	1:50							2	4:00	H
25	1:50							6	8:00	I
30	1:50							14	16:00	J
40	1:40						5	25	32:00	L
50	1:40						15	31	48:00	N
60	1:30					2	22	45	71:00	O
70	1:30					9	23	55	89:00	O
80	1:30					15	27	63	107:00	Z
90	1:30					19	37	74	132:00	Z
100	1:30					23	45	80	150:00	Z
120	1:20				10	19	47	98	176:00	**
180	1:10			5	27	37	76	137	284:00	**
240	1:10			23	35	60	97	179	396:00	**
360	1:00		18	45	64	93	142	187	551:00	**
480	0:50	3	41	64	93	122	142	187	654:00	**
720	0:50	32	74	100	114	122	142	187	773:00	**

Depth (feet): 130

Bottom time (min)	Time to first stop (min:sec)	70	60	50	40	30	20	10	Total ascent (min:sec)	Repetitive group
10								0	2:10	*
15	2:00							1	3:10	F
20	2:00							4	6:10	H
25	2:00							10	12:10	J
30	1:50						3	18	23:10	M
40	1:50						10	25	37:10	N
50	1:40					3	21	37	63:10	O
60	1:40					9	23	52	86:10	Z
70	1:40					16	24	61	103:10	Z
80	1:30				3	19	35	72	131:10	Z
90	1:30				8	19	45	80	154:10	Z

Depth (feet): 140

Bottom time (min)	Time to first stop (min:sec)	90	80	70	60	50	40	30	20	10	Total ascent (min:sec)	Repetitive group
					Decompression stops (feet)							
10										0	2:20	*
15	2:10									2	4:20	G
20	2:10									6	8:20	I
25	2:00								2	14	18:20	J
30	2:00								5	21	28:20	K
40	1:50							2	16	26	46:20	N
50	1:50							6	24	44	76:20	O
60	1:50							16	23	56	97:20	Z
70	1:40						4	19	32	68	125:20	Z
80	1:40						10	23	41	79	155:20	Z
90	1:30					2	14	18	42	88	166:20	**
120	1:30					12	14	36	56	120	240:20	**
180	1:20				10	26	32	54	94	168	386:20	**
240	1:10			8	28	34	50	78	124	187	511:20	**
360	1:00		9	32	42	64	84	122	142	187	684:20	**
480	1:00		31	44	59	100	114	122	142	187	801:20	**
720	0:50	16	56	88	97	100	114	122	142	187	924:20	**

* See No Decompression Table for repetitive groups
**Repetitive dives may not follow exceptional exposure dives

U. S NAVY STANDARD AIR DECOMPRESSION TABLE

Depth (feet)	Bottom time (min)	Time to first stop (min:sec)	90	80	70	60	50	40	30	20	10	Total ascent (min:sec)	Repetitive group
150	5										0	2:30	C
	10	2:20									1	3:30	E
	15	2:20									3	5:30	G
	20	2:10								2	7	11:30	H
	25	2:10								4	17	23:30	K
	30	2:10								8	24	34:30	L
	40	2:00							5	19	33	59:30	N
	50	2:00							12	23	51	88:30	O
	60	1:50						3	19	26	62	112:30	Z
	70	1:50						11	19	39	75	146:30	Z
	80	1:40					1	17	19	50	84	173:30	Z
160	5										0	2:40	D
	10	2:30									1	3:40	F
	15	2:20								1	4	7:40	H
	20	2:20								3	11	16:40	J
	25	2:20								7	20	29:40	K
	30	2:10							2	11	25	40:40	M
	40	2:10							7	23	39	71:40	N
	50	2:00						2	16	23	55	98:40	Z
	60	2:00						9	19	33	69	132:40	Z
	70	1:50					1	17	22	44	80	166:40	Z

Depth (feet)	Bottom time (min)	Time to first stop (min: sec)	110	100	90	80	70	60	50	40	30	20	10	Total ascent (min: sec)	Repetitive group
170	5												0	2:50	D
	10	2:40											2	4:50	F
	15	2:30										2	5	9:50	H
	20	2:30										4	15	21:50	J
	25	2:20									2	7	23	34:50	L
	30	2:20									4	13	26	45:50	M
	40	2:10								1	10	23	45	81:50	O
	50	2:10								5	18	23	61	109:50	Z
	60	2:00							2	15	22	37	74	152:50	Z
	70	2:00							8	17	19	51	86	183:50	Z
	90	1:50						12	12	14	34	52	120	246:50	**
	120	1:30				2	10	12	18	32	42	82	156	356:50	**
	180	1:20			4	10	22	28	34	50	78	120	187	535:50	**
	240	1:20			18	24	30	42	50	70	116	142	187	681:50	**
	360	1:10		22	34	40	52	60	98	114	122	142	187	873:50	**
	480	1:00	14	40	42	56	91	97	100	114	122	142	187	1007:50	**
180	5												0	3:00	D
	10	2:50											3	6:00	F
	15	2:40										3	6	12:00	I
	20	2:30									1	5	17	26:00	K
	25	2:30									3	10	24	40:00	L
	30	2:30									6	17	27	53:00	N
	40	2:20								3	14	23	50	93:00	O
	50	2:10							2	9	19	30	65	128:00	Z
	60	2:10							5	16	19	44	81	168:00	Z

* See No Decompression Table for repetitive groups
**Repetitive dives may not follow exceptional exposure dives

U.S NAVY STANDARD AIR DECOMPRESSION TABLE

Depth (feet): 190

Bottom time (min)	Time to first stop (min: sec)	110	100	90	80	70	60	50	40	30	20	10	Total ascent (min: sec)	Repetitive group
5												0	3:10	D
10	2:50										1	3	7:10	G
15	2:50										4	7	14:10	I
20	2:40									2	6	20	31:10	K
25	2:40									5	11	25	44:10	M
30	2:30								1	8	19	43	63:10	N
40	2:30								8	14	23	55	103:10	O
50	2:20							4	13	22	33	72	147:10	Z
60	2:20							10	17	19	50	84	183:10	Z

Depth (feet): 200

Bottom time (min)	Time to first stop (min:sec)	130	120	110	100	90	80	70	60	50	40	30	20	10	Total ascent (min:sec)
5	3:10													1	4:20
10	3:00												1	4	8:20
15	2:50											1	4	10	18:20
20	2:50											3	7	27	40:20
25	2:50											7	14	25	49:20
30	2:40										2	9	22	37	73:20
40	2:30									2	8	17	23	59	112:20
50	2:30									6	16	22	39	75	161:20
60	2:20								2	13	17	24	51	89	199:20
90	1:50					1	10	10	12	12	30	38	74	134	324:20
120	1:40				6	10	10	10	24	28	40	64	98	180	473:20
180	1:20		1	10	10	18	24	24	42	48	70	106	142	187	685:20
240	1:20		6	20	24	24	36	42	54	68	114	122	142	187	842:20
360	1:10	12	22	36	40	44	56	82	98	100	114	122	142	187	1058:20

Depth (feet): 210

Bottom time (min)	Time to first stop (min:sec)	130	120	110	100	90	80	70	60	50	40	30	20	10	Total ascent (min:sec)
5	3:20													1	4:30
10	3:10												2	4	9:30
15	3:00											1	5	13	22:30
20	3:00											4	10	23	40:30
25	2:50										2	7	17	27	56:30
30	2:50										4	9	24	41	81:30
40	2:40									4	9	19	26	63	124:30
50	2:30								1	9	17	19	45	80	174:30

Depth (feet): 220

Bottom time (min)	Time to first stop (min:sec)	130	120	110	100	90	80	70	60	50	40	30	20	10	Total ascent (min:sec)
5	3:30													2	5:40
10	3:20												2	5	10:40
15	3:10											2	5	16	26:40
20	3:00										1	3	11	24	42:40
25	3:00										3	8	19	33	66:40
30	2:50									1	7	10	23	47	91:40
40	2:50									6	12	22	29	68	140:40
50	2:40								3	12	17	18	51	86	190:40

U.S NAVY STANDARD AIR DECOMPRESSION TABLE

Depth (feet)	Bottom time (min)	Time to first stop (min:sec)	130	120	110	100	90	80	70	60	50	40	30	20	10	Total ascent time (min:sec)
230	5	3:40													2	5:50
	10	3:20											1	2	6	12:50
	15	3:20											3	6	18	30:50
	20	3:10										2	5	12	26	48:50
	25	3:10										4	8	22	37	74:50
	30	3:00									2	8	12	23	51	99:50
	40	2:50								1	7	15	22	34	74	156:50
	50	2:50								5	14	16	24	51	89	202:50
240	5	3:50													2	6:00
	10	3:30											1	3	6	14:00
	15	3:30											4	6	21	35:00
	20	3:20										3	6	15	25	53:00
	25	3:10									1	4	9	24	40	82:00
	30	3:10									4	8	15	22	56	109:00
	40	3:00								3	7	17	22	39	75	167:00
	50	2:50							1	8	15	16	29	51	94	218:00
250	5	3:50												1	2	7:10
	10	3:40											1	4	7	16:10
	15	3:30										1	4	7	22	38:10
	20	3:30										4	7	17	27	59:10
	25	3:20									2	7	10	24	45	92:10
	30	3:20									6	7	17	23	59	116:10
	40	3:10								5	9	17	19	45	79	178:10
	60	2:40					4	10	10	10	12	22	36	64	126	298:10
	90	2:10		8	10	10	10	10	10	28	28	44	68	98	186	514:10
260	5	4:00												1	2	7:20
	10	3:50											2	4	9	19:20
	15	3:40										2	4	10	22	42:20
	20	3:30									1	4	7	20	31	67:20
	25	3:30									3	8	11	23	50	99:20
	30	3:20								2	6	8	19	26	61	126:20
	40	3:10							1	6	11	16	19	49	84	190:20
270	5	4:10												1	3	8:30
	10	4:00											2	5	11	22:30
	15	3:50										3	4	11	24	46:30
	20	3:40									2	3	9	21	35	74:30
	25	3:30								2	3	8	13	23	53	106:30
	30	3:30								3	6	12	22	27	64	138:30
	40	3:20							5	6	11	17	22	51	88	204:30

U.S NAVY STANDARD AIR DECOMPRESSION TABLE

Depth (feet)	Bottom time (min)	Time to first stop (min:sec)	130	120	110	100	90	80	70	60	50	40	30	20	10	Total ascent time (min:sec)
280	5	4:20												2	2	8:40
	10	4:00												5	13	25:40
	15	3:50									1	3	4	11	26	49:40
	20	3:50									3	4	8	23	39	81:40
	25	3:40								2	5	7	16	23	56	113:40
	30	3:30							1	3	7	13	22	30	70	150:40
	40	3:20						1	6	6	13	17	27	51	93	218:40
290	5	4:30												2	3	9:50
	10	4:10										1	3	5	16	29:50
	15	4:00									1	3	6	12	26	52:50
	20	4:00									3	7	9	23	43	89:50
	25	3:50								3	5	8	17	23	60	120:50
	30	3:40							1	5	6	16	22	36	72	162:50
	40	3:30						3	5	7	15	16	32	51	95	228:50
300	5	4:40												3	3	11:00
	10	4:20										1	3	6	17	32:00
	15	4:10									2	3	6	15	26	57:00
	20	4:00								2	3	7	10	23	47	97:00
	25	3:50							1	3	6	8	19	26	61	129:00
	30	3:50							2	5	7	17	22	39	75	172:00
	40	3:40						4	6	9	15	17	34	51	90	231:00
	60	3:00	4	10	10	10	10	10	10	14	28	32	50	90	187	460:00

Extreme exposures—250 and 300 ft

Depth (ft)	Bottom time (min)	Time to first stop (min:sec)	200	190	180	170	160	150	140	130	120	110	100	90	80	70	60	50	40	30	20	10	Total ascent time (min:sec)
250	120	1:50							5	10	10	10	10	16	24	24	36	48	64	94	142	187	684:10
	180	1:30					4	8	8	10	22	24	24	32	42	44	60	84	114	122	142	187	931:10
	240	1:30					9	14	21	22	22	40	40	42	56	76	98	100	114	122	142	187	1109:10
300	90	2:20					3	8	8	10	10	10	10	16	24	24	34	48	64	90	142	187	693:00
	120	2:00			4	8	8	8	8	10	14	24	24	24	34	42	58	66	102	122	142	187	890:00
	180	1:40	6	8	8	8	14	20	21	21	28	40	40	48	56	82	98	100	114	122	142	187	1168:00

No-Decompression Limits and Repetitive Group Designation Table for No-Decompression Air Dives The No-Decompression Table serves two purposes. First it summarizes all the depth and bottom time combinations for which no decompression is required. Secondly, it provides the repetitive group designation for each no-decompression dive. Even though decompression is not required, an amount of nitrogen remains in the diver's tissues after every dive. If he dives again within a 12 hour period, the diver must consider this residual nitrogen when calculating his decompression.

Each depth listed in the No-Decompression Table has a corresponding **no-decompression limit** given in minutes. This limit is the maximum bottom time that a diver may spend at that depth without requiring decompression. The columns to the right of the no-decompression limits column are used to determine the repetitive group designation which must be assigned to a diver subsequent to every dive. To find the repetitive group designation enter the table at the depth equal to or next greater than the actual depth of the dive. Follow that row to the right to the bottom time equal to or next greater than the actual bottom time of the dive. Follow that column upward to the repetitive group designation.

Depths above 35 feet do not have a specific no-decompression limit. They are, however, restricted in that they only provide repetitive group designations for bottom times up to between 5 and 6 hours. These bottom times are considered the limitations of the No-Decompression Table and no field requirement for diving should extend beyond them.

Any dive below 35 feet which has a bottom time greater than the no-decompression limit given in this table is a decompression dive and should be conducted in accordance with the Standard Air Table.

Example—

Problem—In planning a dive, the Master Diver wants to conduct a brief inspection of the work site, located 160 feet below the surface. What is the maximum bottom time which he may use without requiring decompression? What is his repetitive group designation after the dive?

Solution—The no-decompression limit corresponding to the 160 foot depth in the No-Decompression Table is 5 minutes. Therefore, the Master Diver must descend to 160 feet, make his inspection and begin his ascent within 5 minutes without having to undergo decompression.

Following the 160 foot depth row to the 5 minute column, the repetitive group designation at the top of this column is D.

NO-DECOMPRESSION LIMITS AND REPETITIVE GROUP DESIGNATION TABLE FOR NO-DECOMPRESSION AIR DIVES

Depth (feet)	No-decompression limits (min)	A	B	C	D	E	F	G	H	I	J	K	L	M	N	
10		60	120	210	300											
15		35	70	110	160	225	350									
20		25	50	75	100	135	180	240	325							
25		20	35	55	75	100	125	160	195	245	315					
30		15	30	45	60	75	95	120	145	170	205	250	310			
35	310	5	15	25	40	50	60	80	100	120	140	160	190	220	270	310
40	200	5	15	25	30	40	50	70	80	100	110	130	150	170	200	
50	100		10	15	25	30	40	50	60	70	80	90	100			
60	60		10	15	20	25	30	40	50	55	60					
70	50		5	10	15	20	30	35	40	45	50					
80	40			5	10	15	20	25	30	35	40					
90	30			5	10	12	15	20	25	30						
100	25			5	7	10	15	20	22	25						
110	20				5	10	13	15	20							
120	15				5	10	12	15								
130	10				5	8	10									
140	10				5	7	10									
150	5				5											
160	5				5											
170	5				5											
180	5				5											
190	5				5											

Residual Nitrogen Timetable for Repetitive Air Dives

The quantity of residual nitrogen in a diver's body immediately after a dive is expressed by the repetitive group designation assigned to him by either the Standard Air Table or the No-Decompression Table. The upper portion of the Residual Nitrogen Table is composed of various intervals between 10 minutes and 12 hours, expressed in minutes: hours (2:21 = 2 hours 21 minutes). Each interval has two limits; a minimum time (top limit) and a maximum time (bottom limit).

Residual nitrogen times, corresponding to the depth of the repetitive dive, are given in the body of the lower portion of the table. To determine the residual nitrogen time for a repetitive dive, locate the diver's repetitive group designation from his previous dive along the diagonal line above the table. Read horizontally to the interval in which the diver's surface interval lies. The time spent on the surface must be between or equal to the limits of the selected interval.

Next, read vertically downwards to the new repetitive group designation. This designation corresponds to the present quantity of residual nitrogen in the diver's body. Continue downward in this same column to the row which represents the depth of the repetitive dive. The time given at the intersection is the residual nitrogen time, in minutes, to be applied to the repetitive dive.

If the surface interval is less than 10 minutes, the residual nitrogen time is the bottom time of the previous dive. All of the residual nitrogen will be passed out of the diver's body after 12 hours, so a dive conducted after a 12 hour surface interval is not a repetitive dive.

There is one exception to this table. In some instances, when the repetitive dive is to the same or greater depth than the previous dive, the residual nitrogen time may be longer than the actual bottom time of the previous dive. In this event, add the actual bottom time of the previous dive to the actual bottom time of the repetitive dive to obtain the equivalent single dive time.

Example—

Problem—A repetitive dive is to be made to 98 fsw for an estimated bottom time of 15 minutes. The previous dive was to a depth of 102 fsw and had a 48 minute bottom time. The diver's surface interval is 6 hours 28 minutes (6:28). What decompression schedule should be used for the repetitive dive?

Solution—Using the repetitive dive worksheet—

REPETITIVE DIVE WORKSHEET

I. PREVIOUS DIVE:

48 minutes ☑Standard Air Table

102 feet ☐No-Decompression Table

M repetitive group designation

II. SURFACE INTERVAL:

6 hours *28* minutes on surface.

Repetitive group from I *M*

New repetitive group from surface

Residual Nitrogen Timetable *B*

III. RESIDUAL NITROGEN TIME:

98 feet (depth of repetitive dive)

New repetitive group from II. *B*

Residual nitrogen time from

Residual Nitrogen Timetable *7*

IV. EQUIVALENT SINGLE DIVE TIME:

7 minutes, residual nitrogen time from III.

+*15* minutes, actual bottom time of repetitive dive.

=*22* minutes, equivalent single dive time.

V. DECOMPRESSION FOR REPETITIVE DIVE:

22 minutes, equivalent single dive time from IV.

98 feet, depth of repetitive dive

Decompression from (check one):
☐ Standard Air Table ☐ No-Decompression Table
☐ Surface Table Using Oxygen ☐ Surface Table Using Air
☑ No decompression required

Decompression Stops: _____ feet _____ minutes

_____ feet _____ minutes

_____ feet _____ minutes

_____ feet _____ minutes

Schedule used _____ _____ feet _____ minutes

Repetitive group _____

RESIDUAL NITROGEN TIMETABLE FOR REPETITIVE AIR DIVES

*Dives following surface intervals of more than 12 hours are not repetitive dives. Use actual bottom times in the Standard Air Decompression Tables to compute decompression for such dives.

Repetitive group at the beginning of the surface interval

Group	Z	O	N	M	L	K	J	I	H	G	F	E	D	C	B	A
A																0:10 12:00*
B															0:10 2:10	2:11 12:00*
C														0:10 1:39	1:40 2:49	2:50 12:00*
D													0:10 1:09	1:10 2:38	2:39 5:48	5:49 12:00*
E												0:10 0:54	0:55 1:57	1:58 3:22	3:23 6:32	6:33 12:00*
F											0:10 0:45	0:46 1:29	1:30 2:28	2:29 3:57	3:58 7:05	7:06 12:00*
G										0:10 0:40	0:41 1:15	1:16 1:59	2:00 2:58	2:59 4:25	4:26 7:35	7:36 12:00*
H									0:10 0:36	0:37 1:06	1:07 1:41	1:42 2:23	2:24 3:20	3:21 4:49	4:50 7:59	8:00 12:00*
I								0:10 0:33	0:34 0:59	1:00 1:29	1:30 2:02	2:03 2:44	2:45 3:43	3:44 5:12	5:13 8:21	8:22 12:00*
J							0:10 0:31	0:32 0:54	0:55 1:19	1:20 1:47	1:48 2:20	2:21 3:04	3:05 4:02	4:03 5:40	5:41 8:40	8:41 12:00*
K						0:10 0:28	0:29 0:49	0:50 1:11	1:12 1:35	1:36 2:03	2:04 2:38	2:39 3:21	3:22 4:19	4:20 5:48	5:49 8:58	8:59 12:00*
L					0:10 0:26	0:27 0:45	0:46 1:04	1:05 1:25	1:26 1:49	1:50 2:19	2:20 2:53	2:54 3:36	3:37 4:35	4:36 6:02	6:03 9:12	9:13 12:00*
M				0:10 0:25	0:26 0:42	0:43 0:59	1:00 1:18	1:19 1:39	1:40 2:05	2:06 2:34	2:35 3:08	3:09 3:52	3:53 4:49	4:50 6:18	6:19 9:28	9:29 12:00*
N			0:10 0:24	0:25 0:39	0:40 0:54	0:55 1:11	1:12 1:30	1:31 1:53	1:54 2:18	2:19 2:47	2:48 3:22	3:23 4:04	4:05 5:03	5:04 6:32	6:33 9:43	9:44 12:00*
O		0:10 0:23	0:24 0:36	0:37 0:51	0:52 1:07	1:08 1:24	1:25 1:43	1:44 2:04	2:05 2:29	2:30 2:59	3:00 3:33	3:34 4:17	4:18 5:16	5:17 6:44	6:45 9:54	9:55 12:00*
	0:10 0:22	0:23 0:34	0:35 0:48	0:49 1:02	1:03 1:18	1:19 1:36	1:37 1:55	1:56 2:17	2:18 2:42	2:43 3:10	3:11 3:45	3:46 4:29	4:30 5:27	5:28 6:56	6:57 10:05	10:06 12:00*
NEW → GROUP DESIGNATION	Z	O	N	M	L	K	J	I	H	G	F	E	D	C	B	A

REPETITIVE DIVE DEPTH	Z	O	N	M	L	K	J	I	H	G	F	E	D	C	B	A
40	257	241	213	187	161	138	116	101	87	73	61	49	37	25	17	7
50	169	160	142	124	111	99	87	76	66	56	47	38	29	21	13	6
60	122	117	107	97	88	79	70	61	52	44	36	30	24	17	11	5
70	100	96	87	80	72	64	57	50	43	37	31	26	20	15	9	4
80	84	80	73	68	61	54	48	43	38	32	28	23	18	13	8	4
90	73	70	64	58	53	47	43	38	33	29	24	20	16	11	7	3
100	64	62	57	52	48	43	38	34	30	26	22	18	14	10	7	3
110	57	55	51	47	42	38	34	31	27	24	20	16	13	10	6	3
120	52	50	46	43	39	35	32	28	25	21	18	15	12	9	6	3
130	46	44	40	38	35	31	28	25	22	19	16	13	11	8	6	3
140	42	40	38	35	32	29	26	23	20	18	15	12	10	7	5	2
150	40	38	35	32	30	27	24	22	19	17	14	12	9	7	5	2
160	37	36	33	31	28	26	23	20	18	16	13	11	9	6	4	2
170	35	34	31	29	26	24	22	19	17	15	13	10	8	6	4	2
180	32	31	29	27	25	22	20	18	16	14	12	10	8	6	4	2
190	31	30	28	26	24	21	19	17	15	13	11	10	8	6	4	2

RESIDUAL NITROGEN TIMES (MINUTES)

APPENDIX D COMPRESSION TREATMENT TABLES

TABLE 1A—RECOMPRESSION TREATMENT OF DECOMPRESSION SICKNESS AND GAS EMBOLISM USING AIR

TABLE 1A NOTES—

1. Use—treatment of pain-only decompression sickness when oxygen cannot be used and pain is relieved at a depth less than 66 feet.

2. Descent rate—25 ft/min.

3. Ascent rate—1 minute between stops.

4. Time at 100 feet—includes time from the surface.

TABLE 1A

Depth (feet)	Time (minutes)	Breathing Media	Total Elapsed Time (minutes)
100	30	Air	30
80	12	Air	43
60	30	Air	74
50	30	Air	105
40	30	Air	136
30	60	Air	197
20	60	Air	258
10	120	Air	379
0	1	Air	380

TABLE 1A DEPTH/TIME PROFILE

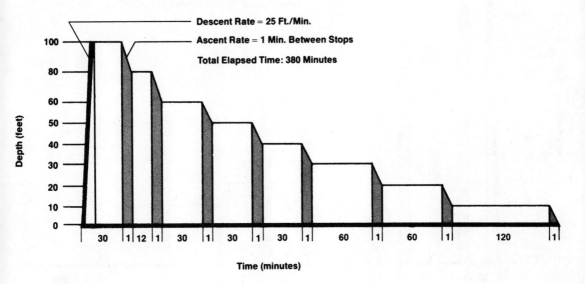

Descent Rate = 25 Ft./Min.

Ascent Rate = 1 Min. Between Stops

Total Elapsed Time: 380 Minutes

TABLE 2A—RECOMPRESSION TREATMENT OF DECOMPRESSION SICKNESS AND GAS EMBOLISM USING AIR

	Depth (feet)	Time (minutes)	Breathing Media	Total Elapsed Time (minutes)
1. Use—treatment of pain-only decompression sickness when oxygen cannot be used and pain is relieved at a depth greater than 66 feet.	165	30	Air	30
	140	12	Air	43
	120	12	Air	56
2. Descent rate—25 ft/min.	100	12	Air	69
3. Ascent rate—1 minute between stops.	80	12	Air	82
4. Time at 165 feet—includes time from the surface.	60	30	Air	113
	50	30	Air	144
	40	30	Air	175
	30	120	Air	296
	20	120	Air	417
	10	240	Air	658
	0	1	Air	659

TABLE 2A DEPTH/TIME PROFILE

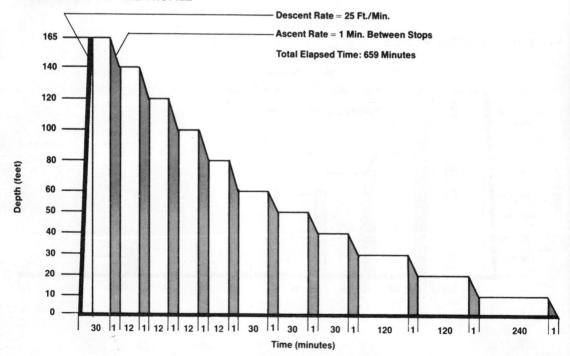

Descent Rate = 25 Ft./Min.

Ascent Rate = 1 Min. Between Stops

Total Elapsed Time: 659 Minutes

TABLE 3—RECOMPRESSION TREATMENT OF DECOMPRESSION SICKNESS AND GAS EMBOLISM USING AIR

1. Use—treatment of serious symptoms when oxygen cannot be used and symptoms are relieved within 30 minutes at 165 feet.

2. Descent rate—as fast as possible.

3. Ascent rate—1 minute between stops.

4. Time at 165 feet—includes time from the surface.

Depth (feet)	Time	Breathing Media	Total Elapsed Time (hrs:min)
165	30 min.	Air	0:30
140	12 min.	Air	0:43
120	12 min.	Air	0:56
100	12 min.	Air	1:09
80	12 min.	Air	1:22
60	30 min.	Oxygen (or air)	1:53
50	30 min.	Oxygen (or air)	2:24
40	30 min.	Oxygen (or air)	2:55
30	12 hr.	Air	14:56
20	2 hr.	Air	16:57
10	2 hr.	Air	18:58
0	1 min.	Air	18:59

TABLE 3 DEPTH/TIME PROFILE

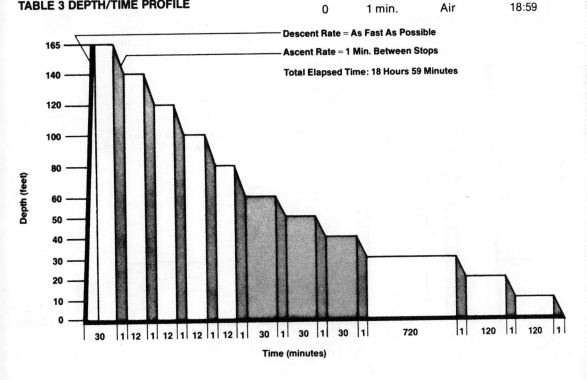

Descent Rate = As Fast As Possible

Ascent Rate = 1 Min. Between Stops

Total Elapsed Time: 18 Hours 59 Minutes

TABLE 4 — RECOMPRESSION TREATMENT OF DECOMPRESSION SICKNESS AND GAS EMBOLISM USING AIR

1. Use—treatment of serious symptoms or gas embolism when oxygen cannot be used and when symptoms are not relieved within 30 minutes at 165 feet.
2. Descent rate—as fast as possible.
3. Ascent rate—1 minute between stops.
4. Time at 165 feet—includes time from the surface.

Depth (feet)	Time	Breathing Media	Total Elapsed Time (hrs:min)
165	½ to 1½ hr.	Air	1:30
140	½ hr.	Air	2:01
120	½ hr.	Air	2:32
100	½ hr.	Air	3:03
80	½ hr.	Air	3:34
60	6 hr.	Air	9:35
50	6 hr.	Air	15:36
40	6 hr.	Air	21:37
30	11 hr.	Air	32:38
30	1 hr.	Oxygen (or air)	33:38
20	1 hr.	Air	34:39
20	1 hr.	Oxygen (or air)	35:39
10	1 hr.	Air	36:40
10	1 hr.	Oxygen (or air)	37:40
0	1 min.	Oxygen	37:41

TABLE 4 DEPTH/TIME PROFILE

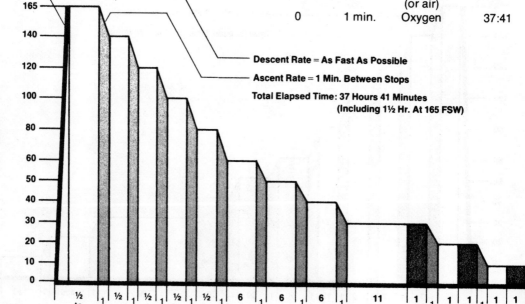

Descent Rate = As Fast As Possible

Ascent Rate = 1 Min. Between Stops

Total Elapsed Time: 37 Hours 41 Minutes
(Including 1½ Hr. At 165 FSW)

TABLE 5—MINIMAL RECOMPRESSION, OXYGEN BREATHING METHOD FOR TREATMENT OF DECOMPRESSION SICKNESS AND GAS EMBOLISM

1. Use—treatment of pain-only decompression sickness when oxygen can be used and symptoms are relieved within 10 minutes at 60 feet. Patient breathes oxygen from the surface.
2. Descent rate—25 ft/min.
3. Ascent rate—1 ft/min. Do not compensate for slower ascent rates. Compensate for faster rates by halting the ascent.
4. Time at 60 feet begins on arrival at 60 feet.
5. If oxygen breathing must be interrupted, allow 15 minutes after the reaction has entirely subsided and resume schedule at point of interruption.
6. If oxygen breathing must be interrupted at 60 feet, switch to TABLE 6 upon arrival at the 30 foot stop.
7. Tender breathes air throughout. If treatment is a repetitive dive for the tender or tables are lengthened, tender should breathe oxygen during the last 30 minutes of ascent to the surface.

Depth (feet)	Time (minutes)	Breathing Media	Total Elapsed Time (minutes)
60	20	Oxygen	20
60	5	Air	25
60	20	Oxygen	45
60 to 30	30	Oxygen	75
30	5	Air	80
30	20	Oxygen	100
30	5	Air	105
30 to 0	30	Oxygen	135

TABLE 5 DEPTH/TIME PROFILE

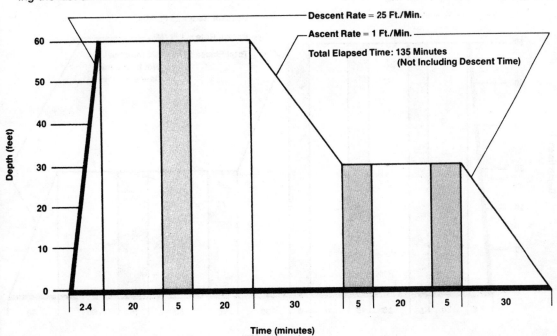

Descent Rate = 25 Ft./Min.

Ascent Rate = 1 Ft./Min.

Total Elapsed Time: 135 Minutes (Not Including Descent Time)

Depth (feet)

Time (minutes)

TABLE 6—MINIMAL RECOMPRESSION, OXYGEN BREATHING METHOD FOR TREATMENT OF DECOMPRESSION SICKNESS AND GAS EMBOLISM

1. Use—treatment of decompression sickness when oxygen can be used and symptoms are not relieved within 10 minutes at 60 feet. Patient breathes oxygen from the surface.

2. Descent rate—25 ft/min.

3. Ascent rate—1 ft/min. Do not compensate for slower ascent rates. Compensate for faster rates by halting the ascent.

4. Time at 60 feet—begins on arrival at 60 feet.

5. If oxygen breathing must be interrupted, allow 15 minutes after the reaction has entirely subsided and resume schedule at point of interruption.

6. Tender breathes air throughout. If treatment is a repetitive dive for the tender or tables are lengthened, tender should breathe oxygen during the last 30 minutes of ascent to the surface.

Depth (feet)	Time (minutes)	Breathing Media	Total Elapsed Time (minutes)
60	20	Oxygen	20
60	5	Air	25
60	20	Oxygen	45
60	5	Air	50
60	20	Oxygen	70
60	5	Air	75
60 to 30	30	Oxygen	105
30	15	Air	120
30	60	Oxygen	180
30	15	Air	195
30	60	Oxygen	255
30 to 0	30	Oxygen	285

TABLE 6 DEPTH/TIME PROFILE

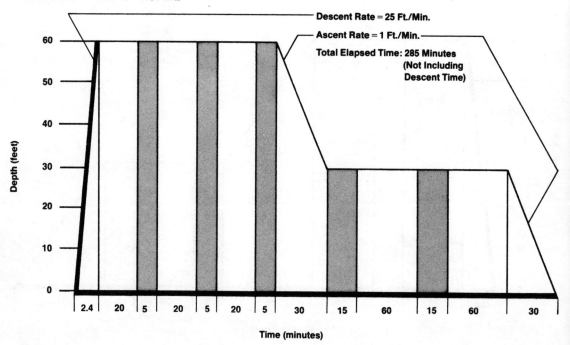

Descent Rate = 25 Ft./Min.

Ascent Rate = 1 Ft./Min.

Total Elapsed Time: 285 Minutes (Not Including Descent Time)

Depth (feet)

Time (minutes)

TABLE 5A—MINIMAL RECOMPRESSION, OXYGEN BREATHING METHOD FOR TREATMENT OF DECOMPRESSION SICKNESS AND GAS EMBOLISM

1. Use—treatment of gas embolism when oxygen can be used and symptoms are relieved within 15 minutes at 165 feet.

2. Descent rate—as fast as possible.

3. Ascent rate—1 ft/min. Do not compensate for slower ascent rates. Compensate for faster ascent rates by halting the ascent.

4. Time at 165 feet—includes time from the surface.

5. If oxygen breathing must be interrupted, allow 15 minutes after the reaction has entirely subsided and resume schedule at point of interruption.

6. Tender breathes air throughout. If treatment is a repetitive dive for the tender or tables are lengthened, tender should breathe oxygen during the last 30 minutes of ascent to the surface.

Depth (feet)	Time (minutes)	Breathing Media	Total Elapsed Time (minutes)
165	15	Air	15
165 to 60	4	Air	19
60	20	Oxygen	39
60	5	Air	44
60	20	Oxygen	64
60 to 30	30	Oxygen	94
30	5	Air	99
30	20	Oxygen	119
30	5	Air	124
30 to 0	30	Oxygen	154

TABLE 5A DEPTH/TIME PROFILE

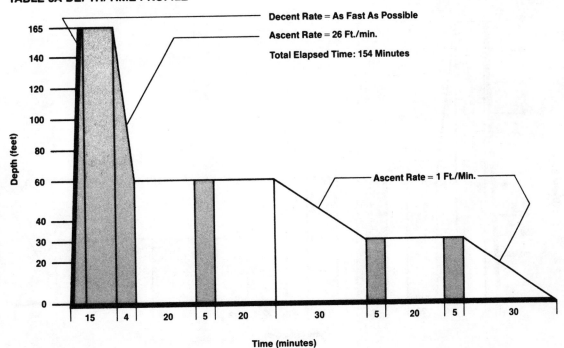

Decent Rate = As Fast As Possible

Ascent Rate = 26 Ft./min.

Total Elapsed Time: 154 Minutes

Ascent Rate = 1 Ft./Min.

Depth (feet)

Time (minutes)

TABLE 6A—MINIMAL RECOMPRESSION, OXYGEN BREATHING METHOD FOR TREATMENT OF DECOMPRESSION SICKNESS AND GAS EMBOLISM

1. Use—treatment of gas embolism when oxygen can be used and symptoms moderate to a major extent within 30 minutes at 165 feet.

2. Descent rate—as fast as possible.

3. Ascent rate—1 ft/min. Do not compensate for slower ascent rates. Compensate for faster ascent rates by halting the ascent.

4. Time at 165 feet—includes time from the surface.

5. If oxygen breathing must be interrupted, allow 15 minutes after the reaction has entirely subsided and resume schedule at point of interruption.

6. Tender breathes air throughout. If treatment is a repetitive dive for the tender or tables are lengthened, tender should breathe oxygen during the last 30 minutes of ascent to the surface.

Depth (feet)	Time (minutes)	Breathing Media	Total Elapsed Time (minutes)
165	30	Air	30
165 to 60	4	Air	34
60	20	Oxygen	54
60	5	Air	50
60	20	Oxygen	79
60	5	Air	84
60	20	Oxygen	104
60	5	Air	109
60 to 30	30	Oxygen	139
30	15	Air	154
30	60	Oxygen	214
30	15	Air	229
30	60	Oxygen	289
30 to 0	30	Oxygen	319

TABLE 6A DEPTH/TIME PROFILE

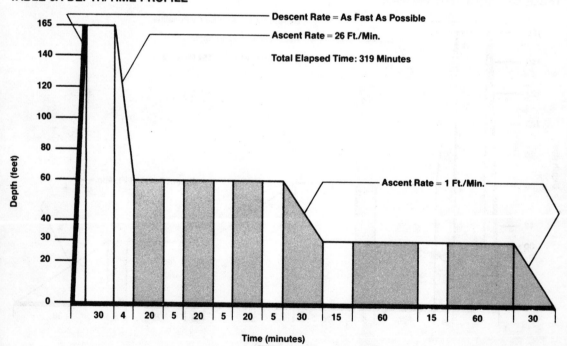

Descent Rate = As Fast As Possible

Ascent Rate = 26 Ft./Min.

Total Elapsed Time: 319 Minutes

Ascent Rate = 1 Ft./Min.

Depth (feet)

Time (minutes)

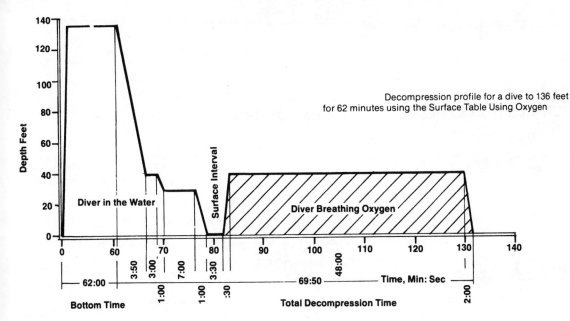

Decompression profile for a dive to 136 feet for 62 minutes using the Surface Table Using Oxygen

Surface Decompression Table Using Oxygen The application of the Surface Table Using Oxygen requires a recompression chamber with an oxygen breathing system as described in Paragraph 16.1.

The ascent rate to the first decompression stop, or to the surface if no stops are required, is 25 feet per minute. The ascent time between each stop, and from the 30 foot stop to the surface, is 1 minute.

Once the diver is on the surface, his tenders must remove his breathing apparatus and his weight belt and assist him into the recompression chamber within 3½ minutes. Pressurization of the chamber with air should take about 30 seconds. This means that the total elapsed time from when the diver leaves the 30 foot water depth to when he reaches the 40 foot recompression depth must not exceed 5 minutes.

As soon as the diver enters the chamber he must begin breathing pure oxygen via an approved mask breathing system. He is to remain on oxygen down to and throughout the designated 40 foot stop time. While the diver is breathing oxygen, the chamber must be ventilated.

Upon completion of the designated 40 foot chamber stop, the chamber should be depressurized to atmospheric pressure at a constant rate over a 2 minute period. During ascent, the diver is to remain on oxygen.

Should the diver develop oxygen toxicity problems, or the oxygen breathing system fail, the diver should be decompressed according to the Surface Decompression Table Using Air disregarding all time spent breathing oxygen.

Example—

Problem—Determine the decompression schedule for a dive to 136 feet for 62 minutes using the Surface Table Using Oxygen.

Solution—The correct decompression schedule for a dive to 136 feet for 62 minutes is the 140/65 schedule. The decompression profile is illustrated above.

Surface Decompression Table Using Air

The Surface Table Using Air should be used for surface decompression after an air dive when a recompression chamber without an oxygen breathing system is available. Also, if oxygen breathing must be stopped at any time when decompressing on the Surface Table Using Oxygen, the applicable chamber stops listed in the Surface Table Using Air must be carried out in their entirety.

The total ascent times of the Surface Table Using Air exceed those of the Standard Air Decompression Table. The advantages of using this table are strictly those of maintaining the diver in a controlled, closely observed environment during decompression.

When employing the Surface Table Using Air, the diver should ascend from the last water stop at 60 fpm. The time spent on the surface should not exceed 3½ minutes and the rate of descent to the first chamber stop should be 60 fpm. The total elapsed time for these three procedures must not exceed 5 minutes.

D-23

SURFACE DECOMPRESSION TABLE USING OXYGEN

Depth (feet)	Bottom time (min)	Time to first stop or surface (min:sec)	Time (min) breathing air at water stops (ft) 60	50	40	30	Surface interval	Time at 40-foot chamber stop (min) on oxygen	Surface	Total decompression time (min:sec)
70	52	2:48	0	0	0	0	TOTAL TIME FROM LAST WATER STOP TO FIRST CHAMBER STOP NOT TO EXCEED 5 MINUTES	0	2-MINUTE ASCENT FROM 40 FEET IN CHAMBER TO SURFACE WHILE BREATHING OXYGEN	2:48
	90	2:48	0	0	0	0		15		23:48
	120	2:48	0	0	0	0		23		31:48
	150	2:28	0	0	0	0		31		39:48
	180	2:48	0	0	0	0		39		47:48
80	40	3:12	0	0	0	0		0		3:12
	70	3:12	0	0	0	0		14		23:12
	85	3:12	0	0	0	0		20		29:12
	100	3:12	0	0	0	0		26		35:12
	115	3:12	0	0	0	0		31		40:12
	130	3:12	0	0	0	0		37		46:12
	150	3:12	0	0	0	0		44		53:12
90	32	3:36	0	0	0	0		0		3:36
	60	3:36	0	0	0	0		14		23:36
	70	3:36	0	0	0	0		20		29:36
	80	3:36	0	0	0	0		25		34:36
	90	3:36	0	0	0	0		30		39:36
	100	3:36	0	0	0	0		34		43:36
	110	3:36	0	0	0	0		39		48:36
	120	3:36	0	0	0	0		43		52:36
	130	3:36	0	0	0	0		48		57:36
100	26	4:00	0	0	0	0		0		4:00
	50	4:00	0	0	0	0		14		24:00
	60	4:00	0	0	0	0		20		30:00
	70	4:00	0	0	0	0		26		36:00
	80	4:00	0	0	0	0		32		42:00
	90	4:00	0	0	0	0		38		48:00
	100	4:00	0	0	0	0		44		54:00
	110	4:00	0	0	0	0		49		59:00
	120	4:00	0	0	0	3		53		63:00
110	22	4:24	0	0	0	0		0		4:24
	40	4:24	0	0	0	0		12		22:24
	50	4:24	0	0	0	0		19		29:24
	60	4:24	0	0	0	0		26		36:24
	70	4:24	0	0	0	0		33		43:24
	80	3:12	0	0	0	1		40		51:12
	90	3:12	0	0	0	2		46		58:12
	100	3:12	0	0	0	5		51		66:12
	110	3:12	0	0	0	12		54		76:12
120	18	4:48	0	0	0	0		0		4:48
	30	4:48	0	0	0	0		9		19:48
	40	4:48	0	0	0	0		16		26:48
	50	4:48	0	0	0	0		24		34:48
	60	3:36	0	0	0	2		32		44:36
	70	3:36	0	0	0	4		39		53:36
	80	3:36	0	0	0	5		46		61:36
	90	3:12	0	0	3	7		51		72:12
	100	3:12	0	0	6	15		54		86:12

SURFACE DECOMPRESSION TABLE USING OXYGEN

Depth (feet)	Bottom time (min)	Time to first stop or surface (min:sec)	Time (min) breathing air at water stops (ft)				Surface interval	Time at 40-foot chamber stop (min) on oxygen	Surface	Total decompression time (min:sec)
			60	50	40	30				
130	15	5:12	0	0	0	0		0		5:12
	30	5:12	0	0	0	0		12		23:12
	40	5:12	0	0	0	0		21		32:12
	50	4:00	0	0	0	3		29		43:00
	60	4:00	0	0	0	5		37		53:00
	70	4:00	0	0	0	7		45		63:00
	80	3:36	0	0	6	7		51		75:36
	90	3:36	0	0	10	12		56		89:36
140	13	5:36	0	0	0	0		0		5:36
	25	5:36	0	0	0	0		11		22:36
	30	5:36	0	0	0	0		15		26:36
	35	5:36	0	0	0	0		20		31:36
	40	4:24	0	0	0	2		24		37:24
	45	4:24	0	0	0	4		29		44:24
	50	4:24	0	0	0	6		33		50:24
	55	4:24	0	0	0	7		38		56:24
	60	4:24	0	0	0	8		43		62:24
	65	4:00	0	0	3	7		48		70:00
	70	3:36	0	2	7	7		51		79:36
150	11	6:00	0	0	0	0		0		6:00
	25	6:00	0	0	0	0		13		25:00
	30	6:00	0	0	0	0		18		30:00
	35	4:48	0	0	0	4		23		38:48
	40	4:24	0	0	3	6		27		48:24
	45	4:24	0	0	5	7		33		57:24
	50	4:00	0	2	5	8		38		66:00
	55	3:36	2	5	9	4		44		77:36
160	9	6:24	0	0	0	0		0		6:24
	20	6:24	0	0	0	0		11		23:24
	25	6:24	0	0	0	0		16		28:24
	30	5:12	0	0	0	2		21		35:12
	35	4:48	0	0	4	6		26		48:48
	40	4:24	0	3	5	8		32		61:24
	45	4:00	3	4	8	6		38		73:00
170	7	6:48	0	0	0	0		0		6:48
	20	6:48	0	0	0	0		13		25:48
	25	6:48	0	0	0	0		19		31:48
	30	5:12	0	0	3	5		23		44:12
	35	4:48	0	4	4	7		29		57:48
	40	4:24	4	4	8	6		36		72:24

Surface interval: TOTAL TIME FROM LAST WATER STOP TO FIRST CHAMBER STOP NOT TO EXCEED 5 MINUTES

Surface: 2-MINUTE ASCENT FROM 40 FEET IN CHAMBER TO SURFACE WHILE BREATHING OXYGEN

SURFACE DECOMPRESSION TABLE USING AIR

Depth (ft)	Bottom time (min)	Time to first stop (min:sec)	Time at water stops (min) 30	20	10	Surface Interval	Chamber stops (air) (min) 20	10	Total ascent time (min:sec)
40	230	0:30			3			7	14:30
	250	:30			3			11	18:30
	270	:30			3			15	22:30
	300	:30			3			19	26:30
50	120	:40			3			5	12:40
	140	:40			3			10	17:40
	160	:40			3			21	28:40
	180	:40			3			29	36:40
	200	:40			3			35	42:40
	220	:40			3			40	47:40
	240	:40			3			47	54:40
60	80	:50			3			7	14:50
	100	:50			3			14	21:50
	120	:50			3			26	33:50
	140	:50			3			39	46:50
	160	:50			3			48	55:50
	180	:50			3			56	63:50
	200	:40		3			3	69	80:10
70	60	1:00			3			8	16:00
	70	1:00			3			14	22:00
	80	1:00			3			18	26:00
	90	1:00			3			23	31:00
	100	1:00			3			33	41:00
	110	:50		3			3	41	52:20
	120	:50		3			4	47	59:20
	130	:50		3			6	52	66:20
	140	:50		3			8	56	72:20
	150	:50		3			9	61	78:20
	160	:50		3			13	72	93:20
	170	:50		3			19	79	106:20
80	50	1:10			3			10	18:10
	60	1:10			3			17	25:10
	70	1:10			3			23	31:10
	80	1:00		3			3	31	42:30
	90	1:00		3			7	39	54:30
	100	1:00		3			11	46	65:30
	110	1:00		3			13	53	74:30
	120	1:00		3			17	56	81:30
	130	1:00		3			19	63	90:30
	140	1:00		26			26	69	126:30
	150	1:00		32			32	77	146:30
90	40	1:20			3			7	15:20
	50	1:20			3			18	26:20
	60	1:20			3			25	33:20
	70	1:10		3			7	30	45:40
	80	1:10		13			13	40	71:40
	90	1:10		18			18	48	89:40
	100	1:10		21			21	54	101:40
	110	1:10		24			24	61	114:40
	120	1:10		32			32	68	137:40
	130	1:00	5	36			36	74	156:40

Surface Interval column (vertical): SURFACE INTERVAL NOT TO EXCEED 5 MINUTES — TOTAL TIME FROM LAST WATER STOP TO FIRST CHAMBER STOP

SURFACE DECOMPRESSION TABLE USING AIR

Depth (ft)	Bottom time (min)	Time to first stop (min:sec)	50	40	30	20	10	Surface Interval	Chamber stops (air) (min) 20	10	Total ascent time (min:sec)
100	40	1:30					3			15	23:30
	50	1:20				3			3	24	35:50
	60	1:20				3			9	28	45:50
	70	1:20				3			17	39	64:50
	80	1:20				23			23	48	99:50
	90	1:10			3	23			23	57	111:50
	100	1:10			7	23			23	66	124:50
	110	1:10			10	34			34	72	155:50
	120	1:10			12	41			41	78	177:50
110	30	1:40					3			7	15:40
	40	1:30				3			3	21	33:00
	50	1:30				3			8	26	43:00
	60	1:30				18			18	36	78:00
	70	1:20			1	23			23	48	101:00
	80	1:20			7	23			23	57	116:00
	90	1:20			12	30			30	64	142:00
	100	1:20			15	37			37	72	167:00
120	25	1:50					3			6	14:50
	30	1:50					3			14	22:50
	40	1:40				3			5	25	39:10
	50	1:40				15			15	31	67:10
	60	1:30			2	22			22	45	97:10
	70	1:30			9	23			23	55	116:10
	80	1:30			15	27			27	63	136:10
	90	1:30			19	37			37	74	173:10
	100	1:30			23	45			45	80	189:10
130	25	2:00					3			10	19:00
	30	1:50				3			3	18	30:20
	40	1:50				10			10	25	51:20
	50	1:40			3	21			21	37	88:20
	60	1:40			9	23			23	52	113:20
	70	1:40			16	24			24	61	131:20
	80	1:30		3	19	35			35	72	170:20
	90	1:30		8	19	45			45	80	203:20
140	20	2:10					3			6	15:10
	25	2:00				3			3	14	26:30
	30	2:00				5			5	21	37:30
	40	1:50			2	16			16	26	66:30
	50	1:50			6	24			24	44	104:30
	60	1:50			16	23			23	56	124:30
	70	1:40		4	19	32			32	68	161:30
	80	1:40		10	23	41			41	79	200:30
150	20	2:10				3			3	7	19:40
	25	2:10				4			4	17	31:40
	30	2:10				8			8	24	46:40
	40	2:00			5	19			19	33	82:40
	50	2:00			12	23			23	51	115:40
	60	1:50		3	19	26			26	62	142:40
	70	1:50		11	19	39			39	75	189:40
	80	1:40	1	17	19	50			50	84	227:40

Surface Interval: NOT TO EXCEED 5 MINUTES — TOTAL TIME FROM LAST WATER STOP TO FIRST CHAMBER STOP NOT TO EXCEED 5 MINUTES

SURFACE DECOMPRESSION TABLE USING AIR

Depth (ft)	Bottom time (min)	Time to first stop (min:sec)	Time at water stops (min)					Surface Interval	Chamber stops (air) (min)		Total ascent time (min:sec)
			50	40	30	20	10		20	10	
160	20	2:20				3			3	11	23:50
	25	2:20				7			7	20	40:50
	30	2:10			2	11			11	25	55:50
	40	2:10			7	23			23	39	98:50
	50	2:00		2	16	23			23	55	125:50
	60	2:00		9	19	33			33	69	169:50
	70	1:50	1	17	22	44			44	80	214:50
170	15	2:30				3			3	5	18:00
	20	2:30				4			4	15	30:00
	25	2:20			2	7			7	23	46:00
	30	2:20			4	13			13	26	63:00
	40	2:10		1	10	23			23	45	109:00
	50	2:10		5	18	23			23	61	137:00
	60	2:00	2	15	22	37			37	74	194:00
	70	2:00	8	17	19	51			51	86	239:00
180	15	2:40				3			3	6	19:10
	20	2:30			1	5			5	17	35:10
	25	2:30			3	10			10	24	54:10
	30	2:30			6	17			17	27	74:10
	40	2:20		3	14	23			23	50	120:10
	50	2:10	2	9	19	30			30	65	162:10
	60	2:10	5	16	19	44			44	81	216:10
190	15	2:50				4			4	7	22:20
	20	2:40			2	6			6	20	41:20
	25	2:40			5	11			11	25	59:20
	30	2:30		1	8	19			19	32	86:20
	40	2:30		8	14	23			23	55	130:20
	50	2:20	4	13	22	33			33	72	184:20
	60	2:20	10	17	19	50			50	84	237:20

Surface Interval: NOT TO EXCEED 5 MINUTES

TOTAL TIME FROM LAST WATER STOP TO FIRST CHAMBER STOP

INDEX

8